A pulsed ruby laser (see Index) pierces a sapphire crystal at the RCA Laboratories in Princeton, N.J.

THE BOOK OF
POPULAR
SCIENCE

Volume 7

INCORPORATED
New York

Distributed in the United States by
THE GROLIER SOCIETY INC.

Distributed in Canada by
GROLIER OF CANADA LIMITED

Cover photograph: all the colors of the rainbow are produced as natural sunlight is refracted through these prisms.

Herbert Matter, courtesy
Wyandotte Chemicals Corp.

Standard Book Number 7172-1200-9
Library of Congress Catalog Card Number: 69-10053

CONTENTS OF VOLUME VII

Modern mammals of land, air and sea and extinct reptiles of past ages evolved from a common ancestor — the cotylosaur.

THE LIFE OF MAMMALS

History, Structure and Habits of Earth's Dominant Animals

BY IAN McT. COWAN

THE animal class of the mammals, or Mammalia, includes a great many familiar forms — horses, cows, dogs, domestic cats, house rats and mice, sheep, goats and rabbits, to name only a few. It also numbers such exotic creatures as elephants, giraffes, rhinoceroses, gorillas, sperm whales, dolphins, vampire bats, kangaroos and platypuses. All these animals, familiar and exotic, have certain features in common. They are highly active vertebrates (animals with backbones), having large brains and a keen awareness of their surroundings. They are warm-blooded and possess a waterproof skin more or less covered with hair. The young are born alive(except for the platypus and spiny anteater) and suckle milk from the mammary, or milk, glands of the female. (The word "mammal" comes from the Latin *mamma:* "breast," a glandular organ that secretes milk.)

The mammals, including man himself, are the dominant animals of the world. They live wherever life is possible — on Arctic ice sheets and in tropical rain forests, on mountain crags and a mile below the surface of the sea, in underground burrows and at the tops of the tallest trees, in fresh-water lakes and streams and also in the air. They vary in size from the minute pigmy shrew of North America — 2 inches in body length and weighing about as much as a dime — to the blue whale, a giant 100 feet long and weighing some 130 tons. Today there are roughly 3,500 distinct species of mammals; there are about 15,000 species and subspecies.

Mammals are comparative newcomers to the animal population of the earth. We can trace their descent back to the cotylosaurs, a reptile group that lived in the Carboniferous period, about 225,000,000 years ago. The cotylosaurs were sluggish and clumsy animals that crawled on their bellies with legs sprawled to the side. Many of them probably lived in or near water, but laid their tough-shelled eggs on dry land. Their bodily processes of digestion and respiration were slow. As a result, they released energy slowly from the foodstuffs they ate; they generated little body heat. They depended for warmth upon the temperature of the external surroundings.

When the temperature was high, the pace of life quickened somewhat. The cotylosaur moved more rapidly and ate more, bolting comparatively large pieces of food: insects and the flesh of amphibians and other reptiles. When temperatures were low, the life processes almost came to a standstill. Stored food, in the form of body fat, was utilized, but no new food was consumed.

of the mammallike reptiles, a gradual lengthening of the front and hind legs took place. The feet came more and more to point forward instead of to the side, and the legs were brought in under the body. Thus the body was lifted off the ground. The bones of the pelvis fused to form a single bony structure. These changes permitted the animals to move about more efficiently and rapidly.

The primitive reptile Dimetrodon (left) and the domestic cat (right), a modern mammal, are both descended from the reptiles known as cotylosaurs. The darkened areas in the two drawings indicate skeletal structure.

From the cotylosaurs, directly or indirectly, evolved all of the reptiles: the modern forms — turtles, crocodiles, lizards and snakes — and those that we know about only from fossil remains. The cotylosaurs were also ancestors of the animals known as mammallike reptiles.

The mammallike reptiles began their evolution some 215,000,000 years ago. Some were carnivorous (flesh-eating); others, herbivorous (vegetation-eating). They all had one feature in common: a hollow in the skull behind the eye, which accommodated large jaw muscles. In time the mammallike reptiles became more and more like mammals. By about the beginning of the Jurassic period (150,000,000 years ago), a population of carnivorous mammallike reptiles seems to have given rise to small animals that clearly possessed the characteristics of mammals. The mammallike reptiles themselves became extinct.

How did a sluggish, sprawling reptile develop into an active, warmblooded mammal? We mentioned that the cotylosaurs crawled on their bellies. During the rise

In the mammallike reptiles certain bones hinged the lower jaw with the skull. By a remarkable transformation, these hinge bones came to have a different function in the mammals. They became part of a chain of bones in the middle ear — a chain that transmits vibrations from the eardrum to the inner ear. As a result of this and other changes, the lower jaw of mammals is now formed of only one bone.

Another change affected the nature of the teeth. From a row of simple, spike-like teeth, which the reptiles possessed, there developed the incisors, canine teeth and cheek teeth, or molars, of the mammals. These teeth were set in sockets of the jaw. On the crowns of the molars evolved several cusps, or points. The mammal's teeth could more efficiently nip off pieces of food, shear and grind it.

A secondary bony palate developed in the roof of the mammal's mouth. This structure, now found in all mammals, separates the nasal, or air, passages from the food passages. Consequently, the mammal can hold food in its mouth, chew it

In this drawing we show the skull and brain of a typical reptile (an alligator) and two mammals (a dog and a man). 1: skull of alligator; 2: skull of dog; 3: skull of man; A: brain of alligator; B: brain of dog; C: brain of man. The brain case enclosing the brain has expanded in the evolution of the higher mammals, making possible greater brain development.

and still continue to breathe; it does not have to bolt its food. Moreover, the secondary palate makes suckling possible.

The bony case enclosing the brain expanded during the evolution from mammallike reptile to mammal. This permitted greater brain growth and development. Especially important was the development of the cerebral cortex, a covering of gray

A further change involved the heart, which came to be divided into four chambers. Through this development, blood carrying oxygen from the lungs to the heart is kept entirely separate from the blood pouring into the heart from the rest of the body. As a result, the tissues constantly receive a rich supply of oxygen, picked up in the lungs.

TURTLE'S HEART   ALLIGATOR'S HEART   COW'S HEART

Three types of hearts. The initial letters "L.," "R.," "A.," and "V." stand, respectively, for "left," "right," "auricle" and "ventricle." The turtle's heart has three chambers; the cow's, four chambers. The alligator's heart has only three chambers, but one of these — the left ventricle — is divided into two distinct sections.

matter over the cerebral hemispheres. The cerebral cortex is a complex area of nerve cells; it is concerned with higher processes such as thinking and reasoning.

The changeover from reptile to mammal involved important alterations in the internal structure. For one thing, a sheet of muscle appeared, separating the thoracic, or chest, cavity from the abdominal region. This muscular partition is the diaphragm of mammals; it allows these animals to supplement rib breathing with belly breathing. Rib breathing, which occurs in the reptiles, is produced by muscular movements of the rib cage; it is not so efficient as belly breathing.

Oxygen is necessary for converting food substances into energy. The food of mammals is broken into small pieces, through chewing, before being swallowed; consequently it can be quickly digested in the stomach and intestine. The digested food particles are rapidly transported to the tissues by the circulatory system.

With a greater supply of oxygen and food in its tissues, there is a greater output of energy. Some of this goes into muscular work, making the mammal more active. Some takes the form of heat, which, carried by the blood, warms the body and causes many of its chemical reactions to proceed at a quicker rate.

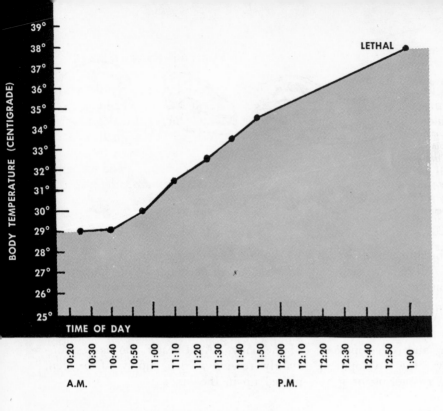

BODY TEMPERATURE (CENTIGRADE)

39°
38°
37°
36°
35°
34°
33°
32°
31°
30°
29°
28°
27°
26°
25°

LETHAL

TIME OF DAY

10:20 10:30 10:40 10:50 11:00 11:10 11:20 11:30 11:40 11:50 12:00 12:10 12:20 12:30 12:40 12:50 1:00

A.M.   P.M.

The body temperature of a typical reptile, such as an alligator, varies within wide limits, according to the external environment. This is strikingly shown in the above graph, adapted from one in the *Bulletin of the American Museum of Natural History,* Volume 86, Article 7. An alligator was tethered to a stake and subjected to the heat of direct sunlight for several hours (from about 10:20 A.M. to 1:00 P.M.). The body temperature gradually arose, as indicated, until a lethal, or fatal, point was reached (about 1:00 P.M.) In mammals there is generally little change in body temperature, except in hibernation (see Index).

As body temperature rises, the mammal's body requires more fuel (food), a greater consumption of oxygen and a higher production of carbon dioxide and other waste products. As a result, blood circulation is increased. Of course this requires increased filtration of the blood by the kidney.

The kidney of a mammal not only filters the blood of salts, sugar, water and wastes, such as urea, but also reabsorbs the sugar and most of the salt and water. Consequently a highly concentrated urine is produced, and water is conserved within the body.

The mammals developed a covering of hair, insulating the body against both excessive heat and cold. They also evolved an efficient control of their surface blood vessels. Because of this, blood can be turned, or shunted, away from the surface when body heat needs to be conserved during cold weather. In hot weather and during physical activity, the body temperature is kept down by dilating these same surface blood vessels. They then radiate heat; they also lose a watery fluid that escapes to the skin surface by way of the sweat glands. When a mammal sweats, the skin is moistened; evaporation of this moisture cools the body.

The milk glands of mammals secrete a rich, balanced, liquid diet for newborn offspring. Because this offspring depends for survival on its mother's milk, it is under parental care for some time.

The extended period of infant care clearly distinguishes the mammals from the reptiles, which do not give further attention to their young once the eggs are laid or the young are born. (Some reptiles bear living young.)

During the period of infant care, the young mammal has time to develop and learn a variety of responses. When it leaves the protection and guidance of its parent, it is fitted to modify its actions in the face of varying circumstances.

We pointed out that the first mammals probably arose about 150,000,000 years ago. These primitive mammals evolved into different types.

One group, the monotremes, has persisted down through the ages and is represented today by the platypus and spiny anteaters. They have fur and feed milk to their young, but they are very much like reptiles in many respects. For example, the waste products of the intestine, the urine and the sperm or eggs pass into a common chamber, called the cloaca, from which they are discharged. (The name "monotreme" means "single hole" in Greek.) This is the condition found in reptiles. The bones making up the shoulder and hip are very reptilian, as are certain features of the skull. Females lay reptilelike eggs.

Another group of primitive mammals, called pantotheres, were small creatures, omnivorous in habit: that is, they would eat almost anything. Sometime in the early Cretaceous period (120,000,000 years ago), the pantotheres gave rise to the marsupial mammals on the one hand and the placental mammals on the other.* These two groups changed but little during the long Cretaceous period, which lasted some 60,-000,000 years.

---

* The young of marsupial mammals are carried, from a very early stage of their development, in a marsupium, or pouch. Placental mammals retain their young within the body until development is quite complete. The name "placental" is derived from the placenta, a structure by means of which the fetus is nourished and discharges wastes in the uterus, or womb.

There are various differences between the skin of a mammal, such as man, and that of a reptile. Reptilian

During this time the reptiles, including the large and small carnivorous and herbivorous dinosaurs, ruled the land. The mammals continued to be small creatures; many of them probably lived in trees and were active only at night. The marsupials were omnivorous animals, the placentals were insect eaters.

By the end of the Cretaceous period (60,000,000 years ago), the dominant reptiles had dwindled in numbers or had become extinct. Cold and dry uplands had been created by the building of mountains and other geological changes. In these uplands the large reptiles were at a fatal disadvantage. The mammals, however, flourished under the changed conditions because they were warm-blooded creatures, and also because of their unrestricted diet, their exploratory activities and their more efficient reproduction. The extinction of

skin lacks glands and is drier than that of mammals. The epidermis is thinner; there is an absence of hair.

HUMAN SKIN

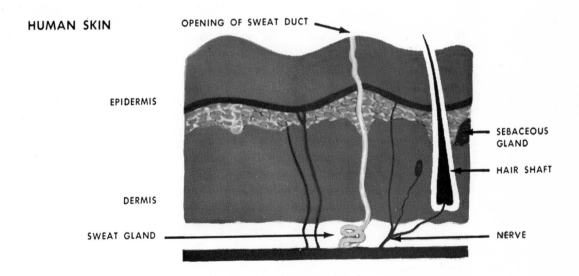

OPENING OF SWEAT DUCT

EPIDERMIS

DERMIS

SWEAT GLAND

SEBACEOUS GLAND

HAIR SHAFT

NERVE

SKIN OF REPTILE

EPIDERMIS

DERMIS

most of the reptiles left empty environments that could be filled by the mammals. The marsupials and placentals adapted to these new niches, changing more and more in form and habits until they occupied and exploited all the places where it was possible for them to live.

The female of the marsupial, as we have noted, rears her young in a special pouch on her belly. The marsupial embryo develops from a comparatively large-yolked egg cell in the female's uterus, or womb. While in the uterus, the embryo receives little or no nourishment from the mother; the young is born in a very undeveloped condition. (The newborn opossum is no larger than a bee.) It crawls into the shelter and warmth of the pouch, where the mammary glands are located, and hangs on to one of the nipples; milk is pumped into the young by the mother. The young remains in the pouch, attached to a nipple, until development is complete. Then it leaves the pouch to feed on its own, but frequently returns for protection.

Placental mammals differ in their manner of reproduction. The embryo develops from an egg cell having very little yolk. A membrane surrounding the embryo fuses with tissue lining the uterus of the female. This complex intergrowth of tissues from the wall of the uterus and from the embryo is the placenta. In this structure, blood vessels from the mother's and embryo's circulatory systems come into close contact. Though there is normally no exchange of maternal and embryonic blood, dissolved substances are transferred

between the two systems. Food and oxygen diffuse from the mother's blood into her developing young. Carbon dioxide and wastes, such as urea, are given off by the embryo to the maternal blood stream. When the young placental mammal is born — that is, delivered from the mother's uterus — it is in an advanced stage of development.

The placentals also differ from marsupials by having a more expanded brain case and a greater development of the cerebral hemispheres. They lack the cloaca, or common chamber for wastes and sex products, found in all the monotremes and marsupials. They are more aggressive and efficient than the marsupials. When they compete directly with marsupials for living space or food, the pouched mammals are usually bested.

Mammals and their environments

Mammals do not live in a vacuum. They must cope with the many factors of their environment — temperature, amount of moisture, humidity, light, vegetation, other species of animals and members of their own species. Some mammals are less adaptable than others. For example, the giant panda (a bearlike mammal) can live only in bamboo forests, subsisting on bamboo shoots; the koala, which is an Australian marsupial resembling a teddy bear, survives only if the leaves of one or two kinds of eucalyptus trees are available to it for food. On the other hand, the brown rat can live almost anywhere and

The young of the opossum, a typical marsupial. The young opossums have been taken out of the pouch of the mother in order to show their undeveloped state at birth. Each is firmly attached to a teat of the mother.

Water holes are vital to animals that feed on vegetation and to those that devour other animals. Not only do flesh-eaters need water themselves, but they prey on the herbivores living in the vicinity of water holes.

eat anything and has spread over most of the globe.

Though mammals are warm-blooded and generally control their internal temperature, the external temperature affects them. The white rat, for example, can maintain a nearly constant temperature when outside temperatures range from $-13°$ to $+104°$ F. If the outer temperature goes much beyond these extremes, the animal's own temperature regulation breaks down with fatal results.

Arctic foxes are active in winter even when the temperature drops to $-60°$ F.; during blizzards the animals dig shelters in the snow. On the other hand, the armadillo, woodchuck, hamster and some other rodents hibernate during winter; their body temperature actually falls to a level only slightly above that of the environment. Bears also sleep in winter, but this is not true hibernation; for by burning a rich store of body fat their body processes continue at a rate that is only slightly lower than normal.

High humidity is important for small bats; their wing membranes dry out if the humidity falls much below 85 per cent. Moles also require dampness, and their burrows are usually very humid. They will die if forced from their burrows by a prolonged dry spell.

The abundance of water is very important, for many mammals drink a great deal. The large African herbivores, such as the antelopes, zebras, elephants, giraffes and buffalo, regulate their movements according to the water sources. These sources are also vitally important to animals such

as lions, leopards and hyenas. Not only do they need water themselves, but they find their prey among the herbivores that live in the general vicinity of water holes.

Some mammals drink dew or rain water running off foliage when there is no temporary or permanent water supply. Others get along with the water contained in their animal or vegetable food. This is true of many carnivores, rabbits and hoofed mammals, as well as certain desert rodents, such as pocket mice and kangaroo rats.

Most strictly land-living, or terrestrial, mammals are capable of swimming. Certain mammals spend much or all of their time in water; they include the platypus, water opossum, water shrew, beaver, muskrat, water civet and otter. These animals are usually sleek of body and have dense fur; most have elongated, pointed snouts. The feet are usually completely or partially webbed; the tail is often flattened horizontally or from side to side.

The most completely aquatic mammals are the seals, manatees and whales. They have streamlined spindle-shaped, or torpedolike, bodies with extremely short necks and no external ears. The front limbs are converted into paddles, and, in the case of seals, the hind legs too. Whales and manatees lack hind legs but have broad horizontally flattened tails; some whales, such as the fast-swimming killer whales, even possess a fleshy fin on the back.

Several factors permit the aquatic mammals to remain submerged for some time. For one thing, these animals renew the air in their lungs, when breathing at the surface, more completely than do terrestrial animals. In addition to the oxygen in the lungs, extra oxygen is taken up by blood that flows from the lungs into special networks of blood vessels. Once a dive is made, the heartbeat slows down; blood continues to flow in the brain and other vital centers but is shut off from the rest of the body. Thus the oxygen of the blood is not quickly exhausted. A dive may be prolonged without the animal being forced to come to the surface for air.

Light is another environmental factor that affects mammals. A great many species remain secluded during the day and become active only at sundown or after dark. This is true of numerous small mammals, such as bats, flying squirrels, badgers, shrews, rats, mice, anteaters and raccoons, to mention a few. Other species, including moles, monkeys, tree squirrels and ground squirrels, are most active by day. The large-hoofed mammals and the cats, foxes, coyotes and rabbits may be active day or night.

In addition to regulating daily activity, light also controls the time of mating in some mammals. For example, the reproductive glands of the ferret mature as the amount of daylight increases each day during the spring. On the other hand, with such mammals as goats and deer, a decrease in the amount of daylight per day, as in the fall, stimulates reproductive activity.

Light may also govern the molting cycle.* When daylight decreases day by day in the fall, weasels replace their summer pelage of brown with one of white. They change again to a brown coat when daylight increases in the spring. This is true of the snowshoe rabbit, which has a brown summer pelage and a white winter one.

When mammals such as sheep, dogs and white rats go from low to high altitudes, their red blood cells increase in number. At sea level, sheep, for example, have 10,500,000 red blood cells per cubic millimeter of blood. At an elevation of 16,000 feet their red blood cells increase to 16,-000,000. This increase is an adaptation

---

* The pelage, or hair, of mammals is shed in periodic molts. Some mammals molt in spring and autumn; others, only in the autumn.

for the high altitudes, where the amount of oxygen in the atmosphere is reduced. Since the red blood cells carry oxygen, more of them are needed in order to supply the body tissues with sufficient oxygen. The llama, vicuña and viscacha (a rodent), which permanently live in the Andes at elevations of 12,000 to over 15,000 feet, have an even better adaptation. Their hemoglobin (pigment of the red blood cells) has a much greater capacity for carrying oxygen than does the hemoglobin of lowland-living species.

Certain mammals dig shelters in the soil; others live entirely underground. The platypus, various marsupials, many rodents and rabbits, armadillos and carnivores, such as foxes and skunks, dig simple shelters in which to sleep, hide and bring forth and care for their young. Voles, hamsters and various ground squirrels, including woodchucks and chipmunks, store food and hibernate, during winter, in their burrows. The truly subterranean mammals such as the marsupial mole, the true moles, the mole rats and the pocket gophers dig nesting chambers, chambers for storing food, connecting galleries and galleries in which they hunt food. They are completely adapted for an underground life, having thick, short hair and strong, oversized digging claws on the front feet. Their eyes are minute or missing; external ears are lacking or almost so. Moles hunt underground insects, insect larvae and earthworms; the mole rats and gophers feed on plant roots and tubers.

Plants serve mammals in many important ways. Grassy clumps, patches of weeds, bushes and the crowns of trees afford ideal places for small mammals to take shelter from the elements and escape the attack of carnivores and birds of prey. Kangaroos, deer, various antelopes, buffalo and elephants find the forest a good refuge.

Vegetation attracts hordes of insects, which provide food for numerous small mammals, including opossums, shrews, hedgehogs, bats, civets, skunks and certain ground squirrels and monkeys.

A number of mammals live in trees and only rarely descend to the ground.

An accomplished acrobat
— the spider monkey.

Among the most specialized of these animals are certain monkeys and apes. They have developed great dexterity with their hands and feet. The thumb and great toe can be opposed to the other fingers and toes of the hand and foot; this permits a very good grasp of tree branches. The whole hand and wrist are exceptionally mobile, and the long arms can move in almost any direction because of the great freedom in the shoulder joint. Gibbons and spider monkeys are very good at swinging by their arms from branch to branch. Some South American monkeys, such as spider and howling monkeys, possess a prehensile, or grasping, tail as an additional means for climbing and remaining secure in the trees.

Tree squirrels live only where there are trees. They cling to a trunk or branch by their sharp claws. A sloth spends its life upside down in trees, using enlarged, hooklike claws to hang from a branch; it travels on the ground only with great difficulty.

Some mammals glide, sometimes for considerable distances, from tree to tree. This is true of the flying lemurs, flying squirrels and the squirrellike marsupials known as flying and gliding phalangers. All have a furry membrane along the sides of the body extending between the front and hind limbs. When gliding, the membrane is stretched so that the animals almost float through the air like parachutes.

Plants serve numerous mammals as food. These animals are adapted in various ways for a vegetarian diet. Fruit-eating bats, for instance, have flattened

grinding teeth. Some bats even possess an elongated tongue for feeding on nectar. The monkeys and apes eat a considerable variety of foods; vegetation forms a good part of their diet. The stomachs of guerezas — monkeys of tropical Africa — are divided into a number of open sacs, which aid in digesting leafy food. The aquatic sea "cows" (manatee and dugong) are herbivorous mammals that use their lips to crop aquatic plants; these are digested in a complex stomach. Bears eat a good deal of plant food, including roots and berries.

Rodents and rabbits are well-known plant eaters. Their front teeth, or incisors, are formed like chisels and are used for gnawing; the molars are developed for grinding. Rabbits eat fresh, green food voraciously. Some of this is completely digested in the intestines; in this case the waste is excreted normally. Some of the green food, however, is fermented for a while in the caecum, which is a blind pouch off the large intestine. The food is then excreted, eaten again and passed through the digestive tract a second time. More energy can be obtained from a given quantity of food as a result.

Rodents often have storage places for food; hamsters, voles, squirrels and kangaroo rats store various seeds, bulbs, tubers, roots, nuts or mushrooms. The beaver provides itself with a winter supply of branches and trunks of poplar, aspen, cottonwood and willow, from which it gnaws the bark. The material is submerged near the animal's lodge sufficiently deep in the water to prevent its being caught in the ice.

Among the most specialized of the herbivores are the kangaroos and hoofed mammals. Kangaroos have a single pair of lower incisor teeth with sharp inner edges, perfect for cutting grass. The horses and their kin crop grass and other vegetation with gripping incisors in the upper and lower jaws. Deer, cattle and their relatives possess only lower incisors;

The howling monkey, an inhabitant of South America, is at home in the trees. It uses its prehensile, or grasping, tail in moving from branch to branch.

9

ESOPHAGUS

RETICULUM

OMASUM

ABOMASUM
(TRUE STOMACH)

RUMEN

COW'S STOMACH

Four-chambered stomach of the cow. Food first enters the rumen; from this it passes into the reticulum, where it is made into small masses, known as cuds. These are cast up to the mouth, where they are chewed at leisure. When swallowed again, the food passes to the omasum and from there to the abomasum (true stomach).

these work against a horny pad on the upper jaw for cropping. The tongue helps bring food to the mouth. It is covered with horny projections; it is large, mobile and pointed and can be considerably extended out of the mouth. The molar teeth of all these mammals have broad, grinding surfaces. The molars of the elephant are immense; this huge animal collects plant food with its trunk.

In the digestive system of kangaroos, deer, cattle and some other mammals, there is a chamber or sac in which bacteria break down the cellulose of plants so that the products can be used by the animal. Bacterial action takes place in the large intestine of horses. Deer, giraffes, antelopes, cattle, sheep and goats all have a complex, four-chambered stomach. Food is received into the first two stomachs when it is initially swallowed; here bacteria reduce the food to a cud (pulp). This is brought back into the mouth for chewing; later it is swallowed and further digested in the last two stomachs. Animals digesting food in this way are called ruminants.

Carnivores have teeth specialized for their flesh-eating habits. In general the incisors are developed for nipping and piercing, and the canines are elongated into daggers that stab and slash. Certain cheek teeth — called carnassials — in the upper

and lower jaws are formed into blades; as the jaws close, the carnassials shear past each other, like the blades of a pair of scissors and so cut or slice flesh and sinew. The hinder molars, not needed for grinding, are usually reduced in number and size; dogs and bears, however, have fairly well-developed molars that serve a grinding function. The hyenas possess massive bone-cracking teeth.

The land-living carnivores are strong and quick-reacting animals. Some can deliver powerful blows with their sharply clawed front feet. Many are strongly muscled in the limbs, allowing for climbing, leaping or the rapid pursuit of prey. The cheetah, or hunting leopard, the fastest of all terrestrial animals, can reach a speed of 65 to 70 miles an hour over a comparatively short distance.

Marine carnivores, such as the seals, lack carnassial teeth but have simple, pointed teeth used for catching and holding fish. The walrus' tusks are modified canine teeth that root up bottom-living crustaceans and mollusks; these are ground by the walrus' broad, crushing cheek teeth.

Certain whales, such as porpoises, sperm whales and killer whales, have simplified teeth, capable of grasping fish and squids or tearing apart the flesh of birds, seals and other whales. Other whales, such as the blue whale, possess a series of sheets of baleen — a horny substance — hanging down from the roof of the mouth. The baleen is frayed along the inner edge. It strains out plankton (see Index) from the water after the whale has engulfed a mouthful of water and animals.

The jaguar, a big land-living carnivore, can deliver powerful blows with its sharply clawed front feet.

The giant armadillo is protected by bony plates. Its front claws are sometimes used as defensive weapons.

Many mammals feed on insects. The winged mammals called bats catch insects while on the wing by opening the very large mouth. It is believed that the species that have a membrane between the hind legs may sometimes curve this membrane, in flight, so as to form a cup. The cup dips insects out of the air; the bat bends down its head, while still in flight, and eats its prey out of this pocket.

Certain mammals eat ants or termites almost exclusively; they include the spiny anteaters, the marsupial anteater, the true anteaters, the scaly anteaters (or pangolins) and the aardvark. Though they are not related to one another, these mammals have several features in common. The front feet possess stout digging claws for ripping apart termite and ant nests. The snout is elongated, and from it can be extended a long, thin tongue, sticky from the secretions of well-developed salivary glands. The teeth are reduced in size and number.

**How mammals protect
themselves from enemies**

Mammals can protect themselves from their natural enemies in various ways. One of the most obvious protective measures is to run away. Kangaroos and hares, for instance, have long hind legs that give them good speed in a bounding escape flight. The hoofed mammals have slender, elongated, running-type legs that lift the body high off the ground; the animals run on their toenails, which are modified into hoofs.

An escaping mammal, if pressed too closely by an attacker, may seek to defend itself. Various methods are employed. The anteaters and sloths lash out with their long, strong claws; rodents and opossums bite their enemies. Hoofed mammals kick out with their feet, or use their tusks, horns or antlers.

Sometimes, instead of running away, many mammals may freeze on the spot. This is common with young fawns; their lack of movement and their dappled coat generally cause them to be overlooked by a predator. Hares will remain motionless until one comes close to them; then they bound away in a zigzag flight. The opossum "plays dead," lying limp with eyes closed and tongue hanging out of its partly opened mouth.

Many of the smaller mammals move about only at night or under the cover of vegetation or under fallen leaves and other debris of the forest floor. The large cud-chewing hoofed mammals come out into the open to feed rapidly. They then quickly return to cover, where they chew the cud and digest their food at leisure and in security.

Armadillos and pangolins are armored with horny plates or scales. When danger threatens they roll up so that only the protected surfaces of the body are exposed to an attacker. Hedgehogs, porcupines and spiny anteaters are protected by hairs that are modified into sharp spines or quills.

Civets, mongooses and skunks spray an attacker with an evil-smelling liquid — a secretion from modified sebaceous glands (see Index) in the region of the anus.

Many mammals are patterned or colored in such a way that they blend well with the background. If they refrain from moving, it is usually all but impossible to make them out. For example, the white winter coat of many weasels, foxes, hares and lemmings blends with the snow. Many desert mammals are pale buff or tawny, "melting in" beautifully with the desert soils.

**The social
life of mammals**

Apart from the relations between a mother mammal and her young, a host of social relations exist among the adults and young of a population. Among the most conspicuous of these is dominance, in which one individual ranks over one or more of its fellows. The more dominant animal eats first; it displays aggressive behavior toward its inferiors. In a given mammal

Herd of elephants. These huge animals, like many other mammals, are social creatures and usually travel about in large groups.

population, male 1, say, dominates males 2, 3 and 4; male 2 dominates males 3 and 4; and male 3 dominates male 4. The same order may follow among females and among the young. The males dominate the females; the adults dominate the young.

Family groups are common among certain mammals. For example, the American beaver lives in a group consisting of two adults, the young of the current year and often the young of the year before. When the young reach maturity they are driven away. Howling monkeys form clans consisting of several adult males, a greater number of females and a variable number of young.

Fur seals and sea lions live in herds for the greater part of the year. During the breeding season, the adult males form harems of several females. At this time immature individuals and adult bulls that have not been able to gather any cows make up a separate group. A number of other species of seals live in herds but never form harems. The males and females breed at random.

Elephants, members of the horse family, hippopotamuses, many of the piglike mammals, giraffes, vicuñas, a majority of the deer and most of the cattle, antelopes, sheep and goats are social creatures. Generally the males associate with one or several females only during mating time. After breeding, the males abandon their mates or harems and establish herds of males only or else lead a solitary life. The females and young collect in a herd of their own, "controlled" by an adult female leader.

Certain mammals are not social. The chipmunk is intolerant of any others of its species. Only for mating do the sexes come together; and immediately afterward the male and female become antagonistic toward one another. The female associates with her young only as long as they remain in the nest. Bears, too, join company only to mate. During the rest of the year, the males live by themselves; the females, however, are followed by their cubs for a fairly long time.

Most mammals do not roam about at random; they restrict their explorations and food-searching activities to a home range. The mammal's lodging place — nest, burrow, thicket or other shelter — is within this range. There are also various places where the animal can attend to its comfort. For example, deer include in their home range wallowing places in which

12

Spiny anteater: order Monotremata.

Duck-billed platypus: order Monotremata.

to take mud baths. The badger has a particular spot for sunning itself. Zebras, bears and bison use termite nests or trees as "rubbing posts." In general, the size of the range of a particular mammal depends upon the amount of food available for its needs. Tigers, lions, wolves and bears have an extensive home range. At the other extreme there is the woolly opossum, which may stay in a single tree for several months.

Though many mammals spend the whole of their lives within a home range, some species migrate; that is, they travel from one area to another and back again. We discuss these migrations in the article Animal Migrations, in Volume 9.

Classification
of the mammals

There are eighteen orders of living mammals in the class Mammalia. The monotremes, belonging to the first order, are reptilelike and only remotely related to the rest of the mammals. The second order is made up of the marsupials. The animals grouped together in the remaining sixteen orders are placental mammals. Following is a brief account of the different orders.

Monotremata: duck-billed platypus, spiny anteaters. The monotremes are like reptiles in certain features of their skeleton and their egg-laying habit. They burrow and make nests to help protect the young. When adult, monotremes lack teeth. The platypus, of Australia and Tasmania, has a flattened bill covered with soft skin, and uses it to stir the mud of streams and lake bottoms as it seeks insect larvae, worms, mussels and snails. Its tail is flattened and its feet are webbed. Spiny anteaters, which possess a mixture of spines and hair on the back, have elongated faces and tongues adapted for eating ants. Spiny anteaters live in Australia and New Guinea.

Marsupialia: opossums, pouched mice, native cats, Tasmanian devil, Tasmanian wolf, banded anteater, pouched mole, bandicoots, opossum-rats, phalangers, koala, wombats, rat kangaroos, wallabies, kangaroos. These pouched mammals are found mainly in Australia and surrounding islands; the opossum-rats and opossums occur in South, Central and North America. Female marsupials usually have a pouch, or fur-lined pocket — the marsupium — in which the larvalike young complete their development. The marsupial's brain is small.

There are pouched mammals that resemble rats, mice, rabbits, woodchucks, squirrels, flying squirrels, moles, anteaters, small bears, otters, cats and wolves. The largest living marsupial is the giant red kangaroo, weighing two hundred pounds and standing seven feet high when raised up on its powerful tail and hind legs. The smallest is the shrew opossum of Brazil; it weighs less than a half dollar.

Insectivora: solenodon, tenrecs, golden mole, hedgehogs, elephant shrews, shrews, moles. These are small, secretive, mostly ground-living and nocturnal animals that feed on insects or are omnivorous. The snout is elongated; the cerebral hemispheres are small. There are five toes on the front and hind feet. Insectivores have a full complement of teeth — incisors, canines, premolars and molars. Some species still possess a cloaca; and the regulation of body temperature in many insectivores seems to be imperfect.

The solenodon, from Cuba and Haiti, and the tenrecs, from Madagascar, are somewhat like hedgehogs. The golden mole and elephant shrews are found in Africa; hedgehogs, in the Old World. Moles occur in Asia, Europe and North America; one kind, the desman of Europe, is an aquatic form with webbed feet. The mouselike shrews are found almost everywhere; some are aquatic in habit.

Dermoptera: colugos, or flying lemurs. The colugos, from the East Indies and the Philippines, are much like insectivores except that they are adapted for gliding. Broad, furry skin folds extend, at the side of the body, between the front and hind legs and onto the tail; when the colugo stretches its legs, the animal becomes a furry kite, gliding long distances from one tree to another. Colugos are the size of squirrels. They have foxlike faces; they eat leaves, flowers and fruit. When sleeping, they hang upside down from a branch, with all four feet grasping it.

Wallaby: order Marsupialia.

Elephant shrew: order Insectivora.

Flying lemur: order Dermoptera.

Bat: order
Chiroptera.

Giant anteater: order Edentata.

Chiroptera: bats. These are the only mammals that can truly fly, doing so by flapping their wings. The bats are essentially insectivores. They have greatly elongated bones in the front limbs and fingers for supporting the wing membranes. The hind legs are weak, making the animals almost helpless on the ground; they cannot walk, but can crawl and climb. When resting, bats hang upside down clutching a support with the clawed toes of the hind feet.

Bats are found on all continents, except Antarctica, and most oceanic islands. Large fruit-eating bats live in the tropics and subtropics of the Old World; the largest of these, called flying foxes, have a five-foot wing span. Most of the smaller species feed mainly on insects, which they catch on the wing. Several bats catch fish by hovering over the water's surface and seizing the quarry with their hind feet. Vampire bats, of Central and South America, feed on blood; they pierce the skin of large mammals with special pointed incisor teeth and lap the blood oozing from the small wound.

Edentata: anteaters, sloths, armadillos. The edentates are close relatives of the insectivores but are specialized for climbing and digging. Well-developed, long and stout claws arm the feet. The diet is somewhat restricted; hence, the teeth are reduced in number and are simplified. Additional joints in the backbone make edentates very strong. The brain is comparatively small, having poorly developed cerebral hemispheres. Edentates occur in South and Central America; one species, the nine-banded armadillo, is found in the southern part of the United States.

The anteaters have an elongated, tube-shaped snout, which is used to probe anthills and termite nests. They lack teeth. Sloths, which have a round head and a short face, are leaf eaters. They have no front teeth; the back teeth are simplified and lack a covering of enamel. Armadillos are covered by armor; shields of small flat bones in the skin, topped by horny plates, cover the shoulder and hip areas. Between these bony shields are bands of horny plates giving flexibility to the back. The top of the head and the tail are protected also by horny plates. As with the sloths, there are no front teeth; the teeth along the sides of the jaw are simple pegs without enamel. Armadillos feed on insects, carrion and whatever else they can find on the ground. They are excellent burrowers.

Pholidota: pangolins, or scaly anteaters. The pangolins are like anteaters but have evolved independently from an insectivore ancestor. They have an elongated snout, large claws and no teeth. Flattened, leaflike, horny scales cover the back and sides of the body from the nose to the tip of the long tail. These scales, which are composed of fused hairs, overlap like the scales of a pine cone. Pangolins live in tropical Africa and Asia; they are nocturnal, and several species can climb trees very well.

Primates: tree shrews, lemurs, lorises, galagos, tarsiers, New World monkeys, Old World monkeys, apes, man. The primates are closely related to the insectivores and apparently directly evolved from them. They have five digits, with nails instead of claws, on each hand and foot. The teeth are much like those of the insectivores. The diet is usually unrestricted, though vegetable matter makes up a good part of it.

The primates are adapted for living in trees and have developed great dexterity with their fingers and toes, permitting the efficient grasping of tree branches and the manipulation of objects. These animals have developed their vision to a high degree. Because the eyes look forward, making the fields of vision overlap, primates enjoy vision with depth. A flexible neck permits the eyes to be turned in any direction. The primates surpass all other animals in mental development. The brain, especially the cerebral hemispheres, is large. After birth, the young primate takes an unusually long time to develop and depends on parental guidance during much of its immature life. Family life is well established.

Primates are mostly forest-living animals of the Old and New World tropics and subtropics. Man, with the aid of his inventions, lives in almost all environments anywhere on the earth.

Rodentia: mountain beaver, tree squirrels, ground squirrels (including marmots, woodchucks, prairie dogs, chipmunks), flying squirrels, pocket gophers, pocket mice, kangaroo rats, beaver, New World mice (including wood, pack and cotton rats), hamsters, lemmings, voles (including muskrats, meadow mice), antelope rats, mole rats, bamboo rats, Old World rats and mice (introduced everywhere and including house rats and mice),

Gorilla: order
Primates.

Sloth: order Edentata.

Pangolin: order Pholidota.

African tree mice, dormice, jumping mice, jerboas, porcupines, Guinea pigs, capybaras, pacas, chinchillas, coypus and many others. There are more species of rodents than all other species of mammals combined.

Rodents have just four front teeth, two in the upper jaw and two in the lower one; these form large, sharp-edged chisels used for gnawing. Ridges on the cheek teeth permit the thorough grinding of hard grain and other plant material. Rodents are usually herbivorous; but they often eat insects and some species are omnivorous.

The skull of the rodent is long and low. The forelimbs are flexible enough for climbing, running and handling food. Usually there are five toes on each foot. Some rodents that are adapted for hopping have elongated, powerful hind legs and comparatively short front limbs.

Rodents have a great capacity for reproduction; this and their generally small size account for their great success in the world. They occur almost everywhere. Rodents would be the dominant mammals of the earth except for one thing — they are not so intelligent as we are.

Lagomorpha: pikas, or conies, hares, rabbits. These superficially resemble rodents but are not closely related to them. They have chisellike front teeth, but unlike rodents, the lagomorphs have a second, smaller pair of incisor teeth in the upper jaw. The cheek teeth cut vegetable food rather than grind or crush it.

Pikas are small, compact, short-legged mammals with short, rounded ears; they live in mountainous country of Eurasia and North America. Rabbits and hares are short-tailed, long-eared mammals adapted for hopping and running swiftly; the elongated hind legs give the power for long leaps, while the front limbs take up the shock of landing. Rabbits and hares occur in the Northern Hemisphere and have been introduced in Australia.

Cetacea: toothed whales (including river dolphins, beaked whales, sperm whales, narwhal, dolphins, killer whales, porpoises), whale-bone (or baleen) whales (including rorquals, humpbacked whales, blue whales, right whales). Cetaceans are highly specialized for an aquatic life. There is little or no hair on the body. Beneath the skin is a thick layer of oil-impregnated fibrous

tissue — the blubber; it may insulate the body or serve as a food-storage tissue.

The nostrils of whales (except those of the sperm whale) lie on the top of the head; the nasal passages go directly to the lungs by crossing the back of the throat in a species of closed tube. The brain of the whales is large and is highly developed; there is no sense of smell, but whales are keenly sensitive to water vibrations. The newborn whale is fed milk pumped into it by the mother. The young one seizes the mother's teats; these lie in a partially closed pouch that prevents the baby from swallowing too much sea water as it nurses.

The toothed whales have few or numerous simple, peglike teeth. The male narwhal has a single upper tooth that projects straight out of the front of the head as a long tusk. In the whalebone whales sheets of baleen, hanging down from the roof of the mouth, strain tiny organisms out of the water. Whales vary in size from small, five-foot species to giants one hundred feet long. They live in all oceans; some species frequent the fresh waters of large tropical rivers.

Carnivora: dogs, wolves, foxes, hunting dogs, bears, racoons, pandas, weasels (including ferrets, minks, wolverines, badgers, skunks, otters), civets, mongooses, hyenas, cats (from the lion to the domestic tabby), ear seals (including fur seals, sea lions), walrus, true seals (including common, harbor and harp seals, elephant seal). These mammals are highly specialized for hunting medium-sized to large prey. They usually have lithe and powerful bodies. The jaws are strong. Generally there are four or five toes, armed with sharp claws, on each foot. Carnivores have large, well-developed brains; they are extremely alert mammals with quick and well-co-ordinated movements. One or more of the senses of smell, vision and hearing are keen. Not all carnivores, by any means, eat flesh entirely; some species, such as the pandas, are vegetarians.

Land-living carnivores are either adapted for climbing or for running with great speed, though normally only over short distances. The seals and walrus are marine carnivores, streamlined of body; the feet have been transformed into paddles with webbing between the toes. Carnivores are native to all continents or their surrounding waters, and have also been introduced in Australia.

Jack rabbit: order Lagomorpha.

Right whale: order Cetacea.

Walrus: order Carnivora.

Aardvark: order Tubulidentata.

African elephant: order Proboscidea.

Tubulidentata: aardvarks. These short-legged, nocturnal, African mammals are the size of a small pig. The head is long and pulled out into an elongated tubular snout. Long, slender ears surmount the head. The tail is heavy and tapering. With its powerful front legs and sharp, flat nails, the aardvark digs burrows and tears up the nests of termites upon which it feeds. The cheek teeth are small cylinders lacking enamel; there are no incisors or canine teeth.

Proboscidea: Asiatic and African elephants. These are the largest of land mammals. The flexible muscular trunk is formed by the elongation of the nose and upper lip. The trunk's tip is a sensitive grasping organ. Tusks are protruding upper incisor teeth, which continue to grow long after adulthood is reached. Vegetable food is ground up by the enormous, tall, cross-ridged, cheek teeth. Elephants walk almost on the tips of the five toes of each foot. The brain is large.

Hyracoidea: hyraxes. The hyraxes, of Africa and Asia Minor, resemble rabbits somewhat in appearance and habit, though they have short ears and some live in trees. Two upper front, chisel-shaped incisors oppose four incisor teeth in the lower jaw. The cheek teeth are large and have grinding surfaces for crushing vegetable food. The four toes on the front feet and the three on the hind feet end in small, hooflike nails.

Sirenia: dugong (or sea cow), manatees. The naked-skinned sirenians are related to the hoofed mammals but are modified for an aquatic mode of life. The body is streamlined, and the head is low, ending in a blunt, bristly snout. The brain is small. Manatees live along the Atlantic coasts of Africa and the tropical Americas, sometimes going far up the larger rivers; the dugong inhabits the coasts of the Red Sea, Indian Ocean and western Pacific.

Perissodactyla: horses (including asses and zebras), tapirs, rhinoceroses. These are the hoofed mammals with odd-numbered toes. In these animals the axis of the foot passes through the mid-dle, or third, toe, which is best developed. The horse has one functional toe on each foot; the tapirs and rhinos, three. The toes end in hoofs. Horses have elongated limbs specialized for swift running; the tapir's legs and feet are short and stocky. The odd-toed hoofed mammals have a full set of incisor teeth for cropping plants.

Wild horses occur in Asia and Africa; but domestic forms are world-wide in distribution. The rhinoceroses, of Africa and Asia, carry horns that are formed of clumped masses of hair without a bony core. Tapirs, which live in the East Indies and Central and South America, have the nose elongated into a short, flexible trunk.

Artiodactyla: pigs (including water hog, wart hog, babirussa, peccaries), hippopotamuses, camels (including llama, vicuña), chevrotains, deer (including musk deer, muntjak, fallow deer, elk, moose, caribou), giraffe, pronghorn, cattlelike mammals, antelopelike mammals, goatlike mammals. These are the hoofed animals with even-numbered toes; the axis of the foot passes between the third and fourth toes. There are either two or four functional toes, usually bearing hoofs, on each foot. In many of these mammals the incisor teeth are replaced by a horny pad against which the lower incisors bite when cropping plants. The canine teeth of some species are elongated into tusks used for fighting; in other species the canines are small or lacking. The rear cheek teeth have excellent grinding surfaces. The brain is moderately well-developed, and the senses of smell, sight and hearing are usually very good. Those forms called ruminants — such as deer, giraffes, cattle and their kin — have the stomach divided into four compartments. The horns of cattle and antelopes are formed of a horny material over a bony core. Deer antlers are bony outgrowths, which are shed periodically. The even-toed hoofed mammals are native to all continents except Australia, where domestic forms have been introduced, and Antarctica.

See also Vol. 10, p. 275: "Mammals."

Tapir: order Perissodactyla.

Dugong: order Sirenia.

Wart hog: order Artiodactyla.

UNUSUAL PETS *

How to Collect and Keep Wild Creatures

BY JOHN C. ORTH

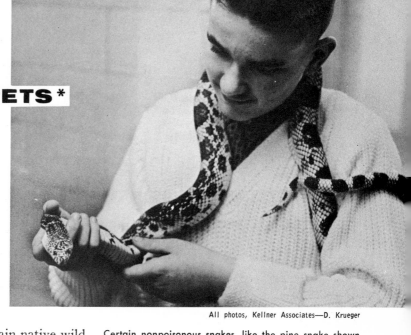

All photos, Kellner Associates—D. Krueger

Certain nonpoisonous snakes, like the pine snake shown here, make excellent pets. Never try to make a pet of a poisonous snake, such as a rattlesnake or a copperhead.

PROPERLY cared for, certain native wild animals make wonderful pets. You must always remember, however, that from the moment you capture and cage a wild creature, you take on certain responsibilities. You become its provider and its protector. It goes without saying that it is inhuman to make an animal a captive and then to neglect or mistreat it.

Various states in the United States and provinces in Canada have laws against collecting and keeping certain forms of wildlife. This is particularly true in the case of mammals and birds, although some regions also protect amphibians and reptiles of certain species. However, there are many forms of animal life that you can keep without a permit if you are sincerely interested in collecting, studying and exhibiting them in a home zoo. Before you attempt to keep any wild creature as a pet — especially a bird or a mammal — find out what the law is where you live. You can get information from your wildlife or game commissioner, a game warden or perhaps an Audubon club.

Some creatures, such as foxes, raccoons, woodchucks and certain kinds of birds and reptiles, do not take to captivity readily when they are caught as adults. Do not try to keep them, because fierce animals

in captivity will give you no particular satisfaction. On the other hand, many of these animals often make fine pets if caught when young.

It is advisable to keep birds and also the larger mammals, such as raccoons, foxes and opossums, out of doors. All of our small native mammals and birds, except those that hibernate or migrate, can be left outdoors in winter provided they have good shelter boxes to protect them from the elements. Reptiles and amphibians will do better if kept indoors.

Mammals are particularly responsive, but many other forms of animal life make satisfying pets. By observing the habits and actions of all these animals closely, you will learn many interesting things. You may even unearth new facts about them.

If there is a zoo in your vicinity, by all means visit it. Study the cages of small animals and the methods used to care for the animals. The keepers will probably be very glad to give you useful hints, if you ask questions.

This article will deal mainly with the kinds of animal life that need to be kept in some sort of cage. Other articles in THE BOOK OF POPULAR SCIENCE tell how to keep insects and other small creatures.

Editor's note: We wish to acknowledge the co-operation of the following in the preparation of photographs for this article: Staten Island Zoo: Natural Science Center for Young People, American Museum of Natural History; Mrs. Robert A. Winston and family; Mrs. Emmett Garrick and family.

Certain wild-animal pets will have to be confined in cages at all times. Below we show a cage for a small mammal. The metal tray fits into a space left in the front. In some cases, wild-animal pets, particularly those caught when very young, can be given a considerable amount of freedom. At the right are two young raccoons which have the run of their owner's yard and which live in the tree house in which they are shown here.

How to build a home for a small mammal

It may seem a bit odd to discuss cages before we take up the matter of collecting animals. You must keep in mind, however, that once an animal is captured, an adequate cage must be ready to receive it, or one must be built immediately. It is cruel to confine an animal in a small space where it cannot be properly cared for. When building a cage for a mammal or bird, remember that this creature has been used to unlimited freedom of movement. Hence the larger the cage, the better. Of course, no matter how roomy it is, it still confines the animal to some extent. Strangely enough, however, captive animals often get used to their cages after a short period of time. At the Bear Mountain Trailside Museums, animals seem to look to their cages for protection. Many times when one of these animals has been given its freedom, it has returned to its cage. If the door has been left open, it has entered.

Cages for squirrels, raccoons and other climbing animals should be at least 6 feet high and no less than 4 feet square. Ground-dwelling animals, such as the woodchuck, skunk and fox, do not need a high cage, but do require more room for movement on the ground. The minimum size of the bottom of the cage for woodchucks and skunks is 4 feet by 6 feet; for more active animals, such as foxes, it should be at least 4 feet by 10 feet. Every part of the floor must be within easy reach for cleaning. For the framework, 2-inch by 4-inch wood construction is best; but 2-inch by 2-inch pieces, if properly braced, will prove quite satisfactory.

The floor can be made of wood planking; however, concrete or heavily painted sheet iron is best for good cleaning. A cage set directly on the ground is unsatisfactory, unless it can be moved from one spot to another without too much effort. The reason for this is that the ground becomes fouled quickly and the cage bottom cannot be thoroughly cleaned. Another disadvantage is that unless adequate underground guards are provided, the animal will probably be able to dig its way out with ease.

Wire should be attached to the framework on all four sides. It should be nailed on from the inside; otherwise the animals, whatever their species, will be very likely to chew the framework. The size of the wire you will use will depend on the kind of animal you want to keep. For an all-purpose cage, 1-inch by 1-inch welded wire is best. It is advisable to roof over a tall cage entirely; a pitch toward the back of about one inch to the foot will be enough to carry off the rain. In the case of long, low cages,

Here are two traps for small animals. Above is a simple drop trap. The stick is pulled out by the trapper when the animal is under the trap. At the right is a bait trap. The door (1) is held open by a cord (2), passing through a hole in the frame (3), and by a ring (4), held in place by a pin (5). When the animal pulls the bait (6), the pin slips out of the ring. The door is released and it falls shut, trapping the animal.

only one third or one half should be roofed. For the door, use a heavy, well-braced wooden frame, covered with wire of the same size used on the cage.

Every cage should be provided with a shelter box into which the animal can retire when sleeping or during bad weather. This box should furnish adequate space for the animal. The opening, however, should be just large enough so that it can enter. The object is to protect the animal from drafts; this is particularly important in the case of tiny babies.

Most animals require a certain amount of sunlight if they are to thrive and the cage should be placed accordingly. In areas where temperatures soar, select a cool, well-shaded situation where the cage will receive a certain amount of morning or late-afternoon sun. In more temperate regions, locations more exposed to the sun are permissible. However, the cage should never be put in a place where the heat will become intolerable to the animal. When the temperature becomes high, hose down the area around the cage, as well as the cage itself. Always bear in mind that some sunlight is essential but that too much can be fatal.

Some animal fanciers prefer to keep an inch or two of soft wood shavings or other absorbent material on the bottom of cages. This practice has certain advantages as far as cleaning is concerned. The great disadvantage is that the shavings often become mixed with food and water and may cause your animals to suffer from indigestion.

The best way to keep a large cage clean is to put nothing on the floor and to hose it out at regular intervals; in good weather, the cages dry rapidly. It is often advisable to apply some mild disinfectant to the bottom of the cage before using the hose.

For mammals of chipmunk size or smaller, you can buy excellent cages at a pet shop; these are of all-metal construction for the most part. If you are handy with tools, it is a simple matter to build small cages to meet any requirements.

Collecting and feeding small mammals

Before you can keep a wild animal pet, you must first catch it. Although you can buy excellent live traps, it is part of the fun of this hobby to build your own traps. Many of them consist of a small cage with a door, or doors, that will close when the animal either steps on a treadle or tugs on the bait. There are various ways in which the tripping mechanism can be constructed; one of them is illustrated on this page. The traps should be built in such a way that the animal will not be injured either by the springing of the trap or by its frightened efforts to escape. Once it has been trapped, the best way to get an animal to its cage is to carry it home in the trap. Set the trap in the cage and open it, leaving the animal free to get out into its larger quarters. If you

Raccoon approaching a garbage-can trap. The bait is set at the bottom of the can, which is tilted at an angle. A plank is set against the can so that it forms a ramp from the ground. Once the animal is in the can, it will not be able to get out, since the inside of the can has been coated with Vaseline or with machine oil.

cannot put the trap in the cage, hold it up to the open door of the cage and let the animal out.

There is another kind of trap, in which no tripping mechanism is used. It consists of a large open receptacle, such as a garbage can. Set bait at the bottom of the can and tilt the can at an angle which will lead an animal to believe that it can get out. To make it easier for the animal to get at the bait, a plank is set against the can so that it forms a ramp from the ground to the edge of the receptacle. It is easy enough for the animal to enter the can, but impossible for it to get out, for the inside has a light coating of Vaseline or machine oil. A large-mouthed gallon jar set into the ground so that the top is level with the surrounding earth can be used in the same way to trap small mammals, such as mice.

Those who find it difficult to do live-trapping can always enlist the services of a farm boy. He is generally wise in the ways of nature, and for a small fee he will keep you supplied with an excellent variety of animals for your home zoo.

We discuss later the food to be given to your small mammal pets. All but very young mammals should be fed once a day. For nocturnal animals, late afternoon is the best time; for the others almost any time will do. Feed at the same time each day; it will be interesting to note how impatient the animals become when feeding time is near. Young animals should be fed several times a day. Babies that have not been

weaned require frequent meals of warm milk, fresh or canned; they must be fed slowly with a small nursing bottle or a medicine dropper. It is very difficult to raise sucklings. It is best not to try to do so unless the babies have been abandoned or are lost.

You can learn only by experience how much food to give an animal at each feeding. It should always be a little on the hungry side after feeding time; this will keep it alert and active. Your pets should never look fat and lazy. This is a sure sign of overfeeding, which may result in ill health. Cod-liver oil should be mixed with the food two or three times a week, and fresh water should always be present.

Some mammals that can be kept as pets

Opossums are among the easiest animals to livetrap. In fact, an opossum will often trap itself by getting into a garbage can from which it cannot withdraw. Food is no problem, as table scraps (cooked vegetables and meat), supplemented with prepared dog food and occasional morsels of raw meat, will do nicely.

Moles and shrews are among the hardest animals to keep in captivity. Moles are difficult to capture with live traps; but quick work with a spade on a lawn that they frequent usually brings good results. You will have to have patience and a knowledge of their habits if you are to succeed in trapping them. Shrews can usually be caught in small live traps by using meat or peanut butter as bait. A fair-sized aquarium with from 4 to 6 inches of soft, damp (not moist) earth is satisfactory for moles; shrews will do best in a terrarium. (See Index, under Aquariums; Terrariums.) Both moles and shrews require almost constant feeding. They will relish insects, worms and raw meat.

Raccoons can easily be livetrapped by using meat or fresh fish for bait. If adults are caught, they should immediately be released as they seldom make good pets. Young ones are inclined to be a bit quarrelsome at first, but with careful handling they will become very tame. Patience and a pair of heavy leather gloves are necessary. These animals usually accept table scraps, supplemented with dog food, raw meat and various fruits. Of course, there should always be a large pan of fresh water in the cage.

Skunks are among the easiest of animals to keep in captivity; they make ideal pets if captured when young. It is not absolutely necessary but often advisable to have captive skunks descented by a veterinarian. Table scraps, meat and prepared dog food are acceptable to skunks. These foods should not be given in large quantities, as the animals tend to become very fat and sluggish when they are overfed.

Foxes should not be kept in captivity unless you have ample acreage. They are inclined to be smelly, no matter how well their cages are disinfected and cleaned. The aroma of fox wafted by the breezes may be quite offensive to a neighbor living nearby. The pups are usually very tractable, but as they grow older they become quite snappy; as a result, adults make poor pets. It is best to release them when they are grown up. Dog food and raw meat with occasional table scraps usually suffice for these animals.

Woodchucks make good pets only when they are young. Adults are savage and can cause serious damage to cage and captor alike with their long, chisellike incisor teeth. Young that have wandered too far from their home burrow may often be run down and caught with a long-handled net. All sorts of vegetables (carrots are a must), apples and many wild, broad-leaved plants

form an adequate diet. As the woodchucks are true hibernators, they should not be left out of doors over the winter.

Much that we just said about woodchucks applies to ground squirrels and chipmunks. Adults should be released if trapped and only the young should be kept as pets. Fruits, nuts and various grains are good foods for them. They are easily trapped in small live traps baited with peanut butter or the foods they ordinarily eat.

Squirrels tend to remain wild if captured as adults, with the exception of the flying squirrel. Young that have just left the nest are often easy to catch and make excellent pets. As squirrels are very active, they must have large, roomy cages; an old tree with several branches should be set into the floor. Feed them nuts, assorted fruits and vegetables and, occasionally, meat.

Mice and rats of many species can be kept in captivity and most of them will do well. Small live traps, baited with peanut butter, bacon, nuts or fruit will usually

Raccoons make fine pets if captured when young. This four-month-old specimen loves to be held and fondled.

These lively little ferrets delight in frolicking in and around the hollow log. Obviously they are very tame.

catch them. The sunken gallon-jar trap, already mentioned, will catch some of the smaller kinds. Dried grasses and strips of cloth should be placed in the cage so that a nest can be built. Don't forget that mice and rats (particularly rats) can bite. Handle them with care until you are certain they can be trusted. Carrots, lettuce, fruit, nuts, grain, prepared pellets and meat (occasionally) should be fed to them.

Porcupines often eat vegetables, fruits, dry bread and the tips of hemlock, elm and aspen branches.

Wild rabbits usually do not make good pets. Those that have been captured when young are apt to be shy and nervous even when they reach maturity. Any undue commotion may literally frighten them to death. If you want to keep rabbits in captivity, there are many domestic varieties that are extremely hardy and make excellent pets. A variety of vegetables and prepared rabbit pellets are the best foods.

Armadillos are most interesting pets and can usually be caught quite easily. Although they are mostly nocturnal, they occasionally move about during the daytime. Soft fruits, raw chopped meat and cooked eggs are excellent food for these animals.

Few wild birds may be kept without a permit

Because of federal and local restrictions, only a very few kinds of birds may be kept in captivity without a permit. This is generally difficult to obtain.

Wild geese and ducks are carefully protected by law. You should not make any plans for keeping these birds without first getting in touch with the wildlife authorities. There are, however, a number of domesticated species that may be kept without a permit. Because a fairly large investment is required, you should be sure that you know how to keep these birds properly before you purchase any. You will find ample information on this subjects in books such as the following:

REGINALD APPLEYARD, *Ducks; Breeding, Rearing, Management;* Poultry World, London, 4th edition.

——, *Geese; Breeding, General Management;* Poultry World, London, 3rd edition.

F. J. S. CHATTERTON, *Ducks and Geese and How to Keep Them;* Cassel and Company, London, 8th edition.

Hawks and owls are sometimes kept as pets if local conservation regulations permit. The young of certain species, particularly red-shouldered, red-tailed, broad-winged and sparrow hawks and barred, great horned and screech owls, are most likely to adjust themselves to living in a cage. Adult owls may be caged with fairly good results; it is much more difficult to keep hawks in captivity. Adult-hawk-trapping should be left to the professional. Young owls and hawks are best fed freshly killed mice, but, as they get older, chunks of horsemeat (and an occasional mouse) are usually adequate. An excellent source of natural food may be found in animals freshly killed by automobiles.

Crows, jays and magpies are related, and their cage and food requirements are the same. They need a large cage with an inch or two of sand in the bottom and a number of perches. Only young birds should be caged, for adults caught wild seldom become adjusted to a cage. As the young grow to maturity they make ideal pets. The birds will do very nicely on a diet of shelled nuts, mixed grain, sunflower seed, chopped meat, chopped carrot, lettuce and assorted fruits.

Quails and pheasants are considered to be game birds, and they are protected by law. A permit for keeping and raising them may usually be obtained without too much trouble from your local conservation department. Books such as Jean T. Delacour's

Pheasant Breeding and Care, All-Pets Magazine, Fond du Lac, Wisconsin, 1953, and David B. Greenberg's Raising Game Birds in Captivity, D. Van Nostrand Company, New York, 1949, will supply much useful material on raising these birds.

Songbirds cannot be legally caged without a permit. However, you can attract them to your property by means of various kinds of feeding stations. (See Index, under Feeding devices.)

Turtles and other reptile pets

Turtles are among the easiest animals to keep in captivity. They should be kept out of doors only during the warmer months of the year. Indoors or outdoors they should never be constantly in sunlight. A large aquarium, with from 5 to 6 inches of water and a few flat rocks rising above the surface, is ideal for most varieties (but not for box, wood and gopher turtles). Generally speaking, the turtles that will thrive in the aquarium eat only food that has been dropped into the water; some will take food from your hands but will then have to get the food wet before eating it. Pieces of fish, raw meat, aquatic plants, earthworms and insects form about the best food. The aquarium water should be changed daily.

Box, wood and gopher turtles are essentially terrestrial and, therefore, require

This crow was formerly a prize attraction at the Children's Zoo in the New York Zoological Park (the Bronx Zoo). It is now the pet of a private family.

Feeding a baby box turtle. A mealworm, which is held with a pair of tweezers, is given to the turtle (A). The little animal then greedily gobbles up the worm (B).

cages with only a small pool of water. In captivity, they do well on melons, bananas and soft fruits, and will also occasionally eat earthworms. As the gopher tortoise is a powerful digger, be sure that the floor of the cage is well constructed.

Alligators are protected by law in some areas, but they may still be collected in others. They may also be obtained in pet shops. Only small specimens up to a foot in length should be kept by an amateur. Larger ones can be extremely dangerous. They are best collected by means of a hand net or noose on a long pole and should be handled by holding behind the head. Their food and cage requirements are about the same as for the aquatic turtles, except that they do not feed on vegetation of any kind.

Lizards generally get along best in a desert terrarium. They should be exposed to sunlight or to the rays of a sunlamp for a short time each day. In keeping lizards such as the chameleon, fence lizard and skink, try to reproduce as closely as possible the habitat where they were caught. These little animals should be fed on mealworms and other forms of insect life. Water should be provided by spraying down the cage. The little droplets that will collect on the rocks and plants will furnish the necessary water for these animals.

Snakes may be purchased from animal dealers, but it is more fun to hunt them. One word of caution to the amateur — be sure you know the poisonous snakes of your region before you go snake collecting. You can acquire a good knowledge of the habits and habitat of each species from the FIELD BOOK OF SNAKES OF THE UNITED STATES AND CANADA, by Karl P. Schmidt and D. D. Davis, G. P. Putnam's Sons, New York, 1941, or FIELD BOOK OF NORTH AMERICAN SNAKES, by Raymond L. Ditmars, Doubleday and Company, New York, 1939, and that will make for more successful collecting. You will be most likely to find snakes in or under rocks, old boards and logs, in sheltered brush piles, along the edges of streams, under the loose bark of trees and along old stone walls and foundations. A broom handle with a 6-inch angle iron screwed to one end is a good device to use for pinning down snakes, as well as for turning over old boards and logs. Caution: if you are in poisonous-snake country, never put your fingers under rocks or logs or similar hiding places of snakes.

When pinning down a snake, it is always best to pin down the top of the head and then to pick up the animal just behind the head. There is a widespread belief that the best way to catch a snake is to pin it down just *behind* the head. The trouble is that if you hold down the snake in this way, it may be able to move its head just enough to bite you when you try to pick it up. Use heavy leather gloves in handling the larger nonpoisonous species. There is nothing better than a cloth bag or sack for transporting snakes. *Do not try to collect poisonous snakes; leave them for the professionals.*

Most species of snakes are not too difficult to keep in captivity. A solid cage with a glass front and a screen top is easily constructed. The cage should open from the top for cleaning and feeding; the size will depend on the size of the snakes that are to be kept. Fine gravel or coarse sand and a few large rough stones are to the liking of most of these reptiles. Place a broad-bottom water dish that cannot be easily tipped over in the cage; provide branches or small logs for the species that like to climb.

Highly nervous species, such as the racers and whip snakes, often do not do well in captivity. Watch these animals closely. If they do not quiet down and accept food, it is best to release them before they fret themselves to death.

A good feeding of live food once a week is all that a snake requires. The animal should be allowed to take all it wants. A good indication that it is not getting enough food is the formation of slight folds of loose skin toward the tail. When feeding or cleaning the cages of aggressive snakes, wear a leather glove. This is adequate protection from the strike of our native nonpoisonous species.

Ring-necked snakes like a diet of earthworms, but will take small toads, salamanders and various soft-bodied insects.

Hog-nosed snakes are difficult to keep for any length of time unless a quantity of toads can be kept on hand for food.

Green snakes are insect eaters exclusively. It is useless to try to keep them unless a good supply of insect life is readily available.

Racers and whip snakes, as we have pointed out, are hard to keep because of their nervous nature. Young ones that will accept frogs, mice and insects sometimes do quite well, however.

Indigo snakes are excellent for handling because of their gentle disposition. They will readily accept frogs, fish, mice and other foods.

Rat, fox, chicken, bull, gopher, corn snakes and pilot blacksnakes, which are

In capturing a snake, it is best to pin down the top of the head, as shown (A), and then to pick up the animal just behind the head (B, C). A beginner should be sure he knows the poisonous snakes of his region before he goes collecting; he should not try to capture poisonous snakes.

This cage for a snake has glass sides and a screen top. A water dish and a branch have been set in the cage; a paper towel covers the floor.

among the largest of our native species, can also be handled very easily. Their favorite foods are live mice and rats.

King snakes feed on snakes in a state of nature. Many, however, will accept mice in captivity.

Milk snakes are popularly supposed to enter barns where cows are kept in order to obtain milk from them! This is an old wives' tale; they actually are searching for the mice found in such places. To keep them happy in captivity, give them plenty of mice.

Water snakes are aggressive and very smelly creatures and, therefore, are not ideal pets. They are easily kept in captivity, however, on a diet of fresh fish (either whole or in pieces) and frogs.

Brown and red-bellied snakes are small, inoffensive creatures. They can be fed on earthworms and soft-bodied insects.

Garter and ribbon snakes are easily kept on a diet of frogs and toads; small individuals may prefer earthworms and soft-bodied insects. Ribbon snakes seem to have a special fondness for fresh fish, either whole or cut into strips.

Salamanders, frogs and other amphibians

Salamanders may be divided into three general groups: those that are aquatic, those that occasionally frequent water (some only during the breeding and egg-laying season) and those that are terrestrial. In order to collect and keep salamanders, their habits should be carefully studied.

Aquatic species are best collected with a seine or hand net. Use a hand net to catch salamanders found in or under rotted logs, old boards and flat rocks. If you use a car for collecting, cruise slowly along unfrequented roads on warm, rainy nights; you will sometimes see hundreds of these animals crossing the road. In spring, certain of the larger species gather in large numbers in small pools and ponds to mate and lay their eggs.

Use an aquarium for the aquatic species of salamanders and a terrarium with a pool of water for the others. Remember that these creatures like cool, moist conditions; extreme dryness or heat will kill

them quickly. Change the water in the aquarium or terrarium when any signs of fouling appear. Since many salamanders are able to climb the vertical glass sides of a terrarium, a piece of glass should be used as a cover. The glass should not rest tightly on the top, but should be raised to a distance of about one sixteenth of an inch to allow for some ventilation.

Hellbenders, mud puppies, spotted newts and axolotls can be kept in an aquarium with coarse gravel or flat rocks in the bottom. The aquarium should be filled to within an inch or two of the top and should be kept as cool as possible. A glass or wire top is necessary, as these animals may otherwise escape. The food should consist of tadpoles, earthworms and small fish.

For terrestrial species and for red efts (immature spotted newts), a cool terrarium with a pool of water is most satisfactory. Earthworms, mealworms and other soft-bodied insects are excellent foods.

Frogs and toads are found in many different places. Some frogs are most easily collected by hand or in a hand net along the borders of lakes, ponds and streams; others, in wet meadows; still others, in wooded areas. Toads, for the most part, favor open areas, though they are occasionally found elsewhere. All native frogs and toads come to water, whether it be a puddle in a wagon rut or a lake, in order to mate and lay their eggs. By collecting the eggs, you can learn a great deal about the life history of these animals. When the eggs hatch, keep only a dozen or so of the tadpoles; release the rest of them in some nearby pond. A simple aquarium with plenty of aquatic plants will suffice for the eggs as well as for the tadpoles. The tadpoles will feed on bits of chopped liver, algae and crushed worms.

Spring peepers, toads, tree frogs and wood frogs can best be kept in a terrarium with a small pool of water. The other varieties do well in an aquarium with several inches of water. Several flat rocks should be so placed that the frogs can emerge from the water occasionally. All sorts of insect life and earthworms are excellent foods for these animals. The water in the aquarium should be replaced daily.

SCIENCE AND PROGRESS

(1815-95) V

BY JUSTUS SCHIFFERES

NEW VOYAGES OF DISCOVERY

THE daring sea voyages of the fifteenth and sixteenth centuries were undertaken primarily to discover new lands and found new empires. With certain notable exceptions, the overseas and overland expeditions of the seventeenth and eighteenth centuries were sent out to establish colonies or to convert native peoples or to find new sources of raw materials. In the nineteenth century, a number of exploring expeditions were launched, after careful preparation, with the express aim of adding to man's knowledge of the globe he inhabits. Vast areas of North and South America and Africa, to say nothing of the

The man who touched off this great movement of exploration was America's famed scientist-president Thomas Jefferson. On April 30, 1803, the United States had acquired by purchase from the Emperor Napoleon a vast region called Louisiana, extending from the Mississippi to the Rocky Mountains and from Mexico to the Lake of the Woods. President Jefferson decided to send out an expedition to explore this vast new addition to the fledgling republic.

As leader of the expedition, he selected his one-time private secretary, Captain Meriwether Lewis (1774–1809), who

Sacajawea, an Indian squaw, guiding the Lewis and Clark Expedition.

sea bottom and the Arctic and Antarctic regions, were revealed to mankind. These expeditions, undertaken without thought of immediate gain, often opened up unexpected natural resources, which later were fully exploited.

During the nineteenth century, the continent of North America was more thoroughly explored than any other; by the end of the nineteenth century, its vast expanses had been quite accurately mapped.

hailed from Albemarle County, Virginia. Lewis chose as his second-in-command Lieutenant William Clark (1770–1838), also a native Virginian but then residing in Kentucky. These two men organized the Lewis and Clark Expedition whose purpose was, in Jefferson's words, "to trace the Missouri to its source, to cross the highlands [that is, the Rocky Mountains] and follow the best water communication from thence to the Pacific Coast."

The trip down the Ohio, up the Mississippi and then up the Missouri to its Great Falls was accomplished by means of river boats and canoes with much labor but little danger. In April 1805, Lewis and Clark sent sixteen of their men back down the Missouri by keelboat with specimens, gifts for the President and careful accounts of what they had already seen and what they had learned from the Indians.

The party that went on included, in addition to its leaders, twenty-six soldiers and rivermen; Clark's Negro servant York, an amazing sight to the Indians, who had never seen a black man before; two French hunters and the Indian wife and half-breed papoose of one of them. The Indian squaw, Sacajawea, a remarkably intelligent woman who acted as guide and interpreter, was as much responsible as anyone for the success of the expedition. She was familiar with the territory between the Missouri and Columbia rivers, for she had been a member of a Shoshone tribe that had dwelt in this area.

The expedition passed the Three Forks of the Missouri, above Great Falls; then the explorers obtained horses from the Indians and crossed over the Great Divide. At last they came to the Columbia River, teeming with salmon. They sailed down the river and in November 1805 reached the Pacific Ocean where the Columbia empties its waters. The return journey was made by the same route the next year. The information that Lewis and Clark brought back about the Great Northwest encouraged fur trading and then settling in this region. Within a single generation the Oregon Trail rivaled the Santa Fe Trail as a road to the West.

Baron Alexander von Humboldt, famous German naturalist, traveler and statesman, exploring the Orinoco River in South America.

Lewis and Clark were not the first white men to reach the Pacific by the land route; they had been anticipated by a young fur trader, Alexander Mackenzie (1755?–1820), in the employ of the Northwest Fur Company. This venturesome young man had journeyed by canoe in 1789 from Fort Chippewyan along the Great Slave Lake and down the river that now bears his name to the Arctic Ocean. In 1792–93, Mackenzie made an overland journey from Fort Chippewyan to the Pacific coast near Cape Menzies. At the top of a large rock bluff overlooking Vancouver Bay, Mackenzie wrote in red grease paint an inscription, since chiseled in the rock, which summed up his achievement:

"Alexander Mackenzie, from Canada, by land, the twenty-second of July, one thousand seven hundred and ninety-three."

The interior of North America was explored by fur traders like the famous Missouri Legion, by Indian scouts like Kit Carson and by religious exiles like the Mormons; it was mapped and surveyed by railroaders and geologists. A journey "unequaled in the annals of geographical exploration for the courage and daring displayed in its execution" was made in the summer of 1869 by an American geologist, John Wesley Powell (1834–1902), who later became the director of the United States Geological Survey. He termed his magnificent adventure a "modest boat trip down the Colorado [River]"; as a matter of fact, it was a hazardous feat that has seldom been repeated. Powell explored the cavernous depths of the Grand Canyon. He reported that two great natural agencies had sculptured the face of the valley of the Colorado and the Southwest in general; these agencies were the upheaval of land masses and the erosion of their surfaces. Control of erosion, particularly of topsoil, remains a vital problem today.

There were also notable explorations of South America in the nineteenth century. No man did more to reveal the mysteries of the continent than the German naturalist, traveler and statesman Baron Alexander von Humboldt (1769–1859).

This versatile man, a Prussian by birth, was educated at Goettingen, Freiberg, Frankfurt and Berlin. His early travels took him to Belgium, Holland, England and France. They served as a fitting prologue to his notable five-year trip of exploration to South America.

In the year 1799 he set out on this famous trip aboard the Spanish frigate Pizzaro, with the French botanist Aimé-Jacques-Alexandre Bonpland as his companion. In the course of the five years that followed, Humboldt thoroughly explored South America: its rivers, its mountains, its plants, its skies, its people. The luxuriant vegetation fascinated him; the strange animals and sea creatures fired his imagination. "Even the crabs are sky-blue and gold!" he exclaimed. He followed the course of the Orinoco through tropical jungles, and he established its connection with the upper Amazon. He crossed the Andes four times, exploring the interior of Ecuador and Peru. At length he returned to Europe by way of Mexico and the United States. He was welcomed back to Europe with joy and enthusiasm. He had been gone so long that his friends had given him up for dead.

Upon his return Humboldt settled in Paris and began a notable career as a writer and lecturer on scientific subjects. He soon became one of the most famous men in Europe. He penned a narrative in French of his journey up the Orinoco under the title of VOYAGE TO THE EQUINOC-TIAL REGIONS OF THE NEW CONTINENT; he also wrote a series of technical books on climate, temperature and plants, mostly in French or Latin. In 1827, he reluctantly returned to Germany at the bidding of his royal master, the King of Prussia. Two years later, at the age of sixty, he launched upon his last great journey — a nine-thousand-mile jaunt through the Ural and Altai mountains of Asiatic Russia.

Humboldt spent the last years of his life in Berlin, receiving visitors, exchanging correspondence with the great of the world and writing his most ambitious work, called THE COSMOS. This work, in five volumes, was published from 1845 to 1862 (the last volume appeared after his death). It sought to provide an accurate and complete description and a unified conception of the entire physical world. Understandably it has become outmoded in many respects; yet it remains a superb monument to a great man.

Humboldt's contributions to science were many and lasting. In the course of his travels he accumulated a great mass of geographical data. He discovered the cool current that sweeps up the west coast of South America from the Antarctic Ocean and that now bears his name. He climbed mountains to prove that temperature decreases with height above sea level. He pointed out that the very nature of plants and animals is controlled by the climate and terrain they inhabit. He studied the origin of tropical storms and the changes in the

The good ship *Beagle* in the Strait of Magellan.

earth's magnetic force from the equator to the poles; he also devoted much attention to "magnetic storms," a name that he himself coined. Meteorology became a much more exact science in his hands. He made an intensive study of volcanoes; he advanced the theory, still held, that zones of volcanic activity follow a definite line of cracks in the earth's crust. To quote Goethe, Humboldt was "without a rival in extent of information and acquaintance with existing sciences."

Humboldt's writings provoked a renewed interest in scientific exploration. Inspired by his example, many naturalists now betook themselves to the vast plains and tall mountains of South America. For example, a British expedition, sent out in 1831 in the small ship Beagle, of the British Navy, did important work in surveying various areas of the continent: Patagonia, Tierra del Fuego, Chile and Peru. The Beagle also explored many islands of the Pacific and Atlantic. Young Charles Darwin, who, as we shall see, was destined to stir up the greatest scientific controversy of the nineteenth century, traveled aboard the Beagle as "naturalist."

After the close of the Napoleonic Wars, Britain turned her attention to the exploration of Africa, called the Dark Continent because comparatively little was known about it. British explorers discovered Lake Chad and the mouth of the Niger, and explored the regions between Lake Chad and Timbuctoo. Protestant missions were organized on the Guinea coast in South Africa and in the dominions of Zanzibar. The missionary David Livingstone (1813–73) crossed the Kalahari Desert from north to south in 1849. In the years that followed he traversed the African continent from the west to the east; in the course of these wanderings he discovered Victoria Falls (1855).

In 1866 he set out on his last journey of discovery. After a time the world lost all trace of him. James Gordon Bennett, the fabulous managing editor of the New York HERALD, interested himself in the matter; he sent out the British-born reporter Henry Morton Stanley (1841–

In the Galapagos Islands, Charles Darwin discovered these lizard species: left, *Tropidurus pectinatus;* right, *Tropidurus multimaculatus.*

1904), born John Rowlands, to find the famous missionary-explorer. Stanley came upon Livingstone in Ujiji in 1871 and uttered the memorable salutation, "Dr. Livingstone, I presume." Livingstone continued his explorations in Stanley's company for a time; he went on alone after the newspaperman's departure. At last, worn out by disease and fatigue, he succumbed in 1873. In the following year, Stanley explored the Congo River.

Other Englishmen made notable discoveries in Africa. In 1862 John Hanning Speke (1827–64) proceeded along the river that flows from Victoria Nyanza (Lake Victoria) and, following it into Egypt, answered once and for all the age-old question, "Where does the Nile obtain its waters?" Another explorer of the mighty Egyptian river was Samuel Baker (1821–93), who discovered Albert Nyanza, the principal western reservoir of the river. Portuguese, Germans, French and Italians also made notable explorations in Africa. By the end of the century much of the mystery of the Dark Continent had been dissipated.

In the nineteenth century, the British made many surveys of their vast possessions in India. One of these surveying

STANLEY AND LIVINGSTONE

expeditions resulted in the most important development in geology since the time of Hutton. This was the theory of isostasy. It resulted from a survey undertaken in 1823 by Sir George Everest (1790–1866), the man for whom the tallest peak in the world — Mount Everest — is named.

Like all surveyors, Everest used a plumb line to level his instruments. According to the theory of gravitation, the plumb line, wherever it is used, should point directly to the center of the earth. It was soon observed, however, that the direction of the line in northern India was different from its direction in southern India. This deflection was attributed to the gravitational attraction of the nearby mass of the Himalaya Mountains. Joseph Pratt (1811–71), a British clergyman and mathematician who spent many years in India as Archdeacon of Calcutta, set out to examine the deviation of the plumb line. He found that the line was attracted far less by the overwhelming mass of the Himalayas than had been expected.

The explanation of this phenomenon was offered by George Biddell Airy (1801–92), English Astronomer Royal and President of the Royal Society. He held that the Himalayas are made up of comparatively light rock, while the plain of the Ganges, to the south, has a denser rock structure. Hence the deviation of the plumb line in the direction of the Himalayas is not so great as it would be if the mountains and the plain had the same density. Airy also advanced the idea that the tablelands and mountains of the earth rest upon a mass of lava. "It appears to me," he said, "that the state of the earth's crust lying upon the lava may be compared with perfect correctness to the state of a raft of timber floating upon water."

According to Airy, the mountains of the Himalayan range and the plains of the Ganges, as well as heights and depressions all over the world, press down upon the underlying sea of lava. They are in balance because the lower-lying lands are heavier than the peaks and mountain ranges. This is the theory of isostasy, or general equilibrium in the earth's crust. The name "isostasy" was first applied in 1889 by the American geologist and army officer Clarence Edward Dutton.

The British took the lead in exploring the depths of the ocean with the famous Challenger Expedition. The Challenger, a wooden corvette of 2,306 tons, was fitted out by the British Navy, "at a cost no more than that of keeping the vessel in commission," for the purpose of exploring the open ocean in every quarter of the globe. Much of the credit for inspiring the voyage of the Challenger belongs to the scientific director of the expedition, Professor Charles Wyville Thomson (1830–82) of the University of Edinburgh.

The Challenger, Captain G. S. Nares commanding, left Portsmouth jetty on December 21, 1872, with a full complement of scientists on board. The route was south to Madeira, thence to the Canaries, the West Indies and north as far as Nova Scotia; south again to Cape Verde, to the Cape of Good Hope, Australia, the China Sea, Japan, along the west coast of South America, through the Strait of Magellan and back to England. When the ship finally dropped anchor at Spithead, England, on May 24, 1876, it had logged 68,890 nautical miles.

The scientists aboard the ship — "philosophers," the bored naval officers called them — were particularly concerned with what they might find at the bottom of the sea. As a result, they laid the foundations of the modern science of oceanography, which seeks to solve the riddles of the deep. The birthday of this science, according to J. Y. Buchanan, one of the Challenger's scientists, was February 15, 1873, when, forty miles south of Tenerife, the ship took the first of its 362 official "stations." A dredging bucket, suspended on ropes, was lowered into 1,890 fathoms of water to see what could be dragged up from the bottom of the ocean. The temperature of the water at different depths was also recorded. The mud from the bottom of the sea proved cold enough to chill a bottle of champagne.

The Challenger Expedition was fruit-

The Challenger Expedition of 1872–76 was the first to collect the following species of deep-sea fish (top to bottom): *Ceratias carunculatus, Ceratias uranoscopus, Melanocetus murrayi, Bathypterois longicauda*.
From "Challenger Reports"

ful indeed. Through numerous analyses of samples, it established the chemical composition of sea water throughout the globe. It made the first comprehensive analysis of the sea bottom. It also exploded a number of myths. It disproved the belief that bathybius, a slimy substance found in the sea, represented vast masses of floating protoplasm. Buchanan showed that this so-called protoplasm is simply a precipitate of calcium sulfate in sea water. The Challenger's scientists also proved that Huxley and others were wrong in supposing that chalk was constantly being laid down on the ocean floor by the shells of tiny sea creatures. Finally, they showed that the "lost continent of Atlantis" — Plato to the contrary — was just not there.

In the year 1880, Thomson issued the first of fifty volumes of Challenger RE-PORTS, containing an account of the expedition and its findings. Upon his death, in 1882, his brilliant young assistant, Canadian-born John Murray (1841–1914), carried on the publication of the REPORTS, completed in 1895. These reports are still "the indispensable starting points for the study of marine biology." Since the oceans cover so large a proportion of the earth's surface, it is truly amazing that the serious study of its composition and its inhabitants should have been so long delayed.

Explorers of the
Arctic and Antarctic

The barren wastes of the Arctic and Antarctic also attracted explorers in the nineteenth century. One of the foremost of these sturdy adventurers was Sir John Franklin (1786–1847), a British naval officer who had served at Trafalgar and the Battle of New Orleans. He headed four successive Arctic expeditions, beginning in 1818; the last one, which set out in 1845, never returned. Between 1850 and 1857 his heartbroken wife Jane (nee Griffin) fitted out five ships to search for her husband. At last indisputable evidence was found that Sir John's ship had been deserted and that he and the rest of his party had been lost. Jane Griffin Franklin was honored for her services to geographical science by receiving, in 1860, the gold medal of the Royal Geographical Society.

In the last decades of the nineteenth century it became a point of honor among nations to be the first to reach the North and South Poles. England, Norway, Sweden, Austria and the United States all entered the race; many different routes to each pole were explored.

Traveling first by ship and then by dog sled through bitter icy wastes, explorers edged closer to the North Pole, representing the northernmost point of the earth — 90 degrees north latitude. By the end of the century Fridtjof Nansen of Norway and Captain Umberto Cagni, of the Italian Duke of Abruzzi's expedition, had gone beyond the 86th parallel north. It was not until April 6, 1909, that the Pole was finally conquered by the determined American naval officer Robert E. Peary, who had made five previous attempts to reach the goal. The Norwegian Roald Amundsen was the first to reach the South Pole (December, 1911). One month later (January 18, 1912) valiant Captain Robert F. Scott of the British Navy also attained the goal; on the return trip he and his companions lost their lives.

In time the importance of these continuing expeditions became apparent. The northern polar route for air traffic between Europe and America has the most startling possibilities in both peace and war. The weather stations that have been set up in the far north have made weather forecasts more accurate than before. As for the Antarctic regions, they hold immense mineral treasures that some day will add greatly to the world's resources.

Today there are comparatively few regions upon the surface of the globe still to be explored. But science has set up new goals for modern explorers. Armed with microscopes, telescopes, cyclotrons, Geiger-Mueller counters, they seek to ferret out the secrets of the physical universe — the mysteries of the life that fills the earth, of the atoms, of the visible heavenly bodies, of the infinite space that is as yet beyond our ken.

Continued on page 156.

PROGRESS IN CHEMURGY

New Riches down on the Farm

BY WHEELER McMILLEN

A FIELD of ripening oats in July makes a pretty picture. The tall, slender stalks bow to the slightest breeze; a few long leaves reach out from the stalks. The sheathed grains clustering at the tips shine like green and gold bells.

When man has extracted the kernel for food and gathered the straw to bed down his livestock, has he made full use of the oat plant? Not very long ago the answer to this question would have been "Yes." Now another story can be told.

A manufacturer of breakfast foods looked out one day upon the mountain of oat hulls that was rising near his factory. A small part could be ground up for livestock feed; but the market was small. The rest of the hulls were fit only to be tossed into the boiler fires; that is, unless someone found a new use for them.

A chemist did. He found that oat hulls yield a chemical compound called furfural. At first there was no known use for furfural, but laboratory workers kept experimenting with it until their curiosity began to pay dividends. They discovered that in the refinement of lubricating oils furfural would dissolve out the substances that made these oils gummy. Soon the petroleum industry was buying entire tank carloads of furfural.

Then some one found synthetic resin adhesives are even more adhesive when furfural is added. Modern grinding tools and abrasives are made by cementing millions of tiny particles of great hardness. They are made to stick together by adhesives that are tough and resistant to heat and water.

Overhead vapors, rich in furfural, pass to decanter

Vapor from digester passes to stripping column

Stripping column

Cottonseed hulls, corn cobs and rice hulls are stored in silos

Pressure cooking in digester with steam and dilute sulfuric acid changes carbon structure of raw materials

Digester

Residue

Still bottoms—undesirable high-boiling compounds—are led out of bottom of stripping column

Boiler plant

PROCESSING

OF FURFURAL

Residue from digester is dried. Some is used as fuel in boiler plant; some serves as fertilizer or in manufacture of glue

Furfural now plays an important part in the cementing process.*

The demand for furfural grew so much that supplies of oat hulls were not enough. Then another farm product found a new market. Corncobs became the raw material for furfural, and nowadays most of this versatile chemical is made from them. Nor was this the end of the story. The spent corncobs, after the furfural has been extracted from them, are formed into charcoal briquettes and sold as fuel for outdoor cooking.

This story of the modern uses of oats and corn shows how science takes materials that used to be thrown away and creates useful products that add to man's wealth and promote his welfare. We give the name of chemurgy to such industrial uses of plant

material. The word "chemurgy" was coined in the twenties of the present century from the Egyptian root word *chem* and the Greek word *ergon*. Literally it means "putting chemistry to work."

Chemistry — more specifically, organic chemistry — is indeed the key science in chemurgy. Organic chemistry has created a wide range of useful products — fuels, dyes, explosives, plastics, rayon and nylon, among others. Its raw materials are cellulose, proteins, starches, sugars and other natural compounds — substances that are readily available in plant life. It is the organic chemist's endless search for such materials that has made the rise of chemurgy possible.

A few pioneers began to promote the idea of chemurgy in the 1920's, when farm surpluses in the United States were a national problem. They pointed out that nearly half the tonnage grown by farmers consisted

* For a number of years, furfural was used extensively in the manufacture of nylon. It has now been replaced by cheaper materials, which are used in the production of nylon intermediates.

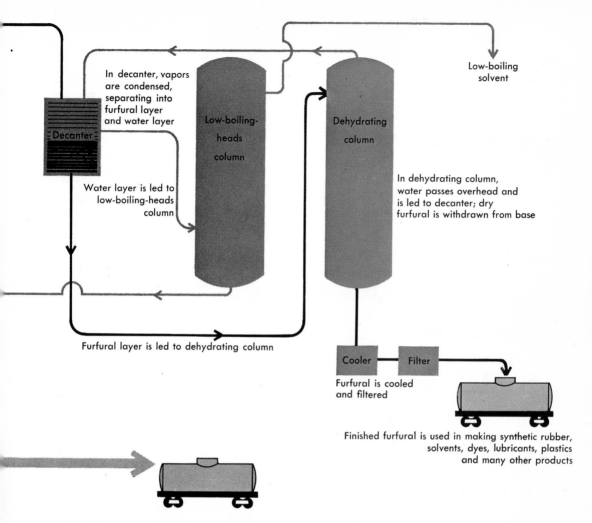

In decanter, vapors are condensed, separating into furfural layer and water layer

Decanter

Low-boiling-heads column

Dehydrating column

Low-boiling solvent

Water layer is led to low-boiling-heads column

In dehydrating column, water passes overhead and is led to decanter; dry furfural is withdrawn from base

Furfural layer is led to dehydrating column

Cooler

Filter

Furfural is cooled and filtered

Finished furfural is used in making synthetic rubber, solvents, dyes, lubricants, plastics and many other products

of potential chemical raw materials, such as straws, stalks and culls (rejected parts of the crop), for which there were no commercial markets. These agricultural materials would be especially attractive to industry because they would be inexhaustible. It is a sad fact that nature either does not replace minerals that are consumed, or else replaces them at a rate that can not begin to keep pace with our consumption. Plant raw materials, on the contrary, are always renewable. With many crops the entire production of a year may be consumed, except for seed, and then renewed by another year's growth.

The idea of applying chemurgy on a wide scale gradually took root. In the spring of 1935, a number of men prominent in agriculture, industry and science were invited to attend a conference at Dearborn, Michigan, in order to discuss the possibilities of chemurgy. As a result of this

conference, the National Farm Chemurgic Council, Inc., was established. In 1955, its name was changed to the Council for Agricultural and Chemurgic Research, or the Chemurgic Council, for short. Its headquarters are now in New York City. This Council serves as a clearing house of information. It brings the subject of chemurgy to the attention of large numbers of people and it promotes support for public and private research.

Congress brought about a long forward step in chemurgic research in 1938. As an amendment to the agricultural act of that year, it provided for the establishment of four regional laboratories to be devoted entirely to finding new uses for farm products. These laboratories were set up at or near Philadelphia, New Orleans, Peoria and San Francisco. To each one was assigned a program of research in the crop generally grown in the nearest area. The laboratory

At the left, in the photograph, are shown several rolls of cigarette paper. At the lower right, we see the tow (that is, processed flax straw) from which the paper was produced.

Peter J. Schweitzer Division, Kimberly-Clark Corporation

buildings, costing $2,000,000 each, were completed and opened in 1940. Each laboratory was provided with space for erecting pilot-plant equipment, where new processes could be tested on a semicommercial scale.

A number of state experiment stations and universities are now taking part in chemurgic research. So are many industrial laboratories. Nearly every large food-processing company has also become a chemical manufacturer in order to make the maximum use of the materials at hand. As for chemical companies, they have naturally made an intensive search for the raw materials supplied by agriculture. Regional research institutions in several areas have also turned their attention to the development of new industrial uses of agricultural resources. Among organizations of this kind are the Midwest Research Institution, at Kansas City, the Southern Research Institute, at Birmingham, the Texas Institute of Technology and Plant Industry, at Southern Methodist University, Dallas, and the Southwest Research Institute, at San Antonio.

Chemurgy arose in the United States and has received by far its greatest development in that country. But there has been wide interest in the chemurgic idea elsewhere. The Chemurgic Council includes members from more than thirty nations; and farm chemurgic councils have been set up in other lands.

The goals of chemurgy

Chemurgy attacks the problem of finding new industrial uses for plants in various ways. (1) It seeks new uses for the plants now commonly grown as crops. (2) It tries to find profitable uses for the wastes and residues of agriculture. (3) It develops new strains of established crops. (4) It seeks new and more profitable crops.

New uses for old crops

Chemurgic research has made old crops more valuable by providing new industrial uses for them. Milo maize has long been grown in Kansas, Oklahoma and Texas. It is a species of corn whose grain develops at the top of the plant where the corn carries its tassel. It has long been valued as a feed grain, but until recently it had no industrial market.

Chemurgic researchers in the corn-products industries developed processes for making the grain into starch. A multi-million-dollar plant for this purpose started operations at Corpus Christi, Texas, in 1949. The plant supplies a market for thousands of acres of Texas milo maize; it

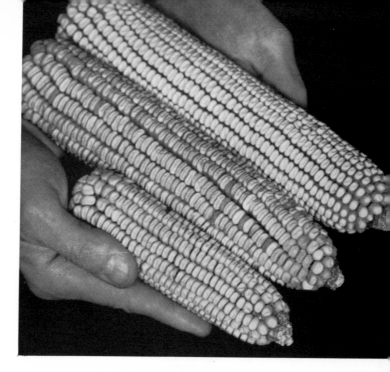

At the top is an ear of ordinary corn, which contains something like 25 per cent amylose. The center ear has from 50 to 60 per cent amylose; the bottom ear, from 70 to 75 per cent.

ARS—USDA

produces starch, dextrins, syrups and other products. Dextrose produced from milo maize is used in large quantities for the processing of cold rubber for tires.

Profitable uses for agricultural wastes

The development of furfural is one illustration of how a waste farm material has been turned to profitable account. Here is another case in point.

Until the 1930's, nearly all the cigarette paper used in the United States was made by factories in France from old rags of linen (a flax product) collected in Central Europe. It then occurred to several manufacturers in the United States that the cigarette paper might be made from seed flax straw. The crop had been harvested, not for the fiber to be made into linen, but for the seed, from which was processed linseed oil, an important ingredient in paints. The flax straw was considered worthless. In some areas it was considered even worse than useless; it had to be raked up and burned since it did not decompose readily on the ground.

In the late 1930's, after a substantial research and development effort, the Ecusta Paper Company of Pisgah Forest, North Carolina, the Peter J. Schweitzer Company of Elizabeth, New Jersey, and the Smith Paper Company of Lee, Massachusetts, began to manufacture cigarette paper from seed flax straw. Today, Ecusta and Schweitzer * supply practically all the domestic requirements for cigarette paper (small quantities are imported). A certain amount of the processed fiber also serves for Bible paper, airmail stationery and currency paper. Most of the flax straw used for these operations is grown in the North Central States, primarily Minnesota and the Dakotas; some of it is produced in Texas, Montana, and California. The Howard Smith Paper Company of Beauharnois, Canada, is manufacturing cigarette paper from Canadian-grown seed flax.

Many other important industrial materials have been created from agricultural wastes. For example, bagasse, the fibrous substance that is left over from sugar cane after it has been pressed in the mill was once considered useful only as an inefficient but cheap fuel in the boiler houses of sugar mills. It is now being made into sturdy fiber board and other useful products. A syrup prepared from cull apples has been used instead of glycerin in order to keep the tobacco in cigarettes moist and even-burning.

* Ecusta is now a division of Olin Mathieson Chemical Company. Schweitzer, having previously absorbed the Smith Paper Company, is now a division of Kimberly Clark.

High-amylose corn — a new strain of an old crop

Amylose corn is one of the fascinating new chemurgic developments. Ordinary starch, which is a principal constituent of corn, is made up of globe-shaped molecules, and because of its starch corn has hundreds of industrial uses. However, corn also has some long, straight-chained molecules, known as amylose. Chemists believed that if a strain could be developed that had, say, three-fourths or more of amylose molecules, the starch would find many more profitable markets. So plant breeders, led by a young Illinois farmer, set out to produce a high-amylose corn. Their efforts, after a few years, resulted in strains with more than sixty per cent of amylose molecules and also individual plants that ran much higher.

Meanwhile the chemists, with enough of the new starch for experimentation, made it into a transparent food wrapping which can be eaten along with the frankfurter, candy or whatever it may contain. They demonstrated that the long molecules could greatly improve some kinds of paper. Many other uses are probable.

PROCESSING AND USES OF THE SOYBEAN

Whole-bean storage

Steam drying reduces moisture of bean particles to 3%

Whole beans fed into cracking rolls

Tempering conveyers heat particles to 275° F.

Pressurized bean cake is expelled

Bean particles are forced into horizontal barrel; in this, a screw subjects particles to increasing pressure

Oil is pressed through gaps in the bars of which barrel consists, and drops to settling tank

Oil is passed through filter

Some oil is returned to wash and cool expeller barrel

The search
for new crops

The search for useful new crops is an important part of chemurgic research. In some cases these new crops replace old ones that, for one reason or another, are no longer profitable.

In the years preceding the great depression of the 1930's, American farmers grew so much wheat and cotton that profitable markets could not be found. Because of the low prices, farmers could not prosper, and they had to receive substantial help in the form of large government subsidies. Chemurgists believed that in many areas it would be well to introduce other crops, which would command a higher price than wheat or cotton and which would supply materials that the nation lacked, instead of adding to surpluses. They attacked the problem with all the resources of organic chemistry, plant-breeding and agricultural engineering. The result was the development of several alternate crops, which had hitherto not been particularly important in the United States or had never before been introduced.

The photo (left) shows a soybean plant. It has been a food crop in China for thousands of years; in the United States it was grown mostly for hay and hog pasture until the 1920's. Now many products come from soybeans.

W. Atlee Burpee Co.

SYNTHETIC MILK, BUTTER AND CHEESE

CATTLE FEED

PAINT

PLASTICS

OLEO-MARGARINE

COOKING OIL

SOYBEAN MEAL

SOYBEAN OIL

INK

FABRIC DYES

Above: cluster of tung fruit; below: the castor bean. Because of its drying properties, tung oil has been used for many years as an ingredient in paints and varnishes. It has been found that the oil derived from the castor bean compares favorably with tung oil for this purpose.

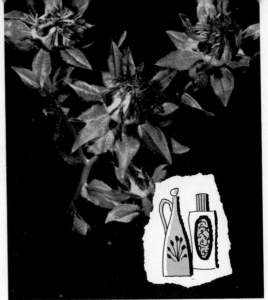

Safflower (above), a thistlelike herb, may be grown in semiarid regions or in irrigated land. The oil of this plant, refined by conventional methods, is used for cosmetics, drugs, food preparations and paints; the oil-free cake is ground into meal, mostly for livestock feed.

The most important of these crops is the soybean. This plant has been a staple food crop in China, particularly in Manchuria, for several thousand years; and as a matter of fact it was not unknown to America before the rise of chemurgy. Early in the nineteenth century, it had been brought to the Western Hemisphere by sailing-ship captains, and it had flourished in a small way. But no one had found much use for the plant; it was grown mostly for hay and for hog pasture. Not until after 1920 was as much as 1,000,000 bushels harvested in a year in the United States.

In the last year of the nineteenth century, American agricultural experiment stations began to look into the possible industrial uses of soybeans, and these experiments were continued in the first two decades of the twentieth century. It was shown that oil pressed from the soybean could be used for a variety of products. In the early twenties, oil mills began to recognize the importance of soybean oil, and farmers planted more and more of the beans.

Chemurgists became fascinated by the soybean; they found it the most versatile crop known to science. An almost infinite variety of industrial products can be produced from soybean oil and meal. To meet the demand for these invaluable raw materials, more and more acres have been planted to soybeans; annual production has grown until it exceeds 600,000,000 bushels a year. In Canada, too, the soybean has become an important crop.

The oil makes up one-fifth of the soybean, and more than twenty thousand tank carloads of it are separated every year. More than half the oil goes into cooking fats, about one-fifth into margarine and about one-twelfth into salad oils. The remainder is used for paints, lacquers, linoleum, oilcloth, window shades, printing inks, putty, insecticides, disinfectants and soap. The meal that remains after the oil is removed has become a foremost ingredient in livestock and poultry feeds. The meal is also used in the manufacture of industrial products like adhesives, textile fibers, waterproofing for textiles, waterproof glue, spreaders for insect sprays, finishing waxes, paper-sizing materials and plastics.

The soybean has become increasingly important as a food. Among the products we now get wholly or in part from the soybean are baked beans, canned green beans, breakfast foods, candies, chocolate drinks, coffee substitutes, crackers, flakes, flavorings, flour, infant foods, macaroni products, milk substitutes and soups.

Guar has been grown and cultivated for several thousand years in India, where it is used principally for animal feed. When mannogalactan mucilage, derived from the seeds of this plant, is mixed with paper pulp, the pulp yields an opaque paper with excellent printing qualities.

Above: guayule plant. Below: roots of the kok-sagyz, a Russian species of dandelion. The latex from which rubber is made has been obtained from both these plants, though not in commercially significant quantities. It is believed that kok-sagyz may yet be a profitable crop.

Thus, largely through the work of the chemurgist, the soybean has become a major crop in the United States and its cultivation has been steadily increasing. It is produced principally in the Midwestern states. The fields in which it grows would otherwise have been planted to corn, wheat and other crops which in normal years might produce surpluses.

Within the past few years safflower, a type of thistle, has become a successful crop in California, western Nebraska and eastern Colorado. Safflower seed yields up to 40 per cent of oil. The oil, which the ancient Egyptians used in their lamps, is sold for food preparations, drugs and cosmetics, as well as for paint. Because of its chemical structure, it is believed to prevent cholesterol deposits in the arteries (see Index, under Cholesterol), and much of it is sold for this and other pharmaceutical uses. More than 200,000 acres are planted each year, and the demand has been growing.

Tung oil is a valuable ingredient in paints and varnishes because of its drying properties. The United States had to import all its tung oil from China and Japan until the twentieth century, since the tung tree, from which the oil is derived, was unknown in the Western Hemisphere. In 1905, a few nuts were sent to America from China, and were planted at Brookville, Florida. Now, in Florida, Mississippi, Texas and other states along the Gulf Coast, tung orchards flourish on thousands of acres. Yet not nearly enough is grown to meet the demand. Because supplies of tung oil were insufficient, chemists cast about for another substance that would do some of its work. Finding no natural oil that was satisfactory, they tried to see what they could do by changing the composition of known oils. They found that by eliminating water (H_2O) from the molecules of castor oil they could produce a substance that was nearly as good as tung oil for many purposes. The castor beans that yield the oil in question are now imported chiefly from Brazil and India. But tests have shown that the plant grows readily in much of the United States, especially in the area between the cotton and corn belts. Commercial production of the castor bean is now well established in the Southwest.

Thus far we have dealt with the introduction into a country of crops that are well established elsewhere. In some cases, the "new" crops were new in the sense that they had not yet been cultivated anywhere on a commercial scale. As a matter of fact, we have hardly begun to tap the immense plant resources of the world. Well over

300,000 plant species have been identified by botanists. Yet man uses extensively not more than 2,000 species, and probably not more than 1,000 species are cultivated anywhere as crops.

The legume called guar (*Cyamopsis tetragonalaba*) was recently introduced to cultivation as a result of chemurgic research. Not long ago, paper manufacturers decided that they could make better paper if a material called mannogalactan mucilage were mixed in the pulp. The paper would be opaque and it would have better printing qualities. The only known source of the material was the carob bean, the product of a locust tree common in the Mediterranean regions. The total available supply, however, was much less than the industry required. Experts launched a search for some other plant that would yield the same product. It was found that guar, which is native to India, produces an abundant yield of a small seed from which the mannogalactan mucilage can be extracted. Guar is now being grown and processed in Texas.

In the effort to create a domestic rubber supply during World War II, experiments were made with two plants that had never been widely cultivated. One of these was the guayule, a shrub growing in the desert areas of southwestern United States and northern Mexico. It was found that the guayule can be cultivated and processed to yield natural rubber. However, since guayule rubber costs more than that obtained from the rubber tree (*Hevea brasiliensis*), the cultivation of the guayule shrub has not made extensive progress.

Another substitute for the rubber tree is a Russian species of dandelion, known as kok-sagyz. It is the roots of this plant that yield the latex from which rubber is made. Seeds were obtained from Russia and test plantings were made at various American state experiment stations. There were substantial yields of kok-sagyz in some of the northern stations; and extraction of the latex proved to be neither difficult nor costly. These tests were abandoned under wartime stress. The experimenters learned enough, however, to indicate that kok-sagyz might some day become a profitable crop.

The effects of chemurgy

There is no doubt that chemurgy has taken its place as a powerful industrial factor. What will its effects be?

For one thing, it will tend to decentralize industry. There is a growing tendency to erect processing factories near the farms where their raw materials grow. As more and more of these materials are made available for industry, processing plants will become more widely distributed. Since manufacturing costs are lower in rural communities, this development will benefit industry. It will benefit the workers, since they will be able to live amid more pleasant surroundings than in the crowded and smoky areas of big cities. It will also be a boon to the communities in which plant-processing enterprises are located; it will make more wealth available for health departments, schools and roads.

From the viewpoint of national defense, the development of new industrial products from agricultural crops will be helpful to the United States and Canada and other nations which have to import certain necessary materials from distant lands. If a war should interrupt production abroad or suspend shipping, the supply of imported materials would soon be exhausted and a serious crisis would develop. When the Japanese overran Malaya and the East Indies in 1942, they cut off the chief source of rubber supply for the Allies. Fortunately, the United States carried through a successful synthetic-rubber program; otherwise, the rubber shortage might well have undermined the entire war effort.

Chemurgy, then, will serve as a shield in time of war. It will also actively promote peace by raising the standards of have-not countries. It will enable farmers to make more effective use of the crops that now flourish in their fields, and to add new, profitable crops. It will make possible the variety of production that is the best guarantee of prosperity. Thereby it will help to do away with the poverty and discontent that breed wars.

See also Vol. 10, p. 282: "Chemurgy."

MODERN RESEARCH PROJECTS

Progress in science is due to the ceaseless activities of research workers in many different lands. Some investigators are engaged in basic research. They seek to add to our general knowledge of science; they are not primarily concerned with the applications of the principles they discover. Other research men are chiefly interested in solving specific problems in industry, medicine or other fields. Both types of research activity are indispensable.

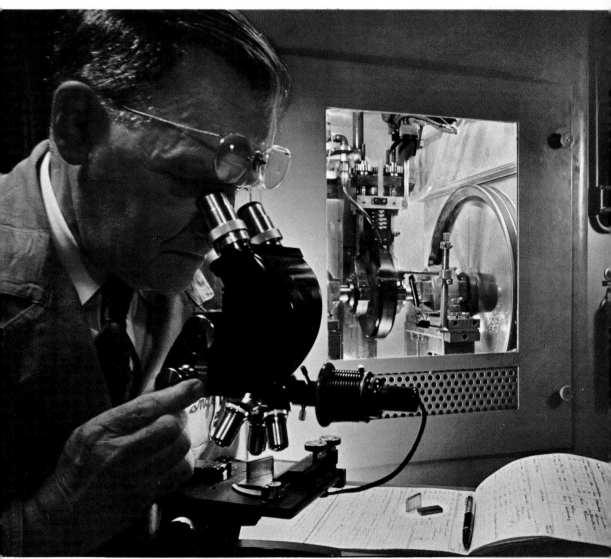

General Motors Corp.

In the General Motors Metallurgical Engineering Department laboratory. The wear-test machine shown at the right is subjecting automobile parts to a series of grueling tests. At the right a skilled research worker is examining a wear-test sample under the microscope.

General Motors Corp.

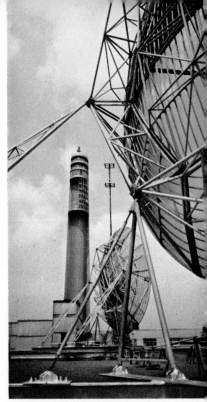

International Tel. & Tel. Corp.

Automobile manufacturers carry on extensive research operations in order to better their product and meet competition. Above we see the 330-acre Technical Center area, the research headquarters of the General Motors Corporation. It surrounds an artificial lake covering an area of 22 acres.

Federal Telecommunication Laboratories, at Nutley, New Jersey. The parabolic antennas in the foreground transmit radio waves.

Brookhaven National Laboratory

Firing a rocket-propelled research missile over the Atlantic Ocean from the pilotless aircraft research station at Wallops Island, Virginia. The missile was tracked through its delicate instruments and also by radar and moving pictures; a speed 5.6 times that of sound was recorded. (Sound travels at the rate of about a fifth of a mile per second.) The Wallops Island Station is run by the National Aeronautics and Space Administration.

National Aeronautics and Space Administration

Cosmotron at the Brookhaven National Laboratory, Upton, Long Island, New York, with the shielding removed for maintenance purposes. The cosmotron is designed to accelerate protons, which ultimately reach an energy of 3,000,000,000 electron volts. This is comparable to the energy of some cosmic rays; hence the name "cosmotron."

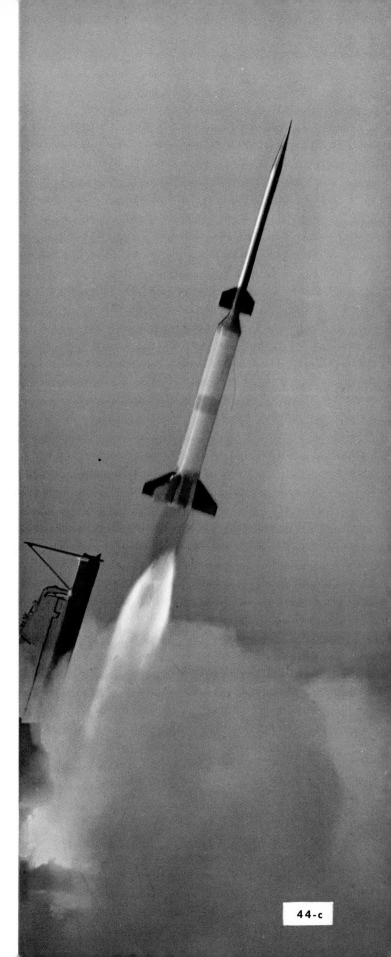

This photograph, taken in January 1954, shows the first atomic submarine engine — the Mark I — being tested in the National Reactor Testing Station in Idaho. The second engine of this type — the Mark II — was later installed in the *Nautilus*, the world's first atomic submarine. Here we see the submarine "hull," containing the atomic power plant, set within an immense tank that contains sea water.

Below: an essential step in the search for new antibiotics. Molds that produce promising antibiotics are isolated and grown in test tubes containing agar. Such colonies are kept constantly on hand in laboratories conducting antibiotic research.

Westinghouse Electric Corp.

Chas. Pfizer & Co., Inc.

44-d

VARIABLE STARS

Eclipsing Binaries, Novae, Supernovae and Others

EVEN to the unaided eye, many of the stars display beautiful tinges of color. These colors are enormously increased in splendor and beauty by the telescope, which also reveals the delicate tints of many stars that without its aid appear white. Antares is a wonderful ruby red. Somewhat less deep and rich in tone is another red star, Betelgeuse. Aldebaran and Arcturus are red-orange. The sun is, of course, yellow; Procyon is yellowish white; Sirius is white with almost a bluish cast; Mirzam is definitely bluish. These illustrate the color range of all the stars in the sky, red to blue-white; but there are a hundred delicate tints in between — lilacs, amethysts and greens, forming a beautifully colored pattern in the night skies.

Homer, Cicero and some other ancient writers described Sirius, the Dog Star, as red, though it is today very clearly white. Can stars, then, change color? They can and do. It has been determined that the color is an index of temperature, red stars being comparatively cool (around 2,000°–2,600° centigrade) and blue-white stars being hottest (up to 50,000°). These are surface temperatures. Inside the stars, temperatures go up to tens of millions of degrees.

Astronomers believed formerly that all blue-white stars were "young" stars and that red ones were "old," with yellow and orange ones in between. Nowadays the accepted theory is that stars progress from red toward white.

This is what probably happens: a "young" star is a diffuse mass of elements in gaseous form. Its color is reddish, which means it is comparatively cool. (If you heat an iron red-hot, it is far cooler than if you heat it white-hot.) But it is,

nevertheless, hot enough so that many atoms are excited; they lose electrons. This means, of course, that they lose mass. The star contracts. Contraction creates pressure, and greater heat and nuclear reactions take place, in which some mass is lost but great energy is created. The star grows progressively hotter. Its color changes from red to orange to yellow to white to blue. For some reason that is not understood, in its hottest blue-white state a reversal sets in. The star starts to cool off, changing color again, growing white, yellow, orange, red and, finally, losing its luminosity, becoming a cold, dead mass. According to this theory of a star's life history, Sirius might possibly have been red "when Homer smote 'is bloomin' lyre," though it is white now and at some future date will be red again.

Sirius also changes periodically in brightness, or apparent magnitude. Thousands of stars do this. They are called variables. The variables have been classified according to the reason for their changing brightness. Sirius belongs to the class of eclipsing variables. That means that Sirius has a companion star, and the two revolve around a common central point. At times the smaller companion, or Sirius B, gets between Sirius A and the earth, cancelling out some of the luminosity of Sirius A.

Two-star companionships of this sort are called binaries, and very beautiful and impressive some of them are when viewed through a telescope. Stars that to unaided vision seem but a single point of more or less doubtful color reveal themselves in the telescope as pairs, displaying amazingly lovely harmonies of color, either contrasted or graded in pleasing nuances.

Algol, perhaps the best-known of the eclipsing binaries, was the first to be discovered by astronomers. Perhaps the ancients suspected that it was out of the ordinary; at any rate, the name "Algol," which means "the demon" in Arabic, may have referred to the bizarre quality of the supposed star's light, alternately becoming brighter and then dimming.

It was an English deaf-mute, John Goodricke, who in the year 1783 first discovered the nature of Algol's fluctuations. He advanced the theory that what appeared to be a single star was really made up of two: a bright star and a fainter companion that eclipsed the bright star as it revolved around it. He noted that the light of Algol becomes dimmer at intervals of about two days and twenty-two hours. Goodricke's theory was later fully confirmed.

Much has been learned since his day about the two stars that make up the eclipsing binary Algol. The brighter of the two — the primary star — has a diameter three times that of the sun. Its companion is somewhat larger, but is fainter by three magnitudes. The centers of the two stars are about 13,000,000 miles apart. Their orbits are almost edgewise to the earth; they are inclined from the edgewise position by only 8° or so.

Another interesting eclipsing binary is Zeta Aurigae. It is made up of a blue star, whose diameter is about seven times that of the sun, and a red star, with a diameter about fourteen times that of its companion. The two stars have approximately the same apparent magnitude. They revolve about each other once every 972 days, eclipsing each other at intervals as they move in their orbits. First we see a partial eclipse, lasting thirty-two hours, then a total eclipse of thirty-seven days and finally another thirty-two-hour partial eclipse.

The components of certain eclipsing binaries are so close together that they appear as a single star even when viewed through the most powerful telescope. They have been discovered and studied, however, with the spectroscope. The two stars of a typical binary of this kind approach the earth and then recede from it in their orbits, unless these are at right angles to the line of sight of an observer on the earth. The motions of the stars can be analyzed with the help of the spectroscope because, in accordance with the Doppler effect (see Index), the lines in their spectra shift to the violet as they approach the earth and to the red as they recede from it. Binary systems that are analyzed by means of the spectroscope are called spectroscopic binaries.

The variable stars that we have considered hitherto in this chapter are called extrinsic variables. The changes of brightness that we note in them are brought about by external factors, such as eclipses. We shall now take up the intrinsic variables. These are the stars that vary in brightness because of various physical changes that take place in them.*

The novae,
or new stars

A fascinating class of intrinsic variables are the exploding stars known as novae, or new stars. They were given that name because to the older astronomers they appeared to be newly created. We realize now, however, that a nova is not "new"; it is a pre-existing star upon which an explosion has taken place.

A faint star, perhaps too faint to be seen by any except the most powerful telescopes, begins to be more brilliant. Within the space of a few days it becomes thousands of times brighter than it was before. After some days of maximum brilliance, the luminosity begins to fade. Ultimately, the star is about as faint as it was before. This would seem to indicate that the outburst is far more superficial than it would appear to be. The explosion of novae occurs without warning. On the average, they increase about 60,000 times in brightness, corresponding to thirteen magnitudes. Always the growth of brilliance in a nova is extremely rapid and its fading is gradual.

* Certain variables are both extrinsic and intrinsic. They are eclipsing binaries that also undergo internal changes.

A nova is designated by the word "Nova," followed by the genitive (possessive form) of the constellation in which it occurs and the year in which the outburst took place. For example, when we refer to Nova Persei 1901, we have in mind the nova that appeared in the constellation Perseus in the year 1901.

The brightest nova of which we have definite record appeared in the constellation Cassiopeia in November 1572; it was observed by the great Danish astronomer Tycho Brahe. Nova Cassiopeiae 1572, to give it its technical name, became so bright that it could be seen in daylight. It faded very gradually and finally disappeared from view in the spring of 1574. There were no telescopes in those days; otherwise, it would have been visible some time longer. Another particularly brilliant nova was observed by the German astronomer Johannes Kepler in 1604, in the constellation Ophiuchus; it remained visible to the naked eye for about eighteen months. This nova became known as "Kepler's star."

Astronomers speak of the "explosion" of a nova; but the term is quite misleading. It is not to be compared, say, to the detonation of a charge of dynamite. It occurs, rather, in the form of a series of powerful jets or sprays, ejecting vast quantities of material from the star. Its effect has been described as suggesting a Roman candle.

A gaseous envelope develops around a nova. In certain cases, this envelope is spherical. Sometimes it is elliptical; in such instances, it is probably composed of several "shells," each corresponding to a different explosion. Occasionally an envelope attains fantastic size. The one that formed around Nova Aquilae 1918 was something like 1,000,000,000,000 miles in diameter after about twenty years. The Crab Nebula in the constellation Taurus shows an envelope that has been expanding for hundreds of years. It seems to have been formed by a nova that appeared in the year 1054, according to Chinese and Japanese records. (Apparently, it was not observed in the West.) Actually, the outburst must have taken place four thousand years or so before 1054, since it would take that length of time for its light to reach us.

A number of novae explode only once. In others, which are called recurrent novae, two or more outbursts take place. These novae rise to maximum brilliance more slowly than those that explode only once, and they take less time to return to their former faintness. They also have smaller ranges of magnitude than most novae. Among the recurrent novae are Y Coronae Borealis, RS Ophiuchi and U Scorpii.

We can only conjecture about the cause or causes of the explosions that result in the formation of novae. It was formerly held that they were due to collisions between stars, or between a star and a nebula. Few take this theory seriously now. For one thing, how could we explain recurrent novae on the basis of collisions? We would have to assume that a single star collides again and again with some celestial object in the course of a century. This would be beyond the range of probability.

It is more likely that a nova arises as the result of the sudden release of internal energy. Perhaps this energy release is brought about by a gradual increase in temperature, which finally triggers a nuclear explosion. At the present time, all this is pure speculation.

The spectacular stars called supernovae

In some cases, the explosions accompanying the rise of novae are particularly spectacular. Such out-of-the-ordinary novae are known as supernovae. The first one recorded by astronomers appeared in 1885 in the central region of the galaxy called the great spiral in Andromeda. It was of the seventh magnitude; it was a tenth as bright as the spiral itself and ten times as bright as the average nova. At first, astronomers did not consider it as differing appreciably from the other novae known at this time, since the great spiral in Andromeda was thought to be a nebula and much nearer to us than it actually is. Once it was realized how far away from the earth the so-called spiral nebula is, it became obvious that this particular "new star" was an extraordinary one.

We pointed out that the explosion that causes the average nova to become so brilliant does not have far-reaching effects — that is, comparatively speaking. It is estimated that a nova throws off only a thousandth part, or even less, of the matter that it contains. The supernova is affected much more by an explosion; as far as we can judge, it throws off the greater portion of its mass. Furthermore, it does not return to its former state after the explosion takes place. If we adopt the internal-energy theory to account for the rise of supernovae, the energy release must be far greater than in the case of novae.

The pulsating
variable stars

The pulsating variables make up another important group of intrinsic variable stars. They have received the name "pulsating" because they grow alternately brighter and fainter according to a more or less definite pulse, or rhythm. The pulsating variables may be divided, rather arbitrarily, into two groups: long-period and short-period. In the first group, the period from one peak of brightness to the next ranges from a hundred days to a thousand; in the second group, from less than one day to about fifty.

Long-period
variable stars

The stars with the longest period are the large red giants, with low density and low surface temperature. Variations in brightness are not altogether regular. These stars are all fairly bright when they reach their maximum brilliance and have conspicuous variations; hence they can be studied by the amateur astronomer with a small telescope or even a pair of binoculars.

The long-period star called Mira, in the constellation Cetus, is the prototype of the long-period variable; as a matter of fact, the name "Mira stars" is sometimes given to them. Mira was the first long-period variable to be discovered. It was first observed by David Fabricius, a German theologian and astronomer, in 1596; he thought he had found a nova. It was seen again in the year 1638. The astronomers of that time also assumed that it was a nova, at first, but they soon became aware of its true character as a periodic variable. The star aroused the admiration of the older astronomers. They hailed it as *stella mira* ("wonderful star," in Latin); that is how the name "Mira" was derived.

Mira has a period of about 332 days. Neither the maximum nor the minimum brilliance in a given cycle can be determined beforehand with any precision. Either may be hastened or delayed by a week or two and occasionally by as much as forty days. There are also considerable variations in intensity of light. The maximum brightness of the star has been known to reach almost the first magnitude. In 1779, Sir William Herschel noted that Mira was almost equal in brilliance to Aldebaran, a first-magnitude star. At other times, however, Mira fails to attain the fifth magnitude at the peak of its brightness.

Its minimum brilliance is more uniform, on the whole, but it, too, is subject to irregularity. It usually falls between the eighth and tenth magnitudes, but it has been known to be considerably fainter than this limit. In 1783, for example, Sir William Herschel could find no trace of the star in a telescope in which all stars down to the tenth magnitude were visible.

If we consider the whole range within which Mira has been known to vary, we find that the light it emits at certain periods is about ten thousand times as great as that emitted at other times. In its usual range of brilliance, however, it is from twelve to fifteen hundred times brighter at maximum than at minimum.

In spite of its variations, we can mark a certain pattern — an average of waning and waxing. At intervals of about eleven months, the star begins to brighten. The progression from minimum to maximum brightness takes something like a hundred days. Mira retains its brilliance for some weeks; then it subsides to its former level of brightness. It takes the star almost twice as long to pass from maximum to

In the above photo, the arrow points to the star now called Nova Aquilae 1918 before the outburst that made it a nova. Below, we see how much brighter the star (indicated here too by an arrow) became.

Yerkes Observatory

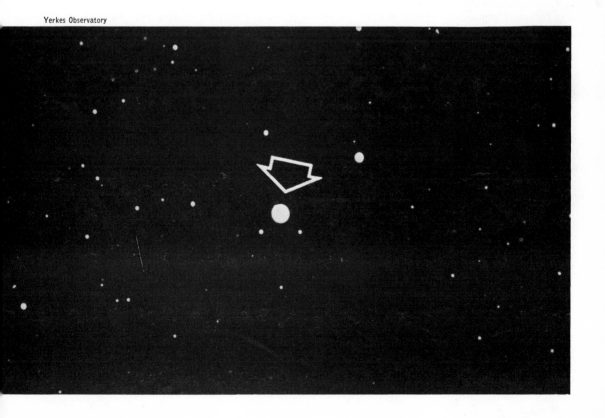

minimum brightness as from minimum to maximum. Considering the average of its performance, it remains at a high level of brilliance for about two months and at a low one for about four. It spends the rest of the time changing from one level to the other.

Another famous long-period variable is Chi Cygni. This striking star, which is of a beautiful scarlet color, is more than six thousand times as bright when it is at maximum brilliance than when it is faintest. It waxes and wanes in periods of about four hundred days through a range of eight magnitudes.

Mira and Chi Cygni show exceptionally wide ranges of fluctuations. The average amount of variation in seventy-five long-period variables that were kept under close observation at Harvard University was found to be five magnitudes. This means that the average long-period variable gives out a hundred times more light at maximum brightness than it does when at minimum.

Spectroscopic examination has shown that the increase in the brilliance of long-period stars is caused by periodical outbursts of incandescent gases, chiefly hydrogen. It is still not clear why these outbursts take place.

The short-period variable stars

The intrinsic variables with the shortest periods are called the RR Lyrae stars, because the first of the group to be studied was RR Lyrae (the star named RR in the constellation Lyra). They have been discovered in considerable numbers in the globular clusters; for this reason they are sometimes known as cluster-type variables. Their periods range from about an hour and a half to a little over a day. They remain at their peak of brightness for a very short time; they are at minimum brightness for a comparatively prolonged period. It is extremely difficult to observe these stars; often they can be studied only by photographic means.

Even at maximum brightness, they are so faint that we have identified only about fifteen hundred out of an estimated total of a hundred thousand in our own galaxy. As for the RR Lyrae stars in other galaxies, we shall probably never be able to discover more than an insignificant fraction. So far, astronomers have identified only a few in the neighboring galaxies.

Far better known are the Cepheid variables. Their name is derived from Delta Cephei, a star that can be made out with the naked eye. The total period of Delta Cephei from minimum to minimum is nearly five and a half days, and its light varies from a magnitude of 3.7 to 4.4. It takes only a day and a half for the star to reach maximum brilliance, while the descent to minimum requires four days. About fifteen hours after the downward progression begins, the star maintains the same degree of brilliance for a short time before resuming its declining course.

The average period of the Cepheid variables in our own galaxy is about seven days. Changes in magnitude vary from less than half a magnitude to somewhat more than a magnitude — a comparatively slight range.

Following are the periods and the variations in magnitude of a few representative members of the Cepheid variable group:

Name	Period (days)	Magnitude
SU Cassiopeiae	2.0	6.1-6.4
Delta Cephei	5.4	3.7-4.4
Zeta Geminorum	10.2	3.7-4.1
1 Carinae	35.5	3.6-4.8
SV Vulpeculae	45.1	8.4-9.4

We show the variations in brightness of a star by the so-called light curve, in which we plot brightness against time. Generally we cannot make observations of a variable star throughout the cycle of its variation, if the cycle is a day or more in length, because of the alternation of day and night. Hence we have to establish the light curve of a variable star from the data we obtain on different nights. It is a tribute to the perseverance and ingenuity of astronomers that they have been able to plot so many of the light curves.

These curves show considerable variation in the Cepheid variables. In some, the curve is smooth; in others, a steep ascent is followed by a gentle downward slope, which means, of course, that they brighten more rapidly than they grow faint.

Almost all the changes in brightness in Cepheid variables are due to the changes in temperature at the surface of the stars. The surface is hottest when the star is the brightest and coolest when the star is the faintest. The Cepheid variables that have the longest periods are the coolest.

Early in this century, a new and valuable method for sounding the depths of space was discovered by Henrietta S. Leavitt, an astronomer on the staff of the Harvard College Observatory, as a result of a study made by her of the Lesser Magellanic Cloud, in the southern heavens. This cloud was rich in Cepheid variables. Presumably all of these stars were at about the same distance from the earth. When Miss Leavitt had suitably arranged these Cepheids according to their period and brightness, she found that a definite relationship existed. The brighter the star, the greater the time that was required to go through the period of change from one time of maximum brightness to the next. If the distance and actual luminosity of any one of the Cepheid variables could be found, it would be possible to determine the luminosities and distances of other Cepheids from their periods. This conclusion was born out by Harlow Shapley's investigations of variable stars in globular clusters. Astronomers now determined the distances of several of the brighter Cepheids found in the heavens, and by using these results were able to calculate the distances of various other Cepheids on the basis of the period-luminosity relationship.

The Cepheids with like periods are assumed by the period-luminosity relationship to have the same intrinsic brightness. Consequently, the difference in observed brightness shows a difference in distance from us. We know that the light that we receive from a given source at a given distance will be four times as great if we halve the distance and only one-fourth as great if we double the distance. Let us suppose, by way of example, that a lighted candle is held at a distance of ten feet from us. If the candle is then set five feet from us, we receive four times as much light; if, on the other hand, it is moved to a distance of twenty feet from us, we receive only a fourth as much light. Utilizing this law of inverse relationship, we can tell that if a Cepheid variable appears to us to be sixteen times as bright as one with the same period (and therefore the same intrinsic brightness), it must be four times nearer to us than the other Cepheid variable in question.

Will our sun ever become a nova?

Astronomers are sometimes asked whether there is any danger that the sun might explode and become a nova or supernova. First, let us point out that the radiations of stars (including the sun) — their light, heat and other forms of electromagnetic energy — are the effects of nuclear reactions involving hydrogen. (We describe these reactions in the article The Sun, Our Star, in Volume 3.) It is when a star is reaching the end of its hydrogen supply that stellar explosions begin.

Suppose, now, that the supply of hydrogen in the sun should run low. The nuclear-reaction cycle would be affected. Other reactions in the sun's gases might then produce the periodic explosions we have observed in novae; or there might be a gigantic supernova explosion in which the sun would collapse and flare up and then cool down. In either case, the effect on earth would be disastrous. The oceans would start to boil and the lands would melt.

However, stellar explosions seem to occur in a star's old age; and the sun is quite young. Another point to note is that huge and very bright stars use up their hydrogen much more rapidly than smaller, dimmer ones; their span of life may be only a few hundred million years. The sun is not very massive and not very bright. As far as we know, it has enough hydrogen fuel to last for over 10,000,000,000 years.

See also Vol. 10, p. 269: "Stars and Constellations."

PRINTED CIRCUITS

How Metal Ribbons Replace Mazes of Wires

ELECTRONIC science has progressed so rapidly that it has often shown signs of bogging down under its own weight. This would have been apparent if one had glanced into the chassis of any television set a few years ago. To track down a minor fault in the set, a repairman often had to thread his way through a bulging, tortuous maze of wires and other circuit elements. Many exasperated engineers referred to this maze as a "can of worms" or as "spaghetti." In the manufacture of television receivers, each individual wire had to be placed and soldered by hand, using up valuable time and raising the costs of production.

The problem was particularly acute in military weapons, such as long-range jet bombers and guided missiles, in which electronic apparatus play an all-important role. As these weapons became more complicated, electronic devices took up more room, encroaching upon valuable space that should

have been used for other purposes. A point of diminishing returns seemed to be approaching. It became clear that electronic circuits would have to be simplified.

This goal has now been accomplished. Electrical circuits, with all their connections, can now be printed on flat panels, in much the same way as words are printed on paper with ink. The "ink" in the circuits may be any one of the many conducting metals (such as copper, silver and tantalum) that have been used in industry.

Printed circuits look something like the mazes familiar to puzzle-lovers. Flat ribbons of metal form the conducting pathways; they are carried on a dielectric, or electrically insulating, base material. Plastics, ceramics, glass and many other kinds of insulating base materials are available; laminated thermosetting plastics are particularly popular. (See Index, under Thermosetting plastics.)

Intricate mazes of electric wiring such as this are being replaced by prefabricated printed circuits.

A. T. & T.

Circuits are manufactured by many different processes. About 75 per cent are made by a variation of the photoengraving system used for books and magazines. The unprocessed panel is a laminated plastic to which a thin foil of metal — from 1/1000 to 4/100 of an inch thick in the case of copper — is bonded by heat and pressure

Printing circuits by the photoengraving process

The wiring scheme of the circuit is first mapped out in two dimensions, and then a highly precise drawing is made of the circuit pattern. A photographic negative of the pattern, in the same size as the eventual finished product, is then taken. The copper surface of the panel is coated with a photographic emulsion. Next, the negative is pressed against this coated surface in a vacuum printing frame and exposed to light from a carbon arc lamp.

Clear areas in the negative, which correspond to the conducting paths of the circuit, allow light to act on the emulsion under the negative. These exposed areas are not dissolved when the panel is put in a developer; instead, they are hardened and made acid-resistant by the action of the developer. The areas that have not been exposed to light are dissolved by the developer, uncovering the copper below. Thus, the circuit is traced in a hard, acid-resistant coating over a copper surface.

After cleaning and inspection, the panel is placed in an etching fluid. Uncoated areas of copper are eaten away by the solution, baring the plastic underneath. The circuit pattern, protected by the acid-resistant coating, is left intact.

Photoengraving can reproduce very fine lines and allows rigid dimension control. Many other manufacturing methods are also used. Circuits can be applied to ceramics by the silk screen process, using metal paints. Metal foil backed with adhesive can be stamped on plastic bases with heavy dies in the shape of the circuit pattern. Metal can also be sprayed directly against the base through pattern stencils. In another method, a film of tantalum is deposited in a vacuum on ceramic or glass

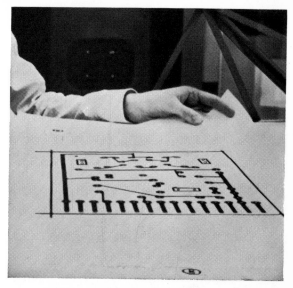

Adjusting a circuit pattern before photographing it with a high-precision copying camera.

blanks. Part of the film is then etched away to form the required circuit.

Some circuit elements must stand up under abrasive wear or corrosive agents. By adding an electroplating step to the photoengraving process, the circuit pattern can be given a tough protective layer of a nickel-rhodium alloy.

Both sides of a panel can be printed with circuits. Holes can then be punched through the laminate and plated with conductive metal to form connections between the circuits on the two sides.

Once the panels are completed, all the circuit connections are soldered in a single operation, which is known as "dip soldering." In this, the panel or assembly of panels is floated on the surface of a molten solder bath. Complete assemblies may be protected with a coating of insulating plastic, such as polyethylene.

The first printed circuits developed on a mass-production basis were for radio proximity fuzes for artillery shells in World War II. The proximity fuze detonated a projectile when it was within range of its target, even before actual contact was made with the latter. A tiny radio set in the nose of the shell sent out radio waves, which were reflected back to the set from the target. The proximity fuze would hardly have been a practical device without the use of printed circuits.

Photos, Bell Telephone Laboratories

Above: the light-sensitive surface of the copper is masked by the negative and exposed to an arc light; later the pattern will be developed and etched.

Left: before printing, the circuit-pattern negative gets a final check. A technician carefully retouches the negative to sharpen the wiring lines.

Printed circuits used with subminiature components, such as the tiny transistor shown below, reduce the cost and complexity of electronic devices.

Printed circuits have found a great many applications since that time. They have made possible the mass production of electronic equipment on a vastly increased scale. They have made such equipment more reliable than before; they have saved space and weight. Printed circuits now serve in practically all types of electronic devices. They have been made available to the general public in radio and television receivers, pocket transmitters and hearing aids. Tiny transistors have been substituted for bulky, fragile electronic tubes in many of these devices. A pocket radio set with printed circuits and transistors can outperform many an older portable set ten times its size.

Electrical wiring behind the dashboards of automobiles is being rapidly replaced by printed circuits. The use of these devices in combination with transistors has made car radios more trouble-free than before; and yet there has been no sacrifice in tonal quality.

Printed circuits have been widely used in electronic computers. They have resulted in notable savings in space and in increased reliability. They have come to play an essential role, too, in the control systems of guided missiles, artificial satellites and manned capsules.

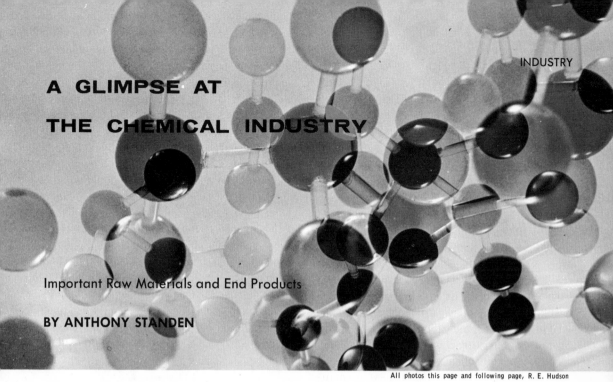

INDUSTRY

A GLIMPSE AT
THE CHEMICAL INDUSTRY

Important Raw Materials and End Products

BY ANTHONY STANDEN

All photos this page and following page, R. E. Hudson

WHAT is the chemical industry? One might say, I suppose, that this is the industry that makes chemicals; but such a definition would leave much to be desired. Just what is a chemical, after all? Presumably, it is a pure chemical substance (an element or compound) and not a mixture. Thus, sulfuric acid is a chemical, and the manufacture of sulfuric acid is undoubtedly a part of the chemistry industry. So is the manufacture of vinyl chloride, which reaches the consumer in the form of a great many plastic articles. But common salt and sugar, with which all of us are familiar, are also pure chemical substances. Yet properly considered, the preparation of these substances for the consumer has nothing to do with the chemical industry. Salt is simply dug out of the earth or evaporated from brine, and sugar is an agricultural product. We shall have to modify our first definition, then, to read "the chemical industry *uses chemistry* to make chemicals from other chemical substances."

The truly chemical industries, which manufacture chemicals, are seldom well known to the public. This is because we, as consumers, do not ordinarily make use of chemicals in their pure form. Instead, they are converted into products that reach the consumer only after a number of operations. Consider the chemical ethylene glycol, for example. If you drive an automobile, you are familiar with one of the products in which ethylene glycol is used — antifreeze. You would almost certainly not ask for this product under its chemical name of ethylene glycol; you would call for a particular brand of antifreeze.*

The products of the chemical industries may have a number of different uses. Ammonium nitrate, for example, is used as an explosive and also as a fertilizer. A certain amount, too, goes into the production of nitrous oxide ("laughing gas"), an anesthetic used in dentistry. Hydrazine, a chemical derived from ammonia, is an important fuel for rockets. It is also the starting material for the manufacture of isoniazid, a drug used in the treatment of tuberculosis. (See Index, under Isoniazid.)

In the chemical industry, the same product may be derived from quite different sources. Ethylene glycol can be manufactured from ethylene (derived from petroleum). It can also be prepared from formaldehyde (which can be made from coal, air and water) or from natural gas or from petroleum.

The part that chemistry plays in industry is by no means confined to the preparation of chemicals by the chemical industry. It is of great importance, for example, in

* *Editor's note*: Antifreeze preparations do not consist of pure ethylene glycol. They contain other ingredients, including a rust inhibitor, which prevents the formation of rust.

55

metallurgy, which is concerned with the extraction of metals from their ores and their preparation for practical use. The metallurgical processes of smelting and refining are chemical processes. They were utilized in very distant times when the chemistry of reducing ore to metal was a trial-and-error affair, and not understood. Many other industries — glass, ceramics, paper, leather, beer, wine and food, to name only a few — also depend on chemistry. All these are examples of *chemical-process industries*. They work with materials that are changed chemically in the process of manufacture, but the end product is not a pure "chemical" that will be used by some other industry. Many of the chemical-process industries are discussed in other articles of this set.*

As a matter of fact, there is some chemistry in practically any industry that can be mentioned. For example, chemical processes are used in the preparation of the ink used in a newspaper printing plant. In a textile mill (quite apart from the fact that it may be using modern synthetic fibers — products of chemistry), there are many chemical operations in the sizing, scouring and conditioning of fibers for the successive operations. We should bear in mind, too, that any industrial product has a definite chemical composition; and usually the chemical composition of the product is a matter of importance.

In the preceding paragraphs, we have given a preliminary survey of the part that chemistry plays in industry. We shall now devote our attention to the raw materials from which chemicals are made. We shall tell how these materials are processed, and we shall consider a few of the uses to which the end products are put.

* *Editor's note:* See the starred articles in the Index under the entry Industry.

Steps by which the plastic polyvinyl chloride forms from molecules of chlorine and ethylene, shown with models. The black globes are carbon (C) atoms; the light globes, hydrogen (H) atoms; gray globes, chlorine (Cl) atoms; the connecting dowels are chemical bonds. In the top and second photos, a molecule of chlorine gas, with two chlorine atoms (Cl_2), and a molecule of ethylene gas (C_2H_4), with two carbon and four hydrogen atoms, react to form a molecule of vinyl chloride (C_2H_3Cl). In the third and bottom photos, several vinyl-chloride molecules polymerize (join) to form polyvinyl chloride.

The raw materials
of the chemical industry

For very large segments of the chemical industry, the most important raw materials are coal, petroleum, natural gas, limestone, salt and sulfur. To these may be added phosphate rock and fluorspar and a certain number of more specialized materials. Note that these substances are all minerals. The chemistry industry proper does not at present use organic (plant and animal) products to any great extent to make pure chemicals. However, chemical-process industries, such as the paper, textile and plastics industries, use large quantities of organic materials. Paper is made from wood. Vegetable and animal fibers are still in wide use in the textile industry. Agricultural products, such as cellulose, soybeans and others go into the processing of various plastics.*

The fossil fuels and the
chemicals derived from them

The name "fossil fuels" is given particularly to coal, petroleum and natural gas. They have all been derived from fossil organic substances — animal and vegetable. They go back one or more geological periods, and they have been transformed through the operation of a variety of natural forces.** At one time, the fossil fuels were used primarily as fuels. They still serve that purpose; but they are also now reckoned among the important sources of chemical raw materials.

Coal. The chemicals derived from coal are generally a by-product of the process whereby bituminous coal is converted into coke. This coking, as it is called, takes place in so-called by-product coke ovens (see Index), in which the coal is heated in the absence of oxygen. The solid matter remaining in the ovens is coke. The gas and vapors that result from the coking are piped to special equipment, where they are made to yield fuel gas, ammonia and coal tar.

Ammonia (NH_3), a compound of nitrogen and hydrogen, is a most useful chemical. It serves in the synthesis of plastics, drugs, dyes and many other substances. A dilute solution of ammonia in water is a well-known cleansing agent in the home. Anhydrous (dewatered) ammonia gas is used as a refrigerant because of the ease with which it can be converted to the liquid state. Ammonia is vitally important for fertilizers (either as ammonia or in the form of ammonia products). When ammonia is mixed with air and passed over a catalyst, it yields nitric acid:

$$NH_3 + 2O_2 \rightarrow HNO_3 + H_2O$$

"A molecule of ammonia (NH_3), reacting with 2 molecules of oxygen ($2O_2$), yields a molecule of nitric acid (HNO_3) and a molecule of water (H_2O)."

Nitric acid leads to the manufacture of explosives, fertilizers (when combined with unchanged ammonia to yield ammonium nitrate, NH_4NO_3) and to other products.

Coal tar is an important by-product of the coke ovens. After it is piped from these ovens, it is dried, heated and distilled, yielding a viscous liquid or solid called pitch,* as well as a number of other products, some of which can also be obtained by "stripping" (taking the substances from) the coke-oven gas. These products include benzene (C_6H_6), toluene (C_7H_8), naphthalene ($C_{10}H_8$), anthracene ($C_{14}H_{10}$), phenol (C_6H_5OH) and cresol (C_7H_7OH). They are chiefly hydrocarbons — that is, compounds made up of hydrogen and carbon. More specifically, they are known as cyclic hydrocarbons because the atoms that make up their molecules form one or more rings. (*Cyclos* means "ring" in Greek.) Thus, benzene has the structural formula

* Editor's note: For the use of agricultural *products* as raw materials for chemical-process industries, see the article on Progress in Chemurgy, in Volume 7.

** Editor's note: See Index, under Fossils. For an account of the formation of coal, petroleum and natural gas see the articles on Earth's Dark Treasure (Coal), Volume 1; Our Liquid Gold (Petroleum), Volume 4; Natural Gas, Volume 5.

* Editor's Note: for the various uses of this substance, see the Index, under Pitch.

The cyclic compounds are now being made increasingly from petroleum products.

Benzene is used extensively in the manufacture of chemicals, particularly styrene and phenol. Toluene is especially well known as an ingredient in the explosive trinitrotoluene, better known as TNT. Phenol and some of its derivatives are powerful germ-killers; but phenol is notably important in the synthesis of phenolic plastics. Naphthalene yields various dyes. Cresol is a good disinfectant and a useful agent for froth flotation, which is a special method for separating ores from the minerals containing them.

Petroleum and natural gas. Petroleum, or crude oil, is a mixture of many different kinds of hydrocarbons. They are separated by a first step called fractional distillation. First the crude oil is heated and converted into a vapor. Then, since the different hydrocarbons have different boiling points, they condense at different places in a tall fractionating tower and are collected separately. To refine the oil further, a number of processes may be used. In "cracking" — sometimes with the aid of a catalyst (catalytic cracking) — large molecules are broken down into smaller ones; this is especially important in the manufacture of gasoline. For other products, a process called polymerization, or building-up of large molecules from smaller ones, is used. Liquefied petroleum gas (LPG) is also one of the products of the fractional distillation of petroleum. The refining of petroleum is discussed in detail in the article Our Liquid Gold, in Volume 4.

Natural gas often occurs together with petroleum; they are both found in the minute pores of certain rocks, including sandstone and limestone. Natural gas consists mostly of methane (CH_4), with small amounts of other hydrocarbons; in some cases it contains helium, sulfur and carbon dioxide, which may be extracted. The gas can be processed to yield carbon black, but it is used very often as a fuel, being sent long distances through pipelines.

The chemicals derived from petroleum and natural gas are known as petrochemicals. These chemicals have become immensely important in the chemical industry; they account for about 30 per cent of the entire chemical production of the United States. They include such essential chemicals as benzene (C_6H_6), phenol (C_6H_5OH), methane (CH_4), ethane (C_2H_6), propane (C_3H_8), butane (C_4H_{10}), ethylene (C_2H_4), acetylene (C_2H_2), butadiene (C_4H_6), butylene (C_4H_8), isoprene (C_5H_8) and isobutylene (C_4H_8). These in turn yield an astonishing variety of still other fundamental and highly useful chemicals.

A rather special petrochemical product is carbon black. This substance is prepared by burning petroleum fractions or natural gas in air that is insufficient for complete combustion. Carbon black is very important as an essential ingredient in tires. It is also used, although to a lesser extent, in printer's ink.

Practically all petrochemicals have been derived from other sources besides petroleum and natural gas, and some still are derived from such sources. As we saw, such chemicals as benzene, phenol and acetylene are still produced from coal tar. Ethyl alcohol was formerly derived exclusively from agricultural sources. Acetone was produced by the distillation of wood and later by the fermentation of various agricultural products. Butadiene, used for synthetic rubber, was made from ethyl alcohol during the first World War. All of these chemicals are derived chiefly or entirely from petroleum and natural gas at the present time.

From the three fossil fuels mentioned above — coal, petroleum and natural gas — the so-called synthesis gases can be derived. The processes involved in the manufacture of synthesis gas include partial oxidation by air, oxygen or steam, with or without a catalyst, and sometimes at high pressure. These processes can be made to yield either ammonia synthesis gas, a mixture (not a compound) of hydrogen and nitrogen; or a methanol synthesis gas, a mixture (again, not a compound) of hydrogen and carbon monoxide.

When ammonia synthesis gas is compressed, slightly heated and passed over a catalyst, it yields ammonia:

$$3H_2 + N_2 \rightarrow 2NH_3$$

CATALYST

GAS PURIFIER

CIRCULATING PUMP

CONDENSER

METHANOL

HEATING COIL

CO + H₂

CO + H₂

CO + H₂

METHANOL

The synthesis of methanol (wood, or methyl, alcohol) is carried out by reaction between carbon-monoxide gas (CO) and hydrogen gas (H₂), promoted by the presence of a catalyst. These gases are purified, heated and then led to the catalyst, which is usually some metallic oxide; the methanol (CH₃OH) is condensed.

Adapted from "The Chemistry of Organic Compounds," by J. B. Conant and A. H. Blatt, 4th edition, © 1952, The Macmillan Company

"3 molecules of hydrogen ($3H_2$) plus a molecule of nitrogen (N_2) yield 2 molecules of ammonia ($2NH_3$)."

Methanol synthesis gas is made into methanol, by a high-pressure catalytic reaction:

$$2H_2 + CO \rightarrow CH_3OH$$

"2 molecules of hydrogen ($2H_2$) plus a molecule of carbon monoxide (CO) yield a molecule of methanol (CH_3OH)."

Methanol is made into formaldehyde, which is a constituent of a large number of plastics.

Chemicals derived from chlorine

Chlorine (Cl_2) is a greenish-yellow gas, with an irritating odor. It has a suffocating effect when introduced in sufficient quantities into the respiratory system; in fact, it has been used as a poisonous gas in warfare. It also happens to be a valuable source of different chemicals.

All the chlorine used in the chemical industry is derived from sodium chloride, NaCl, which is simply common table salt. Sodium chloride is decomposed by causing an electric current to be passed through it. This can be done in two ways. In one way, the electric current goes through a bath of molten salt and splits it into the elements chlorine and sodium. As for the sodium produced in this way, it is needed to synthe-

size certain dyes, and as a cooling medium for certain nuclear reactors. Sodium chloride can also be decomposed by passing electric current through a solution of sodium chloride in water. The main product is chlorine; the co-product is sodium hydroxide (NaOH), a large-tonnage chemical used in the manufacture of soap, textile manufacture and petroleum refining. Sodium hydroxide underlies many other important operations in the chemical industry.

The chlorine derived by electrolysis from sodium chloride can be made to react with the hydrocarbons obtained from fossil fuels. This results in the chemicals known as chlorohydrocarbons—a word that denotes compounds containing carbon, hydrogen, chlorine and no other element. The chlorohydrocarbons are versatile materials. They are used in making more than one kind of synthetic rubber as well as the antiknock compound in gasoline. They also serve in the production of paint removers, refrigerants, vinyl plastics, several types of insecticides and in electric insulation, as well as in dry cleaning and in fireproofing.

Sulfur is another important chemical raw material

Sulfur enters the chemical industry from several sources. Among the more important of these are sulfur-containing deposits in Sicily, Louisiana, Texas and parts of Mexico. At one time, the sulfur deposits of Sicily were the chief source of the world's sulfur; they still account for considerable quantities.

Most of the world's sulfur is produced in the United States from the free deposits in Texas and Louisiana. It is not necessary to mine the sulfur; it is taken out by the method known as the Frasch process. A hollow iron casing is driven down into the sulfur-bearing deposits. Within this casing are three concentric pipes. Superheated water, at a temperature of about 165° C., is forced down between the two outer pipes onto the ore bed. Since the melting point of sulfur is only 110°-120°, the hot water melts the sulfur. Compressed hot air is pumped down the innermost pipe. A mixture of hot water, hot air and molten sulfur is then forced up to the surface in the form of a froth through the space between the innermost pipe and the one next to it (see picture on page 61). The sulfur obtained in this way contains almost no impurities.

Sulfur is also obtained as a by-product of some smelting processes. The ores of many valuable metals, such as copper and zinc, are sulfides — that is, compounds of sulfur and the desired metals. When these ores are "roasted," freeing the metals, the sulfur is obtained in the form of sulfur dioxide, from which sulfuric acid is then derived. A certain amount of sulfur is also obtained from "sour" natural gas — the bad-smelling hydrogen sulfide, H_2S.

Most sulfur is converted into sulfuric acid (H_2SO_4), which is manufactured in greater quantities than any other chemical. The preparation of sulfuric acid is described elsewhere in THE BOOK OF POPULAR SCIENCE (see Index, under Sulfuric Acid — Preparation of). The uses of sulfuric acid are legion. It serves in the manufacture of fertilizers. It is indispensable in steel "pickling" — removing the rust that covers manufactured steel at various stages of processing. It serves in petroleum refining and in the manufacture of rayon, detergents, dyes (for textiles) and pigments (for paint). It is often used, too, as a reagent in the chemical laboratory.

Free sulfur also has many uses. It is a basic material in vulcanizing (see Index); it is an active material in many fungicides. It serves in various medicinal products, such as sulfur ointment, to combat various microorganisms. The compound sulfur dioxide (SO_2) is used in preserving fruits.

Photo: Hooker Chemical Corporation. Diagram: Adapted from material furnished by Hooker Chemical Corporation

CONCRETE TOP
HYDROGEN OUTLET
CHLORINE GAS OUTLET
BRINE INLET
SIGHT GLASS
BRINE LEVEL
COPPER CONDUCTOR ON CATHODE
CAUSTIC OUTLET
PERFORATED STEEL CATHODE COVERED WITH DIAPHRAGM
GRAPHITE ANODES
CONCRETE BOTTOM
COPPER CONDUCTOR TO ANODES
INSULATOR

Hooker cell for producing chlorine (Cl_2) by electrolysis (electrical decomposition) of brine — a water solution of sodium chloride (NaCl), or common salt. The chemical reactions caused by current passing from negative electrodes (cathodes) to positive electrodes (anodes) liberate chlorine from its union with the metal sodium (Na), and hydrogen (H_2) from the water (H_2O). Another important product of this process is sodium hydroxide (NaOH), better known as lye. The photo above shows Hooker cells in action.

FIELD CONTROL STATION

PRODUCING WELL

HOT WATER PLANT

BARREN ANHYDRITE

BARREN CAP ROCK

SULPHUR DEPOSIT

BOTTOM OF WELL IN SULPHUR DEPOSIT

COMPRESSED AIR

LIQUID SULPHUR

HOT WATER

Adapted from material furnished by Texas Gulf Sulphur Company

LIQUID SULPHUR

LIQUID SULPHUR

BARREN CAP ROCK

SULPHUR DEPOSIT

HOT WATER

COMPRESSED AIR

HOT WATER

HOT WATER

HOT WATER

BARREN ANHYDRITE

LIQUID SULPHUR

BOTTOM OF WELL IN SULPHUR DEPOSIT

Frasch process for raising sulphur from underground deposits. Three concentric pipes, 6, 3 and 1 inches in diameter respectively, lead down to the sulphur. The top and bottom parts of the pipe system are enlarged in sectional view at the right and below to show details. Pure hot water is pumped down the space between the 6-inch and 3-inch pipes to the sulphur, which is melted by hot water penetrating it through holes in the outer pipe. Melted sulphur sinks and then enters the 3-inch pipe. Compressed air from the central, 1-inch pipe aerates the sulphur, forming a froth that moves upward through the 3-inch pipe to the surface.

Limestone — a plentiful, cheap and useful chemical raw material

Limestone is made up mostly of calcium carbonate; it often contains various other compounds, such as magnesium carbonate and some compounds of iron and aluminum. There are vast limestone deposits in every continent; most were laid down in areas that were formerly covered by the sea. Many deposits were derived from the shells of sea creatures that lived millions of years ago; others from calcium carbonate that was contained in seawater and that was precipitated. Limy muds were formed in the course of the ages; these solidified into limestone deposits, which became available to man as the oceans receded and the land was raised.

Vast quantities of limestone are used in the smelting of iron ore. Here limestone is used as a flux: that is, it fuses with various impurities in the iron ore and carries them off as slag. This process is discussed in the article on The Story of Steel, in Volume 1.

When limestone is heated in a special kind of kiln, called a limestone kiln, it yields calcium oxide (quicklime) and carbon-dioxide gas, as indicated in the formula

$$CaCO_3 \xrightarrow{heat} CaO + CO_2$$

Contact process for making sulphuric acid (H_2SO_4). At far left, sulphur is burned to produce the gas sulphur dioxide (SO_2), which is then passed through a series of chambers where dust is removed, it is washed in water and then dried in sulphuric acid. The SO_2 is next purified in arsenic and led to the catalyst (usually a compound of vanadium), which causes SO_2 to combine with oxygen (O) to form sulphur trioxide (SO_3). SO_3 is absorbed in sulphuric acid to form $H_2S_2O_7$; water is added to make sulphuric acid.

Adapted from "Introductory Chemistry," O. W. Nitz, © 1961, permission, D. Van Nostrand Company

It is used in making mortar for building purposes. It also serves in many chemical operations, such as glassmaking, sugar refining and water treatment.

In a very special use of lime, it is mixed with coke from coal (or petroleum) and heated to make calcium carbide, CaC_2. When water is added to calcium carbide, acetylene, C_2H_2, is obtained. This is used sometimes, though on a small scale, to make a very brilliant light; it is also used in welding and other operations requiring a hot flame. Actually, however, its most important use is as an intermediary compound in the manufacture of many chemicals.

Fluorine, a chemical raw material with various specialized uses

Fluorine is the most active, chemically, of all the nonmetallic elements; it is the most electronegative of all.* Hence it combines readily with almost all the chemical elements. In fact it has been made to react with xenon and krypton — so-called noble gases. (See Index, under Noble gases.) Fluorine is a pale-yellow, highly poisonous gas. A number of its compounds are toxic but, under certain circumstances, may have health-giving properties, as we shall see.

* *Editor's note*: For a discussion of the electronegative series, see the Index, under Electrochemical series.

Fluorine is found in nature as an element in various compounds. The most important source of the element is fluorspar, calcium fluoride, CaF_2, which has long been used in metallurgy to lower the melting points of various ores. Fluorine is also a constituent of the mineral cryolite (Na_3AlF_6), which is used in the processing of aluminum. (See Index, under Cryolite.) Elementary fluorine is generally obtained by the electrolysis of hydrogen fluoride (HF).

Fluorine and its compounds have a variety of industrial uses. Hydrofluoric acid (HF) reacts with glass and therefore is used to etch glass in the manufacture of thermometers, chemical containers and decorative glassware. This acid is also used to remove various impurities from stainless steel.

Certain gases, such as the Freons, containing fluorine, carbon, chlorine and sometimes hydrogen, are ideal as refrigerants, particularly because they are nontoxic. These compounds are also used as propellants in aerosols, put in spray tubes to deliver insecticides, shaving creams, cake icing and other preparations.

The name fluorocarbons denotes compounds consisting of carbon and fluorine atoms. They have found many uses: among other things, as insulation for electric wire and in the manufacture of plastic tubing. A fluorocarbon called PTFE (for polytetrafluorethylene) has become well known in the kitchen, because of the fact that water will not wet it. PTFE is better known by some of the trade names, such as Teflon, among others, given to it. It has remarkable non-stick properties; if a pan has been coated with the substance, you can fry eggs without any butter or fat, and they will not stick to the pan. PTFE is an example of an abherent — the opposite of an adherent. An adherent, or adhesive, makes things stick; an abherent prevents them from sticking. PTFE is remarkably smooth and slippery (feel the inside of a nonstick frying pan). For this reason it is sometimes used for bearings that never need lubricating.

Certain fluorides (fluorine compounds) have been very much in the news of recent years. They have been added to water in very small quantities in many communities, because fluorides markedly lessen the number of cavities that develop in the teeth. An excess of fluorides, such as sometimes occurs in certain natural waters, may have some bad effects. For one thing, they may cause teeth to become mottled. (See the Index, under Fluoridation.)

Industries that utilize the products of the chemical industry

We have turned the spotlight on some important raw materials of which the chemicals of industry are made. There are many others, which we have not been able to discuss for lack of space. Let us now briefly consider a few of the industries that make extensive use of chemicals.

The fertilizer industry. This is now a huge industry in the United States; it will become increasingly important throughout the world as efforts are redoubled to feed the world's rapidly and dangerously increasing population.

Three principal elements have to be provided in suitable form in fertilizers. These are nitrogen, phosphorus, and potassium.

Nitrogen is supplied very largely from ammonia derived from fossil fuels. Ammonia for fertilizers is available in several forms. It may be used as ammonium nitrate; or it may be combined with phosphates, as ammonium phosphate; or it may be used as urea. A certain amount of the nitrogen used in fertilizers is supplied from sodium nitrate, a mineral that occurs naturally in Chile. A certain amount, too, is derived from ammonium sulfate, recovered as a by-product from the conversion of coal into coke.

Phosphorus is obtained as phosphate rock. It has to be treated with sulfuric acid, or in various other ways, to make it applicable as a fertilizer. These methods of treatment also lead to phosphorus products that are valuable in other ways, such as laundry chemicals. (In some plants, fluorine, which occurs with the phosphates, is recovered, in a form suitable for fluoridating water.) Phosphorus can be used in various forms as a fertilizer — as superphosphate, triple superphosphate and phosphoric acid, which can be converted into ammonium phosphate.

Diagram of cell for production of fluorine gas (F_2). Hydrofluoric acid (hydrogen fluoride, HF) is decomposed by electricity to yield free fluorine and also hydrogen gas (H_2). The interior sides of the steel cell and the central partition act as cathodes, or negative electrodes; the anodes (positive electrodes) are of carbon. HF is mixed with a conducting solution, or electrolyte, so that electric current is able to pass.

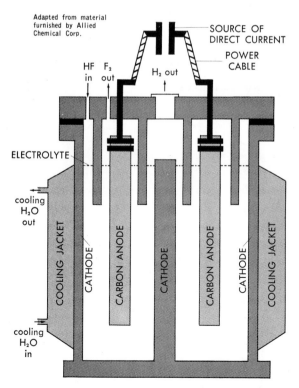

Adapted from material furnished by Allied Chemical Corp.

SOURCE OF DIRECT CURRENT

POWER CABLE

HF in
F_2 out
H_2 out

ELECTROLYTE

cooling H_2O out

cooling H_2O in

COOLING JACKET

CATHODE

CARBON ANODE

CATHODE

CARBON ANODE

CATHODE

COOLING JACKET

Potassium, in the form of several of its salts, is obtained from mines. The principal sources are Germany, France and the United States, in that order. Potassium compounds, nitrogen compounds and phosphorus compounds are mixed together in most of the fertilizers used nowadays. In many cases there are added small quantities of trace elements, that may be necessary in certain regions. These trace elements include zinc, molybdenum, copper and boron.

The explosives. Allied in some ways to the fertilizers are the explosives. These substances are not used by any means exclusively as ammunition for warfare. In peacetime, various explosives are used in mining, quarrying, demolition work, prospecting for petroleum and sometimes the excavation of oil and gas wells.

Many explosives (like many fertilizers) contain nitrates, or compounds obtained from nitric acid. Ammonium nitrate is important; it cannot be made to explode by itself but it is an ingredient of many explosives. Cellulose nitrate (sometimes called guncotton) and glyceryl nitrate (also called nitroglycerin) * are important nitrogen-containing explosives. The well-known explosive dynamite

* The preferred names are cellulose nitrate and glyceryl nitrate.

was originally glyceryl nitrate absorbed in kieselguhr. Today many modified forms are available, often containing ammonium nitrate. Many modern explosives are in plastic form. The old-fashioned gunpowder, a mixture of potassium nitrate with smaller amounts of charcoal and sulfur, is much less used now than formerly. It serves sometimes in ceremonial salutes. Explosives are discussed in detail in Volume 8; see the Table of Contents.

The dyeing industry. The chemistry of dyes is one of the classical triumphs of the organic chemist. Starting with the products of coal tar, he has synthesized thousands of dyestuffs, ranging through the colors of the rainbow. They have not only matched and duplicated nature's colors, but have surpassed them in uniformity, brilliance and permanence. The ultimate consumer is constantly in contact with dyes produced through chemical means. The garments that you wear are practically all dyed (your undergarments may be no more than bleached). If you look around the room your eye will light on dyed products in the rugs that cover the floor, in the paint or wall paper on the wall, in curtains, lamp shades, plastic fixtures, books, book jackets, pictures, color photographs and decorated objects.

Manufacture of viscose rayon involves chemical alteration of raw cellulose into a thick (viscous) liquid which can be forced into the shape of fibers; the fiber is then chemically converted back into a cellulose similar in composition to the original material. Cellulose from wood pulp or cotton, in the form of sheets, is steeped in a tank of caustic soda, which unites chemically with the cellulose to form alkali cellulose. The wet sheets are then squeezed through rolls and shredded; next they are aged in a special bin. The alkali-cellulose crumbs are then put into mechanical

Diagrams on this page and following page, adapted from material and photo furnished by FMC Corporation, American Viscose Division

CELLULOSE SHEETS

SQUEEZE ROLLS

Alkali Cellulose Crumb

AGING BIN

Xanthate Crumb

CONTINUOUS STEEPING TANK
(Caustic Soda Solution)

SHREDDER

MECHANICAL CHURN
(Carbon Disulfide)

The drug industry. In the early years of this century, the German researcher Paul Ehrlich was a pioneer in the investigation of new organic chemicals to find those with curative action against various diseases. In those days chemotherapy — the use of chemicals to heal disease — was something new and striking. Today, the use of synthetic drugs, made from a bewildering variety of chemicals, has become universal. The sulfa drugs and the antibiotics have revolutionized the practice of medicine. The medicament that the doctor last prescribed for you was manufactured, in all probability, in a large establishment from a variety of organic chemicals. You can be sure, too that in this establishment many researchers are engaged in a constant search to find new synthetic drugs to be used against diseases that have not yet been conquered.

The textile industry. There was a time when the only fibers used for making textile fabrics were derived from cotton (from the cotton plant); wool (from the fur of sheep); silk (from the cocoon of the silkworm); and linen (from the stems of flax). These fibers are all polymers; that is, they are made up of atoms of several different elements, arranged in a repeating pattern so as to form a very large molecule. Many naturally occurring substances besides those we just mentioned are polymers. Among these is rubber. On page 56 of this article we show a typical polymer being formed.

Chemists have now learned how to make entirely synthetic polymer fibers. The first was a modified natural polymer. Cellulose, either from cotton or from wood, was dissolved in a solvent, which could be either "xanthate" (a compound containing carbon and sulfur) or "cuprammonium" (made from a copper salt and ammonia). This solution was then squirted out through extremely fine holes into a "bath" of a chemical that would undo the chemical change brought about by the xanthate or cuprammonium. This would practically restore the original cellulose, only very slightly changed in its chemistry, but now in the form of continuous filaments. The resulting product was first called "artificial silk." This name was given up, however, because, although the product is very glossy, it is not really the same as silk. It is now called rayon. It is manufactured in extremely large quantities, and people often wear garments made of it; suits, dresses and the like. It is also used in tire cords.

Another way of treating cellulose is to dissolve it in acetic acid, ultimately producing cellulose acetate. It was originally called

churns, to which carbon-disulfide compound is slowly added. This chemical reacts with the alkali cellulose to form cellulose-xanthate crumb, orange in color. The xanthate is now dissolved in caustic soda to form viscose solution, which is aged in a tank and then filtered to remove any dirt. The viscose is then of the right consistency and is fed into the spinning tank. There it is forced through the fine holes of the spinneret into an acid bath; the fibers thus formed are thereby converted into cellulose—the familiar rayon. The fibers are then collected and removed.

MIXING TANK
(Caustic Soda Solution)

Viscose Solution

AGING TANK

FILTERS

Solution

SPINNING TANK

SPINNING MACHINE
(Sulfuric Acid Bath)

acetate rayon; but it is now simply known as acetate. It is decidedly different from regular rayon; for one thing it needs a much lower ironing temperature.

Fibers such as rayon and acetate are called semisynthetic, since they start with a natural fiber. The first fully synthetic fiber to be successful was nylon, which belongs to the chemical family of the polyamides. Nylon was developed just before World War II. It came providentially just in time to be used as parachute material. Parachutes had formerly been made of silk, but since most silk came from Japan, which was at war with the United States, this was no longer obtainable in adequate quantities. Nylon is used very widely in textiles and in tire cord. It has many other uses.

Polyester fibers (Dacron is the best known brand name) and acrylic fibers (such as Orlon and Acrilan) followed, and they are in wide use. A newer fiber than these is Spandex, which is exceptionally useful in formfitting underwear.

Plastics. Also included among the synthetic polymers is the very large class of materials known as plastics. The first plastic was a modified form of cellulose. It was made by taking cellulose nitrate (closely related to the materials used in explosives) and making it more flexible by the addition of camphor (from a tree that grows in the Far East). The most serious disadvantage of celluloid was that it was flammable. It was largely replaced in time by a variety of other plastics, including the formaldehyde group, the vinyl group and newer cellulose derivatives that are not flammable. The plastics are discussed in detail in the article called The Growing World of Plastics in Volume 8.

They are used in innumerable applications: gadgets in the home; automobile parts; plastic garden hose; raincoats; instrument panels; electric plugs; buttons; game counters; and tablewear. Methyl methacrylate and styrene plastics can be made in beautifully clear and transparent form. They can be used, say, for hairbrush handles and electric light fixtures, as well as for embedding decorative objects and for "piping" light.

Synthetic rubber. Rubber is indispensable in modern life; it has innumerable uses in homes, industries and hospitals, in farms and play areas. It has been supplemented by synthetic rubber. Not all the rubber synthetics have all the qualities of the natural product, but each is equal or even superior to the natural product for certain purposes. The problem of making synthetic rubber was solved years ago. This fascinating development is discussed in the article on The Story of Rubber, in Volume 6.

The electrical industry. This industry uses many chemical products. Sulfuric acid, diluted with water, serves as the electrolyte (see Index) in lead-acid storage batteries. The surface coatings of electric motors are made of resinous materials—a product of the plastics industry. Synthetic rubbers, including silicone, butyl and nitrile rubbers, are used for wire and cable insulation and couplings. High-temperature insulation is provided by the oxides and carbides of many metals.

In this short article, I have given you a brief glimpse of the chemical industry, one of the largest in the United States. It is very high, indeed, in its "capital investment" per employee; which is another way of saying that the amount of equipment and apparatus is very large compared to the number of employees. This is reflected in the typical appearance of a chemical plant. It is in utter contrast to, say, a machine shop, or the composing room of a newspaper, where there are always plenty of busy people around. Typical of a chemical plant would be large pieces of equipment, often in extraordinary shapes with no moving parts and with hardly any humans in attendance. You do not even see the product! Mostly it is in vessels, or reactors, or flowing along pipelines. Then, right at the end of the operation, the product is poured into a railroad tank car, or distributed by long-distance pipeline. And yet, as I have shown you in the preceding pages, these products enter into practically everything that we actually use. And newer chemicals are being produced each year.

See also Vol. 10, p. 280: "Chemistry—Industrial Applications."

JET-PROPULSION PROGRESS

A New Era in the History of Aviation

BY JAMES J. HAGGERTY, JR.

ON AUGUST 27, 1939, the first flight of a jet-propelled airplane took place, and a new era in the history of aviation was ushered in. It has been an era of exciting progress. Planes powered by jet engines (also called reaction engines) are not subject to the power limitations imposed on piston-driven planes; as a result they have attained speeds and altitudes that even the most visionary scientist would hardly have predicted previously.

The principle of jet propulsion is quite simple. All jet-propelled craft are operated, wholly or in part, by jets of hot gases spurting from a tube — the jet nozzle — at the rear of the plane. At one time it was thought that these gases struck the air at the rear of the plane and then bounced back, causing the plane to move forward. What actually happens is this.

The thrust of gases out of the jet nozzle produces an equal thrust against the front part of the engine. This is an example of Newton's third law of motion: that for every action, there is an equal and opposite reaction. It is this "equal and opposite reaction" that accounts for the recoil of a gun that has just been fired. In the case of the jet plane, as hot gases spurt out of the jet nozzle, there is a "recoil" — a push against the front part of the engine. Since there is no thrust against the rear part of the engine, which is open to the outer air, the forward push propels the plane.

Practical work on jet propulsion applied to aircraft started long before 1939. The first to explore the field was A. A. Griffith, whose name has been all but forgotten. Griffith, a scientist with the British Royal Aircraft Establishment, conceived

This jet-propelled fighter is the F-86E Sabre Jet. It was developed by the United States Air Force.

EJECTOR SEAT

TURBOJET ENGINE

COMPRESSOR COMBUSTION TURBINE
CHAMBERS

U.S. AIR FORCE
0579

TAIL PIPE

SPEED BRAKES

INTAKE

GUN CAMERA

ENGINE
NOSE CONE

FUEL TANKS

SIX 50-CAL. MACHINE GUNS
(Three each side)

AMMUNITION

North American Aviation, Inc.

the idea of employing a gas turbine engine to propel an airplane; the turbine was to drive a propeller. He conducted some preliminary tests in the late 1920's.

In the meantime a young flyer of the Royal Air Force, Frank Whittle, had also been studying the application of the gas turbine to aircraft propulsion. His ideas differed from Griffith's in one very important respect. He proposed to eliminate the propeller; the plane would be driven entirely by the engine exhaust. The Air Ministry felt that Whittle's proposed engine had no military application and therefore it refused to finance the construction of an experimental engine. For several years, Whittle was unable to go forward with his project. In 1935, however, he obtained financial backing and in the following year he founded Power Jets, Ltd., a company devoted to jet research.

Power Jets, Ltd., constructed a prototype engine that was bench-tested in the spring of 1937. By current standards it

an airframe, which was to be powered by the first Whittle engine designed expressly for flight — the W-1. In May 1941, the airframe-engine combination was successfully flown for the first time. The engine provided a meager 850 pounds of thrust. (Thrust is the term used in the measurement of jet power; at 30,000 feet and at a speed of 375 miles per hour, one pound of thrust is the equivalent of one horsepower.)

Although Whittle is commonly held to be the father of jet propulsion, his jet engine was not the first to power an airplane in flight. In Germany, Hans von Ohain had been working on the jet principle since 1935, independently of Whittle and apparently unaware of Whittle's research. By 1937 Von Ohain had successfully benchtested a small jet engine. On August 27, 1939, Von Ohain's Heinkel 178, powered by a jet engine called the Heinkel S3B, made the first successful jet-powered flight in the history of aviation. The en-

Diagram showing turbojet parts and how they work.

Curtiss-Wright Corp.

was not much of an engine, and it fell considerably short of Whittle's expectations; but it proved that jet propulsion was feasible. The company built a second and then a third engine. By the middle of 1939 the Air Ministry had changed its mind concerning jet propulsion. It decided to sponsor the construction of an engine designed for actual flight, and at the same time contracted for a new airplane in which the revolutionary engine could be used. The Gloster Aircraft Company received the contract for the construction of

gine developed slightly more than 1,000 pounds of thrust. In Italy, a Caproni-Campini plane made a jet-propelled flight on August 27, 1940.

Jet-propelled planes played no part in the early years of World War II. Later the Germans developed a pilotless jet plane, known as the V-1, or flying bomb or buzz bomb, which was launched from sites on the western European coast; the first one was fired on June 12, 1944. The V-1 flew until its fuel was exhausted; then it dived to earth and exploded. The Germans also

The Stratotanker-Stratoliner, a tanker transport plane which is driven by four jet engines.

built a huge rocket, called the V-2, which was first fired on September 8, 1944; it crashed into target areas in England at a speed much greater than that of sound.

Piloted jet planes appeared toward the end of the war. The British introduced the combat plane known as the Gloster Meteor I; it was powered by the Rolls Royce Welland engine, based on the original Whittle design. The Germans countered with the Messerschmidt 262, a jet fighter with a Junkers 004 engine. Neither the Gloster Meteor I nor the Messerschmidt 262 had much of a war record.

In the United States, jet-propulsion progress had lagged from lack of official interest, although some American engineers experimented with the principle in the late 1930's. In the early 1940's both the General Electric Company and the Westinghouse Electric Corporation began to work on jet-propulsion engines. In October 1942, the Bell XP-59, with a GE I-16 engine, took to the air. June 1944 marked

the highly successful debut of the Lockheed XP-80, which was powered by a GE turbojet known as the I-40 and later as the J-33. The P-80 became America's first operational fighter.

Jet propulsion made tremendous progress in the years immediately following the end of World War II, as engine efficiency increased. The cold war with Russia, the Korean "police action" and the continuing international tension lent new impetus to jet development, particularly as applied to fighters and bombers. Today engines of 10,000 pounds of thrust or even more are common.

There are four basic engine types that use the jet-propulsion principle: the rocket, the turbojet, the turboprop and the ramjet. There are also several variations and combinations of these types.

The rocket principle goes back many hundreds of years, but it has only recently been applied to aircraft. Germany put two rocket-powered aircraft into the air during

This is an experimental ramjet model shown in flight.

World War II, and one of them, the Messerschmidt 163, saw brief but ineffective service as a combat craft. Since the war, rocket engines have been used extensively as power plants for guided missiles and unmanned research planes.

A rocket engine is really only a combustion chamber in which fuel, either solid or liquid, is burned. The resulting gases expand enormously under intense heat and are forced out from the rear of the rocket tube at high velocity, creating thrust. Unlike other types of jet engines, the rocket does not draw air from the atmosphere; it carries its own oxygen with it, in the form of liquid oxygen or a compound, such as hydrogen peroxide.

The great disadvantage of rocket power is the extremely high rate of fuel consumption; most rocket engines can fly for only a few minutes. The chief advantage of the rocket lies in its ability to generate very high thrust in a comparatively small package. Rockets called jato units have been attached to jet planes or propellered planes to provide extra power for take-offs. (The word "jato" comes from "jet-assisted take-off.") Planes powered exclusively by rockets are still in the experimental stage. Because the rocket does not require air, it is the only known power plant that could be used in spaceships flying beyond the earth's atmosphere.

The United States has been actively engaged in developing rocket planes. The first one, the MX-324, took to the air in 1944. The SX-1, or X-1, was the first aircraft to exceed the velocity of sound (in 1947). It was powered with four alcohol and liquid-oxygen rockets, developing a total thrust of 6,000 pounds. In 1953 and 1954, the X-1A attained an altitude of more than 90,000 feet and a speed well above 1,600 miles an hour. The X-2 bettered these marks in 1955, reaching an altitude of 127,000 feet and flying at 2,200 miles an hour. Its rocket engine had a thrust of 16,000 pounds and could be controlled more effectively than the ones in earlier experimental craft. A number of other rocket planes were designed to solve different research problems. Generally, they were somewhat modified versions of the machines we have mentioned above.

The X-15 is a particularly powerful rocket vehicle. Equipped with a rocket engine fueled with liquid oxygen and ammonia and developing a thrust of 50,000 pounds, the X-15 can fly at more than 3,600 miles an hour 100 miles above the earth. As the first manned spaceship, it will answer many questions about travel in the uppermost reaches of our atmosphere.

The rocket power plants that are used in missiles are of two basic types. Some have only a short range and require only a brief duration of power. Power duration is longer in long-range missiles; after the fuel is used up, the rocket continues its flight on the momentum provided in this way. We give more details on rockets in another article. (See Index, under Rockets.)

The jet-type engine best known to the layman, perhaps, is the turbojet (turbine-jet). In this form of propulsion, air is

Fuel is injected and burned in the afterburner. This causes further expansion of the gases escaping from the engine, adding to the basic thrust and increasing the velocity.

In the early days of jet development, the turbojet engine used a great amount of fuel; continued research, however, has made its operation much more economical. Fuel consumption in this type of engine is measured by the pounds of fuel required to create one pound of thrust for an hour. At first it took well over one pound of fuel to create one hour's thrust-pound; in some modern engines, however, the consumption rate is as low as three fifths of a pound of fuel for an hour's thrust-pound. This is not much higher than the comparable rating of a piston engine. It is believed that the jet engine will use even less fuel than the piston engine in the not too distant future.

FUEL ENTERS HERE   IGNITER-FLAMEHOLDER

AIR IN

AIR IN

There is no turbine in the engine of the ramjet.

FUEL PUMPS AND CONTROLS

COMBUSTION CHAMBER

Curtiss-Wright Corp.

◀ DIRECTION OF FLIGHT

drawn from the atmosphere through intakes, usually located either in the nose or the wing roots of the plane. The air is compressed, led into a combustion chamber, mixed with injected fuel and ignited. The resulting gases are forced rearward at high velocity. They drive a turbine connected to the main engine shaft on which the compressor is mounted. Then they escape through the nozzle; the reaction from the spurt of gases provides thrust. The escaping gases therefore not only propel the plane but also serve to compress the air drawn in through the intakes.

Some turbojet engines are equipped with a device called an afterburner, or reheat tube. This is simply a tail pipe attached to the rear of the engine proper.

Speed is the major advantage offered by the turbojet type of engine, although up to the present time such speed has been obtained at the expense of range. Today, there are several types of jet-propelled craft capable of exceeding the speed of sound (about 660 miles per hour at high altitude) in level flight.

A variation of the turbojet principle is the turboprop (turbine-propeller) engine. The intake, compressor, combustion and turbine units are like those of the turbojet. The difference is that most of the energy released by the escaping gases is used to drive a propeller; some of it, however, provides thrust as the gases escape. Thus propeller drive and exhaust thrust are provided by a single engine.

The turboprop represents a compromise between the jet and the piston engine. It is slower than the jet but uses less fuel; it is faster and freer of vibration than the piston motor. It burns more fuel than the latter; but it can use low-grade fuel, costing less than aviation gasoline.

The ramjet, or "flying stovepipe," is the simplest of the jets that draw in air, since it has neither compressor nor turbine. Essentially it is a long tube containing a fuel injection system and a spark plug. To work effectively the ramjet must be moving at high speed; to operate most effi-

less interceptor" developed by the United States Air Force. The Bomarc is fired from the ground, using a rocket engine for the take-off. By the time the rocket fuel is exhausted, the Bomarc has attained a speed at which its two ramjets can operate efficiently. Ramjets are capable of far greater power than anything yet attained by turbojets; but they also have a very high rate of fuel consumption.

In all ramjet applications to date, the engine has been used in combination with the rocket or the turbojet. It is conceivable that it may be developed into an auxil-

PROPELLER   AIR COMPRESSED HERE   FUEL ENTERS   IGNITER   TURBINE

AIR IN

AIR IN

Diagram of turboprop engine driving a propeller.

Curtiss-Wright Corp.

COMBUSTION CHAMBER

← DIRECTION OF FLIGHT

ciently it must travel at speeds in excess of Mach 2. (Mach, or the Mach number, named after the Austrian physicist Ernst Mach, is the ratio of the speed of a body to the speed of sound in the surrounding atmosphere; therefore Mach 2 is twice the speed of sound.) Compression is provided by the so-called ram effect — that is, the sudden compression of the air as it enters the tube at high velocity; no mechanical compression is required. The compressed air passes through the combustion chamber; here the burning fuel creates the working gas, which is expelled rearward as thrust.

Because of the high speed required for ram compression, the ramjet has as yet found no application in manned aircraft. For one thing, having no mechanical compressor, it is incapable of taking off from the ground, that is, at zero speed. It does, however, have an application in guided missiles which operate within the atmosphere, such as the Boeing Bomarc, a "pilot-

iary power plant for combat fighters, which are now approaching the speeds at which a ramjet can operate. In such applications it would probably be used only for combat emergency power, as the afterburner is used today. It would not necessarily replace the afterburner, which could be used on take-off and in climbing.

Jet power is being applied at a rapidly increasing rate to commercial aviation. Today, giant turboprop and turbojet airliners, measuring well over a hundred feet in length and in wing span, carry up to two hundred or more passengers each, on sustained flights of thousands of miles and, in some cases, at velocities near the speed of sound.

Great Britain was the pioneer in the turboprop field. In 1950, Vickers-Armstrongs brought out the Viscount, a four-engine turboprop transport that has since become highly successful in Europe and in North America. The Viscount model 840 seats up to 75 passengers; with its four

2,080-horsepower Rolls-Royce engines, it cruises at 400 miles an hour; the maximum range may be 1,650 miles.

The Vickers Vanguard 952 is a much larger turboprop machine than the Viscount. Its four Rolls-Royce engines generate over 5,000 horsepower apiece; it can transport as many as 139 passengers and cruise at 424 miles per hour. The Vanguard's extreme range is 3,400 miles; its cruising ceiling, as much as 24,000 feet.

The Bristol Britannia 320 is another large English turboprop transport, with four Proteus engines of 4,445 horsepower each. Its maximum passenger capacity is 139; its cruising speed, about 400 miles an hour; its maximum range (at 357 miles per hour), nearly 4,700 miles. A number of other passenger and freight turboprop planes are manufactured in Great Britain.

Great Britain has also led the world in civilian turbojet flying. In 1951, the British Overseas Airways Corporation began long-range jet service between London and Johannesburg, South Africa, with the de Havilland Comet 1. After some serious accidents the Comet was improved, until today it is one of the most widely used jet liners. The Comet 4C is powered by four Rolls-Royce engines of 10,500 pounds thrust each, cruises at 509 miles per hour at 33,000 feet, carries up to 99 passengers and has a range of 2,450 miles.

Other countries have followed Britain's lead in the jet race. In the United States, the Boeing Company flew the first American jet-powered commercial transport — the 707 prototype — in 1954. Several different models of this four-engine plane are now being used by a number of airlines the world over. These craft are among the largest jet passenger planes in existence; they are powered with Pratt and Whitney or Rolls-Royce engines of different types, each providing a thrust of 12,500 to 18,000 pounds. An intercontinental version, the Boeing 707-320, has a wing span of 142½ feet and a total length of nearly 153 feet. It can carry 189 persons, cruise at better than 600 miles per

This plane, shown here in flight, is the British Vickers Viscount turboprop.

British Information Services

hour and fly over 4,700 miles at heights of up to 40,000 feet.

Convair is bringing out two jet transports, the 600 and the 880. The Convair 600, with four General Electric engines, can fly 635 miles an hour at 35,000 feet; its maximum range is 4,400 miles and its maximum passenger capacity, 121 persons. Each jet motor of the 600 is equipped with an additional turbine and fans at the rear; these devices compress the air flowing through the engine and exhaust it through special openings, thus increasing the operating efficiency. The slightly smaller Convair 880 has four General Electric jet motors, each with 11,200 pounds of thrust, and is able to haul as many as 110 persons. Its extreme range is over 4,300 miles; its highest cruising speed, 615 miles an hour at 25,000 feet. The 880 can reach 40,000 feet in altitude.

The Douglas Aircraft Company has also entered into commercial jet aviation with its DC-8 airliner. Four Pratt and Whitney or Rolls-Royce jet motors push the intercontinental version of this craft through the air at a height of 30,000 feet and at speeds approaching 600 miles an hour, for a range of well over 5,000 miles. At 550 miles per hour, the range is nearly 7,000 miles. Seating capacity for up to 176 persons is provided.

The Lockheed Electra 188 is a turboprop craft of medium capabilities. Its four Allison engines, each rated at 3,750 horsepower, can maintain a speed of more than 400 miles an hour; the general range is from somewhat over 2,700 miles to more than 3,000 miles. Passenger capacity is 66 to 98 persons.

The U.S.S.R. (Russia) has come out with an amazing variety of regularly used jet and turboprop transport planes in a relatively short time. Its Tu-104 went into routine service in 1956. This is a twin-jet craft, capable of cruising at better than 500 miles an hour and carrying 50 persons for almost 2,000 miles at nearly 33,000 feet. Its engines develop a combined thrust of close to 30,000 pounds. Modified versions of the 104 have maximum speeds up to 600 miles per hour

or more and have greater passenger capacity (but with reduced range and ceiling). The Tu-110 has four jet motors; it can cruise up to 36,000 feet at nearly 500 miles an hour for about 2,000 miles nonstop. Its highest speed is 620 miles per hour; its passenger capacity, 100 persons.

The Soviets have built one of the largest passenger planes in the world, the Tu-114, a turboprop ship that rivals jet transports in speed and range and exceeds them in carrying capacity. Capable of seating as many as 220 passengers, this giant, powered with four 12,000-horsepower engines, reaches a cruising speed of 565 miles per hour at nearly 30,000 feet of altitude. Its normal range is something like 6,200 miles. The Russians claim that the extreme range of the Tu-114 turboprop is 9,000 miles or even more.

Jet and turboprop airplanes are used for different purposes. The large turbojet serves particularly for longe-range and intercontinental flights or for shorter hauls with large passenger and freight loads. The principal application of the turboprop and the small turbojet is in short-range and medium-range flight, where high speed is not so necessary. Turboprops use less fuel than turbojets and generally they do not require very long runways. In recent years, aeronautical engineers have narrowed the differences in operation and capabilities between the jet and the turboprop airplane to a certain extent.

The future of the jet plane

As the world moves into the era of supersonic and spatial flight, jet and rocket engines will undoubtedly be used to a greater extent, wherever very high speeds are necessary and wherever it is impossible to use propeller-driven craft.

The practical use of atomic power in jet and turbojet machines has still not been realized, but experiments go on. A small nuclear reactor will probably heat air or water to operate the engines, so that a plane will be able to fly around the world without stopping to refuel.

See also Vol. 10, p. 285: "Aviation."

RCA Victor Records

PHONOGRAPHS AND TAPE RECORDERS*

A modern phonographic recording session, with the pianist Gary Grafman at the concert grand. The photograph was taken from the control room at the recording studio.

How Sounds Are Preserved for Future Generations

SOUNDS — the noise of waves breaking on a beach, the stirring tones of a trumpet, the crash of thunder — are really vibrations in the air or in some other medium. If they strike the eardrums of a listener, they cause nerve impulses to arise. These impulses are transmitted by way of the nerves to the brain, where they are interpreted. As a result, we hear the pounding of the waves, the blare of the trumpet and the peal of thunder.

Until the last part of the nineteenth century, there was no way of capturing and re-creating sound waves. Nobody will ever be able to hear again the beautiful voice of Jenny Lind, the exciting piano playing of Franz Liszt or the glorious tones that Nicolai Paganini drew from his Guarnerius violin. But now man has learned how to record the vibrations that make up sound and how to reproduce them at will. Through the medium of the phonograph and the tape recorder, generations yet unborn will be able to listen to our finest singers, violinists, pianists and symphony orchestras. They will hear the voices of our great statesmen and actors.

The phonograph is not a recent invention, as inventions go. As early as 1857, the

* Article prepared with the assistance of the RCA Victor Home Instruments Division.

Frenchman Edouard-Léon Scott de Martinville invented a sound-recording device that he called the phonautograph. It had a speaking horn shaped like a barrel and made of plaster. Connected to the lower end of the horn was a short brass tube. A flexible membrane, stretched over the end of the tube, would vibrate in unison with the sound waves that struck it. A hog's bristle was fastened to the membrane and acted as a stylus, or pen. The end of the bristle pressed against a cylinder covered with smoked paper. When the cylinder was rotated by a hand crank and sound waves struck the membrane, the bristle traced a wavy line on the sooty paper. This line represented a graph, or visible pattern, of a sound wave. However, there was no way of producing actual sound with the phonautograph.

The first man to reproduce sound was Thomas A. Edison, whose fabulous career as an inventor has been described elsewhere in this set (see Index). Edison had developed a telegraph repeater for recording telegraph messages. In this device, the dots and dashes of the Morse code were recorded on a revolving paper disk by an embossing point; the resulting groove spiraled toward the center of the disk. Edison found one day that when he rotated the disk very rapidly and caused the embossing point to pass over the marks already made on the disk, a faint sound was produced.

This effect gave Edison the idea of reproducing sound.

He rigged up a simple apparatus consisting of a membrane connected to a steel point. As he pulled a paraffin-coated paper strip through the device he shouted against the membrane. This caused the point to vibrate in unison with the sound waves. Edison then pulled the paper through the device again and listened breathlessly. A faint but distinct sound could be heard.

On August 12, 1877, Edison made a rough sketch of a talking machine based on the device we have just described. He wrote on the sketch: "Kreusi, make this." Then he gave it to John Kreusi, one of his workers, and explained to the puzzled man that this was a device for reproducing sound. Kreusi laughed at what he considered to be a silly idea but began work on the model.

In a few days, he brought the completed machine to Edison. Then he stood by, grinning, while the inventor prepared to put the device to the test. It consisted of a cylinder with an embossing needle, attached to a diaphragm, at the top. The cylinder could be turned by a hand crank. Edison fixed a sheet of tinfoil around the cylinder and set the needle in position. Then, rotating the cylinder by turning the crank, he shouted into a funnel set at the top of the device:

"Mary had a little lamb,
Its fleece was white as snow."

He now put the needle back at the beginning of the groove that had been made in the tinfoil. When he rotated the cylinder again, the words of the poem could be heard — squeaky but quite distinct. Kreusi

turned pale and exclaimed in German: "Mein Gott in Himmel [my God in heaven]!" Edison gave the name of phonograph to his device. Unlike Scott de Martinville's phonautograph, the phonograph was not merely a sound recorder but also a sound producer.

The first talking machines that Edison devised were little more than scientific curiosities. The sounds they reproduced were scratchy, tinny and unmusical. It was difficult to remove the tinfoil from the cylinder or to replace it without distorting the material and injuring the indentations. Consequently, it was necessary to have a separate cylinder for each new record. Moreover, the motion given to the cylinder by turning a hand-operated crank was not regular, and it caused the sounds to waver in pitch.

After a few months of work and experimentation, Edison laid his phonograph aside in order to busy himself with other inventions. Alexander Graham Bell now began to experiment with sound-recording and sound-reproducing devices. Assisted by his brother, Chichester A. Bell, and by Charles S. Tainter, he developed a talking machine that he called the Graphophone. Patents were issued in 1886 for the device, which represented a considerable advance over the phonograph of Edison. For one thing, the cylinder was rotated by clockwork instead of by hand. There was a permanent cylinder. Over this was slipped a light cardboard cylinder, covered with a thin wax mixture. The stylus engraved the wax as the cylinder rotated.

Edison had returned to his sound-reproducing project in the meantime. He now produced a new machine in which a special wax removable cylinder was em-

RCA Sales Corp.

ployed. The record was cut by means of a tiny agate or sapphire point, which made minute depressions in the wax. The reproducing point, of sapphire, passed over the indentations as the cylinder turned. It communicated its movements to the diaphragm of the recording machine by means of a delicate combination of weights and levers.

At about this time, a German-American inventor, Emile Berliner, developed a phonograph that used a metallic disk instead of a rotating cylinder (1887). Edison had also experimented with disks, but those of Berliner presented an entirely new feature. In both the cylinders and disks of Edison, the record in the wax was formed of a series of little hills and dales, running around the cylinder or disk. The sound waves were represented by actual waves in the wax, each wave sloping upward or downward like the rippled surface of the sea. Berliner departed from this "hill-and-dale" method by causing the engraving stylus to move laterally (from side to side) in the groove. This became known as the "lateral cut" and it was particularly well adapted to the disk type of record. Berliner called his machine the Gramophone. An improved version was marketed by the Victor Talking Machine Company (later to become RCA Victor).

In the course of the years that followed, various improvements were made in both recording and reproduction. By the turn of the century, several companies were marketing the phonograph. Prospective buyers could choose between the lateral-cut disk and the vertical-cut cylinder types. Disks and cylinders were made to rotate by clockwork, which was wound up by hand. A mica diaphragm transmitted the sound waves to the ears of the listener through a big horn, which was fixed to a bracket on the sound box. After 1910, the disk type of phonograph, with the lateral cut, won the day.

The tonal quality of records until the middle of the 1920's left much to be desired. In making a recording, the energy of sound had to be changed directly into mechanical energy. The singing tones of a baritone or the blare of a trumpet may be loud, but the power output of its vibrations cannot begin to compare with the power that is required, say, to light a hundred-watt bulb. As a result, many tone values were lost. Small wonder that the disks of that period seem so unsatisfactory to us. They were popular with a large proportion of the public, but trained musicians had little respect for what they called "canned music."

A most important advance was made when electric recording was introduced about 1925. The sound was directed to a microphone which converted it into electric current. This was greatly amplified by electron tubes and then changed into vibratory movement, which was transmitted to the cutting stylus. In playback, vibrations were produced as the stylus moved over the record. These were changed into electric current, which was amplified before passing to a loudspeaker. Here they were converted into sound waves. The resulting sound was a much more faithful reproduction of the original sounds.

An innovation of the 1930's was the automatic record changer, which could play a number of records with one loading. It was no longer necessary, when playing a long symphony or concerto, to go to the phonograph every few minutes in order to change records. Still, even with a record changer, the music would stop every few

In the photograph at the far left, we see a technician inspecting the grooves on an instantaneous recording. This type of record is played back immediately after cutting; it has a short life. Diagrams A and B give close-ups of a cutting stylus (A) and the record grooves (B).

Reeves Soundcraft

minutes while the next record was being set in place. This annoyance came to an end once and for all when long-playing records were introduced in 1948.

At about this time, magnetic recording and reproduction were first introduced in the United States. (It had been under development in Europe for some time.) In the magnetic system, the original sound pattern was converted into a magnetic field of varying strength. These variations were stored up in magnetized tape.

In the early 1950's, engineers perfected high-fidelity systems that made it possible to hear practically the full range of audible sound. The stereophonic, or twin-channel, system, marked an important development in high-fidelity reproduction.

Monaural disk
recording and reproduction

Until fairly recently, all phonograph records were monaural, or monophonic. That means that a single channel, or transmission path, was used in both sound recording and sound reproduction. A great many records are still produced in this way.

The first step in monaural disk recording is to convert the sounds produced by an orchestra, say, into electric current of varying intensity by means of one or more microphones.* In modern recording, the varying electric pulses produced by the microphone are generally fed to a tape

* The microphone is described elsewhere; see Index.

recorder.* The resulting magnetic tape is edited and a duplicate, called a master tape, is made of it. The magnetic signals of the master tape are then changed into electric signals, representing the same varying pattern that originally came from the microphones. This varying current is enormously magnified as it passes through the electron tubes of an amplifier. Then it is transmitted to a cutting, or recording, head, where it is transformed into vibratory motion.

The vibratory motion is transmitted to the cutting stylus, which makes a groove in a revolving disk. The stylus is of sapphire, synthetic ruby or other hard material; the disk is of aluminum, coated with lacquer or acetate plastic. The turntable on which the disk is set turns at a constant speed—78, or 45, or 33⅓ or 16⅔ rpm (revolutions per minute), according to the type of record. The stylus cuts a V-shaped groove in the coating of the disk—a groove that spirals inward. As the stylus produces this spiral, it moves from side to side, following the pattern of vibrations transmitted by the cutting head. The wiggly pattern of the lateral groove made in this way can easily be seen under a microscope, even one of low power. The width of the groove is carefully regulated. The number of lines per inch ranges from 125 to 550, depending

* Magnetic tape recording is discussed later in this article.

78

This photo shows the two jaws of the stamping press, with upper and lower stampers in place. The operator is affixing a label to the upper stamper; another label will be put on the lower one. A blob of a plastic material, called Vinylite, will be set in the middle of the lower stamper. The jaws of the press will then close, forming the blob of plastic into a phonographic record.

upon whether the record is to be standard or long-playing.

It is possible to play back a recording immediately after cutting. These instantaneous records, as they are called, have a short life, as the original coating on the record is comparatively soft. If disks are to be produced in quantity, the original disk must be duplicated by a rather roundabout process.

First, the original record is coated with silver so that it may become a conductor of electricity; then it is placed in a bath of nickel. Through the process of electroplating (see Index), a coating of nickel is deposited on the surface of the original record, faithfully reproducing the minute windings of the grooves. The plating is then stripped from the disk and is reinforced by a metal backing. The combined plating and backing is called the *master*. Everything in the record surface has been reversed. What was formerly a groove in the original disk is now a ridge; what was formerly a ridge is now a groove.

The master is electroplated in its turn. The plating, separated from the master and backed with metal, becomes the *mother*. It reproduces the pattern of grooves and ridges found in the original record.

The next step is to electroplate the mother. When the electroplating is stripped from the mother, it becomes the *stamper*. The stamper has the same reversed pattern as the master.

To prepare a double finished record (one with two playing sides), a stamper is placed, surface down, in the upper jaw of a hydraulic press. A second stamper, containing another part of the same selection or else a different selection, is placed, surface up, in the lower jaw of the press. After labels have been placed in position, a blob of a plastic material, called Vinylite, is set in place in the middle of the lower stamper. The jaws of the hydraulic press close and the stampers are heated. The Vinylite is flattened out and is formed

into a phonographic disk. The stampers are cooled. Then the jaws of the press open and the finished record is removed. It is practically unbreakable.

We saw that in the recording process, the turntable can be made to run at speeds of 78 rpm, 45 rpm, $33\frac{1}{3}$ rpm or $16\frac{2}{3}$ rpm. The records are played back at the speed with which they were recorded; thus we have 78-rpm records, 45-rpm records and so on.

In the 78-rpm record, which was the standard for many years, the grooves are spaced farther apart than in the other types. Because of this feature and the rapid rate of rotation, the playing time is relatively short — up to about 5 minutes per side for a 12-inch record and 3 minutes per side for a 10-inch record. Contrasting with the 78-rpm records are the microgroove records — those with much smaller and more closely spaced grooves. The $33\frac{1}{3}$-rpm microgroove record plays as long as 27 minutes per record side for a 12-inch record. The $16\frac{2}{3}$-rpm has an even longer playing time — up to 40 minutes per record side. In between the 78-rpm's and the microgroove records are the 45-rpm's. These are only 7 inches in diameter; yet they have as long a playing time as the 78-rpm 12-inch disks. A special variety of 45-rpm — the extended-play (EP) record — plays up to 8 minutes per side.

The $33\frac{1}{3}$-rpm record has become the most popular for extended recordings of

TURNTABLE   TONE ARM   STYLUS

SPEED CONTROL
Elpa Marketing Industries, Inc.

PICKUP

UNDERSIDE
OF PICKUP

Left: turntable with pickup and tone arm.
Above: close-up of the underside of the
pickup, showing the position of the stylus.

all types — symphonies, concertos, canta-tas, operas, dramas. It is generally this type that we have in mind when we refer to long-playing records. Though the 16⅔-rpm has a longer playing time, it has not become nearly so popular. The 45-rpm is the favorite medium for short selections — either one or (in the case of EP) two or more per side. As for the old 78-rpm record, it is becoming obsolete.

Records of different speeds can generally be played on the same phonograph. Often this phonograph is provided with a record changer, which can play as many as twelve records at one loading. The finest record players do not have record changers but play only one record at a time.

The turntable upon which the record is to be put is made to turn at the required speed by an electric motor. The record is set on the turntable by hand or is dropped onto it from a spindle by an automatic mechanism. Then a stylus, or needle, passes over the grooves in the record as the turntable rotates. Modern styluses (or styli) are generally of sapphire or diamond. The diamond stylus is considerably more expensive than the sapphire variety but it lasts much longer and produces less wear and tear on the record.

The stylus is attached to a pickup, which is at the end of a tone arm. In the pickup, the sidewise motion of the stylus as it passes over the wiggles in the groove is transformed into electric pulses of varying strength. There are various kinds of pickups. The crystal type is based on the piezoelectric effect — that is,

the tendency of certain crystals to generate electric current when subjected to pressure. Crystals of Rochelle salt are used. As the stylus twists the crystal element in the pickup, electric current is produced; this will vary according to the motion of the stylus. The ceramic pickup is based on the same effect as the crystal pickup; but its active element is a ceramic material, produced from barium titanate. Both the crystal and ceramic pickups are popular today.

For high-fidelity reproduction, the dynamic pickup is preferred. In this, a coil of wire is attached to the stylus and moves in the field of a permanent magnet. It generates electric current as it moves; the strength of this current will vary according to the pattern traced by the stylus. There are still other types of pickups.

The electrical output of the pickup is amplified and is then transmitted to the loudspeaker. Here the current is transformed into sound frequencies, reproducing the original sounds that were recorded by the microphone.*

For high-fidelity reproduction, the amplifier consists of two parts — a preamplifier and a power amplifier. The former unit provides a certain degree of current amplification and is also equipped with various regulating devices, including tone and volume controls. The output from the preamplifier is fed to the power amplifier, where further amplification takes place. Then it passes to the loudspeaker. In high-fidelity reproduction, there are two

* The loudspeaker is described elsewhere; see Index.

or more speakers, each designed to handle sounds of a certain range of frequencies. There is a woofer for low-frequency sounds and a tweeter for high-frequency sounds. Sometimes there is a midrange unit for in-between frequencies.

Stereophonic disk
recording and reproduction

We pointed out that in the monaural system, there is only one transmission path for recording and only one path for re-production. It is as if the sound had passed into a single ear; hence the name monaural.* Now human hearing is bin-aural, or two-ear. Our ears are separated from one another by the width of the face, and therefore sound waves strike them from somewhat different angles. As a re-sult, it becomes possible to locate quite effectively the direction from which the sound comes.

The binaural principle has been ap-plied to sound recording and reproduction in the stereophonic system, introduced in 1958. Sound passes through two micro-phones, each of which is connected to a separate amplifying and recording system. The resulting recording is played back through two separate reproducing systems, each with its own loudspeaker.

* The word is derived from the Greek *monos*: "alone" and the Latin *auris*: "ear."

In recording a program by the stereo-phonic system, the microphones are placed at a given distance apart. The current out-put from the microphones is amplified and then led to twin cutter heads. These are set side by side at an angle of 45 degrees from the surface of the record and 90 de-grees from each other. A single stylus is connected to both cutter heads. It creates two sets of wiggles, one on one side of the groove, one on the other side.

For playback, in some models, a sin-gle stylus, mounted in a cartridge, is used. There is a twin pickup device, whose two elements are mounted at an angle of 90 degrees from each other. Each element of the pickup is responsive only to the vi-brations caused as the stylus travels over one of the two walls of the record groove. In other models there are twin styluses. There are separate amplifying systems and separate loudspeakers. Stereophonic rec-ords can be played on a single-channel phonograph; but in this case the binaural effect cannot be obtained.

In a quality stereophonic system, with the loudspeakers correctly positioned, we have high-fidelity reproduction at its finest. It introduces a sort of third dimension into the reproduction of sound. Thus the sounds produced by the first violin section of a

The diagram shows a stereo cut-ting stylus at work. The two sets of patterns it creates as it cuts a groove in the lacquer disk are at an angle of 90 degrees from one another. In the photograph, we see a Westrex Stereodisk Cutter. The suction pipe at the right of the stylus draws off flash—that is, particles removed by the sty-lus from the surface of the disk.

RIGHT CHANNEL

LEFT CHANNEL

RCA Victor Records

Shure Brothers, Inc.

Far left: a magnetic stereo cartridge, used in a dynamic pickup system. The diagram next to it shows how such a system works. *A*, the stylus, is connected by a shank, *B*, to a permanent magnet, *C*. *C* can move freely between wire coils *DD* and *EE*, wrapped around U-shaped interlocking cores. As *A* passes over the record groove, its motion is affected by the patterns on the two groove walls. Variations in stylus motion are transmitted to permanent magnet *C*. As the latter moves, current is generated in coils *DD* and *EE*. The current passing through *DD* corresponds to the pattern of one wall of the record groove; the current passing through *EE* corresponds to the pattern of the other groove wall. The electric output of the currents is amplified and it passes to loudspeakers.

symphony orchestra will seem to come from one part of the room where the record is being played; cello sounds will apparently come from another part of the room. When an opera lover listens to a stereophonic recording of a sextet, say, he can readily visualize the positions taken by the different singers on the operatic stage.

Magnetic tape
recording and reproduction

In magnetic recording, or tape recording, there is no stylus making contact with a disk, as in the electric phonograph. Instead, a specially prepared tape moves past the poles of an electromagnet in both recording and playback. The idea of magnetic recording was first worked out in 1898 by the Danish engineer Valdemar Poulsen, using wire instead of tape. It was not, however, until the 1940's that the magnetic system was adopted to any great extent. At first, both steel wire and metal-coated tape were used; nowadays, however, wire has been almost entirely replaced by tape.

In the magnetic system, the vibrations of sound waves are first changed into varying electrical pulses by one or more microphones. These pulses affect the strength of the magnetic field of an electromagnet, known as the recording head, and this field therefore changes constantly. The recording head is ring-shaped, with a small gap between its two poles. The magnetic tape used in the recording process has a plastic or paper base and is coated with a thin layer of iron oxide. As the tape moves past the gap in the recording head, the metallic coating is magnetized.

As we have seen, the strength of the magnetic field in the recording head constantly changes, and the magnetic pattern in the tape will vary accordingly. Hence it will carry, strung out along its length, a complete history of the many changes that have taken place in the strength of the magnetic field in the recording head. Now, as we have seen, the variations in the magnetic field itself have resulted from variations in the sound waves that struck the microphone. Hence the magnetized tape constitutes an accurate record of the original sound waves. Anything producing sound — an orchestra, a large choir, a violin, a singing voice or the conversation of a family group — can be recorded on the tape.

The mechanism for moving the tape past the head is driven by an electric motor. The tape moves from the payoff reel, or spool, upon which it was originally wound, to the takeup reel, upon which it is wound after becoming magnetized. It moves past the head at speeds ranging, according to the particular model, from 30 inches per second to $1\frac{7}{8}$ inches per second. At the slower speeds, the quality of reproduction tends to suffer.

If one wishes to play back the recording, the magnetized tape is moved past another electromagnet, known as a playback head. As the magnetized tape passes by the poles of this head, a small electric current is produced. This will vary in strength according to the magnetic pattern on the tape. The current passes through an electronic amplifying system and then to a loudspeaker. Here it is transformed into sound waves.

Since the magnetized tape is wound on a reel, it takes up very little space. It is subjected to very little friction as it moves past the recording head or the playback head; hence it practically never wears out.

PAYOFF REEL   TAKEUP REEL

INPUT   OUTPUT

RECORDING HEAD   PLAYBACK HEAD

DIRECTION OF
MAGNETIC-TAPE
TRAVEL

RECORDING GAP   PLAYBACK GAP

Diagram showing how a tape recorder works. The vibrations of sound waves are changed into electric impulses of varying strength by a microphone. These impulses (indicated above by "input") affect the strength of the magnetic field of the recording head, which is a magnet. As the tape moves from the payoff reel past a gap in the recording head, its metallic coating is magnetized, the pattern varying according to changes in the magnetic field of the recording head. The tape then moves to the takeup reel. For playback, the tape is moved past a gap in the playback head. A small electric current of varying strength is produced. The current (indicated by "output") passes through an electronic amplifying system and to a loudspeaker; here it is changed into sound waves.

If one so desires, the recording may be erased from the tape so that a new one may be made. This is done by having the tape move past a so-called erase head, which is similar to the recording and playback heads. The erase head applies a high-frequency magnetic field to the tape. This erases the recording and makes the tape ready for another recording.

The stereophonic system has been applied to magnetic tape. In some stereophonic tapes, there are two lengthwise tracks, the upper one serving for one channel, the lower one for the other. Some tapes have four such tracks; others eight.

Magnetic tape has found wide use. It serves in making fine recordings of musical performances. These performances are often, as we have seen, transferred to disks; sometimes they are sold in tape form. Radio studios use tape recordings to keep a record of the programs that go out over the air. Home magnetic recording sets have become very popular. With a tape recorder, a music lover can make recordings of good music coming in over his radio or television set. Thus he can build up an extensive record library at a very modest cost. Tape recording also makes it possible for a musician, professional or amateur, to make fine and inexpensive recordings of his performances.

The use of magnetic tape is not limited to the recording and reproduction of sound.

It has also been used to record black-and-white and color television programs, which can be stored indefinitely and played back any number of times. Information provided by computer systems has been recorded on magnetic tape; so have the radio signals transmitted from artificial satellites.

The optical method of sound production

It should be pointed out that the phonograph and the tape recorder are not the only devices for recording and reproducing sound. The so-called optical system is used in making the sound tracks in moving-picture film. This is basically a photographic process. In recording, sound waves are converted by one or more microphones into varying electric current. The current is amplified and then controls the action of a light modulator. This in turn regulates the amount of light falling upon a photographic film. In one method — the varying-density system — variations in sound are recorded in terms of lighter or darker areas in the film. In another method — the varying-area system — it is the width of the exposed area that varies. In reproduction, a photoelectric cell converts variations in the photographic film into varying electric pulses. These are amplified and converted into sound by the method already described.

See also Vol. 10, p. 287: "Sound Recording."

An adult walrus taking his ease. The walrus is related to the seals; it is a heavily built animal, reaching a length of thirteen feet or so. Its formidable tusks may be almost three feet long.

FIN-FOOTED CARNIVORES

Seals, Walruses and Sea Elephants

A PERSON unfamiliar with sea lions may wonder, when he first sees these comic and entertaining creatures at the zoo or circus, just what kind of animals they are. They have coats of hair like mammals, but their flippers seem to have nothing in common with the feet of mammals. Are these flippers like the fins of fish, or are they like the paddles of the whales and dolphins? The truth is that sea lions are flesh-eating mammals that long ago returned to the sea to live an aquatic life. The limbs of the sea lions and their kin — the walruses and seals — have bones that correspond to those found in the limbs of the land mammals. Moreover, the teeth and skull bones of these aquatic creatures show they are related to the carnivorous, or flesh-eating, mammals of the land.

Scientifically, the seals and walruses are classified in the suborder Pinnipedia, which means fin-footed. The pinnipeds are large, bulky mammals with rudimentary tails. Their external ears are very small or absent altogether. The body hair of the different groups varies from the finest of fur to coarse bristles. The pinnipeds prey upon fish, squids and other mollusks, crustaceans and, occasionally, sea birds. We can trace the pinnipeds back as far as the Miocene period (about 25,000,000 years ago). Some zoologists think that the fin-foots were derived from the earliest and most primitive carnivores called the creodonts. Others believe that they evolved from a later carnivore stock that produced the dogs, bears, weasels and otters. The fossil remains of a mammal with seallike characteristics were found in a Siberian geological deposit that was about 10,000,000 years old. This mammal had a long, slim tail and limbs that indicate it could walk on land as well as swim. It also had features somewhat similar to those of the otter. This ancient carnivore itself could not possibly have been an ancestor of the pinnipeds; however, it may have been derived from the ancestral group that gave rise to the modern seals and walruses.

The limbs of seals and walruses have undergone a strange transformation. The upper and lower leg bones have been much shortened; the front and hind feet have been lengthened. There has been no increase in the number of toes. A web of skin grows between the toes, thus forming the flipper, or fin. The fin-foots, unlike all other aquatic vertebrates, swim entirely by means of their limbs. The two hind legs are directed backward to serve, in swimming, as a substitute for a tail. The front legs are well suited for steering. The eared seals, which include the sea lions and fur seals, can bring their hind legs around in a forward position when they are traveling on the land. This is also true of the walruses. The earless seals, of which the elephant seal is an example, cannot turn their hind limbs forward at all. When on the beaches these animals are barely able to drag themselves along.

Why should seals and walruses retain leglike limbs for land travel when in other respects they are so remarkably adapted for life in the sea? The reason is that all the members of the pinnipeds must leave the water to breed and raise their young and, consequently, need supports on land for their large bodies. When the ancestors of the fin-foots first took to the water, they were probably as agile on the land as most other carnivores. But in time they became adapted to an aquatic environment and came to the land less frequently.

There are three families of pinnipeds. Included in the first (family Otariidae) are the fur seals and sea lions. These animals have long necks, small external ears and front limbs nearly equal to the hind limbs in length. The northern fur seals (genus *Callorhinus*) of the north Pacific and the southern fur seals (*Arctocephalus*) of the Southern Hemisphere possess a luxuriously soft and dense underfur. The sea lions, which lack this underfur, include the California sea lion (*Zalophus*), the northern sea lion (*Eumetopias*) and the southern sea lion (*Otaria*). The California sea lion has a high forehead and glistens black when wet. It gives honking barks. It lives along the coast of southern California and through the central Pacific to New Zealand, Australia and Japan. The northern sea lion, which is larger and has a low forehead, ranges chiefly in the North Pacific, though it will go as far south as southern California.

The walrus is a
large pinniped with tusks

The walrus (*Odobenus*) of the Arctic is confined to a family (Odobenidae) of its own. Its great size and large tusks distinguish it from other aquatic mammals.

The earless, or hair, seals (family Phocidae) lack external ears, have a very short neck and possess forelimbs much shorter than the hind ones. Common seals (*Phoca*) of the northern seas include the small and spotted harbor seal; the ribbon seal, which has yellow bands around its neck, rump and front flippers; the ringed seal, with whitish rings on its sides; and the harp, or Greenland, seal, which has along its sides dark bands that join across the shoulders and over the rump. The large bearded seal (*Erignathus*) of the Arctic is distinguished by bristles on the sides of its muzzle. Another large seal of Arctic waters is the gray seal (*Halichoerus*), a uniformly grayish animal.

The male hooded seal (*Cystophora*) of the North Atlantic differs from other seals by having a pouch atop its forehead and snout. This bag is inflated when the animal becomes annoyed. The closely related sea elephants, or elephant seals (*Mirounga*), are giant species living in the Antarctic, South Pacific and Indian Ocean and off the coast of Lower California.

Other seals of the Antarctic and South Pacific are the crab-eating seal (*Lobodon*), which varies in color from brown to yellowish white; the sea leopard (*Hydrurga*), the largest Antarctic species aside from the elephant seal; Ross's seal (*Ommatophoca*), a small blackish seal; and Weddell's seal (*Leptonychotes*) of the south polar seas, blackish, peppered with silver and gray. The monk seal (*Monachus*) is a large animal, black above and whitish below, inhabiting the waters of the Mediterranean, Caribbean and central Pacific.

Pinnipeds are specialized
for swimming and diving

Pinnipeds are graceful and powerful swimmers. Sea lions, when they are swimming slowly, use their front flippers as paddles. When they go faster, they also work the hind limbs. The elephant seal moves only its rear flippers to swim. Weddell's seal presses together the bottom surfaces of its hind feet and waves this apparatus from side to side. Pinnipeds often dive to considerable depths and remain submerged for some time. The maximum time spent under water has been recorded for several species; for instance, the elephant seal can stay submerged twelve minutes, the harbor seal, fifteen and the harp seal, twenty minutes. How is this possible? First of all, these mammals, unlike land species, almost completely renew the air in their lungs when they breathe. The respiratory center of their nervous system does not respond quickly to an increase of carbon dioxide in the blood and so does not demand more rapid breathing. Finally, pinnipeds, when under water, efficiently distribute breathed-in oxygen so that it goes only to those parts of the body involved in essential activity.

Almost all pinnipeds are gregarious, or social, animals, though the sea leopard, Ross's and the bearded seals seem to lead solitary lives. Of the earless seals, only the male gray seals and elephant seals

Hawaiian monk seal (Monachus schauinslandi).

Northern fur seal (Callorhinus ursinus cynocephalus).

Galapagos fur seal (Arctocephalus philippii).

SEALS AND SEA LIONS

Two fine specimens of the Peruvian "snub-nosed" sea lion (Otaria flavescens).

gather harems of females in the mating season. Some earless seals migrate to their breeding ground, but other species rear their young upon shores or ice floes wherever they happen to be. Sea lions and fur seals, on the other hand, make long migrations to their breeding territories, where the males gather a large number of females together into harems.

Description of a
fur-seal rookery

The bulls arrive at the breeding grounds about the end of May or the beginning of June and take up positions along the shore, awaiting the coming of the cows a few weeks later. The cows are heavy with young when they arrive. Each male now seeks to obtain as many cows for his own harem as possible. He emits loud roars designed to frighten away his competitors. Violent fights ensue; the bulls inflict serious wounds with their sharp, powerful teeth. As the bulls seek new cows, the ones they have already secured may be stolen by other seals farther away from the water's edge.

The stronger the bull, the more mates he obtains. The harems of the large bulls average about thirty cows; some bulls may manage to gather as many as a hundred cows. The competition is so strong and so continuous that the bulls will not leave the beach to feed at sea. As a result, they may go for several months of the year, fighting and mating, without eating at all. In the competition for mates, the larger bulls obviously have the advantage. Apparently, the seals that produce the largest male offspring are favored in the process of natural selection. At any rate, the male seal often weighs five or six times as much as the female.

Shortly after the cow arrives at the breeding ground, she gives birth to the single pup conceived the previous season; about a week later she mates for the next year. Four to six weeks after birth, the seal pup learns to swim. During the summer, the cow frequently swims out to sea to feed, returning at gradually lengthening intervals to nurse her pup. The senses of the seal are apparently so acute that she has no trouble in finding her own offspring among the many thousands she encounters when she returns to the swarming beach. About four months after it is born, the young seal is weaned.

With the approach of winter, the seals move out to sea until the following summer. By this time, the seal pups are far enough along in their development so that they are able to accompany their mothers on the long swim to warmer latitudes. On their migration to and from the summer nesting grounds, seals are subject to attacks by many sea predators, particularly the killer whale, which may swallow as many as twenty or more seals at a single feeding. It is estimated that not more than half of the seal pups ever reach maturity.

Because of its habits, the seal is an easy prey. When the Russians claimed the Pribilof Islands in the eighteenth century, Russian seal hunters wrought havoc among the huge hordes at the rookeries. The seals, quite helpless on land, were clubbed to death by the thousands. They were skinned on the beach and the carcasses simply left to rot. The animals were hunted so avidly that one species, the *Hydrodomalis stelleri,* became extinct within twenty years of its discovery. Several other species became too rare to be hunted profitably. In time the Russian government realized the seriousness of the situation and put a stop to this destruction of valuable resources. Then, in 1867, the islands were purchased from the czars by the United States; the sealing rights were leased to private companies and the slaughter was resumed. As the demand for furs grew, pelagic sealing — that is, catching seals at sea — became common. Since the herds migrated in huge groups at fairly regular times, they were easily located. In the late nineteenth century, over one hundred ships were engaged in sealing. They claimed many cows as their victims. Unfortunately, when a cow was killed, the herd lost not only that female but the pup it was carrying. If the female was killed in the late summer or early fall, it also meant the death of the pup she was nursing.

But the fur seal, happily, has been saved from extinction, at least for the present. The nations most interested in the sealing industry and therefore concerned with the rapid depletion of the herds finally agreed upon measures safeguarding the fur seals. These nations were Great Britain, Russia, Japan and the United States. They drew up a pact called the fur-seal treaty of 1911. Under its terms, sealers of any of these nations could not kill seals at sea in the waters of the North Pacific and adjacent seas north of the 30th parallel. Exceptions were made for the native people of the North Pacific who depend largely upon seals for their subsistence and use primitive methods in hunting them.

The two most important fur-seal rookeries are those located at the Pribilof Islands, Alaska, and the Commander Islands, in the Bering Sea. The Pribilofs belong to the United States and the Commander Islands to Russia. According to the treaty, the management and killing of the fur seals were left to these two countries. Provision was made for Japan and Canada to each receive 15 per cent of the skins taken by the United States and Russia. This fur-seal treaty was terminated in 1941.

A new Alaska fur-seal law, agreed upon by Canada and the United States, still prohibits the killing of seals at sea. Also, the law provides that Canada is to receive 20 per cent of the skins taken on the Pribilof Islands. The remainder of the skins are to be kept by the United States. Sealing operations on the Pribilofs are carried on by natives of the islands who are under the direct supervision of the United States Fish and Wildlife Service.

Since one hardy old male, or bull, seal may maintain up to one hundred cows in a

U.S. Fish and Wildlife Service

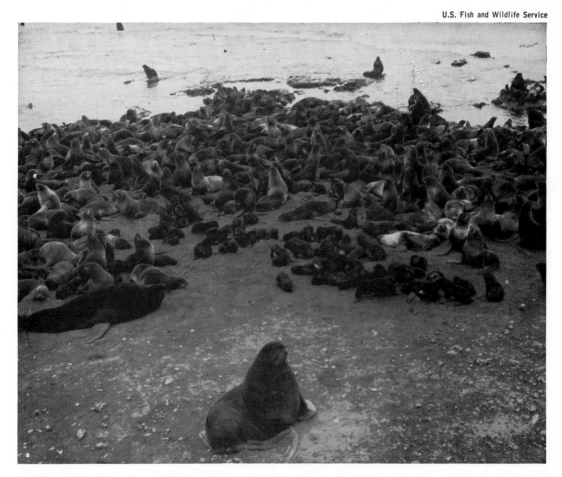

A fur-seal rookery at one of the Pribilof Islands. A large bull is in the foreground.

A baby walrus is nursed by its mother almost two years before its tusks grow enough to help it dig for food.

Zool. Soc. of San Diego

harem, and since an equal number of male and female seals are born, there is an excess of bulls in every rookery. These surplus bulls, which are called bachelors, are either too young or too weak to fight for a harem; they accordingly separate themselves from the rest of the herd. These are the seals that are killed for their pelts. A certain number of bachelors are allowed to escape, however, so that they may become harem masters in the future.

The bachelors are usually killed and skinned, or pelted, in July. The pelts undergo preliminary preparations, such as salting, at the islands. Then they are shipped to a government-supervised factory in St. Louis where they are dressed, dyed and sold at public auction.

The walrus is another fin-foot that may visit the Pribilofs, though it usually keeps to the Arctic seas. It is a good swimmer but cannot endure a long-distance trek such as is made by the fur seal. Often it will climb aboard ice floes and let the ocean currents carry it along. Walruses begin their northward migrations in May, and during the journey young are born and mating occurs. When the Arctic waters freeze over, walruses may go as far south as Labrador in the Atlantic and to the Bering Sea in the Pacific.

The walrus is a ponderous seallike mammal, weighing as much as 3,000 pounds. It has a massive neck, which supports a proportionally small head. Its muzzle is broad and blunt and is studded with coarse, stiff bristles. Short, reddish hairs scantily cover its thick and wrinkled hide. Like the eared seals, the walrus turns its hind feet under its body to assist it when walking on land or ice.

The characteristic mark of adult walruses is the possession of a very fine pair of ivory tusks, which are really elongated canine teeth of the upper jaw. The tusks of the male are quite straight and may grow to a length of thirty-nine inches. Those of the female are shorter, more slender and somewhat curved. The tusks make formidable weapons in defense and in fighting for a mate. They are also efficient tools for digging in the sediment of the ocean floor for mollusks, such as clams, snails and oysters. Besides mollusks, walruses relish starfish and shrimp. When the young, tuskless walrus is still nursing, it will often cling by its front flippers to the mother's neck as she swims and dives in search of food.

Sociable by nature, walruses keep together in small herds, spending their time on shores or on ice floes. Though usually mild in manner, they become aggressive during the mating season, or when attacked or when their young are threatened. Man is their greatest enemy; they also fall victims to polar bears and killer whales.

The prosperity of some Eskimo tribes of the far north depend to a great extent upon the herds of walruses. These Eskimos use every bit of a walrus carcass. The flesh is eaten, the hide is made into leather, the intestines serve as a substitute

and hooded seals are somewhat similar. These animals often migrate together. Early in February they head northward for the Strait of Belle Isle or the Gulf of St. Lawrence, where the young are born, or whelped, sometime in March. Until the young harps are able to swim, they are left on sheets of thin, drifting ice. The old seals leave and approach their babies through holes made in this ice. The hooded seal young are whelped on ridges

Sea elephants are giants among seals. The male has a long, flexible, inflatable snout.

for window glass, the tusks are carved and the oil is burned to provide light.

Of the true, or earless, seals, the harp and hooded seals are the ones chiefly hunted by commercial sealers for their hides and blubber. Like other true seals, they do not move well on land or ice. Not only are the hind limbs of little use, but their fore limbs are quite small and their necks are so short that they can barely lift their heads. Their pelts have long, coarse hair and lack the characteristic underfur of the fur seals. The habits of the harp

of ice, which are approached directly from the sea. Hooded seals scatter in small groups away from the herds of harp seals.

Other true seals are found along rocky coasts or about islands and ice floes of most seas. Certain species even live in inland waters. The Caspian seal dwells in the Caspian Sea; the Baikal seal flourishes in Lake Baikal, which is a large freshwater lake of Eurasia. Since these seals are awkward on land, their presence here suggests that these waters had a former connection with the open sea.

But seals can travel on land, if necessary, — a short way in a long time. It is recorded that a gray seal traversed fully thirty miles of snow-covered land in Norway, the time taken, it is believed, being about a week. Whether they would have endurance enough to find their way from some other watercourse to the inland seas mentioned is, of course, another matter.

Many seals are destroyed on land by polar bears, and many in the waters by killer whales. But the shark is also an enemy of this animal. The common seal along our coasts is called the "harbor" or "leopard" seal. It is one of the small-

Because of lack of space we cannot mention here all the various genera of the true seals; but the sea elephant, or elephant seal, must be noted. This is indeed a prodigious beast, with a length of from to 20 to 22 feet, and a girth of from 15 to 16 feet, these dimensions relating to males only, for the females are considerably smaller. The enormous coating of blubber by which the animal is enveloped is a perfect protection against cold, for it has been found that the body of a sea elephant that has lain for twelve hours in the icy water of the Arctic fully retains its internal heat. Formerly to be found in

N. Y. Zool. Soc.

A California sea lion sunning itself. The animal's coat glistens black when wet.

est of the true seals, rarely exceeding a length of five or six feet, and is whitish in color, heavily spotted with gray. It sometimes finds its way into the Great Lakes or other inland bodies of water having a connection with the sea, but it is nowhere regarded with friendly interest by fishermen whose nets it frequently robs or even destroys in its pursuit of fish. It is found in both the Atlantic and Pacific as far south as North Carolina and Lower California though not abundant south of Maine and British Columbia. It is not as gregarious as other seals and, therefore, in no present danger of extermination.

enormous herds, sea elephants are now relatively few in number.

One species, the California sea elephant, was nearly exterminated in the early years of the twentieth century. Conservation practices in those days were decidedly sketchy, to say the least; the animals had been considered fair prey for years by whalers and sealers. Naturally there had been an indiscriminate slaughter of the helpless beasts; the few that remained made their final bid for life on the island of Guadelupe, off the coast of Lower California. Since there was no law, written or unwritten, to protect them, it seemed only a matter of time before

Herbert J. Pontine

A Weddell seal about to dive for its prey.

were so near to extinction. But the expedition was sent to Guadelupe nevertheless.

The members of the expedition, with true scientific zeal, photographed the animals as they lay on land, then killed them and sent the carcasses home to be preserved. At the same time a horde of whalers and sealers descended upon the island and began their own slaughter of the innocents. The sea elephants on Guadelupe, menaced by commercial killers and scientific killers, seemed doomed to destruction. Fortunately, however, some of the animals either managed to escape detection or else were not

they would all be slaughtered by the rapacious hunters of whales and seals.

But this was not the only threat to their existence. A rich English collector, who had become interested in these huge animals, was appalled to learn that there was not a single adult specimen in any museum in the world. He determined, therefore, to send out an expedition to Guadelupe in order to obtain a number of specimens for museums before the animals should be utterly exterminated. He was hotly denounced by many naturalists and by animal lovers generally. They felt that it was all very well to provide specimens for our museums, but that it was not right to seek specimens of animals that

U.S. Fish and Wildlife Service

The harbor seal frequents harbors and river mouths.

on the island when the slaughter took place. When Guadelupe was visited by an exploring party in 1919, a small herd of the enormous beasts was still holding its own.

These seals breed from February to June; during this period they are often to be found on the shore. Here they are sluggish and ungainly. They appear to be quite unaware that they have a deadly potential enemy in man; they show no signs of fear when humans approach them. When they are attacked, their attempts to escape are pathetically futile, since they move about with difficulty on land and quickly become exhausted. They are more truly in their element when swimming about in the sea; here their chief enemy is the killer whale.

Another species of sea elephant makes its home in the vicinity of various islands in the Antarctic region; the big animals live on friendly terms with their neighbors, the penguins. They have a better chance to survive than their northern cousins.

See also Vol. 10, p. 275: "Mammals."

A fur seal that is found in Australian waters.

Australia News and Information Bureau

Mounds made by *Scapanus townsendi*, a species of mole found in Pacific coastal areas in the United States.

The two upper pictures show *Scapanus townsendi* and its trademark — the surface pushed up by its burrowing.

U. S. Fish and Wildlife Service

A series of typical ridges and mounds made by moles. The sectional view in the foreground shows part of a somewhat deeper runway that connects with the different mounds and also with a hunting path that lies farther underground.

THE INSECT EATERS

Humble Animals That Maintain the Balance of Nature

THE group of small mammals that specialize in eating insects includes the hedgehogs, shrews, moles, tenrecs and solenodons. These insectivores, or insect eaters, as they are called, are widely distributed in the temperate and tropical portions of the Old and New Worlds. Hedgehogs are found in Europe, Asia and Africa; moles and shrews, in those three continents and also in North America. The tailless tenrec dwells in Madagascar; the ratlike solenodon, in Haiti and Cuba. Australia and the oceanic islands have no members of this group. South America has practically none; the only representatives of the insect eaters in that large continent are a small number of shrews.

The insectivores are not seen so frequently as other mammals. They are shy and retiring animals; they are mostly active at night, frequenting places where abundant growths of vegetation serve to attract numerous insects. For the most part they are small-bodied creatures with elongated and mobile snouts and small eyes and ears. They possess musk, or scent, glands, from which a strong-smelling substance is secreted. Their toes are armed with very strong claws; certain species of insectivores use these claws as tools for burrowing into the earth.

The burrowing types of insect eaters, such as the moles, excavate a vast network of tunnels in the ground. The shrews and the hedgehogs, on the other hand, live above ground, though shrews sometimes use the tunnels made by mice. Tree shrews dwell almost entirely in trees; the African otter shrews, the water shrews and the water moles are particularly well fitted for an aquatic type of life. Most of the insectivores supplement their staple diet of insects with worms, snails, lizards and small birds. Shrews often devour mice; otter shrews feed upon fish; hedgehogs and tree shrews consume fruit.

Though the insectivores make up only a small part of today's mammalian population, they are particularly interesting because they show us what some of the first mammals were like. Between 160,000,000 and 230,000,000 years ago, certain reptiles gradually evolved into the mammalian type of animal. The first mammals were quite small; they ate either insects or flesh and they lived in trees. Their small size and tree-dwelling habits undoubtedly helped them escape the attention of the formidable flesh eaters belonging to the dinosaur group. From this early mammalian stock several types of mammals evolved. One branch developed into the egg-laying mammals, such as the duck-billed platypus; another, into the pouch-bearing animals; still another, into the true insectivores. The bats, which still feast upon insects, were an early offshoot from these insectivores.

The insect eaters of today seem to have departed but little from their ancestors. It is true that the hedgehogs now have a coat of bristling spines and that the moles have gone underground to live; but their skeletal structure, teeth and small brains show typically primitive characteristics. Perhaps the shrews have changed least of all; they are still unspecialized, mouselike creatures. The tree shrews, which have larger brains than their relatives, are generally considered to represent a link between the insectivores and the primates, which include the lemurs, the monkeys and the apes.

The tree shrews, also known as tupaias, are now included in the order of Primates, to which man belongs. The name "insectivores" was first applied to the group by the great comparative anatomist Baron Georges Cuvier (see Index).

The characteristics of the true insectivores

Though many animals, such as birds, fish, bats, frogs and snakes, eat insects, they are not all insectivores. The true insectivore is a mammal distinguished by the peculiar character of its teeth. These have the shearlike action of the typical carnivore, as opposed to the grinding action found in most other animals. In addition, the insectivore's teeth are furnished with sharp projections enabling the animal to seize and pierce the body of insects. Nearly all members of the order possess a long, narrow, mobile muzzle. The brain shows several primitive characteristics; large olfactory bulbs (extensions of the brain concerned with the sense of smell), few folded surfaces and an underdeveloped cerebrum. The cerebrum is well developed in the higher mammals, such as the apes. In man this portion of the brain is concerned with the thinking process.

It has been extremely difficult for zoologists to classify the insectivores. The taxonomist (one who classifies living things according to their natural order) looks for similarity of anatomical features when he tries to fit animals into a logical classification. When he deals with the insectivores, he finds that some types have retained many ancient, specialized features, while others have been profoundly modified through the ages.

According to the modern classification, the eight surviving families, arranged according to increasing specialization, are the Solenodontidae (including the solenodon of the West Indies); the Tenrecidae (great tenrec, aquatic tenrec, rice tenrec); the Potamogalidae (otter shrew); the Chrysochloridae (golden mole of South Africa); the Erinaceidae (hedgehog, moonrat, gymnura); the Macroscelididae (elephant shrew); the Soricidae (common shrew, pygmy shrew, short-tailed shrew or "mole" shrew, musk shrew, web-footed shrew); the Talpidae (desman, "shrew" mole, eared shrew mole, star-nosed mole, all the American moles).

The ancestor of the insectivores is believed to have been a hedgehog type. Its teeth and bones have been found in fossil deposits that date back to the Upper Cretaceous period, some 60 million years ago. At this time the climate was changing from warm and humid to temperate and dry. The great reptiles disappeared, and the small, shy, warm-blooded creatures called mammals began to increase and multiply. Certain mammals (the bats) became aerial; some (the whales) became aquatic; others (the hoofed mammals and rodents) became plant eaters; still others (the cats, civets and wolves) became meat eaters. The insectivores, however, followed the ancestral mode of life and became even more specialized in it. Considering the fact that they survived for such a long period of time, the insectivores must have been astonishingly successful in adapting themselves to changes in climate and to the predacious (preying) habits of the carnivorous animals, their greatest enemies.

Adaptations to an underground environment

This phenomenon of adaptation is very important for the modern theory of evolution. An adaptation may be defined as a characteristic that is advantageous to an animal in the particular surroundings in which its life is spent. Sight is a distinct advantage for all animals living on the earth or in the air. Genetic factors (see Index) can cause hereditary poor sight in animals. The blind animal would have to develop other senses such as smell and touch to survive. In an underground environment it would even have the advantage over a sighted animal, which needs vision to orient itself. It is therefore not surprising that the insectivore known as the mole, an animal with small, weak eyes, has successfully survived. Regardless of its visual shortcomings it has evaded its enemies and found food.

In adapting to its environment, this animal chose to lead the life of an underground burrower. The form of its body shows the adjustments made for this mode of living. The mole's head is conical in shape; there is no distinct neck, and the body is in the form of a compact cylinder. The eyes are minute with the power to discriminate only between light and darkness. Some moles even have the eyes covered with a thin layer of skin. External ears are lacking. The soft, thick fur is like velvet, lying smoothly in whatever way it is pressed; thus it keeps friction at a minimum as the mole plows through the soil. The powerful front feet are its digging tools. These feet are very broad and are equipped with stout, strong claws. The

monly occurs in low meadows, gardens and lawns in the eastern half of the United States. The Pacific mole and related species live along the Pacific coast from Lower California to northern Washington. They are similar to the eastern mole but are larger and have a slightly hairy tail. The hairy-tailed mole is a small animal, whose tail is decidedly hairy; it is confined to the northeastern states and southeastern Canada. The most unique American mole is the star-nosed mole, which has a disk of short, fleshy tentacles at the end of its nose. It lives in the eastern states and southeastern Canada. The common European mole represents the mole family in the Old World; it occurs from England and France to the islands of Japan.

A. R. Thompson

The common shrew of Europe and central Asia is one of the smallest and most pugnacious of all mammals.

front legs of some species are set so that the soles of the feet face outward. The feet, fleshy nose and hairy or naked tail are sensitive organs of touch. The mole's sense of smell is keener than its vision. The sense of touch is best developed and is used to locate prey.

Moles inhabit much of the world's north temperate region, but are absent in the Southern Hemisphere. North America has several species. The eastern mole is a moderate-sized animal, five or six inches long, with a short, naked tail. It com-

Moles require a fairly moist, loamy soil, which is easily worked. Their burrows must be humid, for these creatures cannot live long in a dry atmosphere. They prefer open terrain, such as lawns, low meadows and gently sloping hillsides. The star-nosed mole, however, chooses the damp soil and grassy swamps near streams or lakes, while the hairy-tailed mole likes upland wooded areas.

Moles excavate two types of tunnels. There are temporary channels that lie close to the surface, forcing the soil into ridges; there are permanent galleries that run through the soil about a foot or so below the ground. In the tunnels near the surface, the moles hunt for food. The digger literally swims through the soil at an amazing speed. The soil is not removed but merely pressed aside by the mole's body as it forces its way through.

Deeper galleries are more carefully excavated

The deeper galleries are more carefully constructed and serve as passageways to the hunting ground and to the mole's nesting chamber. Using first one front foot and then the other, the mole loosens a bit of soil and passes it back along the side of the body, kicking it to the rear with its hind feet. When a quantity of loosened soil has accumulated, the mole then pushes it along the tunnel to an outlet at the surface; this makes the characteristic molehill. The little insectivore is careful to keep the outlet plugged with dirt when it is not in use. The mole has a keen sense of direction; it digs at about the same level below the surface whether the ground forms a ridge or a hollow. The eastern mole digs tunnels at the rate of about twelve feet an hour. During a mole's lifetime, an extensive network of these tunnels is excavated. Some tunnels may be used in common by dozens of moles living in the same area.

The mole's nesting chamber, or fortress, is excavated about a foot below the surface, under a good-sized mound. If the animal lives close to water, the chamber is located above the water level. Several galleries lead from the upper part of the chamber and form a network of channels around it. It is believed that these may aid in giving proper aeration to the chamber. At the base of the fortress another gallery is excavated. This serves to drain the nesting site of any excess moisture and gives the mole an emergency exit in case of danger. The nest itself is composed of leaves and grass. During the breeding season, female moles construct a similar but smaller nesting chamber in which to have their young. Moles are usually solitary creatures; they defend their fortress and its approaches and their hunting territory against intruders.

Mating occurs during the early spring and occasionally in the fall. The female carries the young in her womb from four to six weeks, depending upon the species. From two to six offspring are produced. The young develop quickly and are ready to take care of themselves when but six or eight weeks old. The eastern mole may live about three years, barring accidents.

Since moles are extremely active creatures, they require a great deal of food to keep themselves alive. It has been estimated that a mole will eat its weight in food every day. Earthworms, beetle larvae, cutworms, adult beetles and snails form the principal fare. Apparently, when there is an abundance of earthworms, moles store them to be eaten later. The mole bites the worm at the front end; this immobilizes the prey but does not kill it.

Moles spend the greater part of their lives underground. Occasionally they come to the surface in order to hunt for prey, to find water and to obtain grass and leaves for the nest. They can swim, sometimes crossing small rivers. The star-nosed mole is an accomplished swimmer and diver. It has even been observed swimming under ice during the winter.

Water moles, or desmans, are semiaquatic insectivores

The active swimmers known as water moles, or desmans, which live in Spain, northern Europe and Russia, are related to the true moles. These animals have webbed hind feet, a vertically flattened tail and long, oily guard hairs that protect the skin and thick fur from water. The elongated, tubular snout forms a proboscis. Desmans construct their nesting chambers in river banks. They prey on small aquatic animals of all kinds, including fish.

The tiny shrew mole is another insectivore related to the moles; it has features of both the shrews and the moles. For instance, its face is long like that of a shrew, but its naked muzzle is molelike. Its moderately broad, stoutly clawed front feet are larger than those of a shrew but not so well developed as those of a mole. Shrew moles live in the humid coastal

The long-eared hedgehog, at the right, is a native of India. Its sharp spines serve as a defense against its enemies.

areas of the northwestern United States. A similar species, the eared shrew mole, occurs in Japan. These insectivores live partly underground, partly on the surface.

Hedgehogs and their kin comprise a family living entirely in the Old World. The common hedgehog has a small rounded body, short legs and tail and a sharply tapering muzzle. Its back and sides are covered with hairs modified into sharp but unbarbed spines, or quills. Coarse hairs clothe the legs, under parts and face. It inhabits Europe and Asia from the British Isles to Korea. Closely related species live in northern and eastern Africa. Southern Asia is the home of two rather curious relatives, the moonrat and the gymnura. These are longer-bodied animals with long pointed muzzles and moderately long tails. They lack spines.

When approached by a predator, the hedgehog rolls into a ball, tucking its head and feet into the center. The erect spines form a formidable defense against attack; this is not a completely efficient defense, however, for weasels, owls, vultures and foxes sometimes made a meal of the hedgehog. The moonrat has an odor peculiarly like that of onions. This may be offensive to certain predators.

The hedgehog is, for the most part, a nocturnal roamer, spending the day in any place that affords warmth and dryness, such as a hollow log, a burrow in an embankment or a den among rocks. It feeds on insects, worms, slugs, birds' eggs, frogs and snakes. In hunting prey, the hedgehog will sometimes take to water, swimming fairly well. It will cross small rivers when pursued. During the winter, it hibernates in a snug retreat; at this time its body temperature may fall to 43° F.

Usually hedgehogs breed twice a year. The gestation period lasts from five to seven weeks, and the number of offspring, which are covered with soft, white spines, average from four to six. A nest of leaves in the shelter of a tree's roots or some hidden burrow serves as a nursery. Here the young remain until a month old; then they follow the mother in her wanderings.

The author has become familiar with the doings of a hedgehog family that sleeps beneath the floor of a summerhouse; his observation of the family has given him an insight into the lives of these insectivores. The hedgehogs feast on the insects of the garden and find an additional food supply in the thousands of frogs living within the boundaries of their domain.

All that they have to do is to eat and drink and be merry. There are only two pitfalls in the garden, yet both have almost proved the undoing of the hedgehogs. One is a miniature lake, which is more easily entered than left. Though there is plenty of water elsewhere for drinking purposes in the garden, a hedgehog once sought to quench its thirst in the water of the lake, blundered in and was almost at its last gasp when it finally was rescued.

The second pitfall is supplied by a steep drop in the ground at one place in the vicinity of the fence that encircles the garden. This results in a penned-in area about a foot wide and many yards in length. Hedgehogs, some of them more than half

The elephant shrew, or jumping shrew, is an inhabitant of Africa. Note the trunklike extension of the snout.

grown, blunder into this "trap" and cannot get out. On one occasion a little mound of stones was built in order to enable two little trapped animals to climb up to the higher ground. A couple of days later, the two were still imprisoned. In spite of their exceedingly sharp claws they had apparently been unable to scale the "wall" that enclosed them; nor had they availed themselved of the bridge provided by the mound of stones.

The nearest relative of the hedgehog is a rat-like animal called the gymnura, or rat shrew. The latter name describes the external characteristics of this animal; but its teeth and its internal structure show that it is closely allied to the hedgehog. The

gymnura is found in Burma, the Malay region, the Philippines and parts of China. There are several species, some as big as good-sized rats, others as small as mice. All are purely insectivorous. The discovery of fossil remains of an extinct genus of gymnura in France has been cited as evidence of the similarity between the fauna of Europe in prehistoric times and that of the present-day Malay Archipelago.

The shrews are widely distributed

The most numerous and widely distributed of all the insectivores are the shrews. The common shrew, or shrew mouse, found in Europe, Asia and North America, is about the size of a mouse and somewhat resembles that animal, particularly in the shape of its body, feet and tail; but it is distinguished from the mouse by its muzzle, which projects far beyond the lip. The common shrew feeds upon insects and their larvae, and inhabits dry places, making a nest of various kinds of leaves and grasses. The young, numbering from five to seven, are born in the spring. Common shrews are very voracious; they sometimes kill and devour one another.

The pygmy shrew is even smaller than the common shrew. Rarely more than three inches in length, this tiny animal is the smallest mammal of the North American continent.

The short-tailed, or mole, shrew is the best-known species in the eastern United States. It is about four inches long, with a hairy tail measuring one inch. It remains quite active in the winter; it is sometimes found burrowing in the snow. At this season of the year it feeds largely on beechnuts as well as chrysalids and larvae.

The tupaia, or tree shrew, is widely distributed in the countries of the Orient. The head with its elongated muzzle is typical of the insectivores and the character of its teeth is unmistakable. For a long time this animal was classed in the order Insectivora, but close inspection of the brain and eyes revealed the animal to be more closely related to the lemurs, belonging to the order Primates.

The African water shrew or otter shrew, although a true insectivore, is an excellent swimmer and fine fisher.

The great tenrec of Madagascar can inflict a severe bite. Note the long muzzle and insectivorous teeth.

The European water shrew can dive and swim with great facility. It feeds mainly on larvae and young fish.

The jumping shrews, also called elephant shrews because of the trunklike extension of the snout, are the African representatives of the tupaias. They are ground animals and move by leaps, after the fashion of the kangaroo. The jumping shrews are entirely restricted to Africa. There are many species of these interesting animals. Some haunt the thick undergrowth; others dwell in stony wastes, where clefts and crannies in the rocks offer a secure haven during the dreaded hours of daylight.

China has an aquatic shrew that is more highly specialized than any of its relatives — the web-footed shrew. The soles of its feet are provided with disclike pads; these enable the animal to grip securely the surface of smooth stones and rock as it seeks its food in a river bed.

The musk shrew—
the bane of insect pests

The musk shrew of India is remarkable for the strong, musky odor that emanates from glands situated on the sides of the body. Though it leaves an offensive musky trail, it is generally tolerated in the houses that it enters, because it feeds greedily on cockroaches and other insect pests.

The otter shrew of West Africa finds a place among the insectivores because of the insectivorous characteristic of its teeth. The muzzle is broad, not pointed, after the fashion of other insectivores; and this expert swimmer's habits — particularly its skill in catching fish — decidedly suggest the otter rather than the shrew.

The tenrecs and the
solenodons are closely related

Among the most fascinating of the insect-eaters are the tenrecs and the solenodons, which are closely related. The former are natives of Madagascar, the latter of the West Indies. The existence of these closely allied animals in such widely separated areas points to ancient land connections that have vanished under the seas.

The great tenrec is the most fearsome beast of the tenrec group. Tailless, it attains a length of sixteen inches and considerable girth; it possesses formidable

N. Y. Zool. Soc.

The little solenodon, above, is an inhabitant of Haiti.

teeth and it can inflict a serious bite. Its diet consists almost exclusively of earthworms; it hunts this prey only during the hours of night. To defend itself against its enemies, the tenrec has developed a formidable coat of armor, consisting of bristles and spines. This animal hibernates like the European hedgehog and it lives in burrows, which it excavates by means of its strong claws. Unlike the hedgehog, however, the great tenrec does not roll itself up into a ball-like form for defense.

One species of tenrec has become aquatic. Another, the rice tenrec, carries its search for insects beneath the roots of growing rice to such lengths as to become a serious pest; more so, even, than the insect pests upon which it feeds. Tenrecs rank among the most prolific of all mammals; as many as twenty-one at one birth have been recorded. The flesh of these animals, especially before they hibernate, is highly esteemed by the natives of Madagascar.

The solenodons, found only in Haiti and Cuba, have long snouts and tails and large ears. The body of the solenodon is hairy; by way of contrast, the tail is naked.

We shall end our account of the insectivores with the animal known as the golden mole. It is to be found in eastern, southern and central Africa. This animal is more nearly related in structure to the tenrec than to the mole; still, in its habits of burrowing and tunneling it is clearly molelike. The ears are tiny; the eyes are buried beneath the skin. The metallic luster of the coat gives the golden mole its name.

See also Vol. 10, p. 275: "The Mammals."

THE SOLAR BATTERY*

How Sunlight is Used to Generate Electricity

OUR star, the sun, radiates energy at the enormous rate of 3.79×10^{33} ergs a second. (See Index, under Ergs.) The earth is so small, comparatively speaking, and so far away from the sun that it receives only about a two-billionth of this energy; yet even this represents a staggering quantity.

We would be able to put our slim quota of solar energy to even better use if we could harness it effectively. Within the last few decades, much progress has been made in this respect. Heat produced by the sun's rays has served to generate electricity indirectly,** to provide warmth for houses and even to cook food. In the useful device called the photoelectric cell, the light of the sun (as well as light from other sources) has been converted directly into electric energy. (See Index, under Photoelectric cells.)

The electric power produced by the photoelectric cell is very feeble. A far more effective device for generating electric power from sunlight is the solar battery, developed by the scientists of the Bell Telephone Laboratories. It is made up of a number of cells, each consisting of a wafer of pure silicon, to which certain impurities have been added.

To have some idea of the workings of a solar cell, let us recall that electrons — particles with a negative electrical charge —

* Article prepared with the assistance of Bell Telephone Laboratories, Inc.
** Solar energy is made to heat a liquid; the resulting vapor runs turbines which are connected to generators of electricity.

revolve around the nucleus of a typical atom in several concentric shells.* Atoms combine with one another through the agency of the electrons that make up the outermost shell. A silicon atom has four electrons in this shell. In a silicon crystal, each atom is normally joined to four of its neighbors by its four outer electrons.

If an electron is jarred loose from a silicon atom by some outer force such as light, heat or electrical energy, it will wander freely through the crystal, leaving a hole in the crystal lattice, or framework. This hole behaves like a positive charge of electricity. Every time an electron from an adjacent atom moves in to fill such gap, it

* Ordinary hydrogen has only one electron; the atoms of hydrogen and helium have only one shell.

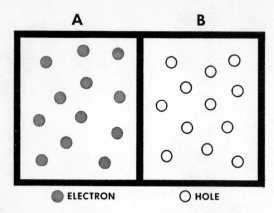

ELECTRON   HOLE

1. If we put arsenic in half a silicon wafer (A), there will be more electrons than holes; if we put boron in the other half (B), there will be more holes than electrons. "Electrons" and "holes" are explained in the text.

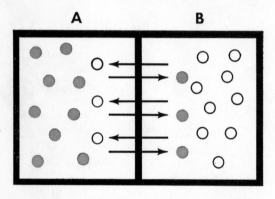

2. The negative electrons and positive holes cross the boundary between A and B. Side B will acquire a negative charge as the electrons pass into it; side A will acquire a positive charge as it receives holes from B.

3. Typical silicon solar cell, described in this article.

Bell Telephone Laboratories, Inc.

PHOTONS OF LIGHT ENERGY FROM SUN

P-N JUNCTION

N-TYPE SILICON

P-TYPE SILICON

ELECTRON FLOW

leaves a new gap behind it. In this way holes can travel from one part of the crystal to another, just as electrons can. When we apply an outside source of energy to a crystal, therefore, a certain number of freely wandering negative and positive charges are created within the crystal. They travel at random and balance one another.

Suppose that we introduce a trace of arsenic in a silicon crystal. The arsenic atom has five electrons in its outer shell. If it combines with four adjacent atoms of silicon (just as a silicon atom would combine with its neighbors), one of the arsenic electrons will be left over and will become a free electron. Even a trace of arsenic contains a very large number of atoms. Therefore we bring about an excess of freely movable electrons by introducing the arsenic. The crystal as a whole remains electrically neutral, since the extra free electrons are balanced by positively charged protons in the nuclei of the arsenic atoms.

There would be a different state of affairs if we put boron in the crystal. Each boron atom has only three electrons in its outer shell. If it combined with four silicon neighbors, the lack of one electron would leave a positive hole in the crystal lattice around the boron atom. As we would be introducing considerable numbers of boron atoms in the crystal, we would now have an excess of positively charged holes. Again, the neutrality of the total crystal would not be affected.

Suppose now that we put arsenic in one half of a silicon crystal (A in Figure 1) and boron in the other half (B in Figure 1). Each half of the crystal would be electrically neutral. Yet the concentration of free electrons would be greater in the arsenic half than in the boron half; and, similarly, there would be more wandering holes on the boron side than on the arsenic side. Since both kinds of charges move about in a haphazard way, they would tend to diffuse throughout the entire crystal, crossing the boundary between A and B. Side B would acquire a negative charge because excess electrons would be passing into it. Side A, on the other hand, would become positively charged, since it would receive an excess

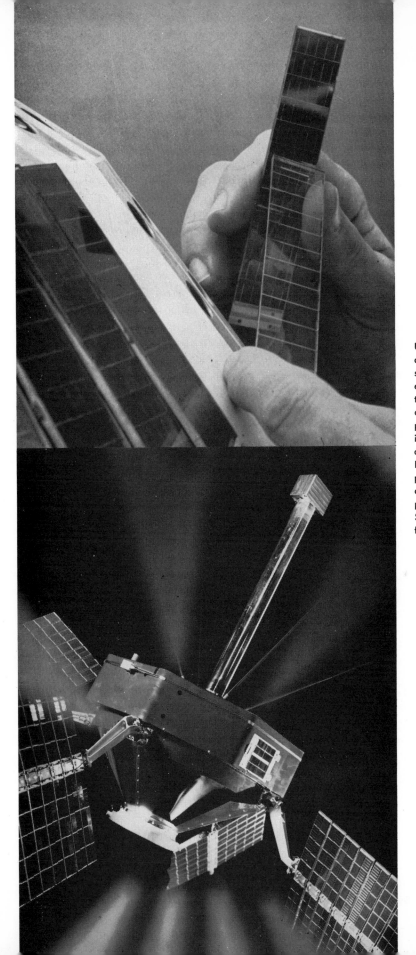

Upper photo: attaching solar cells and transparent sapphire slices to a developmental model of the *Telstar* communications satellite. Solar cells are covered with thin slices of sapphire, set in frames of platinum, in order to protect the cells from space radiation. Lower photo: an S-3 energetic-particles satellite, designed to analyze the energy of charged particles encountered in space. Solar cells are installed on the four paddles of this satellite.

Upper photo: Bell Telephone Laboratories, Inc.
Lower photo: NASA

of holes. (See Figure 2.) These charges would build up as more electrons and holes passed through. In time they would become strong enough to prevent any more diffusion at the boundary. Negatively charged side *B* would repel electrons; positively charged side *A* would repel holes. Equilibrium would be established and we would now have a built-in electric field, as the inventors of the solar battery call it.

We have just such an arrangement in each of the cells that make up the solar battery. Each cell (Figure 3) is a thin wafer. Its body consists of silicon with a trace of arsenic. This is called n-type silicon ("n"="negative") because the addition of the arsenic provides an excess of negative charges. The surface of the wafer is made up of a thin layer of silicon with a trace of boron; this is called p-type silicon ("p"= "positive") because it has an excess of positively charged holes. The boundary between the silicon-arsenic body and the silicon-boron surface is called the p-n junction. The p-type silicon, corresponding to *B* in Figure 1, develops a negative charge; the n-type silicon, corresponding to *A*, develops a positive charge.

To use the solar battery, terminals are attached to the n-type and p-type material, as shown in Figure 3, and the terminals are connected by wiring. When sunlight strikes the surface of the wafer, it knocks out electrons from the crystal lattice in the vicinity of the junction and produces electron-hole pairs. In so doing it upsets the equilibrium established between the n-type and the p-type silicon. Electrons are pulled across the junction into the n-type silicon and holes are pulled into the p-type silicon. Electrons then stream from the negative terminal by way of the electric wiring to the positive terminal. Current will flow in this way as long as sunlight strikes the silicon wafer. Practical solar batteries consist of a number of such wafer-cells set side by side and electrically connected in series.

The solar battery can deliver a maximum voltage of a little more than half a volt in bright sunlight, and a maximum power of about a hundredth of a watt per square centimeter of exposed surface area.

It is estimated that it can convert up to 11 per cent of the sun's energy it receives directly into electric power.

The solar battery was put to work on a very modest scale at Americus, Georgia, in order to provide power for telephone amplifiers, or repeaters. These are required at intervals in a telephone line, in order to maintain the strength of the signal that is being transmitted. The power requirement for such repeaters is small; and it was found that a solar battery could readily meet it.*

The most promising use of solar cells at the present time is in the field of space exploration. They have already been used quite extensively in artificial earth satellites to provide electric power for various purposes. For example, the satellite *Explorer XII*, launched in August 1961 and used in radiation research, had 5,600 solar cells, capable of delivering 5 watts of power.

Solar cells play an important part in the Bell System's *Telstar* communications satellites. These devices receive a radio signal beamed at them from the ground, amplify the signal ten billion times and retransmit it on another frequency.** Each satellite, roughly spherical in shape, has 72 facets. Solar cells are set on most of the facets; there are 3,600 of the cells in all. They are mounted on ceramic bases in platinum frames; coverings of clear man-made sapphire protect them from bombardment by charged particles and tiny meteorites. The *Telstar* solar cells convert sunlight into electricity and charge 19 nickel-cadmium cells. The latter in turn provide power for the electronic circuits in the satellite.

It is believed that as the solar battery is perfected, it will find many useful applications. It should offer some striking advantages. It has no moving parts or corrosive chemicals, such as we find in various other generators of electricity; hence it should have an unusually long life. Besides, the sunlight on which it operates is our most abundant resource.

* The Americus project was technically successful, but was later discontinued.
** *Telstar* is also designed to analyze its own performance and provide information about energetic particles in space.

THE LAW OF PARITY

Significant Discoveries in the World of Subatomic Particles

BY EDMUND GREKULINSKI

THE LAW of the conservation of parity has been considered very important in modern physics. This law states, in effect, that for the absolute universe of space and time, distinctions between left and right and up and down, between an object and its image and so on have no real significance. These directions mean something only to an observer or in spatial relations among objects in various locations.

It is true that in our familiar everyday world, as opposed to the universe at large, distinctions between right and left assume great importance. We find a difference between right and left arms, right and left legs, right and left shoes and gloves. The structures of various organisms tend to be oriented to the right or to the left, more toward one than the other in different groups (the coiling in the shells of snails, for example). Thus, one direction may be preferred over another; even the sun, planets and moons mainly rotate and revolve in a prevailing direction. And

yet, is it not possible to imagine a system like ours in all respects, but constructed on a pattern where directions are the reverse of ours? Except for this one basic difference, would it otherwise differ markedly from the one we now inhabit? Probably it would not.

Consider a pair of shoes. Except for the difference between rightward and leftward directed structures, no one doubts that both shoes are identical in style, size and function. Suppose you have a pair of shoes, *a* and *c*, as shown in Figure 1. If you hold shoe *a* to a mirror, the reflection, *b*, will be identical with shoe *c*, the other shoe of the pair. If we use symmetrical kidney beans instead of shoes in the demonstration (Figure 2), we see that bean *b*, the mirror image of *a*, is exactly the same as bean *c*. We also observe that bean *c* is exactly the same as bean *a* turned upside down. In this case, then, there is no basic difference between the object (bean *a*) and its image (bean *b*).

107

1. Shoe *b* is the reflection of shoe *a* in the mirror; *b* is identical with shoe *c*, the other shoe of the pair.

2. Bean *b* is the mirror image of bean *a*; *b* is also the same as bean *c*, which is simply *a* turned upside down.

Parity in the
subatomic world

If we could directly see the particles that compose the atoms of matter and the waves of energy, we would notice, in certain situations, that particles spinning or moving in one direction tend to be balanced

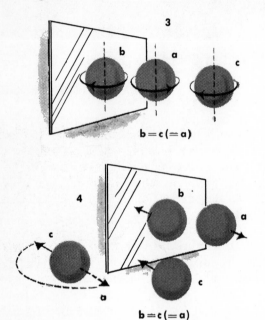

3

b = c(= a)

4

b = c(= a)

3. Ball b is the mirror image of ball a; b is identical with ball c, which rotates in the same direction.
4. Ball b is the mirror image of ball a; b is identical with ball c, which is a turned 180° to the left.
5. Three straight lines, x, y and z, meet at right angles at O and thus define a three-dimensional space.
6. When the same axes, x, y and z, are extended beyond the O point, the extended portions receive minus signs.

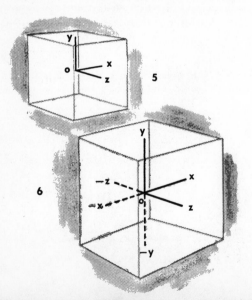

by identical particles spinning or moving the opposite way. To illustrate this aspect of parity, hold a plain ball, *a*, up to a mirror (Figure 3). Ball and image are absolutely identical and cannot be distinguished at all. Now spin the ball between thumb and forefinger along an axis parallel to the plane of the mirror. You will notice that the image of the ball in the mirror spins in the opposite direction. Reflection *b* is identical with a real ball, *c*, rotating in the same direction; *a* corresponds to *c* turned upside down. The introduction of motion into the concept of parity here is of the greatest importance, as we shall see shortly.

Another important factor to consider in balanced motion is symmetry. We illustrated mirror-image parity for the sphere by rotating it, in Figure 3. Suppose now that, as in Figure 4, we move the ball *a* in a straight line directly *away* from the mirror; its image, *b*, of course, will move in the opposite direction. If we move another ball, *c*, directly away from ball *a* (which moves in the opposite direction), ball *c* will correspond exactly to the mirror image *b*. These motions may be considered as symmetrical or balanced. In Figure 4, balls *a* and *c* may be said to constitute a pair. If we turn *a* 180° to the left so that it is "upside down" in relation to its former position, it corresponds perfectly to *c*, even including the arrows. Therefore, *a*, *b* and *c* are identical.

We can detect the nature of particles of subatomic size only indirectly, since they are too minute and move far too rapidly for us to see. We observe how they interact with other particles and waves, and we measure these interactions. But this system of measurement necessarily disturbs the particles, so that we cannot get an exact picture of what and where they are at a given moment. However, using statistics as a guide, physicists can "guess" about the probable positions of particles.

These bodies travel and may also spin, or rotate, on their axes as well. They are affected by electrical and magnetic fields. They react with each other, giving off or forming different particles, as in radioactivity. Some (called electrons) have nega-

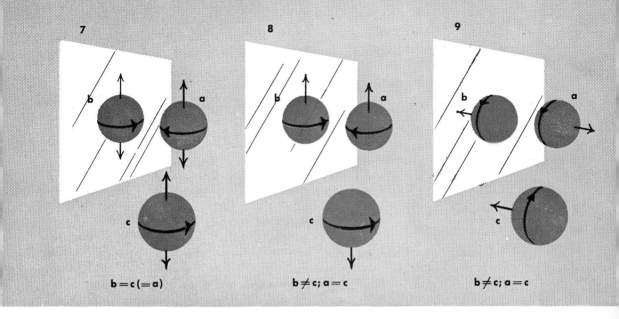

7   8   9

$b = c (= a)$ $b \neq c; a = c$ $b \neq c; a = c$

tive electrical charges; others are positive (positrons and the heavier protons) and still others are electrically neutral (neutrons and the far lighter neutrinos and antineutrinos). Certain particles move freely through space, while others (electrons, protons and neutrons) are also in atoms.

To locate such a particle in three-dimensional space, we construct three straight lines, called axes, at right angles to each other (Figure 5). The position of the particle is related to distances marked off on the three axes, or co-ordinates, which are given arbitrary symbols or letters (usually x, y and z). Suppose this system of axes is reflected in mirrors (Figure 6). We could call the reflections negative (labeling them $-x$, $-y$ and $-z$) to distinguish them from the positive axes, x, y and z, that are being reflected. Axes $-x$, $-y$ and $-z$ might also be called left-handed.

The actual picture in the world of subatomic particles is a bit more complicated than we have drawn it so far. Under certain conditions, groups of particles behave like waves in their motion. Physicists have made a careful study of these wave motions. They have determined that the probable positions of particles can be derived by a formula involving the square of what is called the wave function. (The wave function represents the amplitude, or height, of a wave.) If the axes which determine the position of a particle are reflected and the wave function becomes negative as the axes do, that particle is said to have *odd* parity.

7. Ball *b* is the mirror image of ball *a*; *b* is identical with ball *c*, which is simply ball *a* turned upside down.
8. Ball *b* is the mirror image of ball *a*; but *b* is not the same as ball *c*, which is ball *a* turned upside down.
9. Ball *b* is the mirror image of ball *a*; but *b* is not the same as ball *c*, which is just ball *a* turned about.

If the wave function still remains positive after reflection, however, the parity is called *even*. It is as if, despite the "extension" of the axes into the "negative" region, the particle's "image" is still "positive." In a system with a given number of particles interacting, parity is not supposed to change from the beginning to the end of the process. It is either even or odd, but not both; that is, parity is theoretically conserved.

Certain scientists began to express doubts about the "law" of parity during the 1950's. It was noted that certain particles, called mesons,* during their transformation, or "decay," into other kinds of mesons and various particles, had different parities, although they were absolutely alike in all other respects. One type of meson decays into two other mesons of different mass, each of the two having odd parity, so that the over-all parity is even. This is so because, when two negative quantities are multiplied together, the product is positive. In other words, two "odds" make an "even." Another kind of meson decays

* Mesons are subatomic particles with masses intermediate between those of electrons (which are light) and those of protons (which are heavy). Mesons may be electrically positive, negative or neutral; they occur commonly in cosmic rays or as the result of cosmic-ray activity. Some physicists believe mesons represent the binding force in atomic nuclei.

into three mesons, each of the latter identical with the products of the first-described process and each one also having odd parity; the over-all parity is odd. The reason is that when three negative numbers are multiplied together, the result is negative; or three "odds" make an "odd." The two original mesons (at the beginning of decay) are alike except for their parity — one odd, the other even. It is as if identical objects have different mirror reflections. Even if we assume the same parity for both, then somehow parity has changed in one of the two decay processes above. It would appear that the "principle" of parity has been violated, that certain reactions in the subatomic field are not symmetrical and that there is a difference between right and left and between particle and image.

To test the parity law for mesons, physicists at Columbia University in New York City and at the University of Chicago conducted a number of experiments. The Columbia group of M. Weinrich, L. Lederer and K. Garwin, for example, bombarded a target in a cyclotron (atom-smasher) with protons. As a result, the target emitted a stream of mesons, known as "pi" mesons. The latter then decayed into so-called "mu" mesons (somewhat different from pi mesons) and into extremely light particles with no positive or negative electrical charge — antineutrinos. This process was carried out in a magnetic field, which lined up the mu mesons' axes of rotation in one direction; it also made these mesons spin in a single direction. This was important, because now (unlike the situation in earlier experiments) the movements and positions of the reacting particles could be observed and measured. The mu mesons were then collected in a carbon block, where they in turn decayed, giving off electrons, antineutrinos and neutrinos — light particles with no positive or negative charges (unlike the electrons). It was noted that *more* electrons were emitted in one direction along a mu meson's spin axis than in the opposite one. According to the law of parity, the electrons should have come off equally in all directions or in equally opposed ones, as in Figure 7 (indicated by the arrows).

That is, they were supposed to come off each end of each rotation axis. Parity in this case would have been preserved; note that image *b* is identical with *c*; *a* and *c* constitute a pair, and *a* is *c* turned upside down, so that *a* = *b* = *c*. (Compare this with Figures 1-4.)

The reader should note that each sphere in Figure 7 is symmetrical in that its upper half, with its arrow, is a mirror image of the lower half, with its arrow. That is, imagine a mirror inserted through the equatorial region of each ball, perpendicular to the axis of spin. Figure 7 shows what the situation would be if the law of parity held true.

The actual experimental results are shown in Figures 8 and 9. The meson *a* emits electrons off one end of its spin axis. Its paired opposite, meson *c,* spinning in the *opposite* direction, emits electrons off the *opposite* end of its axis. We see that *a* is *c* turned upside down. Is *a*'s reflection, *b*, identical with meson *c*? It is not, of course. In Figure 8, *b* spins in the same direction as *c*, but its electrons stream off its axis in the opposite direction. In Figure 9, electrons move in the same direction in *b* and *c*, but the spin directions are opposed. It is as if *a* has two different "mirror" images: *b* and *c*.

Other experiments, conducted by Tsung D. Lee and Chien S. Wu of Columbia University, Chen N. Yang of the Institute of Advanced Study and Ernest Ambler of the National Bureau of Standards, indicated similar parity-law violations. This time they occurred in beta-ray emissions (of electrons and positrons) from the aligned spinning nuclei of cobalt atoms. Again one direction was favored over another.

So far, breakdown of the parity principle has been observed only in a few, so-called "weak interactions," involving low orders of energy. In other subatomic processes (strong interactions), parity seems to stand up. Future experiments will have to determine to what extent the law of the conservation of parity holds true. The findings thus far seem highly significant; they indicate that we may have to change our ideas about certain basic concepts.

THE WEEDS

A Standing Menace to Cultivated Crops

BY CLYDE M. CHRISTENSEN

A PLANT can be a thing of beauty and yet not be a joy forever. The bright trumpets of bindweed, a pasture that is sunny with buttercups, Queen Anne's lace in a meadow — here are spectacles to delight the passing motorist. But the farmer finds them less delightful, for the bindweed strangles his corn, the buttercups contain an irritating juice that cattle dislike, and Queen Anne's lace, which is a wild carrot, harbors a destructive weevil. These and other plants that spring up unbidden the farmer calls weeds. This name has nothing to do with plant classification. A weed is any plant growing where it is not wanted.

A dandelion in the front lawn is a weed; it is not a weed when cultivated for fresh greens. Sweet clover sown in the meadow is not a weed; when some of the ripe seeds drift over on the wind to the flower garden, they grow into weeds.

Weeds do enormous harm. In actual figures, many billions of dollars a year are lost, over the world, because of weeds. The sum is greater than the combined loss due to both plant diseases and insects. The loss is likely to be highest in regions where agriculture is most intensive and where the crops and land are of greatest value, but weeds in open-range country are also costly.

The cereal-grain crops offer a good example of the tax we pay on weeds. Seeds of weeds in the grain field are harvested along with the grain. On the average, wheat brought to the elevators contains one per cent of weed seeds. This means that in, say, a billion-bushel wheat crop, ten million bushels of weed seeds were harvested, threshed, stored, hauled to mills or terminals and there removed and disposed of. Even a small percentage of seeds of certain weeds, if blended with the grain, would give an off flavor to the flour. The grower receives a reduced price for his grain when it contains weed seeds.

Weeds that grow in hay or forage crops are of low feed value; many of them are unpalatable to stock, and some are actually poisonous and cause the loss of valuable animals. Others, when eaten by cows, give an unpleasant flavor to milk and butter. Weeds with pointed or spiny seeds or seed pods may get caught in the coats of animals, causing acute discomfort and also reducing the value of wool or hides.

Along railroad rights of way and highways, weeds are often fire and traffic hazards. They clog drainage and irrigation ditches and canals. For example, the water hyacinth, imported to Florida from the tropics, in a short time blocked many coastal and inland waterways. Constant and costly work is now required to keep these channels clear.

Some plant diseases have spread by means of weeds. The stem rust of wheat is caused by a fungus that spends part of its life on the barberry. To aid in controlling this disease, millions of ornamental barberry bushes have had to be uprooted and destroyed. The blister rust of white pines is caused by a fungus that spends part of its life on the leaves of wild and cultivated currant bushes. Some virus diseases that attack cultivated plants may be traced to weeds that not only serve as a source of the virus but also furnish a breeding place for leaf hoppers, aphids and other insects that carry the viruses. A number of insects that directly injure cultivated plants breed on or in weeds.

Hay-fever sufferers know that ragweed (as well as some other weeds and cultivated plants) causes heavy human misery. Poison ivy, poison sumach and other weeds are even worse pests than ragweed.

Probably the greatest harm done by weeds is in competing with crop plants. The weeds grow rapidly and send strong root systems far into the soil. In less than three weeks of growth, a vigorous mustard plant in a grain field will produce more than four hundred feet of roots. A dozen of these plants will produce nearly a mile of roots in three weeks. They rob the crop plants of soil minerals and water, and their leaves screen sunshine from the cultivated plants, further reducing the grower's yield.

Many weeds have remarkable powers of reproduction. An average-sized pigweed will produce from 100,000 to 200,000 seeds in one season, and a large pigweed may ripen 10,000,000 seeds. An annual crop of about 20,000 seeds per plant is a good average for each of 200 different kinds of annual and perennial weeds.

The seeds of many weeds are tenacious of life. In a famous test in Michigan, the seeds of twenty different kinds of weeds were buried in the soil (too deep for growth) in 1879. After forty years, some seeds of ten of the kinds were still able to germinate and, after sixty years, seeds of two kinds were still viable (able to grow). Nearly 70 per cent of the seeds of one weed, the moth mullein, germinated after having been buried in the soil for sixty years.

The seeds of some weeds can lie under water for months, or even years, and can still remain viable.

Quackgrass and certain other weeds can multiply rapidly by underground root stems or by root fragments. Perennial sow thistle and wild morning-glory, two of our most pestiferous weeds, not only produce seeds in abundance, but can also grow from severed roots. A small piece of morning-glory root carried into a field may in one year produce a root system fifteen feet across and extending down twenty feet into the soil. When these roots are cut by a cultivator, each piece will send up a new plant.

Weeds are famous travelers, and every continent today has a weed population made up of both native and immigrant pests.

The seeds are carried in almost every imaginable way. Those of the dandelion and some thistles have a buoyant parachute, called a pappus, on which they can ride for miles, drifting along with the wind. Many burrs, the beggar-ticks and others, have sharp or barbed spines by means of which they attach themselves to the fur of animals or the clothing of man. The puncture vine, a native of the Sahara Desert, has been spread by railroads and is now at home in many fertile lands. Motor cars and airplanes also carry it; the seeds cling to the tires and may be dropped off hundreds of miles from where they were picked up.

Animals and birds swallow seeds whole and later excrete them. When livestock are shipped long distances, seeds are transported in this manner. Farm machinery, especially harvesting machines and threshers, will carry seeds from one field or farm to another. The seeds of a few weeds can be carried by streams or by the water in drainage or irrigation ditches.

Man has only himself to blame for some of the weeds that plague him. Most of North America's worst weeds, for example, are aliens, brought from the other continents. The early colonists, when they set out from the Old World, brought seeds of plants to raise in the New. Almost no at-

Water hyacinths. These plants, imported into Florida, have become a pest, blocking waterways.

tempt was made to insure the purity of this seed stock, and so the common weed pests of these plants came along, too. Before 1700, dozens of different weeds common in Europe had a foothold in New England, and, as time passed, hundreds more were brought in. Not all of them prospered, but many did. Among them was the plantain.

Here are a few examples of weeds that thrive far from their native heaths.

Russian thistle — tumbleweed — was unknown in the United States before 1873. At that time a small amount of flax seed containing some thistle seed was imported and planted in South Dakota. Within ten years the Russian thistle had spread extensively in South Dakota and Missouri, and within another ten years it had infested sixteen states, from Missouri to the west coast.

The Canada thistle is not native to Canada but was brought from Europe early and became established around Montreal. When General Burgoyne's army invaded New York from Canada in 1777, hay brought for the cavalry horses contained thistle seeds. The Americans soon got rid of Gentleman Johnny Burgoyne, but the Canada thistle is now a costly pest in thirty-six states, from coast to coast.

Johnson grass, brought from Turkey, was tested as a forage grass in California. It proved of little value, but soon escaped and became a most detrimental weed along irrigation ditches.

The prickly pear, a kind of cactus, was introduced into Australia from North and South America for use as an ornamental plant. Within a short time it had taken over hundreds of thousands of acres of valuable agricultural land and amounted to almost a national calamity.

If a piece of land is stripped of vegetation and then left idle, weeds are the first plants to take over, and they take possession of the land in definite order. First, annual weeds form a dense cover. They not only hold the soil in place but also, as they rot, enrich the soil. Gradually the annual weeds are replaced and crowded out by biennials, which have the advantage of a two-year lease on life. The biennials are crowded out by perennials. If the climate

L. W. Brownell

The seeds of the milkweed, shown above, are carried far and wide on their buoyant "parachutes."

is suitable, these in turn may give way to forest trees. The trees will persist until fire, flood or other violence of man or nature again lays the ground bare, when the cycle begins anew. You can see the beginning of such a cycle, on a small scale, on newly filled-in lots or abandoned garden plots or even in untended yards around vacant houses in city or country.

Man fights the war of weeds with a variety of weapons, old and new. No one method of fighting will control all weeds, and certain weeds can be stamped out, or checked, only by the use of several methods at the same time. The attack to be chosen depends on the weed concerned, the extent of its infestation, the location and the purpose for which the land is used.

Governments long ago recognized the danger of importing alien weed seeds mixed with other seeds and the danger of introducing new cultivated plants that might become pests. Plant quarantine laws are helpful in this connection. Where there is such a national plant quarantine, seeds, plants or plant parts for propagation can be brought into a country only after rigid inspection at the port of entry; and new plants brought into the country are tested in isolated plots. The tests not only show whether the plants have a tendency to run wild as weeds, they also show whether the plants might be disease-carriers or hosts to harmful insects.

Within some countries, seed for sale is most carefully inspected, and very low limits are set on the kind and number of weed seeds that it may contain.

Cultivation is the time-honored method of keeping weeds in check. In small gardens, the hoe is still the most valuable weed-control tool we have. In large-scale growing, various kinds of cultivators are used. Regardless of the type or frequency of cultivation, it is practically impossible to get rid of all weeds, because seeds remain in the soil, and new seeds are carried in constantly. Cultivation remains, however, one of the most successful means of combating many weeds and the only method of controlling some of them.

Certain weeds are associated with particular crops and can be kept down by rotation of crops. By sowing a field to small grains one year, a cultivated crop, such as corn, the next year and a hay crop, such as sweet clover, the third year, a good share of the weeds associated with each of these crops can be kept in check. A combination of cultivation and crop rotation is the best general means of control.

Along railroad rights of way, highways and irrigation ditches, weeds are sometimes kept in check by burning or mowing, but this is likely to be only a temporary control.

In pineapple and sugar-cane fields in Hawaii, wide strips of heavy paper are laid and the plants are set out through holes in the paper. The weed seedlings, of course, cannot push through the paper, nor can vagrant seeds blown along by the wind find resting place in the soil. This good device is sometimes used in home and market gardens, but it is pretty costly.

Insects may sometimes be called on for aid. The prickly pear, which overran much valuable land in Australia, was controlled by introducing from South America an insect that tunneled through the plants and killed them. It was necessary, of course, to be sure that the insects used would not attack any valuable plants.

Within the last hundred years or so, there have been many attempts to control weeds by means of chemicals. Some of these have been very successful. However, until around 1940 there were almost no chemicals that would kill weeds without injuring other plants or poisoning animals or birds or doing other harm. Now there are chemicals that are highly selective — that is, they poison certain plants but do not injure other plants or animals. One, known as 2,4-D, has had a great deal of publicity. However, it does kill or injure some cultivated plants as well as weeds, and so it must be used with caution. Weed-killing chemicals will doubtless be more helpful in our fight against weeds, but the man with the hoe is likely to be needed for a long time to come.

Du Pont

A growth of poison ivy in a vacant lot in Wilmington, Delaware, is sprayed with ammonium sulfamate.

THE BUILDER'S MATERIALS

A Survey of Substances Used in Every Age

BY JOHN H. CALLENDER

IN HIS extensive career as a builder, man has worked with mud, baked clay, stone, glass, copper, brass, iron, steel, felt, hide, logs, boards, leaves, grass and even snow. Some of these materials he found ready for use; others had to be most carefully prepared before they could serve for dwellings, religious temples and monuments.

All of the builder's materials, so abundant and so varied, may be divided into three general classes: primitive, traditional and modern. Primitive materials are readily available in nature and require very little preparation; they include logs, saplings, reeds, leaves, grass, skins, clay and snow. We list under traditional materials those that have been in use over a long period of time and that require more or less extensive preparation — stone, brick, tile, mortar, timber, plaster, metal, glass and the like. Modern materials include new or relatively new substances such as structural steel, reinforced concrete, vermiculite, fiberboard, plywood and plastics.

The names "primitive," "traditional" and "modern" suggest the order in which building materials were first employed by man. They do not stand for definite historical periods, for both primitive and traditional materials are still popular.

We think of a builder nowadays as a specialist who devotes all his time to his chosen lifework. But the history of building with primitive materials generally shows no such specialization.

Perhaps an example or two will make this clearer. American colonists frequently came to a land of almost unbroken forest. Before a man could settle anywhere and plant crops, he had to clear away the trees.

Many a colonist took the trees that he had cut to make a shelter for himself and his family. Selecting trunks that were straight and uniform in size, he laid one on top of another, notched and lapped the corners and built a log cabin. The spaces between the logs he chinked with clay to make the house watertight, and the log chimney was lined with clay to keep it from burning. The complete house was built by the colonist and his sons, with help from neighbors.

A small log cabin erected by American pioneers.

Of course, the American Indians built with primitive materials. The tribes of the western plains were hunters, especially of the bison that roamed the plains in enormous herds. Bison and deer meat were the food of these tribes; the skins of the animals were fashioned into clothing. It is not surprising to find that the Plains Indians made their houses of these hides, stretched over a pyramidal frame of saplings.

Primitive materials are generally used in their natural state, without processing; but this is not always true. Many Arabs live in tents of cloth woven from sheep's wool,

The massive temple of Rameses II at Abu Simbel, Egypt. It was carved out from the solid rock.

goat's wool or camel's hair. In Mongolia, where the herds are mostly short-haired animals, such as cattle and horses, the tents are covered with felted cloth.

Primitive man occasionally built homes of field stone, putting the rocks in place with a minimum of cutting. More often, stone was reserved for temples to the gods or monuments to heroes.

Traditional materials

Stone

For thousands of years, stone has been without a rival as the material for buildings of a monumental nature — that is, those that are intended to endure and to have dignity and authority. We find the earliest monuments of this sort in ancient Egypt. The Egyptians believed that the earthly body would be needed in the next world, and they invented methods of embalming to preserve the body almost indefinitely. They buried with the body various belongings of the dead person — food, clothing, money, jewelry, cosmetics, musical instruments, books, weapons and toys. The tomb in which the body and all of its possessions were to be buried was built to last "forever."

Nothing seemed more permanent than the stone cliffs that rimmed the Nile Valley; hence, the Egyptians built their tombs of stones cut from these cliffs, or else they carved out tombs in the very cliffs themselves. The tombs withstood the ravages of time and weather and the attacks of all

marauding animals except man. As a building material, the stone of Egyptian tombs has proved to be as durable, thus far, as the Egyptians hoped it would be.

Stone provided a material out of which the images of the gods could be carved; it also seemed appropriate for buildings dedicated to these supernatural beings. The kings, who were considered to be gods, came to live in temple-palaces of stone, as did the high priests. This set the style for the wealthy nobility, who also built stone palaces for themselves.

Greece is a rocky country with rich veins of marble; therefore the inhabitants turned naturally to stone for building after wood became scarce. The architecture of the Greeks, executed in white marble, has been an important influence in Western architecture down to the present day.

The Romans built first of brick, but as they came under the influence of Greek culture, they, too, found stone more beautiful. Instead of using solid blocks of stone, as the Greeks and Egyptians had done, the Romans often put up walls of brick, or rubble or concrete, and faced them with thin slabs of stone. For this purpose, they imported rare marbles and porphyries from distant parts of their vast Empire. These stones were selected for their beautiful colors and patterns, and were often cut and laid in such a way that the veining of adjacent stones formed a pattern. Floors were paved with mosaics, made up of small

This ornate pavement of mosaic work was found in the remains of a Roman villa in Bignor, Sussex.

pieces of stone of various colors. These were usually laid so as to provide an abstract pattern; sometimes, however, they formed definite pictures.

One of the disadvantages of stone, from the viewpoint of Egyptian and Greek builders, was the very short distance that a single stone spanned between supports. This made it impossible for them to build a large open room. The interiors of Egyptian and Greek temples give the impression of a forest of columns. The only way in which the span can be increased in an all-masonry building is by the arch; and it is remarkable that the Egyptians and Greeks, master builders as they were, made no use of the arch. The Romans, however, used it extensively in its various forms, especially the vault and the dome, which permitted them to build vast open halls, uncluttered by columns.

In the Middle Ages, stone continued to be an important building material. As medieval civilization moved northward, a new factor was introduced — the desire for more light. The dimness of the interiors of most earlier buildings had been rather a pleasant relief from the brilliant Mediterranean sun. But in northern Europe, light was desirable and man wanted it in his buildings. By the thirteenth century, there had developed in northern France a method of building in which glass took up a good deal of the space formerly occupied by stone in the side walls. Yet far overhead was a solid stone roof. This construction is known as Gothic.

How was it brought about that walls with so much glass could be made to support roofs of heavy stone? The Gothic builder combined arches to form immensely strong vaults, which could be flung up to great heights. He made most liberal use of clerestories — upper stories that were provided with windows lighting up the interior of the building. He provided support for the building by side structures called buttresses.

Thus, he utilized the natural advantages of stone — its strength and its durability — as a building material and he overcame its disadvantages — its heaviness and its inability to span very far. The natural character of stone is massive, inert strength,

The choir of England's Salisbury Cathedral, a splendid example of medieval stone construction.

exemplified by the Egyptian pyramids. But in the late Gothic cathedrals, stone seems to stretch aloft, to soar, in complete disregard of its natural limitations.

A well-built, solid stone building is as durable a structure as man has ever devised. The forces of nature are rarely able to injure it seriously; masonry buildings have successfully withstood hurricanes, tidal waves, long submersion under water and burial by sand dunes and by volcanic ash. Only a severe earthquake or a major landslide, among natural forces, would be likely to destroy them.

But man can easily raze the sturdiest stone buildings. High explosives, in time of war, have destroyed in a few seconds structures that had stood for thousands of years. In time of peace, too, man has deliberately dismantled buildings, stone by stone, to make way for something else or to get the stone for another building. Most of the picturesque ruins of Rome, such as the Colosseum, are ruins because medieval builders made quarries of them.

In spite of today's wealth of new materials and new techniques of building, stone still seems to be considered the noblest material. Our principal public buildings — cathedrals, railroad stations, museums, libraries and other buildings that are intended to be impressive — are faced with stone, regardless of their construction.

Most desirable are the even-grained stones that are fairly easy to cut, such as sandstone, limestone and marble. If too soft, the stone will probably not be very durable. Some coral limestones can be cut with a knife, but, unless they are stuccoed, they weather very badly. Granite, which is stronger and more durable than limestone but harder to cut, is excellent for foundations and for whole buildings — also for curbstones and paving blocks. In rubble, or roughwork, masonry, as distinguished from ashlar (cut stone), practically any type of stone may be seen. Slate, which splits easily in one plane, makes good flagging and roofing.

Ashlar masonry is usually set in mortar, although the Greeks and the Incas and some other fine masons used none. The purpose of mortar is not to hold the stones together (metal dowels provide for that) but to give a small space between the stones, to allow for minor errors in cutting and to waterproof the joints.

The exposed face of stone masonry may be given various textures, ranging from highly polished to extremely rough, or rock face. Or it may be carved into various designs. The joints may be recessed in such a way as to form a series of channels in the outer surface of a wall. A rugged effect, called rustication, is produced.

Brick and Tile

Second only to stone as a permanent building material and second only to wood as a utilitarian material is brick. It is made of clay, molded into blocks while moist and then hardened in the sun or by fire. Standing midway between wood and stone in cost, brick has been used as a substitute for either or both of these materials in places where they were not available.

The first bricks were hardened by being exposed to the sun. At about the same

Photo by Horydozak

A marble masterpiece: the Thomas Jefferson Memorial, erected in Washington, D.C., in 1941.

time that the Egyptians were first learning to cut stone into blocks and build with it, the people in Mesopotamia discovered that if bricks were baked in an oven, instead of merely being dried in the sun, they would be much harder and more durable. Entire cities were then built of brick, from the most imposing temples and palaces down to the least important buildings.

Brick is perhaps not quite so enduring as stone, but it will last well over a thousand years, which should be durable enough for most purposes. Furthermore, it is fireproof, which wood is not; hence, it is replacing wood in many areas.

Bricks are always laid in mortar. The type of mortar, the width of the joint and the skill with which the work is done all have an important effect upon the appearance, the durability and the waterproof qualities of a brick wall.

A wall consists of at least two thicknesses of brick. In order to tie these two thicknesses together, some of the bricks are turned so that their length extends back into the wall, and only their ends are exposed. These headers, as they are called, may be arranged to form a pattern, which can be quite decorative. The Dutch and Flemish, who are very skillful builders in brick, have developed patterned brickwork to a high point.

In modern times, brick walls are sometimes built with a more or less continuous hollow space between the two thicknesses. This gives better insulation and prevents water from coming through. In this case,

The patterned brickwork of this small house at Lisse, Holland, produces a most pleasing effect.

the two brick walls are tied together, not by headers but by metal ties built into the brickwork.

Brick varies in color, according to the clay; pigments are rarely introduced. Although most bricks are brownish red, they range from deep maroon to light pink and are occasionally in such colors as yellow, buff, gray or dark brown. Face bricks of extra hardness and having special colors and surface textures are sometimes used for the outside of the wall, the remainder of the wall being common brick.

In order to span even a small opening in brick masonry, an arch must be built, or else a lintel (beam) of some other material must be used. The Babylonians, who had no other materials, used the arch extensively. In other countries, stone lintels were often used over small openings, such as windows and doors, and, in more recent times, iron and steel have served the same purpose. But, as in all masonry construction, long spans require the arch in some form.

The Babylonians discovered that, if certain minerals and pigments were added to the surface of clay, they would melt during the firing and form a hard, smooth, glazed surface. These glazed bricks were used decoratively to relieve the monotony of unbroken brick masonry. Glazed clay, generally in thin, flat shapes, called tiles, later became an important building material. Tile has been used for decoration by most people who have built extensively in brick — the north Italians and the Dutch, for ex-

ample. But it was the medieval Mohammedans who carried tile to its highest point of development, especially in Persia and in Spain. There, entire buildings, inside and out, were faced with tile in a thrilling variety of patterns and colors.

Burned clay (terra cotta) has served from ancient times and still serves for roofing tiles and drainage pipes. Hollow building blocks of terra cotta have been much used in modern times for fireproof partitions and walls that do not bear loads. Special firebrick is made for lining the fireboxes of boilers and for other industrial structures where very high temperatures prevail. An extremely hard type of brick is made especially for paving streets.

Wood

Wood is the world's great utilitarian building material. Probably there are more buildings of wood today than of any other substance that is used for building purposes; more space is enclosed by wood than by any other building material.

Wood is in some respects ideal for building purposes. It is still plentiful in many parts of the world and could be grown as

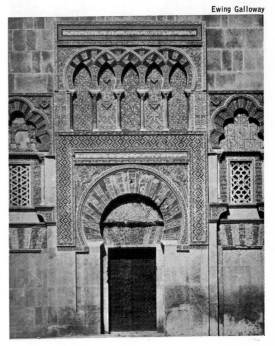

Intricate tile patterns adorn the façade of the Great Mosque in the city of Córdoba, in Spain.

a crop in most other places. Unlike the masonry materials we have been discussing, it is light but very strong for its weight. It is easily worked, is a good insulator, is warm to the touch and springy to the step. It also has certain disadvantages. It is inflammable; it is apt to decay; it shrinks or swells with changes in moisture.

In wood, moderately long spans are easily provided and extremely long spans are quite practical, with the aid of trussing, or bracing. Many medieval buildings with masonry walls had wood roofs. In a few parts of the world, notably Scandinavia and Japan, wood has been used throughout, even for the most monumental buildings.

Wood is America's traditional house-building material. One authority estimates that even today almost 90 per cent of the

FHA

Frame house in Nashville, Tennessee. Frame construction is popular in the United States.

American people live in wooden houses. Formerly, wood construction in both Europe and America was in the form of heavy timbers, hand-hewn and joined together without nails. In the nineteenth century, a new type of construction was introduced into the United States. Slender two-inch by four-inch pieces of lumber formed the uprights of a wall; they were spaced fairly close together and tied, braced and stiffened by a continuous sheathing of one-inch boards nailed to the outside. Houses constructed thus were light, and they could be put up rapidly. This method of building, called frame construction, was regarded at first as an emergency measure for temporary building; today, with certain modifi-

cations, it is a standard practice in the United States.

The softwoods make up by far the greater part of our building lumber. "Softwood" is a technical term for lumber from any coniferous, or cone-bearing, tree, regardless of its hardness; some softwoods, such as long-leaf yellow pine, are much harder than some hardwoods like poplar or basswood.

The framework of the house is most often of Douglas fir, yellow pine, spruce, hemlock or balsam fir. The boards forming the outer surface may be white pine, redwood, cedar or cypress; sometimes yellow pine, ponderosa pine, Douglas fir or hemlock are used.

Millwork (windows, doors, their frames and all kinds of decorative moldings) is usually made of a soft, even-textured wood, with little noticeable grains: white pine, sugar pine and ponderosa pine are most popular. Doors are often made of Douglas fir or of hardwood — birch, gum, maple, oak or walnut. Flooring is almost always hardwood, usually oak, sometimes maple; occasionally it is of yellow pine or Douglas fir. Oak, walnut, mahogany, teak and many other domestic and imported hardwoods provide interior wood paneling in the more luxurious types of buildings.

Plaster and Stucco

Plaster is of ancient origin and has been used all over the world, especially for interiors. A wall may be built with considerable roughness and inequality and with no consideration for appearance if it is later to be plastered. A plastered wall or ceiling can be made to produce an unbroken, smooth white surface, which cannot be achieved by any other means. Plaster may be given various surface textures, or it may be molded or colored, as it is applied.

Elaborately molded plaster ceilings were a feature of English Renaissance mansions. Most of the extravagant ornament of the Italian and Spanish baroque periods was molded of plaster, and such molding was prominent later in the Georgian style of architecture in England. Mural paintings done on wet plaster are known as frescoes, and their beauty, as well as their durability,

The Mission San Fernando, in Los Angeles, California, is an example of fine stucco construction.

may be seen in the examples uncovered at Pompeii and in Crete.

Interior plaster has generally consisted of sand and lime, with some fiber or hair to give it additional cohesion. Gypsum often takes the place of lime, or it may be added to the mixture. Exterior plaster, usually called stucco, must be more waterproof and more resistant to freezing and thawing than interior plaster. Stucco consists of cement and sand with a small amount of lime. It was exceedingly popular in the Italian Renaissance; it has been widely applied to buildings in many lands to cover rubble masonry or poor brickwork.

There are many familiar examples of stucco work in the United States, in the Pennsylvania "Dutch" area and in the Spanish missions of the southwest. Most Latin American buildings of the colonial period are of this type. Many modern suburban dwellings are of stucco or of half-stucco. In Italy and other Mediterranean lands, beautiful effects are produced by colored stucco: reds, pinks, blues, greens and grays are popular.

Plaster may be applied directly to masonry, but in wood construction it must be applied to laths or some other special material to which it will adhere. Laths are thin strips of wood, spaced slightly apart so that the plaster can fill the space between and bulge out behind and thus be keyed securely in place. Wood laths of this type are disappearing, for it takes too long to nail each lath separately in place. Materials to hold the plaster now include expanded metal, welded wire, gypsum board and insulating board.

Hollow blocks of gypsum make good fireproof partitions and other non-load-bearing walls. The plaster is applied directly to these gypsum blocks.

Metal

Until modern times, metal was not a primary building material; but it has long served in connection with other materials. Copper and tin were the most abundant metals of ancient times. Bronze, a mixture of these two metals, was sometimes concealed in stone masonry to key the stones together; sometimes it was exposed. Doors, windows, grilles, railings, hardware, lighting fixtures, fountains and even bathtubs were made of bronze by the Greeks and Romans. Except for bathtubs, bronze is still used for these purposes, by those who can afford it, because it is a strong, handsome metal.

Copper, which can be pounded into thin sheets, has long served for roofing, gutters and downspouts. It has also provided flashing — waterproofing material used to seal a joint in the roof or between the roof and another part of the building. Copper makes fine water piping, for, like bronze, it corrodes but slightly. After years of exposure, it acquires a light, bluish green coating known as a patina.

Lead is another metal with a long and honorable history as a building material. Since ancient times it has been used for roofing, flashing, gutters, downspouts and water piping. (Our word "plumbing" comes from *plumbum*, the Latin word for lead.) It is an important ingredient in the manufacture of paint, glass and ceramic tile. Tin is another noncorroding metal of ancient lineage. Tin roofing and flashing, tin coating on steel sheets, solder (a lead-tin mixture that is part of the plumber's stock in trade) — these are some of the forms in which tin appears in building.

Zinc's most important use today is for coating steel, or galvanizing, as it is called. It is also an important ingredient in the manufacture of paint and wood preservatives. Zinc roofing, flashing and weather stripping are not uncommon.

Brass, a mixture of copper and zinc, serves principally for water piping, door hardware and lighting fixtures. It varies in color, depending upon the proportion of its ingredients, from nearly white to orangered. Most brass is more or less like gold in color; if kept polished, it is attractive.

Iron and its derivative, steel, are so important in our modern civilization that we often call this the Iron Age. Yet they were not essential building materials until about 1850, though from ancient times iron has been important for tools, weapons and armor. In the Middle Ages, wrought iron was widely popular for door hardware, lighting fixtures, railings, grilles, dungeon bars, drawbridge chains and spikes and bolts in wood trusses.

These uses continued with little basic change down to the nineteenth century. In the Renaissance, especially in Spain and Italy, wrought-iron grillwork was developed to a fine art. Iron occasionally reinforced masonry, as in the case of the chains that were put around the base of the great dome of St. Peter's and other Renaissance domes. Wrought iron, hand-forged by skilled blacksmiths, was the only form in which iron had a place in construction until comparatively modern times.

Glass

Glass has been used for windows since Roman times, but not until the late Middle Ages did it become a major item in building. Then, in northern Europe and England, not only the great cathedrals but also royal palaces, town halls, city houses and other types of buildings were opened up with huge expanses of glazed windows. Medieval glass was in small pieces, only a few inches in each dimension. These were set in lead cames — that is, grooved bars of lead that formed a resilient and watertight frame for the precious little "lights," as the small pieces of glass were appropriately called. The glass was hand-blown and quite irregular in surface, texture and color; but it let light in. The people of

northern Europe installed magnificent stained-glass windows in their cathedrals. Glass is sometimes used nowadays for walls as well as for windows.

In the Renaissance, this brave expanse of glass gave way to the small windows of the classical styles, which had originated in the Mediterranean region, where windows were not very important. Then builders discovered the charm of glass as a material for interior decoration. They lined walls with mirrors — the wonderful Hall of Mirrors in the Palace at Versailles is literally a shining example. Small pieces of crystal cut in prisms and hung on chandeliers reflected and diffused candlelight.

Modern materials

Toward the middle of the nineteenth century, building began to feel the effects of the Industrial Revolution. Much work that had been done by hand could be done more cheaply by mass production in factories; and, as labor costs increased, it was necessary to find short cuts in building techniques. New materials were introduced; the most important were steel, reinforced concrete, insulation and sheet materials.

Iron and Steel

The first iron bridges were built in England in the 1840's. As early as 1851 the Crystal Palace, originally set up in Hyde Park, in London, was built entirely of iron and glass. Wrought iron and cast iron began to be used for columns and, occasionally, for girders and beams. In 1889, Gustave Eiffel made the world gasp by building an iron tower in Paris to the dizzy height of almost a thousand feet.

It was in Chicago in the 1880's that the complete steel frame was first used. The steel frame is a continuous cagework of steel columns and beams that forms the skeleton of a building and upon which everything else is hung. The walls do not bear the weight of the building; hence they can be quite thin and of almost any material. Windows can be as large as desired; in fact, the entire wall can be a window.

In steel-frame construction it is almost as easy to build vertically as horizontally.

As soon as the invention of the elevator made skyscrapers practical, man began to build them enthusiastically.

Steel is the form of iron most useful as a building material. It differs from cast iron in that it is not brittle, but malleable — that is, it can be shaped by hammering or pressing or rolling. Wrought iron is also malleable, but cannot be manufactured by mass production. It is, therefore, more expensive, less plentiful and less uniform in quality than steel.

Steel can withstand both compression and stretching; in this respect it may be compared to wood. Long spans are easy in steel construction. Buildings of this material look strikingly different from masonry buildings unless, as is often the case, they have been disguised to resemble masonry buildings.

Steel has two great enemies, fire and corrosion. Although steel does not burn, it loses its strength very rapidly in even a small fire. For protection from both fire and rust, the steel frame is surrounded by at least two inches of fireproof material, most often of concrete, but sometimes of brick, stone, terra cotta or gypsum.

Steel is used for many other building purposes: doors, windows, stairs, decking, roofing, gutters, siding, lath, hardware, plumbing, heating and most other mechanical-equipment items. Cast iron serves for boilers and radiators, as well as for plumbing fixtures and drainpipes.

Reinforced Concrete

Concrete was employed extensively by the Romans and can thus hardly be called a modern material. But when it was discovered in the late nineteenth century that concrete can be reinforced with steel rods, an entirely new type of material was born, unlike anything that had ever been known in building before. Concrete is as durable as any material known to man, and it is capable of supporting enormous loads. It therefore serves for heavy construction — dams, piers, docks, roads, foundations, warehouses and the like. But when reinforced with steel, it can be used, like steel, for long spans and light construction. In

A lofty iron structure: the Eiffel Tower, Paris.

Europe, where structural steel has not been so plentiful or cheap as in America, reinforced concrete may be seen in almost every conceivable type of building.

Concrete, like stone and brick, can stand very high compression but cannot withstand stretching; in other words, it has very high compressive strength and very little tensile strength. But if we embed a steel rod near the bottom of a concrete beam, the steel, which has high tensile strength, will carry the load and thus keep the concrete from cracking. The concrete, in turn, protects the steel from fire and rust. This same principle applies in reinforced brick masonry, the steel rods being placed in the mortar joints or run through holes in the brick.

Concrete is made of portland cement, sand and broken stone or gravel. Portland cement is simply a modern refinement of the various natural cements known to the Romans and later builders. It is made by burning certain limestones and shales together in the right proportions and at a very high temperature.

One of the advantages of concrete is that it is monolithic — it forms a single block.

It can be poured into forms, and it hardens in place so that the whole structure is like one massive stone; there are no joints to worry about. But this is also a disadvantage, since it requires an enormous amount of material and labor to make the forms into which the concrete is poured; besides, a good deal of valuable time is lost waiting for the poured concrete to harden. However, there are now new types of concrete that develop high strengths very quickly and permit the forms to be removed within twenty-four hours after pouring.

Another approach to the solution of this problem is to precast the concrete into blocks or slabs before they are placed in the building. These precast units resemble masonry rather than monolithic concrete. Hollow blocks of concrete are now very widely used as masonry in small buildings. Where appearance is a factor, they are usually stuccoed. Precast joists (beams) and slabs serve for floors and roofs, usually in buildings with masonry walls. Precast wall slabs are among the prefabricated home-building devices.

The difficulty with large precast concrete units is their great weight, which makes shipping and handling very expensive.

Armstrong

Insulating a room with insulating wool in roll blankets. The "wool" is made of fine glass fibers.

Therefore, a great deal of experimental work has been done in an effort to produce lightweight concrete. In one method, the stone in concrete has been replaced by lighter materials such as cinders, slag or vermiculite, a form of mica. Another method consists of omitting the stone entirely and causing the cement and sand to foam like whipped cream before the set. In both cases, the result is lighter weight and better insulation, at the cost of reduced strength and waterproofing qualities. The strength may be greatly improved by introducing wood or straw fibers.

Insulating Materials

When man began to heat his buildings, he found that heat was expensive, and so he began to develop insulating materials that would conserve the heat. These were applied first to the heater itself and to the pipes or ducts that led from it, in order to prevent the loss of heat before it was delivered at the place where it was wanted. Then the walls and roofs of buildings were insulated, so that the heat could not escape easily to the outdoors.

Boilers are insulated by means of two remarkable minerals — asbestos and diatomaceous earth. Asbestos is a rock that is fibrous, like cotton or wool, and the fibers can be woven into cloth or made into paper. Diatomaceous earth is a lightweight limestone formed by the skeletons of countless millions of microscopic plants, called diatoms, that lived in the sea ages ago. These materials are mixed with enough cement to bind them together and are then plastered to the boiler. For pipe insulation, asbestos is mixed with another lightweight mineral, magnesia, usually in preformed sections, which are held in place by metal bands.

Insulating the walls and roof of a building is very much like insulating our bodies by the clothes we wear or the blankets under which we sleep. One popular type of insulation is a sort of "quilt" made up of some woollike or cottonlike material between two pieces of very tough building paper. The stuffing may be made from rock, slag, wood or bark, which has been processed into a fibrous, woolly material, or from a natural material of this type, such as eel grass, kapok or cotton. Occasionally, the filling material in loose form is simply poured into the hollow spaces in the wall. The filler is sometimes of the mineral known as vermiculite; it comes in grains and looks much like a breakfast cereal.

Another type of insulating material does double duty. It is made in the form of a building board and can take the place of wood sheathing or lath or both lath and plaster. These insulating boards are of vegetable fiber, derived from wood, sugarcane, straw and the like. One board is made from old newspapers; it is just as good as the others, and perhaps even better!

The best insulation is a vacuum; the next best is air, provided it does not move freely. All of the insulations that we have mentioned above trap thousands of little pockets of dead air, which, since they cannot move, act as excellent insulators. An insulation that works on an entirely different principle is aluminum foil, which reflects the heat waves in exactly the same way that a mirror reflects light waves.

**The weather stripping
of windows and doors**

A great deal of heat is lost through windows and doors, most of it through the cracks around the edges. Weather stripping is applied to stop this loss. Interlocking metal strips are the ordinary form of weather stripping, but felt or rubber gaskets are not uncommon. Heat loss through the glass itself can be reduced only by adding another piece of glass to form an insulating air space between. This is usually done in the form of a storm sash. There has recently been developed a double glass, with the air space between permanently sealed. It can be installed in any ordinary sash just like a single piece of glass. Plastic is also used for insulation purposes.

Refrigerators and cold-storage rooms must be heavily insulated, and they have a special problem of moisture condensation to contend with. In cases like these, natural cork, pressed into blocks, provides insulation. Foamed glass and foamed rubber

have been developed for this purpose, and foamed plastics have also been tried.

Sheet Materials

With the thin, sheetlike materials known as wallboards, large areas of wall or ceiling can be covered very quickly, and the wall can be painted immediately afterward. About the only disadvantage of the sheet material is that the joints are sometimes unsightly. Some efforts have been made to conceal the joints in order to make the material resemble a plaster wall. It is now becoming more customary to give the joints a **V**-shape and expose them frankly. Most wallboards are for interiors only, but some waterproof types have been developed for the exterior of buildings. In this case, the joints are a practical as well as an aesthetic problem; they must be made weathertight, and this is not always easy.

The first wallboards were made of very heavy cardboard. Next came plaster board, an early sandwich-type board consisting of a thin core of gypsum with faces of heavy paper. Then came the fiber, insulating boards mentioned above. Another type, known as hardboard, is thin and smooth, and, as the name implies, very hard. It may be made of wood fiber compressed under very heavy pressure, or of asbestos and cement or of paper impregnated with a synthetic resin. All of these materials may be obtained already decorated, which saves another step in finishing the building Some of the hardboards have an ename. finish of synthetic resin resembling the glaze of tile; in fact, they may be marked off into squares to imitate tile.

Plywood is a sheet material made up of three or more thin sheets of wood, called veneers, glued together with the grain of each sheet at right angles to that of the adjacent sheet. Since the strength of wood is much higher and its shrinkage is much lower along the grain than across the grain, plywood produces a stable board that is strong in any direction.

Plywood is not a new invention by any means; furniture of this material was made by the ancient Egyptians and by the fine cabinetmakers of eighteenth-century France

VERSATILE
BUILDING
MATERIALS

California Redwood A

Striking redwood ceiling, paneling and window frames in the lobby of a smart hotel in Southern California.

Aluminum Company of America

Alcoa Building, Pittsburgh, Pennsylvania. This handsome, thirty-story structure is sheathed in aluminum panels, which are an eighth of an inch in thickness. Electrical wiring, most of the plumbing, ducts, doors, hardware and trim are aluminum.

Alsynite Company of Ame

Sawing an Alsynite fiber-glass building panel. It is translucent, shatterproof, lightweight and easy to use.

S. C. Johnson & Son, Inc.

Glass walls in a Racine, Wisconsin, research center. Sections of glass tubing are laid horizontally, with synthetic rubber strips between.

Mosaic Tile Co.

Zonolite Co.

Slabs of precast vermiculite concrete used as roof decking. Vermiculite concrete resists fire and rot.

Modern tile work in the headquarters of a building-and-loan company in the city of Cheviot, Ohio.

Portland Cement Assn.

A magnificent concrete structure of advanced design: YMCA Building in Oklahoma City.

and England. But as a building material, plywood was just another wallboard until the middle of the 1930's, when waterproof plywood was developed by using synthetic resin adhesives in a hot press. This made plywood a dependable, weatherproof building material that could be applied indoors or out, structurally or decoratively. It is very important for building purposes.

Most plywood is made of Douglas fir. For decorative effect, plywood can be faced with practically any known wood, including many rare and beautiful imported ones. This has resulted in an increasing use of natural wood as an interior finish, in place of paint or wallpaper.

Two weatherproof sheet materials that have long served for exterior walls and roofs of factories and other utilitarian buildings are corrugated steel and corrugated asbestos-cement board. These thin materials have sufficient stiffness to span several feet between supports and are thus an economical method of enclosing a frame structure.

The development of sheet materials and waterproof adhesives has encouraged a more efficient use of materials in the structural engineering sense. Now we can attach a finishing material to the frame in such a way that both act together as one, and the finishing material actually carries a considerable part of the load. This type of construction is known as stressed-skin. Prefabricated stressed-skin panels are usually of plywood, though they may be of steel, aluminum or fiber board. The hollow spaces in the panels are filled with some insulating material, such as glass wool.

The sandwich-type panel represents an even more advanced step. Imagine a stressed-skin panel of the type we have just described, but with a rigid insulation, like corkboard, instead of glass wool. The faces may then be glued directly to the insulation, and the framing members may be omitted entirely. One material of this type, having a core of fiber insulating board and faces of asbestos-cement board, has been on the market for many years.

During World War II, great advances were made in the development of this type of panel for aircraft construction, and many lightweight panels of amazing strength resulted. The airplane manufacturers first used a core of balsa wood with faces of aluminum. Later, they tried foamed plastic cores, and finally honeycombs of paper impregnated with synthetic resin.

Other Modern Materials

Asphalt served the ancient Babylonians for calking and waterproofing, but modern man has given it many more jobs to do. We all know it in paving and in roofing. The commonest modern roofing material is a felt made of paper and asbestos and impregnated with asphalt. For flat roofs, this felt is applied to the roof in successive layers with hot asphalt mopped between each layer. For sloping roofs, the felt is cut into strips to resemble shingles and is applied like shingles. Asphalt is also pressed into tiles for flooring; coloring matter is added and a number of attractive designs are available.

Linoleum is a resilient, sheet flooring material made of linseed oil and ground cork. It is gaining steadily in popularity, since it gives an attractive and durable floor that has no cracks and is easy to clean. Other modern flooring materials are rubber, cork and plastic.

A number of modern materials will probably become increasingly important in building in the near future. Plastics (synthetic resins) in the form of adhesives and coatings are already very popular, as we have pointed out. In solid form, they have long been used for electrical switch plates and other small gadgets. Aluminum, more plentiful and cheaper as a result of the war, is beginning to serve for roofing, flashing and siding as well as for decorative purposes, and, in the form of foil, for insulation. Stainless steel, also popular as a decorative metal, will doubtless soon find a wider scope.

Scientific research in building materials is neither well organized nor adequately financed; nevertheless, it does go on, and it has already produced gratifying results. To an ever greater extent, the research man is helping to solve the builder's problems.

See also Vol. 10, p. 282: "Construction."

Lederle Laboratories Div. of American Cyanamid Co.

Soil bacteria growing on a nutrient agar medium. These bacteria reproduce by cell division. Though the individual soil bacterium can be made out only with a microscope, clumps of these bacteria can often be seen with the naked eye, as in the photomicrograph at the left.

THAT LIFE MAY CONTINUE

Investigating the Vital Process of Reproduction

BY ROBERT W. MENEFEE

HAVE you observed as you grow older that your life involves many things that seem quite obvious and yet are not understandable or explainable? For example, the feelings that you have about your family and home are quite apparent to you. If you were discussing these feelings, you might talk about your "love" of family or home. But if someone were to ask you for a definition of the word "love," you would probably not be able to give a satisfactory answer.

The biologist, whose field is the study of living things, works with "life," talks and writes about it. But if you ask him to define "life" or explain what it is, he encounters the same sort of difficulty that you would have if you were asked to explain what "love" is.

A possible approach to the problem of defining life is to distinguish between things that are alive and those that are not. In the article What Is Life? in Volume 1 of THE BOOK OF POPULAR SCIENCE, there is an analysis of some of the points of difference between living and nonliving things. One of the most important of these distinctions is that living things can reproduce their kind, while nonliving things cannot do so. It is true that when we consider the reproduction of viruses we are in quite a dilemma. We know that viruses can form crystals and that objects that form crystals (such as table salt, ordinary sugar, dry ice, asbestos and diamond, to mention a few) are not considered to be examples of life. Yet we also know that in certain situations (usually when they are inside living cells) viruses behave very much like living things; certainly they reproduce like living things.*

In general, however, there can be no doubt but that reproduction, or self-duplication, is characteristic of living things. In the following pages, we shall investigate some of the processes of reproduction in plants and animals. This is an exciting area of study for it lies at the very core of life itself. It involves the crucial problem of what must take place in order that life may continue.

If we were to use only our unaided vision in this investigation, we would be greatly handicapped. This is because some of the most significant happenings in reproduction, particularly as they occur in cells, are on too small a scale to be seen with the naked eye. We shall require the assistance of the magnifying device known as the microscope. Microscopes are described elsewhere in this set (see Index). We shall sum up in the following paragraphs some important facts about these useful devices.

* *Editor's note*: Most scientists consider that viruses are on the borderline between living and nonliving things. See the article on The Viruses, in Volume 6.

The microscope, a tool
in the study of reproduction

In the study of reproduction, the biologist often uses the optical microscope, based on light rays. Optical microscopes (sometimes called simply scopes) exist in many varieties, from small, simple hand lenses to very complicated and expensive precision instruments. Regardless of their size and their accessories, however, they are essentially nothing more than frameworks, holding one to many lenses for magnifying specimens so that the viewer may observe an enlarged version.

The amount of magnification is given in terms of diameters. If an object's image, when viewed through the microscope, has an apparent diameter 10 times as large as its actual diameter, the object is said to be magnified 10 diameters, or 10 times (sometimes written 10x). Combinations of lenses multiply, so that two 10x lenses used together would provide $10 \times 10 = 100$ diameters, or 100x.

Lenses must be made so that the image viewed appears enlarged and also clearly visible. The clarity with which objects are seen — the resolving power of the microscope — is particularly important. Inexpensive microscopes will magnify, but the image will be blurred. Microscopes should be purchased in terms of resolving-power capability rather than magnifying capability.

The simplest type of microscope is the hand lens, also known as a simple microscope. It may be mounted on a holder or bracket so that it is rigid and your hands are free. The drawback of simple one-lens magnifiers is that they magnify only a very few diameters. In lenses for such magnifiers, the images are enlarged when the curvature of the lens is increased. As curvature and resulting magnification increases, the size of the lens must be bigger and bigger and soon the lens becomes too bulky to be practical.

Most microscopes contain several lenses and are called compound microscopes. There are usually three lenses in the objective, which is near the specimen, and two lenses in the eyepiece. The lenses are lined up so

Bausch & Lomb

Adjustable illuminated stand magnifier. With the lens tilted, small hand-held objects can be worked on or inspected. If the lens is set parallel to the work surface, any object laid upon this surface will be in focus.

that light from the sample being viewed passes through them in order. This is much more satisfactory than having one huge lens. Not only is the bulkiness reduced, but also the lenses may be made so as to correct or reduce distortions of shape or color.

Compound microscopes must be used when the size of the objects being studied is too small for observation by the eye or a simple lens. The human eye can resolve or see separately points that are not less than about 0.1 millimeter (generally written as 0.1 mm) apart. Simple lenses usually magnify up to about 10x; at that magnification, points 0.01 mm apart may be resolved. Since many cells are only about 0.0001 mm in diameter, it is obvious that the compound microscope is required for their study.

Compound microscopes usually magnify from about 50 to 400 diameters, depending upon the selection of the objective and eyepiece lenses, though magnification of up to 2,000x is possible with certain models. Eyepieces are usually 5 to 10 power; objectives, about 10 and 40 power. If the nosepiece * has three objectives instead of two, the third is often a lower power of 2 or 3. This is a scanning lens; it is used to locate things which appear to be worth further study with the other objective lenses.

The adjustment of a microscope is somewhat like that of a TV set. In both cases, you desire the clearest, sharpest possible picture, and you have various controls

* *Editor's note:* The nosepiece is the endpiece of a microscope body, to which objectives are attached.

EYEPIECE

FOCUSING KNOB

BODY TUBE

NOSEPIECE

OBJECTIVES

INCLINATION JOINT

MIRROR

Bausch & Lomb

Ward's Natural Science Establishment, Inc.

At the left is a standard teaching monocular microscope. It has a triple revolving nosepiece, with 4x, 10x and 43x objectives and a concave mirror. Above we see a variety of prepared microscope slides all ready for use.

for obtaining it. If you learn the purpose of the various control devices, you can get the desired result. On a compound microscope, your controls are those which adjust the amount of entering light and those which adjust the distance of the lenses from the specimen.

It is usually better to adjust the light before you place the glass slide with the specimen on the microscope stage. The light source may be daylight or it may be a small-wattage bulb (40-watt or less). The mirror (or built-in light source on some models), the diaphragm (regulating the size of the opening through which light passes) and the condensor lens (if one is present) are all located below the stage. These are your light adjustments. They should be set so that bright but not glaring light is available with each of the objectives. Blue filters are sometimes used to reduce glare. When the light has been adjusted, a specimen can be placed on the stage. Specimens should be in water on a good-quality optical-glass microscope slide, with a cover glass (also called a slip glass) set upon it. It is usually most efficient to begin with your objective of medium power in place. The biggest problem at this point is to avoid breaking the cover glass. You can prevent breakage by looking at the side of the objective while lowering it until it almost, but not quite, touches the cover glass. Then look in the

eyepiece and turn the coarse adjustment so that the barrel moves up away from the slide. Another important habit to develop is viewing with both eyes open. This may seem difficult at first, but you will quickly become accustomed to it.

Objects such as the parts which make up cells may be too small to be studied with a compound microscope. The tool of choice then becomes the electron microscope. Beginners in the investigation of cells are not likely to have access to such an instrument. It is described elsewhere (see Index).

Sexual and asexual reproduction

Before we begin to investigate reproduction in plants and animals, it would be well to point out that there are two basic types of reproduction. One involves specialized sex cells, called gametes — male cells and female cells. The combining of male and female gametes to form a new individual organism is called *sexual reproduction*. In the other basic type of reproduction — *asexual reproduction* — there is no uniting of gametes. Self-duplication may take place through cell division, or budding or in various other ways.

Asexual reproduction is the more primitive form and in general is far simpler than sexual reproduction. Hence we shall first consider asexual self-duplication.

Investigating asexual reproduction in cells and cell colonies

A common type of organism which is easily obtainable for observation of asexual

Photomicrograph of a *Protococcus* cluster. *Protococcus* is a green alga and reproduces by cell division. The daughter cells that result may separate or may remain together, for a time at least, in smallish clusters.

reproduction is *Protococcus* (also called *Pleurococcus*). It is a one-celled plant belonging to the large plant grouping known as the algae. *Protococcus* is the green film that you will often find on tree bark; it looks somewhat like a thin layer of paint. Gather some of it for microscopic study.

It is better to break off small pieces of bark from the tree and to take these inside before you remove the powdery algae. Place the pieces of bark in a shallow dish containing about one-half inch of tap water. Allow the bark to become well-moistened; then use an object such as a matchstick to scrape off some of the green film onto a microscope slide. Slosh the bark about in the dish and some of the green cells will float off into the water. Place several drops of this water on the scraping that you have put on the slide. Spread the material evenly over the center of the slide and put a cover glass in place.

First observe the specimen under low power. Are the cells arranged in any particular way? Now use the higher powers for viewing the cells. Do you find any differences in cells? Even if you cannot actually see reproduction occurring in cells, you can observe many cells and infer what has happened to them. This technique of observation followed by inference is often employed by scientists, and it is a valuable one. Of course you must realize that the inferences that you form may be in error.

Can you make out single cells? Do you find some cells that are double, with their walls flattened at the point of attachment? How would you explain the presence of these single and double cells? You might infer that two different cells are combining to form one new cell. This does occur in some algae and other organisms and is called conjugation, a form of sexual reproduction. However, in the case of *Protococcus*, the inference would not be correct. The two attached cells were originally a single cell which split to form two cells. This type of asexual reproduction is called *fission*, or cell division. It is a very common form of self-duplication in simple organisms with only one cell, such as *Protococcus*. The same process of cell division accounts for growth in larger and more complex plants and animals.

A special type of microscope called the phase microscope makes it possible for you to see cell details that are not visible in ordinary microscopes. Accessory phase devices are available for most good scopes. If you have a microscope with phase-light control, you will notice a gray body within most cells. This is the nucleus. Did you find any *Protococcus* cells with more than one nucleus? If so, what was the shape of this cell? Did it appear ready to divide? If you were successful in observing such cells with two nuclei, you would probably infer (and correctly, in this case) that the nucleus in a cell divides to form two nuclei prior to the division of the cell to form two cells. The division of the nucleus is called *mitosis* by cytologists — scientists who specialize in the study of cells.*

A variety of fissioning one-celled animals and plants known as protists** may be obtained by preparing a culture jar. A convenient container for this purpose is a wide-mouth gallon jar of the type commonly used by restaurants and cafeterias. Collect a gallon of water from a pond, large pool or other still-water site. Gather some leaves, grass and other decaying vegetation from the bottom of the pond. Put enough of this debris into the jar so that the accumulation

* *Editor's note*: The term "mitosis" is sometimes applied, particularly by embryologists, to the division of cells as a whole.
** This name is applied to protozoans, bacteria, certain algae and fungi and also sometimes to viruses.

Above are four familiar one-celled animals and plants, whose reproductive activities have often been observed. A. The protozoan *Amoeba proteus*. B. *Paramecium*, a protozoan with a slipper-shaped body. C. *Lactobacillus acidophilus*, a milk-souring bacterium. D. *Euglena*, a member of the flagellate group. It has animallike and plantlike characteristics.

will be 2 or 3 inches deep. When you get home, transfer the water to a pot after you have removed the leaves and grass, which are to be dried and kept separately.

Boil the water in the pot for 10 minutes or so in order to provide a sterile environment. After the water has cooled, return it to the jar and drop the vegetation in. Place the culture in a lighted place, but not in direct sunlight. You can begin taking samples with an eyedropper or soda straw from various sites in the jar for microscopic study at intervals of your choice. You will discover dramatic daily changes in the types and numbers of protists as rates of reproduction increase and decrease.

If you wish, you may at any time isolate one type of organism and start a pure culture containing only this type. You will, of course, have to prepare a sterile environment to insure that no other types will appear. This can be done by boiling smaller amounts of water and using smaller bottles. The vegetation that you will add to the culture (timothy hay and foxtail weed are often used) must be boiled for 10 minutes with the water to prevent the introduction of other protists. The addition of a pinch of dried yeast or skim-milk powder should

increase the number of fissioning protists in your culture. If you are successful, you will observe the increased numbers resulting from fission. If you are a diligent and careful observer, you may even observe the process as it is occurring.

An interesting one-celled organism that displays another type of asexual reproduction is the yeast plant used in baking. Obtain a package of dried yeast from the grocery store. Make a culture solution by placing ten dried beans and two teaspoonfuls of grape juice or molasses into a pint of water that has been boiled and then cooled. An ordinary pint bottle used for cream or milk makes a convenient container. Add half of the package of dried yeast. Instead of capping the bottle, stuff the opening with a cotton wad or plug. Place this culture in a warm spot. After a few hours, remove a sample and examine a few drops under the microscope. Can you see evidence of reproduction? The term *budding* is used in describing the self-duplication of yeast cells. Can you see why this term is used to describe the process? You might wish to culture some yeasts found on the surface of fruits, especially grapes. Repeat the above procedure.

A   B   C   D

The Fleischmann Laboratories, Standard Brands, Inc.

How a yeast cell multiplies through budding. A swelling arises at the edge of a cell and enlarges to form a new cell. In the above photos, a cluster of cells has been produced. Photo A was taken at 10:15 A.M.; B at 11:30 A.M.; C at 12:15 P.M.; D at 12:30 P.M.

Observing asexual reproduction in larger organisms

Asexual reproduction can be studied in organisms which are large enough to be seen with just the aid of a hand lens. Bread mold is convenient for this purpose. Place a moist piece of bread and a soaked sponge in a dish. Sprinkle some dust on the bread. Then cover the dish with an inverted pan or lid so that the bread is in darkness. (Homemade bread is preferred since many bakeries add chemicals to their bread to inhibit the growth of mold.)

After a few days, you should see evidence of mold growth. Observe the structure of the white mold with a hand lens. The threadlike structures, which make up the plant body, are called hyphae. Shortly after the mold appears, you should observe some dark objects at the ends of vertical stalks. They are spore cases; they contain asexual reproductive cells called spores. You should examine these mold parts under your microscope. The so-called dissecting microscope is excellent for such observation. This scope, which usually has two eyepieces, is used for observing objects larger than cells. It does not require a transmitted light; hence opaque objects may be viewed with the device. Small insects, molds and other objects in this general size range are best examined with such a tool.

Many organisms are capable of reproducing a new organism from a part of an older one. This is a kind of asexual reproduction, called vegetative reproduction in plants. Several geranium plants, for example, can be produced from a single plant. All that is required is a little time, patience and care. Cut several healthy stems with healthy leaves from a geranium plant; place these, cut end down, into a layer of moist sandy soil. (It is helpful to use one of the inexpensive commercial root-growth-inducing preparations on "cuts" prior to the "plantings.") Pack the moist, but not wet, soil around the cuttings so that they will be upright. After two weeks, make daily examinations of one of the "cuts" by carefully brushing away the soil. What do you observe? You can use some of your cuttings for detailed study and transfer the remainder to flowerpots for further growth. When potting, take a ball of soil with the roots to prevent root breakage.

You can produce several animals from a single one in somewhat the same way as you produced the geraniums. (In animals, as we shall see, the process is not called vegetative reproduction.) An excellent organism for this type of self-duplication is a freshwater flatworm known as a planarian. This animal usually goes unnoticed, since it is relatively small; however, it is large enough to be observed with the naked eye or a hand lens. You can find planarians by turning over submerged stones or vegetation. You can also trap them easily by placing some raw meat (preferably liver) in cheesecloth and tying a string to it. Place this trap in a stream. After a day or two you should find several planaria in your trap. These interesting flatworms show great ability to replace lost parts — a capability referred to as *regeneration*. In some cases, new individuals can be formed.

Transfer your planarians to dishes of cool chlorine-free water. (Tap water may be used if it is boiled for several minutes and then cooled.) Do not feed your planarians for several weeks, since they will do nicely without food for long periods, and stale food often fouls the water. If you do feed the animals, change the water after feeding. Obtain a new single-edged razor blade. Cut some planarians in halves crosswise; cut others in half lengthwise. Place each section in a small separate dish. Attach a label giving the date and type of cut performed. Will you obtain new individuals from these sections?

Left: microscopic view of a planarian. This small flatworm has a remarkable ability to regenerate lost parts. Sometimes a new individual will be formed in this way.

Right: stages in the sexual reproduction of *Spirogyra*. A. A typical *Spirogyra* filament, showing several cells. B. Two filaments, side by side, connected by means of conjugation tubes. C, D. Movement of the contents of the cells in one filament to the cells of the other filament. Here fusion will take place.

A

B

C

D

You can produce two-headed specimens if you cut about a third of the way down the long axis of the body. The cuts may require redoing for a few days since they tend to grow back together. Observe your specimen daily and you will see a remarkable example of regenerative ability.

Investigating
sexual reproduction

In sexual reproduction, two organisms combine to produce offspring. This type of reproduction involves the formation of the specialized reproductive cells known as gametes. They combine and form the cell that grows to become the new organism.

A highly simplified version of sexual reproduction is found in a common water plant — the green alga called *Spirogyra*. It is easily recognized in freshwater ponds and streams, since it appears as masses of fine silklike threads of green. Gather some *Spirogyra*, keeping it in a container with the water in which it was found. Examine some threads with a microscope. If you are careful and fortunate, you may observe a point at which two strands of *Spirogyra* lie close together. At some places, the adjacent cells of the two strands appear to have grown together; at others, the contents of one cell appear to have crossed through the connecting portion and to have joined with the contents of the opposite cell. It is not possible to tell one sex from the other. Biologists refer to the portion that migrates, in this case, as the male gamete; the non-migrating cell portion would be the female gamete. The single cell formed by the union of the two gametes is called a zygote.

The zygote may grow through fission into a new strand of *Spirogyra* which will not be identical with its predecessors. This is the fundamental distinction between asexual and sexual reproduction. Asexual reproduction is a continuation of an existing organism type. Sexual reproduction is also a continuation of an existing type; but the offspring here is a modified version which has resulted from the interaction of the two parents' contributions.

An excellent source of material for observing the development of a zygote is found in most home aquariums containing snails. Fertilized snail eggs are frequently found in small clumps, attached to the glass sides of the aquarium or on the leaves of the water plants. These can be carefully scraped off into a shallow glass dish containing a little water from the aquarium. The eggs may be observed several times a day. A dissection scope is best, but a hand lens can also be used. If you are careful and consistent in your observations, you will see the internal organs of the snails develop. The transparency and ruggedness of the egg cases make them well suited for study.

You probably learned some time ago that certain animals undergo a series of dramatic changes in structure during their development — changes to which the name of *metamorphosis* is applied. It is described

A **B** **C**

D

The four stages of metamorphosis in the house fly (*Musca domestica*). A. Eggs. B. Larvae C. Pupa. D. Adult flies. The name imago is applied to the adult form of an insect.

Picture credits—A: USDA; B,C: Hugh Spencer—Nat. Audubon Soc.; D: Standard Oil Co. (N. J.)

in detail in the article on The Mighty Insect, in Volume 2. An ideal subject for the study of metamorphosis is the common fruit fly, *Drosophila*.

Drosophila is easy to obtain in all but the coldest months. Merely place some overripe fruit in a bottle, and you will quickly attract the flies. Culturing can be done in small bottles. Each is to contain a small piece of ripe banana (approximately one inch long), which has been dipped in some of the yeast solution described earlier. Use gauze or cotton to plug the bottle. Watch for mold, which may stop the growth of the flies. If mold develops, discard the culture and clean the bottle thoroughly before using it for other cultures.

Drosophila eggs may be obtained for microscopic study by smearing banana on a slide and placing the latter in the culture bottle. *Drosophila* will lay eggs on the slide, which can then be removed for viewing. Return the slide to the jar and watch for the second, or larval, stage of development. The pupal stage is the third one. Pupae are usually detected on the sides of the culture bottle. The final adult stage completes the metamorphosis. The time elapsed will be 10 to 15 days, depending upon the temperature and other factors.

Another common insect that displays metamorphosis is the "mealworm," obtainable in pet shops and bait stores; it is the larval state of the beetle *Tenebrio*. *Tenebrio* is very easily cultured. Simply place some

of the larvae in a large jar containing moist oatmeal or bran. Cover the top with cheesecloth or gauze so that the adult beetle cannot escape. The disadvantage in the study of *Tenebrio* for the metamorphosis process is that the life cycle may take from 3 to 5 months. Because of its larger size, however, this insect is easier to study with a hand lens than *Drosophila*.

The snail, fruit fly and beetle that we have just described all reproduce sexually. Males and females are not distinguishable in the snails. It is possible to tell the sexes apart in the case of *Drosophila* because the abdomen of the female has a more pointed tip. It is not likely that you observed the behavior of the mating pairs at the time when the male and female gametes came together. This is more readily studied in larger animals.

Frogs in the spring may be observed with a male astride the back of a female. This procedure, called false copulation, or amplexus, places the male in position to fertilize the female gametes, or eggs, just as they leave the female's body. Fertilized frog eggs are easily found in spring. They appear on pond surfaces in clusters of gelatinous masses. Gather some in a bottle. Observe them daily with the microscope.

In other animals, copulation may permit the introduction of the male gametes, or sperm, into the female's body. The latter procedure permits the retention and protection of the fertilized eggs by the female.

The eggs may be laid, as in birds, or retained until the young are hatched and born alive, as in garter snakes and guppies and most mammals.

Biologists now recognize that many animals will not copulate until a certain pattern of behavior has occurred. This is called "courtship," or "stylized," behavior and has been studied extensively in certain birds. Courtship behavior has become a rapidly developing area of study in the case of many other types of organisms besides birds. Animals such as mice, hamsters and tropical fish may be studied in order to gain information about premating behavior patterns.

Sexual reproduction in plants is quite similar in many ways to self-duplication in the commonly observed animals. There is a significant difference, however, in the manner in which the gametes are produced. In most animals, gametes unite to form a zygote, which then grows to adulthood. The adult, in turn, can produce gametes for the next generation. In plants, however, there is an alternation of generations. The gametes combine to produce a zygote, but the zygote develops into a structure which produces spores instead of gametes. If the spores are provided with the proper environment, they develop into a structure called a gametophyte. The gametophyte can then produce gametes and in this way the reproduction cycle is completed.

This cycle can be studied in the fern plant. The fern commonly seen in the woods or in flowerpots is in the spore-containing, or sporophyte, stage. Obtain some fern fronds (leaves) and examine the underside for brown spots. These are the spore-producing sites. If the spores are allowed to develop, they will grow into gametophytes.

You can culture gametophytes in about 1 to 2 months. Wad paper toweling and pack the wads into a medium-sized flowerpot; then turn the pot upside down on a shallow dish. Place the dish and pot in a container of boiling water for at least two minutes. After the water has cooled, remove the pot and dish. Next, sprinkle spores from fern fronds onto the surface of the inverted pot. Keep water in the dish so

The eggs of the wood frog (right), crowded together in gelatinous masses. The tadpoles that hatch from the eggs are fishlike, legless creatures with gills and long tails.

Amer. Mus. of Nat. Hist.

that the pot is always moist. If you have never seen fern gametophytes, you are going to have quite a surprise when you see what sort of plants develop from the spores.

If water from the gametophyte surface is examined under the microscope from 4 to 6 weeks after the preparation of the culture, you may see swimming male gametes. The ability of these gametes to swim is a common characteristic in both plants and animals. Because of this ability, the male sex cell can move to the female gamete and can fertilize it. The swimming may take place in dew or in water surrounding aquatic plants. In animals, the swimming motion of the male gamete may occur in water or entirely within the female's body, where it has been placed during copulation.

The seed plants are by far the best-known of all; they number more species than all the other plant groups put together. They include cone-bearing plants, such as pines, firs and hemlocks, and flowering plants in amazing variety — water lilies, wheat, beans, onions, date palms, oaks, maples and pumpkins, to mention only a few. The visible plant of a seed plant represents the spore-producing stage. The sexual stage occurs between the production of spores and the formation of sex cells by the spores. The seed plants are discussed in the article Seed Plants, in Volume 3.

The article Flowers, Fruits and Seeds, in Volume 4, discusses the reproductive activities of flowering plants, and the numerous illustrations identify the more important structures involved. Read this chapter carefully. Then examine as many flowers, fruits and seeds as you can and identify the different parts.

THE PHOTOELECTRIC CELL

A Versatile Servant of Mankind

LIGHT SOURCE

PHOTONS

PHOTOEMISSIVE SOLID

ELECTRONS

PHOTOELECTRIC EFFECT

A photoelectric effect (photoemission). The photons of a light source strike a photoemissive solid and impart energy to some of its electrons. These may lift the electrons through the solid and quite off its surface.

SINCE light is a form of energy, it is not surprising that scientists have transformed it into electricity, which is another form of energy. This is brought about by the photoelectric cell, also called the "electric eye." It may be defined as a device for making use of electrical phenomena brought about by light radiation.* The device has made television and talking pictures possible. It has been used to measure light, to open doors without the agency of a human hand, to inspect manufactured articles and so on.

The principles underlying the operation of the photoelectric cell have been known to scientists for many years. The French physicist Alexandre-Edmond Becquerel (1820–91) was probably the first to note that the presence or absence of light produced an electrical effect. He had been experimenting in 1839 with glass-enclosed primary batteries, in which electrodes were immersed in liquid. He noticed that the voltage of his batteries increased as the light falling upon them increased in intensity, and that green light provided the highest voltage. Becquerel also made the important observation that the increase in voltage was proportional to the intensity of the light falling upon his batteries. For a long time, the phenomenon discovered by Becquerel remained a scientific curiosity.

* Some photoelectric cells also react to ultraviolet radiation, which is not visible.

Following a somewhat different approach, Willoughby Smith discovered in 1873 that the resistance offered to the flow of an electric current by the chemical element selenium varied according to the intensity of the light falling upon it. His discovery led to a long series of investigations of selenium and other metals that were affected in the same way. This brought about the development of the photoconductive cell, described later in this article.

In 1888, Wilhelm Hallwachs, a German physicist, discovered a fundamental photoelectric effect. He charged a polished zinc sphere with negative electricity and subjected it to ultraviolet radiation. The zinc ball soon lost its negative charge. The loss did not take place when glass was placed between the ultraviolet radiation and the zinc ball. There was also no loss of electrical charge when the zinc was positively charged. Hallwachs correctly concluded from these results that when ultraviolet light fell upon the zinc ball, the latter lost "negative electricity." This phenomenon is known as the Hallwachs effect. The Russian Stoletow made a further advance by collecting the electricity lost by the zinc ball.

In the years that followed, the Germans Elter and Geitel constructed cells that made use of the metals sodium and potassium and other alkali metals (see Index). They showed that these metals were sensitive to visible light as well as to ultraviolet. These cells of Elter and Geitel were the direct ancestors of the photoemissive type of photoelectric cell, described below.

Another great step forward was taken when the Hungarian Philipp Eduard Lenard and the Englishman J. J. Thomson proved that the loss of "negative electricity" observed by Hallwachs was due to the emission of electrons by the illuminated body. In other words the carrier of the photoelectric current was the electron.

The photo-
electric effect

It was not until the early 1900's that some understanding was obtained of why light may stimulate an electric current in some materials. The theories of Planck and Einstein (see Index) and later work by various investigators have given us the

following picture of the photoelectric phenomenon — in this case, photoemission, or the discharge of electrons into space from a mass of matter (solid, gas or liquid) under the influence of light.

In this situation, a beam of light is thought to consist of a wavelike motion of small bundles or packets of energy known as quanta or photons. (See Index, under Photon theory of light; Quantum theory.) When a photon of given energy strikes the surface of, say, a photoemissive solid, it imparts its energy to an electron, which is part of the substance of the solid (along with many other electrons). This burst of energy may be sufficient to lift the electron through the solid and off its surface into the surrounding space or medium. If enough photons can hit enough electrons with enough energy, a flow of electrons from the surface of the solid is initiated. These electrons can be attracted by a positively charged electrode, called a collector, so that an electric current in a circuit is set up.

It has been found that the more intense the light, the greater the quantity of electrons released from a body's surface, up to a certain limit. But this occurs only with light of a certain range in frequencies or wavelengths. Light of low frequency (low energy) very seldom causes photoemission in most materials; this is the case with the red and infrared portions of the spectrum. (The metal cesium, however, responds to red light.) With light of high frequency (high energy), photoemission takes place even if the light is dim, although the resulting current is very weak. This is particularly true

PHOTOEMISSIVE CELL

Left: a photoemissive cell. When light strikes the electron-emitting substance on the cathode of the cell, electrons are emitted. Negatively charged, they are attracted to the anode, which is positive, and they continue around the circuit back to the cathode.

ELECTRONS

LIGHT

PHOTOTUBE

ANODE   CATHODE

Below: applying the photoemissive effect to a movie sound track. Variations in sound had been previously recorded on the film in terms of lighter or darker areas or of varying width. When the film is run off, as here, a phototube converts variations in the film into varying electric pulses. These are amplified and then converted into sound.

SOUND TRACK

FILM

AMPLIFIER

LIGHT SOURCE

PHOTOTUBE   SPEAKER

of the green, blue, violet and ultraviolet wavelengths, to which many substances react photoelectrically.

Substances that are capable of photoemission show surprisingly similar properties in this respect. They differ primarily in their photoelectric threshold — the frequency of light at which they begin to emit electrons. The electrons that are emitted under the impact of photons are often called photoelectrons, although they do not differ at all in their properties from electrons that are released by other means. In most cases, photoelectrons come from the outermost shells of the atoms involved (see Index, under Electrons — Arrangement of). Many individuals played important parts in the development of photoelectric theory and devices. Lack of space makes it impossible to mention them here.

The types of photoelectric cells

There are three principal types of photoelectric cells:

(1) Phototubes, or photoemissive cells. In these, electrons are emitted by one of the electrodes in a tube when the cell is exposed to light radiation.

(2) Photoconductive cells. Here light causes a change in resistance to the passage of electric current.

(3) Photovoltaic cells, or phototrons. In these, the action of light produces an electromotive force (voltage), without the need for any external source of electrical power for the cell.

There is considerable variation in the design, characteristics and use of these three main kinds of photoelectric cells. Although their applications may overlap in various situations, each is more suited to certain functions, as we shall bring out in the following pages.

Phototubes, or photoemissive cells

One type of phototube is illustrated on the preceding page. It consists of a glass tube, either highly evacuated (that is, with a high vacuum) or else filled with some inert gas, such as argon, at low pressure. The electron-emitting substance, generally a compound of cesium or potassium, is deposited in a thin layer on a half-cylinder of silver or other metal within the tube. The coating represents the cathode, or negative electrode, of the cell. A connection is made between the cathode and one of the cell terminals. As light falls upon the coating — the cathode — it emits electrons.

The cell also contains an anode, or positive electrode, which consists of a wire extending along the axis of the cylinder. It is maintained at a positive potential with respect to the cathode by means of an external battery. The negatively charged electrons emitted by the cathode are attracted to the anode and continue around the battery circuit back to the cathode. Hence the phototube functions as an electric valve. It causes the current output to fluctuate according to the amount of light falling upon it. If the light beam is shut off altogether, the circuit is broken. In this case, the phototube represents an open switch in the circuit. The "switch" is closed when light again falls on the cathode.

In another type of phototube, the cathode consists of a semitransparent layer of the photoemissive substance applied to the envelope, or window, of the tube. A part of the layer is deposited on another layer of a metal that provides the necessary electrical contact. When light falls upon the surface of the layer in contact with the envelope of the tube, electrons are emitted from the inner surface of the layer.

The current output of a photoelectric tube is extremely small; hence it is provided with suitable amplifiers and relays. A gas-filled phototube generates a larger current than a vacuum phototube because of the ionization of the gas by the photoelectrons when light hits the tube. However, it is slower to respond to changes in light intensity than a vacuum phototube; of course, the amount of electrons produced is not simply proportional to the amount of light entering the gas tube. Despite its lesser electrical output, the vacuum phototube must be used where quick response to

LIGHT SOURCE

PHOTOCONDUCTIVE CELL

RELAY

BELL

BATTERY

How a photoconductive cell causes an electric bell to ring. The electrical resistance of the cell drops as the light intensity rises. When the latter goes beyond a certain point, the current becomes strong enough to work a switch. This closes the electrical circuit; as a consequence the bell rings.

small light fluctuations is necessary, as in many kinds of scientific instruments.

Phototubes have a great variety of applications. They serve as sensing elements in detecting and measuring light and other forms of radiation. They are used in light-controlled relay circuits; in these, variations in the intensity of light falling on the cathode brings about current variations.

The phototube plays an important part in sound movies. Variations in sound are recorded in terms of darker or lighter areas in the film or of varying width of the exposed areas. When the film is run off in a movie house, a phototube converts variations in the film into varying electric pulses. Amplified, they are converted into sound.

The phototube plays an important role in television and also in facsimile transmission. These uses are described elsewhere in THE BOOK OF POPULAR SCIENCE. (See Index, under Photocathodes; Facsimile transmission.)

In certain applications, a beam of light is kept focused upon a phototube. Various devices are actuated when an object comes between the light beam and the phototube, thus cutting off the light. This effect is used as a safety feature, preventing a machine such as a press or cutting device from working when the operator comes dangerously close to it. It also serves to open

doors automatically. The door remains shut as long as the beam of light is uninterrupted; when a person stepping in front of the door interrupts the beam, the door swings open.

The current output of cells of the photoemissive type can be amplified many times in the phototubes known as photomultiplier tubes. These are provided with two or more anodes, called dynodes, which emit secondary electrons when struck by the primary electrons emitted by the cathode in response to light. As electrons bounce off from one dynode to another, more and more electrons are emitted. Certain photomultiplier tubes have more than ten dynodes and amplify a current a billion times. Photomultipliers are used where great sensitivity to light and fast response to light radiation are required.

Photoconductive cells

The photoconductive type of cell depends for its action upon the fact that the electrical resistance of certain substances varies with the intensity of the light that strikes them. Resistance usually drops as light intensity rises. A great many different substances display this property, including selenium, boron, germanium, silicon and various compounds. In a photoconductive cell, a thin metal film is deposited on an insulator plate. The film is divided into strips with a thin dividing line between them. Alternate strips are connected. A thin layer of the photoconductive substance is deposited over the metal film; it forms a bridge across the dividing line between the strips. The assembly is enclosed in an evacuated glass tube, and the connections are brought out to terminal prongs attached to the base.

Photoconductive cells play an important part in television (see Index, under Vidicon tubes). They are used in photographic exposure meters when more sensitivity or power is required. They are used with batteries; the photoconductive cells are made of cadmium sulfide or cadmium selenide. Photoconductive cells are also employed in high-speed recording spectroscopy and in detection of infrared radiation.

Photovoltaic, or phototronic, cells

Both photoemissive and photoconductive cells require an external source of voltage before any current flow can take place; this is not a requirement in the photovoltaic (phototronic) type of cell, because an electromotive force is generated within the cell itself when it is exposed to light. This force is used in a variety of different ways, as we shall see.

All of the early cells of this type were "wet cells." They consisted of two electrodes immersed in an electrolyte, or conducting solution. In a typical wet cell, the cathode (negative electrode) was of copper, coated with a copper oxide; the anode

(positive electrode) was of lead; both electrodes were dipped in a solution of lead nitrate. Light falling on the cathode produced an electric current between the cathode and anode; the strength of the current was measured by connecting a galvanometer to the cell.

The modern photovoltaic cell generates electricity when light falls upon the junction, called a barrier layer, between two different types of semiconductors (see Index). In one type, the n-type, conduction is due to electrons, each of which represents a negative charge of electricity — hence the name "n-type" (n = "negative"). In the other type of semiconductor, the p-type, conduction is caused by so-called holes, or gaps, in the crystalline structure of the material. Each hole, in the absence of a negatively charged electron, is therefore considered to represent a positive charge — hence the name "p-type" (p = "positive"). Electrons and holes are considered to move or flow in the electric currents set up under the action of light. The solar cell is a photovoltaic cell; its action has been described in detail in another article, The Solar Battery, in Volume 7.

The photovoltaic cell has been used extensively to detect and measure the intensity of light in photographic exposure meters. It also serves in the relay systems used in automation. It is also finding more and more extensive use in the form of solar batteries, each made up of thousands of solar cells. In the earlier stage of their development, solar batteries were used on a small scale to provide power for telephone amplifiers or repeaters. They have, however, proved to be indispensable in the space program. To name but a few of the spacecraft in which solar batteries have been installed, they are the *Tiros* and *Nimbus* weather satellites; the *Telstar, Early Bird* and *Syncom* communication satellites; the *Lunar Orbiter*, used to survey the moon; *Mariner II*, which approached within 5,000 miles of Venus; and the OAO (*Orbiting Astronomical Observatory*). Solar batteries have been used to charge nickel-cadmium batteries, which in turn provide power for the electronic circuits of the space vehicles.

PHOTOVOLTAIC CELL

LIGHT SOURCE

TRANSPARENT METALLIC FILM

LIGHT SENSITIVE SELENIUM LAYER

METAL BASE

GALVANOMETER

When light photons strike the boundary between two types of material in a photovoltaic cell, the result is an electric current. The strength of the current is measured by a galvanometer, thus indicating the intensity of the light that causes the current. A detailed account of the workings of such a cell is given in the article on The Solar Battery, Volume 7.

THE WONDER-WORKING X RAYS

Radiations That Have Opened New Paths of Knowledge

BY HELEN MERRICK

WITHIN recent years the walls that formerly rigidly separated physics and chemistry have been crumbling away. It now seems prophetic of this trend that one of the first steps toward the discovery of X rays was taken by a scientist who was both a chemist and a physicist, Sir William Crookes, an Englishman (1832–1919).

Crookes was interested in the effects of electrical discharges through gases at low pressure. To help him in his experiments he invented a device that became known as the Crookes tube. It was a tube from which the air had been pumped; this created a vacuum, or rather a partial vacuum, since some air had to remain in the tube if it were to work. Metal wires were sealed into opposite ends of the tube. These wires served as electrodes to which a source of electric current could be attached; the current could then be sent through the air remaining in the device.

One day, after Crookes had been sending a high-voltage current through his tube, he discovered that photographic plates in a closed box nearby had become fogged. He had also observed a mysterious green glow in the tube. Crookes prevented further fogging by removing photographic plates to another room whenever the current was flowing. For some reason the strange phenomenon does not seem to have aroused his curiosity.

Our story skips a few years, to the autumn of 1895. Wilhelm Konrad Roentgen (1845–1923), the German physicist, was puttering with a Crookes tube in his laboratory at the University of Würzburg. Turning on a high-voltage current, he noticed the effects that had already attracted the attention of Crookes: the green glow; the fogging of photographic plates. Roentgen was not satisfied to let it go at that. He tried covering the tube with black paper, through which no visible light could pass, and still something came through that affected a photographic plate. He came to the conclusion that this something must be invisible rays, and he called them "X rays" because "X" stands for the unknown in science. (X rays are also called roentgen rays for their discoverer.)

The story goes that Roentgen, by a lucky accident, also discovered one of the properties of X rays. While he was experimenting with the Crookes tube, some photographic plates in a desk drawer had been fogged. Instead of throwing the spoiled plates away, he developed them. On one plate he was amazed to see the perfect image of a key appear; yet no key had been in the drawer. Then he remembered that a key had been on the top of the desk. The key had been photographed right through the desk by the X rays. Roentgen also found that the rays would pass through his hand when he inserted it between the tube and a plate. In the developed photograph, however, the bones stood out clearly as dark shadows as compared with the flesh. This indicated that the bones, more dense than the flesh, must block the rays to some extent and, therefore, that the rays pass more easily through less dense materials.

The green glow that Crookes and Roentgen saw was light waves being sent out by the glass walls of the tube when electrons bounced against them, as the result of the discharge of electricity through the gas remaining in the tube. (Electrons are atomic particles that carry a negative charge of electricity; and ordinary electric current is really a flow of electrons.) At the same time, the electrons were stimulating the atoms of the glass to send out waves of extremely short length, the X rays. Since then, physicists have learned that X rays are produced when electrons strike any atoms at high speed and, conversely, that when X rays strike atoms, electrons are hurled out.

It was finally proved that X rays are similar to those of ordinary light, though they differ in wave length. This is how it was proved:

Since the time of Sir Isaac Newton (1642–1727) it had been known that visible white light consists of a number of different colors; and that white light may be broken into bands of these colors, since each color has a different wave length. Red, at one end of the spectrum, has the longest wave length; violet, at the other end, the shortest. When white light passes through a prism, each color is bent according to its wave length, red the least and

Early X-ray picture of a hand. The rings have blocked the X rays completely; that is why they appear black.

violet the most, and we get the rainbow array of the visible spectrum.

"Diffraction" is a term used for the property which waves possess of spreading out and interfering with one another when they meet a slit, a hole, or an opaque object of almost the same size as the wave length. One kind of diffraction grating consists of a system of lines drawn very close together on a glass plate. The lines are parallel, equally spaced and there are thousands of them to the inch. The spectrum obtained from such a grating is an interference phenomenon; the waves reinforce one another when their crests come together at any point, and cancel each other out when a crest meets a trough. The result is a system of bands of light and dark, visible on a screen placed behind the grating.

Von Laue proves that X rays are similar to visible light waves

Now a German physicist, Max von Laue, was familiar with the diffraction grating. In 1912, he had the brilliant idea that a crystal, such as diamond or rock salt, might separate X rays into beams of different wave-lengths. This, of course, would prove that they do behave like light waves. A crystal came to mind because by this time physicists suspected (and later proved) that a crystal is a conglomeration of atoms arranged in a perfectly regular plan at very short distances from each other. It seemed to Von Laue that such an arrangement might act as a natural diffraction grating, with openings between the atoms small enough to diffract X rays if they really do have shorter wave lengths than those of visible light.

Von Laue's reasoning was sound. When a narrow beam of X rays was sent through a crystal, dark spots appeared on a photographic plate behind the crystal. It was found that the position of these spots depended on the different wave lengths in the X-ray beam and also on the arrangements of the atoms in the crystal.

Sir William H. Bragg, a British physicist, and his son, Sir William L. Bragg, carried Von Laue's work still further, and soon obtained clear, sharp spectrum lines with X rays. The Braggs discovered what is called the law of crystal diffraction. Using this law, if a scientist knows the wave length of the X rays, he can find out how the atoms are spaced in the crystal. The process can be reversed. If the scientist begins with knowledge of how the atoms are arranged, he can then work out the wave length of the X rays.

To describe all the experiments, theories and calculations that were involved in this work would fill volumes. Summing up, they not only furnished the key to the nature of the X rays but also to the structure of crystals. Most nonliving, solid matter is crystalline in structure.

We know now that X rays are a part of the electromagnetic spectrum. They are related to radio waves, infrared rays, visible light waves, ultraviolet and gamma rays and rays that accompany cosmic radiation. X rays belong in wave length between ultraviolet and gamma rays. (Gamma rays are given off by radium and other radioactive elements.) All electromagnetic waves travel through space at the same speed, about 186,000 miles per second.

The angstrom unit for wave lengths

Wave lengths of the electromagnetic spectrum are expressed in terms of the angstrom unit, named for the Swedish physicist Anders Jonas Ångström (1814–74). One angstrom is 1/100,000,000 (.00000001) of a centimeter, or 1/253,999,800 of an inch. A scientist expresses this value as 1 Å $= 10^{-8}$ cm (centimeters). The symbol λ stands for wave length expressed in terms of angstroms. Thus $\lambda5,890$ means "wave length of 5,890 Å."

Visible light has wave lengths ranging from about 4,000 Å to somewhat more than 7,000 Å. The wave lengths of X rays go from about 1,000 Å to 0.1 Å, overlapping other wave groups.

An important point to remember here is that the shorter the wave length, the greater the energy of the ray; and the greater the energy, the more penetrating the ray will be. For this reason, X rays and the tubes that produce them can be classified as "hard" or "soft." Hard rays have shorter wave lengths than soft rays and hence are more penetrating.

A descendant of the simple Crookes tube with which our story began, the modern X-

Diagram of a modern X-ray tube. Useful rays, streaming through the tungsten target, pass out through a window.

ray tube works on the same principles. It consists of a bulb containing as nearly perfect a vacuum as possible and fitted with electrodes to which high voltage can be applied. The negative electrode is called the cathode. It is usually a filament of tungsten wire wound into a spiral. The positive electrode, the anode, is called the target. It is made of some heavy metal, such as tungsten, and is welded to a copper support, which helps conduct away the tremendous heat generated. To prolong the life of the target, many present-day tubes are fitted with rotating anodes. When an electric current of high voltage is turned on, the cathode is heated white-hot and sends out a stream of electrons, or cathode rays, which are pulled through the vacuum by the high voltage until they reach speeds of thousands of miles per second. They slam against the atoms of the target and, as they strike, a spurt of X rays splashes out from the disturbed material of the target.

To explain where the X rays come from, we must go inside the atom. Whirling around the atom's nucleus, or core, are one or more electrons—in the case of a heavy metal there are many—each in a definite shell, or path. If an electron is forced to jump out of its shell, some kind of ray is emitted. Visible light is sent out when an electron is displaced from an outer shell.

If the disturbance is much more violent, an electron in an inner shell, close to the nucleus, is likely to be dislodged and removed from the atom entirely. The atom cannot remain in this unbalanced state. So an electron from the next outer shell jumps into the vacant place. The second shell is soon filled by an outer electron jumping in, and so on. Balance is restored when the atom picks up a free electron (there are always some free electrons drifting around in a metal) for its outermost shell. X rays are the result of inner-shell disturbance.

How higher
voltages affect X rays

As we have indicated, it requires more energy to displace the electrons close to the nucleus than it does to displace any others in the atom. The higher the voltage in an X-ray tube, the faster the cathode rays will be pulled through it, increasing their energy. As a result the wave lengths of the X rays given off from the target will be shorter, approaching the wave lengths of gamma rays, and the X rays will be more penetrating. In giant X-ray tubes, built to stand millions of volts, the cathode rays may reach almost the speed of light (about 186,000 miles per second) and X rays are produced that will easily go through several feet of concrete.

As we have seen, one of the first properties of X rays to be noticed was their ability to penetrate solid substances such as wood, flesh and metal. However, X rays cannot be focused, or brought to a point, easily as visible light-waves can. One reason for this is that an X-ray beam of the same wave length does not penetrate all substances equally well. We mentioned earlier that the depth of penetration depends partly on the density of the substance. Ordinary X rays, produced at 100,000 volts, pass through flesh easily but through bones less so. "Filters" of aluminum or of copper are often used to refine X-ray beams. The softest rays are absorbed even by air. One of the most effective materials to block X rays altogether is lead. For this reason, glass containing lead is used on many kinds of X-ray equipment to protect those who work with it and are endangered by X rays.

Another important property of X rays is that, like light, they act on the chemicals of photographic plates, fluorescent screens and so on. This X-ray action together with the penetrating property makes it possible to take "shadow" pictures of, say, the inside of the human body or of a metal casting. Bombarded with X rays, some chemicals fluoresce: that is, they glow brightly as long as X rays strike them. One of the best-known uses to which this property has been put is in the fluoroscopic screen, which we shall explain when we take up the medical uses of X rays in more detail.

When a gas, such as the air, is exposed to X rays, it becomes ionized: that is, some of its atoms or molecules acquire an electric charge. (We explain ionization elsewhere in THE BOOK OF POPULAR SCIENCE.) The amount of ionization produced serves to measure the strength of the X rays.

Still another property of X rays is that when they fall on a substance, other rays are given off, which also consist largely of X rays. This "secondary radiation" is partly like that of the original X rays but is also dependent on the kind of substance exposed. It gives the scientist a tool with which to study the structure of matter.

Effect of X rays
on living tissues

X rays also have an effect on living things. When X rays are absorbed, they change the structure of tissues, and these will be "burned" or destroyed if the exposure is long enough. Some kinds of X rays are also able to affect the genes, the elements in the germ cells of reproductive organs by which hereditary traits are passed on from one generation to the next. In this way heredity itself may be changed.

Considering the ability of X rays to probe matter and force it to yield its secrets, however grudgingly, it is hardly to be wondered at that X rays play a prima-donna role on the stage of scientific research. Practical application of new findings frequently follows so swiftly in many fields that it is difficult to separate the pure research from the everyday use.

Perhaps no field has been more rewarding to the scientist than the kind of analysis called X-ray crystallography, which began with the work of Von Laue and was developed further by the Braggs. The methods used in this field are too complicated to discuss within the brief limits of this article. To put it as simply as possible, when a narrow beam of X rays is sent through a crystal, the rays are scattered by the atoms and form a balanced pattern, which can be caught on a photographic plate. Each kind of crystalline solid has its own pattern. One result of this work is that scientists now have an accurate knowledge of the character of X rays sent out by each of the chemical elements, knowledge that has helped to determine the internal

compound by a device that shows the amount of X rays absorbed. The device is so sensitive that it can register the difference between ninety-nine and a hundred sheets of thin paper. One practical use is to measure the amount of "ethyl" in gasoline. X-ray absorptometry is possible because atoms can absorb X rays. An atom of oxygen, say, absorbs the same amount of rays whether it is in the form of the element or in a compound with other elements; and under the simplest conditions, the amount of absorption is the same whether the substance containing the oxygen be a solid, a liquid or a gas. So the amount of energy taken from a beam of X rays passing through a given mass of a substance is always the same, whether the

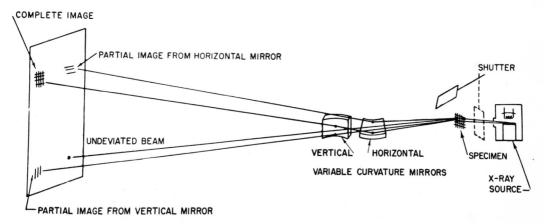

How the X-ray microscope works. The specimen is put in front of a shutter between the X-ray source and two concave mirrors with their faces at right angles to each other. Partial images are produced when rays are reflected from one mirror. The complete image results when rays bend up from the horizontal mirror and then bend out from the vertical mirror. X rays can be bent only at a low angle and only from the surface of a subject (reflection), and not in passing through (refraction). The above diagram has been greatly simplified.

structure of the atoms themselves. In fact, in what is called X-ray spectroscopy, the rays reveal information about the patterns of the electrons inside the atom.

From this kind of research, it has been a fairly easy step to investigate the arrangement of molecules in various chemical substances. They may be "fingerprinted" by the way in which X rays are scattered in passing through.

A comparatively recent development is the branch of science called X-ray absorptometry. Scientists can measure the quantity of certain materials in a chemical

substance is hot or cold, or a gas, a liquid or a solid.

Even art has benefited. X rays can be used to analyze the composition of pigments in oil paintings—to the point where sometimes the painter of what appears to be an "old master" can be identified.

The first X-ray microscope was introduced in 1950. It uses a combination of X rays and visible light-waves; and because of the penetrating power of X rays, it reveals finer detail than is possible with optical microscopes.

In order to increase the penetration of X

rays, scientists have been building ever more powerful machines. A giant among them all is the betatron—really an outsized X-ray tube. This machine was first invented in 1941 by Donald William Kerst, of the University of Illinois. He called it the "betatron," from beta ray, which is a stream of high-speed electrons.

As you may guess, a betatron is an enormously complicated apparatus. Essentially it consists of a doughnut-shaped glass tube, containing a vacuum, that is placed between the poles of a powerful electromagnet. What is called an electron gun is arranged so that it will send a stream of electrons into the tube at a certain angle. Inside the tube, two forces act on the electrons: one makes them follow the curve of the tube, and the other gives them higher and higher speeds, increasing their energy enormously.

TO VACUUM PUMP

ELECTRONS STREAM FROM CATHODE

PATH OF ELECTRONS

X-RAY BEAM

TARGET

Diagram of a betatron. As the path of the electrons is bent and they strike the target, X rays spurt out.

At a chosen instant, they are bent from their curved path and directed to the X-ray target. All this happens in the twinkling of an eye; nevertheless during this time the electrons circle the tube many thousands of times. These operations are repeated over and over again.

In our daily lives, most of us are first introduced to X rays in the office of a dentist or a doctor. From what has been said, you can now understand why X-ray

photography is so helpful in dentistry and medicine. Abscesses at the roots of teeth, an open safety pin in a baby's throat, a bullet in a splintered bone—all can be detected with X rays.

You may also have had your chest, say, examined with a fluoroscope, which makes use of the property of X rays to cause certain chemicals to glow. One advantage, for some purposes, of the fluoroscope over X-ray photography is that the fluoroscope allows a doctor to observe the inside of the body in action.

A fluoroscopic screen consists of a piece of cardboard (which X rays can pass through easily) coated with certain crystals, such as platinobarium cyanide or tungstate of calcium, which fluoresce under X rays. In an examination, the patient stands or lies down between an X-ray machine and a fluoroscopic screen, which the doctor can place against any part of the body. In some cases, such as an examination of the stomach, the patient usually drinks a liquid first, often a compound of barium, which blocks X rays. (Naturally, the liquid is harmless to the patient.) When the current is turned on in the X-ray machine, bones and thick organs, or organs such as the stomach that are full of the barium compound, cast shadows on the screen because they are blocking the X rays, and the rest of the screen glows. For the best results, of course, the fluoroscope should be used in a blacked-out room.

X-ray photography itself has been improved by the development of a method for taking pictures in three dimensions. Heretofore, the pictures were "flat," showing only width and length. The new method adds depth, so that the doctor may see the inside of the body in actual perspective. Another method, invented by a Swedish scientist, Dr. Arne Frantzell, permits pictures of veins and other soft tissues such as muscles, fat and the skin around bones to be taken in great detail.

X-ray photography has also made possible the mass survey of large sections of the population for tuberculosis. The mass chest X-ray units are fitted with photo-fluorescent cameras capable of taking a great

The fluoroscope at work. Special gloves and an apron protect the physician from overexposure to the X rays.

be able to control the dosage precisely. X-ray machines for medical treatments are complicated affairs, with a number of precision measuring devices. Tumors on or near the surface of the body may be treated with X rays produced at 100,000 to 200,000 volts, but tumors that lie deeper may require rays from tubes of higher voltage, running into the millions. "Millions of volts" may sound alarming, but there is no danger of shock. The machines are completely insulated, and the dangerous part of the equipment is kept outside of the treatment room. One of the largest X-ray machines for treatment—2,000,000 volts—thus far built is in use at the Hospital for Joint Diseases, in New York.

A few cases of malignant tumor, considered hopeless, have even been treated with a 23,000,000-volt betatron. There were no harmful effects from the treatment on the patients, and the tumors that could be examined had shrunk.

Improvements in X-ray-treatment techniques are coming fast. An X-ray shield, developed by Dr. Hirsch Marks, of the New York City Cancer Institute, is one example. It permits extremely high-voltage

many miniature X-ray photographs. The X-ray equipment, the camera, and a dark-room for developing the films are grouped together into a truck unit. This is fitted with dressing-rooms, and it can be moved around the country. Widespread surveys of the population and the early diagnosis of cases have greatly reduced the number of tuberculosis victims.

X rays have a place in the treatment of disease, particularly cancer. A cancerous tumor is a new growth of cells which shows a tendency to spread to other areas. Now the action of X rays on living cells is mainly a destructive one. However, young cells and actively growing ones succumb to X-ray action more quickly. Also lymph tissue is more susceptible and some kinds of cancer spread by way of the lymph vessels. Cancerous cells are usually young and grow much more rapidly than healthy ones, so it is possible to adjust the strength of the X rays and limit the exposure with the result that only the cancerous cells are attacked and healthy cells are affected very little, or not at all.

Great care is necessary. The roentgenologist (a medical X-ray specialist) must

Treatment with an X-ray machine. The rays come out of the funnel and are concentrated on the area being treated.

"Shadow" picture of part of an airplane crankcase, showing the position of the studs (white objects).

X rays to be trained on a tumor without damage to healthy cells. Radiation dosage is measured in terms of a unit called the roentgen, "r" for short. Without the shield, the highest safe dosage is about 200 r in air per treatment, up to a total of 3,300 r over a period of four weeks. With the shield, Dr. Marks reported, 1,200 r in air a day may be given for twenty days of treatment—in all, 24,000 r.

The industrial applications of X rays are legion, and we have space to mention only a few here. X rays are used to examine metal coatings, plastics, rubber insulation and so on, whose flaws might not appear on the surface. High-pressure boilers and pipes, for instance, are X-rayed to be sure that there are no weak places that might cause explosions. Some machines are large enough to take an X ray of an entire automobile. Most X-ray machines, however, concentrate on smaller areas.

Shadow pictures can show whether an egg is good or bad, and whether the core of a golf ball is perfectly round.

Airplane propellers are X-rayed periodically, because they show changes in their internal structure some time before they are ready to break.

Up-to-date textile mills also use X-ray equipment. Examination of fibers often shows that a better arrangement of the molecules in a fiber will make it sturdier and so will make stronger cloth.

It was only toward the turn of the century, as we have seen, that Roentgen found the answer to the mysterious green glow in the Crookes tubes and to the fogging in photographic plates. Yet already X rays have probed deeply into the closely guarded secrets of matter and have provided tools that benefit man in thousands of ways. Advances are still being made.

See also Vol. 10, p. 282: "X Rays."

All pictures, General Electric Co.

Series of X rays of a set of teeth. Such pictures give the dentist precise information about the teeth.

LIFE WITHOUT GERMS*

The Answer to a Great Scientist's Question

ALMOST all living creatures, including man, are continually surrounded by a host of microorganisms (tiny living things), including bacteria, algae, viruses and protozoans (one-celled animals). These tiny creatures, also known as germs, or microbes, inhabit the air we breathe, the food we eat, the water we drink and the earth upon which we live. They invade and powerfully affect the blood system, the breathing apparatus and the intestinal tract of animals.

The great French bacteriologist Louis Pasteur (see Index) raised the question whether the higher forms of life could exist at all without microorganisms, particularly those that are found in the intestinal canal. Many biologists pondered over this question. It occurred to some of them that something more than mere theory was involved. Suppose that researchers succeeded in raising animals in a germless environment, so that they would be free of germs during the whole of their lives. These animals would offer the most interesting possibilities in various types of research.

For one thing, they would supply bacteriologists with a supremely useful tool. The bodies of animals normally contain many different kinds of germs. A bacteriologist using such animals can never be certain that the conditions revealed by his microscope are due to the specific germ that he is studying. But if he could experiment with a germfree animal, he could accurately determine the effects of a given germ, since no other microorganism would be involved.

The early efforts of biologists to raise germfree animals were not very successful. By 1913, however, such animals could be kept alive for short periods of time. Later, the life-span of the animals was increased and their growth rates were measured. The first successful results on a truly significant scale were produced in the bacteriological

laboratories of Notre Dame University. The experiments of James A. Reyniers, director of the laboratories, and his associates opened up a new era in the investigation of germfree animals.

Reyniers first became interested in the problem while doing research on the nature of the bacterial cell. He found that his bacteria cultures were constantly being contaminated by unwanted microbes, and he tried to find a way to exclude these unin-

Two types of germs that infect man. *Escherichia coli* (A) is a bacterium found in human body wastes from the colon, a part of the large intestine. B is a species of the bacterium *Streptococcus*; it produces dental carries (that is, tooth decay). The activities of germs such as these can be effectively studied by noting their effects on germfree animals, described in this article.

Medical Audio Dept.,
Walter Reed Army Inst.
of Research

* Article prepared with the assistance of Lobund Laboratory, University of Notre Dame.

Dr. D. B. Scott, Laboratory of Histology and Pathology,
National Institute of Dental Research

The photographs on these two pages show different kinds of isolators, or germfree cages. At the right, we see a group of stainless-steel isolators. The air pressure within the tanks keeps the gloves extended. The technician pushes the gloves back into the tank to work. In this way, the outside of the gloves becomes the inside, next to his hands. The diagram below shows a germfree animal-rearing unit, with the technician's hand inside the tank. The steam clave serves to sterilize food before it is introduced into the isolator.

Photo and diagram, National Institute of Allergy and Infectious Diseases, National Institutes of Health

VIEWING PORT

GLOVE

CHAMBER

FLOOR

STEAM CLAVE

DRAIN

vited organisms. He succeeded in protecting his cultures from contamination by means of containers that could be sterilized and then sealed. To test their effectiveness, Reyniers tried to raise germfree animals in them. After much experimentation he succeeded; the glass containers he used were sterilized with germicide and supplied with air filtered through glass wool. In the years that followed, Reyniers' equipment and techniques were steadily improved. In the apparatus that is used today, microbefree animals breathe sterile air and eat sterile food; they mature, breed and die in a germfree environment. Sterilization is brought about by heat and also by chemicals and ultraviolet radiation.

The basic type of germfree cage, or isolator, that follows the original design is a stainless-steel * cylinder five feet long and three feet in diameter. Welded to one side of the cylinder is a smaller cylinder, called a sterile lock, through which food and other materials are passed from the outside into the sterile cage. Food, instruments and other materials are sterilized in this lock before being transferred into the cage proper. Waste products, cultures and the animals are removed from the main cylinder through the sterile lock.

The cage has a Pyrex observation window, through which experimenters can view the interior. Technicians, stationed outside the cage, handle and feed the animals with arm-length rubber gloves extending into the cage through ports; the gloves are sealed to the edges of the ports. The cage and its contents and the surfaces of the rubber gloves are sterilized by steam under pressure before animals are brought into the cage.

Many different kinds of cages are constructed on this basic design. There are raising cages where animals are housed. There are operating cages in which instruments and animals can be conveniently handled. A special transfer cage makes it possible to transfer animals from one kind of cage to another — for example, from the operating cage to the raising cage.

The steel isolators are being replaced by chambers constructed of plastic material

* The early isolators were constructed of cast iron.

Left: a Reyniers-400 rearing isolator. Above: a technician introducing food into a steam clave that is attached to a Reyniers-type isolator. The food is sterilized in the steam clave before it enters the isolator.

and maintained in an inflated state by low-pressure air. This air is sterilized before entering a chamber by being passed through a cylinder of fiber-glass wool. The device has been developed by Professor P. C. Trexler. Materials are passed into the isolator through a plastic lock, sterilized by a fog of peracetic acid. The plastic isolator is relatively inexpensive and is more adaptable to new experiments than the rigid metal isolator.

The animals used in germfree-life experiments include guinea pigs, chickens, monkeys, cats, dogs, rabbits, rats, mice, insects and even fish. These animals must be germfree to begin with. In the case of mammals, for example, the young are delivered from the germfree womb of a pregnant female by Caesarean operation performed in a sterile operating cage after the mother has been anesthetized and scrubbed well with a germicidal solution. In the case of chicks the matter is simpler. Fertile eggs whose shells are sterilized by the germicide mercuric chloride are placed in a sterile cage where they hatch.

The feeding of newborn animals presents many problems. Young mammals must be fed hourly with a specially prepared formula; later they must be weaned to a solid or semisolid diet. They are fed by hand by means of a small capillary stomach tube. The tip of the tube is a special latex nipple similar to the mother's nipple. Chicks are fed a sterile chick food. All foods are carefully sterilized by steam under pressure.

Once germfree animals breed, the labor of caring for the young is considerably reduced, for the jobs of feeding and weaning no longer have to be assigned to a staff of specially trained technicians.

Each animal is frequently examined to see if it is germfree. Samples of bodily secretions, hair or feathers, food, milk, water, urine and feces are collected. These samples are sealed in test tubes; they are then removed from the cages by way of the sterile lock and are rigorously tested for any traces of living microbes.

The experiments in the germfree laboratories at Notre Dame and other research centers have already answered Pasteur's question about the possibility of life free from germs. These experiments have proved that animals can be born, can be raised and

A plastic isolator, maintained in an inflated state by low-pressure air. The air is sterilized before it enters the isolator by being passed through fiber-glass wool.

Photo and diagram, American Sterilizer Co.

Technicians transferring animals from one plastic isolator to another. The diagram shows how air circulates through a plastic isolator. A blower forces incoming air through an air intake filter. After the air circulates through the chamber, it is exhausted through an air outlet trap.

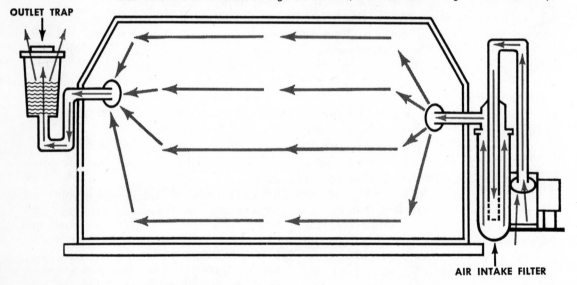

OUTLET TRAP

AIR INTAKE FILTER

can breed in an environment free from microbes. But they have gone far beyond this important point of departure.

For one thing, they have thrown a flood of light on the life processes of animals uncontaminated by germs. We now know that the blood serum of such animals contains few or no antibodies — substances that restrict or destroy the action of bacteria or neutralize their poisons. Germfree animals have fewer white blood cells and less lymphatic tissue than normal animals.

It has been found that the caecum, a blind pouch opening into the large intestine, is greatly enlarged in germfree mice, accounting for up to 30 per cent of the body weight. No one knows why this is so.

When certain antibiotics, such as penicillin and chloromycetin, are fed to normal poultry, the birds grow considerably larger. There is no such increase in growth when these antibiotics are supplied to germfree birds. The reason is probably that the latter, in their sterile environment, have already reached their maximum growth.

Germfree animals have proved exceedingly helpful in the study of tooth decay. It is generally believed that bacteria in the

Experimenting with germfree animals in isolators. Left: rat in caging that permits the collection of products of excretion. These products will be carefully studied. Below: injecting a germfree mouse with disease-carrying microorganisms.

National Institute of Allergy and Infectious Diseases, National Institutes of Health

Dept. of Germfree Research, Walter Reed Army Inst. of Research

mouth are responsible. Since the mouth is contaminated by different kinds of bacteria, it is difficult to single out the actual culprit. The teeth of germfree animals are free from decay, whatever their diet may be. Therefore experimenters are able to determine accurately the effects upon the teeth of specific bacteria introduced into the mouth of germfree animals. They may find out which germs cause tooth decay.

Germfree animals are being used in research in radiation biology, cancer, surgery, respiratory infections and skin and organ transplantation. One advantage in the use of such animals is that they are uniform; they carry no other forms of living agents that might complicate the interpretation of experimental data. The animals will contribute information in the search for the causes of aging, of heart ailments and of diseases of the digestive system.

Researchers utilizing germfree animals are trying to find out whether they require the same food constituents as normal animals. Once this matter has been decided, many important dietary studies will be carried out. Researchers will be able to study, more effectively than ever before, the relation of diet to longevity, constipation, reproduction, lactation (milk production), growth and the development of special systems, such as blood and lymph. They will also be able to learn much about dietary disease, such as pellagra.

At the University of Notre Dame, research programs such as those we have mentioned are carried on in Lobund Laboratory. (The name "Lobund" was derived from "*Laboratories of Bacteriology, University of Notre Dame*.") The laboratory produces in excess of 6,000 germfree mice and 3,000 germfree rats per year. Already such animals have been propagated through a number of generations in the germfree state.

Photo A, below, shows extensive tooth decay in the molar teeth of an ordinary rat on a high sugar diet. Photo B shows the molar teeth of a germfree rat, which has received the same diet as that given the animal in A.

Both photos, Dr. Robert J. Fitzgerald, Laboratory of Microbiology, National Institute of Dental Research; from and copyright by "The Journal of Dental Research"

CARTILAGE CELLS

NERVE CELLS

BLOOD CELLS

MUSCLE CELLS

SKIN CELLS

BONE CELLS

SCIENCE AND PROGRESS
(1815-95) VI

BY JUSTUS SCHIFFERES

THE CELLS OF ANIMALS AND PLANTS

THE cell is the fundamental unit of living things; or, to put the matter differently, living things must be considered as communities of cells. There are certain one-celled animals, like the amoeba, and one-celled plants, like the diatom. Most animals and plants are made up of combinations of cells. Thus, in a human being we find billions upon billions of cells of different kinds — bone cells, skin cells, nerve cells, blood cells and so on. This is the cell theory of organic structure. Rather dimly foreshadowed in the seventeenth and eighteenth centuries, it was first definitely stated in the 1830's.

The seventeenth-century microscopist Robert Hooke was the first to make out the structure of the cell, or, more exactly, the cell wall. Peering through his primitive microscopes (which he had made himself) at thinly sliced sections of cork, he clearly saw that the cork was divided into numerous compartments. These seemed to fit snugly into one another, like the different sections of a honeycomb. Hooke called these compartments *cellulae,* or cells, because they suggested little rooms (which is what *cellulae* really means in Latin). The cells that he first examined belonged to dead plants; he later observed that there were similar structures in living plants.

A little later, the Italian anatomist Marcello Malpighi, studying sections of plants, observed a number of "little bodies, closely massed together and each surrounded by a wall." The Dutch naturalist Anton Leeuwenhoek and the English plant physiologist Nehemiah Grew also made out cell structures in the tissues of animals and plants. None of these investigators, however, had any idea of the nature and the purpose (if any) of these structures. We discuss these early microscopists in the chapter Science Grows Up (1600–1765) II, in Volume 3.

Probably the first man to point out that cell tissue is found in both animals and plants was the German army surgeon, naturalist and embryologist Kaspar Friedrich Wolff (1733–94). Wolff thought of this cell tissue as consisting of a mass of "cell-shaped" structures. The concept was valid enough, as far as it went, but it was expressed pretty vaguely and it does not seem to have created much stir. Wolff had other quite sound ideas. He pointed out, for example, that living creatures are not machines, as certain mathematicians had implied, since, after all, machines cannot, like living creatures, reproduce their kind. He also indicated various similarities in plant and animal development.

Unfortunately for his reputation, however, Wolff often drew conclusions that were not warranted by the facts at hand. If he could not explain something, he was wont to toss off a clever phrase in order to cover up the gap. It is said that Goethe had Wolff in mind when he had Faust remark to Wagner, his pupil, "If you do not understand a thing, simply give it a long name and then everybody will say what a brilliant fellow you are."

The early microscopists had focused their lenses not only on the minute structure of large organisms but also on the tiny creatures that they called animalcula (little animals). A generation or so later, the animalcula came to be known as infusorians, because they were to be found in different kinds of infusions. The German natural philosopher Lorenz Oken (1779–1851) pointed out a possible connection between the tiny infusorians and the higher organisms. In his GENERATION, published in 1805, he compared the infusorians to the "vesicles, or cells" found in larger organisms. "All organized beings," he wrote, "originate from and consist of vesicles, or cells. These . . . are the infusorial mass from which all larger organisms are formed or are evolved." This surprisingly acute observation was quite lost, in Oken's book, amid a flood of wild speculation.

The early investigators of cellular structure were greatly handicapped by the imperfect microscopes that they used. The chief defect of these instruments was chromatic aberration — that is, things placed under their lenses shimmered with all the colors of the rainbow, so that microscopists could not be sure of what they saw. Some of them used their imaginations pretty freely in interpreting what their microscopes revealed — or seemed to reveal. For example, some of them imagined they saw a preformed little man — homunculus — in the head of a human sperm cell.

A Swedish physicist, Samuel Klingenstierna (1698–1765), was the first to show how achromatic lenses (lenses free from color distortion) should be made. Acting under his instructions, the English optician John Dollond, in 1758, constructed the first lenses free from chromatic aberration. It was not until the nineteenth century, however, that microscopes were supplied with these improved lenses. In 1827, the Frenchman Chevalier produced the first achromatic lens system for microscopes, thus making it possible to bring very small objects sharply into view. The Italian Amici began the manufacture of achromatic lenses for microscopes at about the same time. In the 1830's, biologists began using the greatly improved microscopes and they made many striking discoveries.

These drawings of animalcules ("little animals") are from Henry Baker's treatise *Of Microscopes Made Easy*, which was published in London in the year 1785.

Thus the German botanist Hugo von Mohl (1805–72) convincingly demonstrated that new cells in plants — one-celled algae and higher plants alike — arise through the formation of partition walls in old cells. He showed that a definite cellular structure exists in bast (woody fibers), bark and other parts of plants — a point that had been denied by many previous investigators. The Scottish botanist Robert Brown (1773–1858), the discoverer of Brownian movement (see Index), showed that each cell of the orchid and of various other plants has an internal "key spot," which he called a nucleus, or areole. Johannes Evangelista Purkinje (1787–1869), a Czech naturalist, pointed out that the closely packed cell masses in certain parts of animals resemble cell masses found in plants. A French zoologist, Félix Dujardin (1801–60), observed that the life of one-celled animals is bound up with physical and chemical changes occurring in the jellylike substance of which the cell consists.

These investigations were all forerunners of the modern cell theory of organic structure. The cell theory, as we accept it today, was first comprehensively set forth by Schleiden and Schwann. Matthias Jakob Schleiden (1804–81) was born at Hamburg, the son of a distinguished doctor. He first specialized in the law. But his legal practice, in his native city, was so unsuccessful that in a fit of despondency he shot himself in the forehead. Recovering from the effects of this attempt at suicide, he determined to give up the practice of law and to devote himself to the natural sciences.

He obtained a doctor's degree in both philosophy and medicine, won fame with his scientific writings and became a professor of botany at the University of Jena in 1850. Twelve years later he resigned and, after a brief interlude as professor at

The microscope of Chevalier was the first one to use an achromatic lens system.

MATTHIAS JAKOB SCHLEIDEN

Dorpat (now Tartu), in Estonia, he gave up his scientific work. He spent the rest of his life idly wandering through the towns and the pleasant countryside of Germany.

In 1838, he wrote a paper, On Phytogenesis (origin of plants), for a scientific journal called MUELLER'S ARCHIVE FOR ANATOMY AND PHYSIOLOGY. In this paper he presented the idea of the cell as the essential unit of living organisms. He pointed out that plants that consist of but a single cell — like so many algae and fungi — are nevertheless individual, independent organisms. "Plants developed to any higher degree," he wrote, "are aggregates of . . . independent separate beings — that is, cells themselves . . . Each cell leads a double life; one which is independent and has to do with its own development alone; the other which is incidental, as an integral part of a plant. The vital processes of the individual cells . . . form the fundamental basis . . . for vegetable physiology."

All this is perfectly sound; it is accepted by all biologists. When Schleiden tried to explain the origin of cells, however, he went astray. He advanced the erroneous theory that new cells arise by budding from the surface of the nucleus.

The German naturalist Theodor Schwann (1810–82) worked out the cell theory of organic structure at almost the same time as Schleiden. The son of a Prussian bookseller, he studied at Berlin under a renowned physiologist, Johannes Peter Mueller, and after taking his doctor's degree he became Mueller's assistant. In 1838, Schwann was named professor of anatomy at the University of Louvain, in Belgium. Nine years later, he transferred to the University of Liége, also in Belgium, and here he remained until his death. He refused the professorships that were offered to him at German universities, because he objected to the constant quarreling of German professors.

Theodor Schwann's contribution to the cell theory

Schwann's chief contribution to the cell theory was contained in his treatise MICROSCOPIC STUDIES OF THE SIMILARITY OF STRUCTURE AND DEVELOPMENT IN ANIMALS AND PLANTS, published in 1839. He took as his point of departure certain striking resemblances between animals and plants. In the case of animal cartilages, for example, he pointed out that "the most important phenomena of their structure and development correspond to like processes in plants. These tissues originate from cells, which correspond in every respect to those of plants. During development, too, the cells display phenomena similar to those in plants . . . The cells — the membranes and the cell contents, as well as the nuclei [in animals] — are analogous to the parts with similar names in plants."

Schwann observed that the egg from which, when impregnated by a sperm cell, the animal body originates is really a cell. In mammals the egg (or ovum) is microscopically small in size; in other animals, like the hen, it may be quite large. Yet, large or small, all eggs are cells; in them we can distinguish the nucleus, the cell contents and the cell membrane. The egg produces a young animal by cell division. The single fertilized cell divides into two cells, the two into four and so on. The tissues that eventually arise can be distinguished from one another on the basis of the characteristic cells they contain. For example, there are tissues, like the skin, in which the cells are independent but pressed together; there are tissues, like the muscles, in which the cells are extended into fibers.

Schwann summed up his findings by pointing out that every part of every animal or plant is made up either of cells or of the substances that are thrown off by cells; that, to some extent, cells have a life of their own; that the status of this kind of individual life depends upon the life of the organism as a whole.

The cell theory, established by the Karl Ernst von Baer (1792–1876); his treatise ON THE STORY OF THE DEVELOPMENT OF ANIMALS, published between 1828 and 1837, was long held in reverence by embryologists. Von Baer was the first to discover the eggs of mammals ripening in the ovaries and embedded in minute, fleshy nests called Graafian follicles. Examining the embryos of rabbits and dogs, Von Baer showed how the specialized tissues of the growing animal are formed in regular and orderly fashion from the fertilized egg.

While Von Baer's work marked a great advance over previous studies in the field of embryology, he did not have a clear idea of the microscopic structure of tissues. He did not realize that tissues in their

These three drawings show the development of the embryo inside a chicken's fertile egg. They are from Karl E. von Baer's book On the Story of the Development of Animals, published in two volumes from 1828 to 1837.

work of Schleiden and Schwann and sometimes called the Schleiden-Schwann theory, offers a logical and satisfying explanation of animal and plant structure and physiology. After this theory was once definitely stated, no one could successfully challenge it. It was modified in a good many details by later investigators. But the essence of the theory has remained unchanged since it was first formulated.

Out of the cell theory of Schleiden and Schwann arose the new science of cytology (the study of cells). The theory was also destined to influence profoundly many other biological sciences. For example, it revolutionized the science of embryology, which deals with the period of life between the fertilization of the egg and the moment of birth. The great name in the early development of this science is entirety are made up of cells or of the products of cells; nor did he realize that the eggs that give rise to tissues are cells. It was not until the findings of Schleiden and Schwann were adopted by researchers in embryology that this science was put on a firm basis. The first important work of embryology to utilize the cell theory was THE DEVELOPMENTAL HISTORY OF MEN AND ANIMALS, published by Albert von Koelliker in 1861.

The cell theory has become basic in many other sciences: in bacteriology, in pathology, in genetics and in histology, to name only a few. It is one of the great scientific generalizations of all time; it ranks with Newton's theory of universal gravitation and Mendeleev's periodic system of classification of the elements.

Continued on page 370.

General Electric Co.

A 55-inch electromagnet loading machine-shop steel turnings in the salvage department of the General Electric Company's Erie works. The magnet can lift 850 pounds of scrap like this, on the average.

MAGNETS LARGE AND SMALL

What We Know about Magnetism

BY JOHN A. FLEMING

EVERYBODY is familiar with the toy magnet, that mysterious little U-shaped device that picks up needles or pins and that holds them indefinitely, through what seems to be sheer magic. But the magnet is far from being a mere toy. It is an essential part of a great many machines and tools and measuring devices, without which the world's work could not be done. A magnetized needle set within a compass helps the navigator to keep to his course at sea. When you hold a phone receiver to your ear, a magnet records the vibrations set up by the voice of the person talking into the mouthpiece. The electric motor, the electric generator and the ammeter could not possibly work without their built-in magnets.

Magnetism, the natural force that causes magnets to function as they do, revealed itself to men long centuries ago. A number of persons in antiquity knew that the black metallic iron ore called magnetite, or loadstone, had the property of drawing particles of iron to it. The Greek philosopher Thales (640?–546 B.C.) is said to have been the first to call attention to this property, but it may have been known long before. After Thales' time the loadstone was often mentioned in ancient writings; it was sometimes given the name of "magnet," from Magnesia, a district in Asia Minor where large magnetic deposits were to be found.

Socrates remarked, "the stone that Euripides calls a magnet . . . not only attracts iron rings but also imparts to them similar power of attracting other rings, suspended from one another, so as to form quite a long chain, and all of these derive their powers from the original stone." The Roman Lucretius, who lived in the first century B.C., tried to explain magnetism in terms of his atomic theory.

There are many legendary accounts of the properties of magnets. The ARABIAN NIGHTS contains the story of a ship

Loadstones attracting iron objects, as shown in a French treatise on the loadstone by D—, published in Amsterdam in 1687. The properties of the loadstone were known long before that time.

that approached an island made of magnetic rock; the ship fell completely to pieces because all the iron nails were pulled out of it through the attraction of the rock. Other ships, according to legend, avoided a similar fate by substituting wooden pegs for iron nails. There are stories, too, of huge statues of iron and bronze held in mid-air through the force exercised by magnetic domes.

Another tale gives a fanciful account of the origin of the word "magnet." It seems, according to this tale, that one day a shepherd called Magnes was tending his flock on the slopes of Mount Ida, in Asia Minor. Suddenly he noticed that the iron tip of his staff was being pulled toward the ground. He dug up the earth in the vicinity and found that his staff was being attracted by the loadstone in which the place abounded. Thereafter the loadstone was called a magnet in honor of the shepherd who had discovered it. Scholars have pointed out that this story originated long after the word "magnet" was in common use.

In the course of the centuries much of the mystery that once surrounded magnetism has been dispelled. In the place of out-and-out legends and pseudoscientific speculation, we now have at our disposal a respectable amount of scientifically proved fact. Furthermore, we have been able to put the force of magnetism to work for us in a great many different ways.

Today that natural magnet, the loadstone, no longer figures prominently in the

From "Magnetic Phenomena," by S. R. Williams

1. Magnetic lines of force about a bar magnet. Iron filings on a glass plate that is laid over the magnet are aligned along the lines of force.

study of magnetism or in its many applications, for practically all magnets nowadays are artificial. It is easy to make such a magnet out of a steel object, such as a needle, if you have a permanent magnet. Simply draw one end of the magnet along the needle, stroking in one direction only. The needle will become an artificial magnet and will have the property of drawing various particles to it. The original magnet has lost none of its strength; it will be capable of magnetizing any number of other steel needles. Suppose, now, that we break our magnetized needle in two; each of the fragments will be a magnet.

Until about 1820 artificial magnets were made by stroking bars of steel with a loadstone or with an artificial magnet. But then a Danish scientist, Hans Christian Oersted, revealed that a magnetic field can be produced by sending an electric current through a coil of wire, called a solenoid. If this wire is wound around a core of steel, the core will be permanently magnetized when current is passed through the coil. Nowadays the manufacture of artificial magnets is based on this principle.

Every magnet, natural or artificial, produces a magnetic field in the space around it. We can map out this field in various ways. If we place a magnet under a piece of paper whose surface is covered with iron filings, the filings will arrange themselves in lines of force like those shown in Figure 1. We can also use a small compass to mark out the magnetic field about a magnet. If we put the compass in different places in the vicinity of the magnet, it will assume the direction of the lines of force at any given point (Figure 2).

In any magnet there are regions near the ends of the long axis where the attractive forces are greatest. These regions are called the poles of the magnet; the line joining the two poles is the magnetic axis. If a straight, or bar, magnet is suspended so as to move freely in a horizontal plane, the magnetic axis will assume, roughly, a north-south direction.

The pole of a magnet that is directed northward is known as the north-seeking pole, or north pole or positive (+) pole.

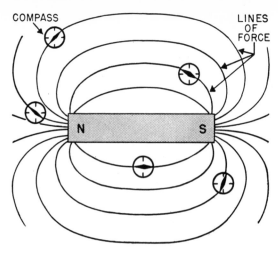

2. The magnetic field about a magnet may be marked out by a compass, which will assume the direction of the lines of force at any point.

The pole that is directed southward is called the south-seeking pole, or the south pole or the negative (—) pole. Similar, or like, poles repel each other; dissimilar, or unlike, poles attract each other.

When a bar magnet is bent double, it forms what is known as a horseshoe magnet. It will attract a given substance more powerfully than a bar magnet of corresponding size. The reason is that since the two poles are close together, the lines of force are crowded in a comparatively small space and exert a greater effect upon their surroundings.

Magnets lose their strength when heated; but they regain it when they become cool again. However, if they reach a temperature that is known as the Curie point, they become entirely demagnetized. The Curie point for iron is about 750° C. (1382° F.); it is different for other magnetic materials. In general, magnets tend to lose their strength as they grow older. To provide longer life, they are aged: that is, they undergo various treatments by heat, shock and repeated magnetizations and demagnetizations in weak alternating fields.

Magnetic lines of force cannot penetrate certain materials as easily as they can penetrate air or a vacuum. Such materials are called diamagnetic ("magnetic across," in Greek) because rods made of these substances tend to take up a position *across*

the field of force of a strong magnet (Figure 3). Bismuth, antimony and most of the other chemical elements are diamagnetic; so are their compounds.

Magnetic lines of force can penetrate other materials more easily than they can penetrate air or a vacuum. Such materials are called paramagnetic ("magnetic alongside," in Greek) because rods made of them tend to line up *alongside* the field of force of a strong magnet (Figure 4). Iron and liquid oxygen are paramagnetic substances.

A few paramagnetic materials are so much more easily magnetized than the rest that they are generally put into a separate class, called ferromagnetic. The ferromagnetic materials derive their name from the fact that one of them is iron (*ferrum,* in Latin). Nickel and cobalt are also ferromagnetic; so are various alloys of these

3. The diamagnetic substance takes a position *across* the field of force.

4. The paramagnetic substance aligns itself *along* the field of force.

metals and a few other materials. Sometimes ferromagnetic substances are called magnetic materials, while all the rest are lumped together as non-magnetic materials.

Magnets that retain their strength for long periods of time are called permanent magnets. They have a wide range of uses in industry and in research. They serve in various measuring devices, such as ammeters, voltmeters, galvanometers, cardiograph recorders, seismographs (earthquake recorders), magnetic compasses, magnetometers and so on. They form an essential part of many kinds of scientific equipment. Temperature, pressure and traffic signals are all controlled by permanent magnets. They are used in certain kinds of lathes, chucks, conveyors, hand tools and separators, and also in various toys and novelties.

Improvements in permanent magnets are constantly being made. New alloys with superior magnetic properties have been developed. Some of these alloys are called quench-hardening steels: that is, they are

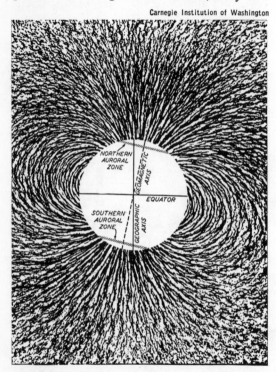

Carnegie Institution of Washington

5. Magnetic field about the earth, represented by the alignment of iron filings along the lines of force on a glass plate laid over a disc magnet.

first heated to a very high temperature and then hardened by rapid cooling, after being "quenched" in water or oil. Quench-hardening steels include alloys of steel with carbon-manganese, tungsten, chromium, cobalt and cobalt-chromium. They all contain carbon, since steel is basically an alloy of iron and carbon.

Other alloys are carbon-free. They include alloys of aluminum-nickel-iron, aluminum-nickel-cobalt-iron (trade name, Alnico), aluminum-nickel-titanium-iron (trade name, Nipermag) and cobalt-molybdenum (trade name, Comol). All these

substances require special casting, grinding, magnetizing and aging treatments.

Not all magnets are permanent. If electric current is passed through wire that is wound around a soft-iron core, the core will be magnetized but only as long as the current is turned on. If the current is shut off, the iron will lose practically all its magnetism; if the current is increased, the iron will have greater magnetic strength. This temporary sort of magnet — a core of soft iron set within a coil of wire through which an electric current is passed — is called an electromagnet.

The electromagnet is used in a great variety of modern electrical devices. It is the heart of the electric motor, and of such devices as the telegraph, the telephone and the electric bell. It serves to separate iron from its ores. Big electromagnets are frequently employed to load and unload iron and steel materials in railroad yards, steel plants and junk yards. Doctors sometimes use electromagnets to remove bits of iron or steel that have become imbedded in the eye.

We pointed out before that a magnet that is free to swing in a horizontal plane adopts, approximately, a north-south position. The reason is that it is attracted by magnetic forces arising within the earth itself. For the earth is a great natural magnet, with a North and South Magnetic Pole, a magnetic axis and a field of force that extends far out into space. Even four thousand miles above the surface of the earth, the magnetic intensity of this field is still one-eighth as great as it is at the surface. The lines of force of the earth's field are parallel to the surface near the equator; but as they approach the two magnetic poles, they bend and converge (Figure 5).

Certain substances within the earth — its magnetic deposits, for example — are highly magnetic; but that is certainly not true of most of the materials that make up our planet. As a matter of fact, a magnet of steel would be something like 10,000 times as powerful as one just as large made of typical earth-stuff. But in view of the earth's size, its total magnetism is pretty awe-inspiring. It is equivalent in effect to that produced by 800 quintillion (800,000,-000,000,000,000,000,000) parallel one-pound magnets if they could be placed at the earth's center or if they could be evenly distributed through the body of the earth with one magnet for about every two cubic yards.

Naturally, if the earth is a huge magnet, other magnets will be influenced by it. The north-seeking pole of a bar magnet, moving freely in a vertical axis, will evidently be attracted to the earth's North Magnetic Pole. It is true that the North Magnetic Pole does not correspond exactly to the geographical North Pole, as we shall see; but if we make certain calculations, we can determine in what direction true north lies. Of course we can then find the other points of the compass. This is the principle of that supremely useful instrument, the magnetic compass.

The south-pointing chariots of the Chinese

The Chinese have been credited with the invention of the compass. It is said that the Emperor Hwang-ti, who lived twenty-five centuries before the birth of Christ, built a chariot on which a dummy, mounted on a pivot, always indicated south. By using this chariot at a time when a thick fog had closed in upon his army during a battle, Hwang-ti was able to defeat the foe. This account is almost certainly mythical. Unfortunately it is difficult to see how much truth there is in later Chinese accounts of south-pointing chariots.

A Chinese document of the third century A.D. contains a statement that a needle enables a ship to follow a southward course. But it is not until the twelfth century that we find in any Chinese work a detailed description of the manner in which a needle is made to point to the south. The invention of the compass has also been attributed to other peoples, including the Arabs, the Greeks and the Etruscans; but there has been no authentic proof of such claims.

The earliest definite mention in European literature of the directive property of the magnet and its use in navigation appears in two Latin treatises by the English-

man Alexander Neckam. These treatises, entitled OF INSTRUMENTS and OF THE NATURE OF THINGS were written toward the end of the twelfth century A.D. The first of these works describes the use of the magnetic needle to indicate the north; Neckam points out that sailors use the needle to find their direction when the sky is overcast and the stars cannot be seen. The second treatise gives a description of a magnetic needle mounted on a pivot.

An early authority on magnetism—Petrus Peregrinus

In the following century, Petrus Peregrinus de Maricourt, a soldier monk, discussed the directive property of magnets in his famous EPISTLE CONCERNING THE MAGNET. "Take a loadstone," he says, "and put it in a wooden cup or plate and set it afloat, like a sailor in a boat, upon water in a larger vessel, where it will have room to turn. Then the stone so placed in the boat will turn until the north pole of the stone will come to rest in the direction of the north pole of the heavens, and its south pole toward the south pole of the heavens. And if you move the stone away from that position a thousand times, a thousand times will it return by the will of God." Peregrinus suggested a number of improvements in the nautical compass.

In the years that followed, the magnetic compass was gradually perfected; but even the most learned had no idea why the needle always pointed in a more or less northerly direction. It was not until the year 1600 that the reason was definitely revealed.

In that year the learned English physician Sir William Gilbert published a treatise called OF THE MAGNET, MAGNETIC BODIES AND THAT GREAT MAGNET THE EARTH. This was one of the greatest scientific works of all time. In it Gilbert, who has been called the Galileo of magnetism, set forth his theory that the earth is a magnet, and that a magnetic compass needle points north because the north-seeking pole of the needle is attracted by the North Pole of the earth. Gilbert also pointed out that the Magnetic North and South Poles do not

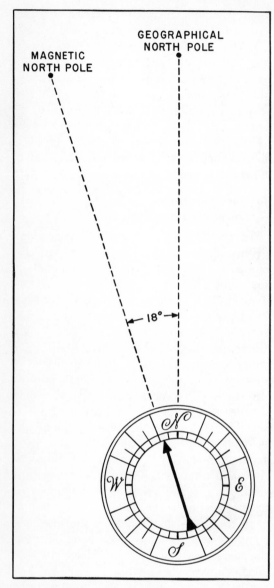

MAGNETIC
NORTH POLE

GEOGRAPHICAL
NORTH POLE

←—18°—→

6. The compass needle that is shown above points in a direction that is 18° west of true north; hence the declination of the compass is 18° west.

the moon and radiations from outer space.

The North and South Magnetic Poles are at quite a distance from true north and south — as much as a thousand miles, or even more. They are constantly shifting their positions. The Carnegie Institution of Washington has determined their average positions for various periods, as shown in the table at the top of the following page. This table indicates that both magnetic poles have shifted in a direction that is generally north by northwest.

The declination
of the compass

Since the magnetic poles of the earth do not correspond to true north and south, it is very important to know how much they diverge; otherwise a navigation officer would have only an approximate idea of his direction. We can find out how great this divergence is by examining the declination of the compass. The declination represents the angle between the magnetic needle, as it points to the North Magnetic Pole, and the geographic meridian — that is, the line passing through a given point on the earth's surface and connecting the North and South Poles of the earth. If the declination is 18 degrees west at a given point, it means that here the compass needle points in a direction that is 18 degrees west of true north (Figure 6).

Another factor that is also important in many calculations is the inclination, or dip, of the compass. To determine this, a magnetic needle, called a dipping needle, is mounted on a horizontal axis and is allowed to swing in a vertical plane. The needle will follow the direction of the earth's lines of force. The dip of the needle represents the angle between the plane of the horizon and the magnetic needle (Figure 7). The dipping needle is vertical at the North and South Magnetic Poles; it is horizontal at the magnetic equator. It occupies intermediate positions between horizontal and vertical at other places on the earth's surface.

The degree of declination or inclination at different points on the earth's surface may be shown on charts (maps) showing

correspond to true north and south. He observed, too, that a magnetic needle free to move up and down dips toward the earth at many places. Gilbert's work laid the foundations for our present-day knowledge of the earth's magnetism.

We realize now that, as a result of the magnetic field surrounding it, the earth and its atmosphere constitute a great magnetic laboratory. In this, nature continually performs her experiments, utilizing as apparatus not only the earth, but also the sun.

Five-year period* ending	Position of North Magnetic Pole	Position of South Magnetic Pole
1945.0	76.1° N., 101.8° W.	68.2° S., 145.4° E.
1950.0	73.0° N., 100.0° W.	68.0° S., 144.0° E.
1955.0	73.8° N., 101.0° W.	68.0° S., 144.0° E.
1960.0	74.9° N., 101.0° W.	67.1° S., 142.7° E.

* Note: Each date represents an official charting epoch.

the entire world or a single region. In preparing a chart showing magnetic declination, the degree of declination is determined at a number of different places. A line is then drawn through all the points where the degree of declination is 0°; another, say, through the places where the degree of declination is 5° and so on. If this method were strictly followed and if the places where the declination is determined were spaced closely enough, it would be found that the lines would form an intricate pattern of complex bends and closed loops. It is customary to smooth out the lines somewhat and to disregard irregular values.

The same method is used in preparing charts showing magnetic inclination. The charts that show lines of equal magnetic declination are called isogonic (having equal angles); those that show lines of equal magnetic inclination are called isoclinic (dipping equally). Both isogonic and isoclinic charts are called isomagnetic. On the next two pages we show a world isogonic chart.

The usefulness of the magnetic compass has been enhanced with the development of the accurate isogonic charts that we have just described. It is true that on large vessels the gyrocompass is now the chief directional instrument. In all such ships, however, magnetic compasses are held in reserve. For, after all, the gyrocompass is dependent on a source of motive power for its operation and it is also subject to mechanical failure. The magnetic compass, on the other hand, practically never goes out of order and the only "power" that is required to run it is the attraction of the North Magnetic Pole.

There are certain more or less regular changes in the earth's magnetic field, known as secular variations. There are secular variations from place to place, from season to season, from Northern to Southern Hemisphere and, for the same place, from year to year. For example, observations made at London indicate that the

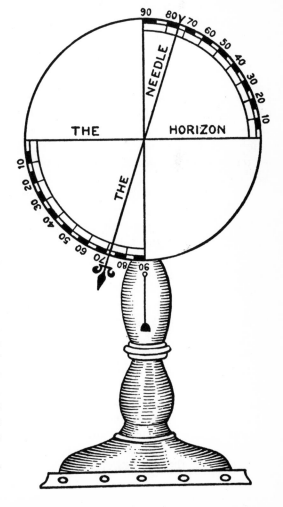

7. Sketch of the dipping needle with which Robert Norman measured dip at London in 1576. The needle, mounted on a horizontal axis, followed the direction of the earth's lines of force.

World isogonic chart for the year 1960, showing the North and South Magnetic Poles and the lines of equal magnetic declination. The magnetic declination of the compass is the same for all points on a given line in the chart. Thus the declination is 10° E. in all places through which the line marked 10° E. passes. Navigators find charts like these invaluable; without them, the compass reading would give only a rough idea of true north.

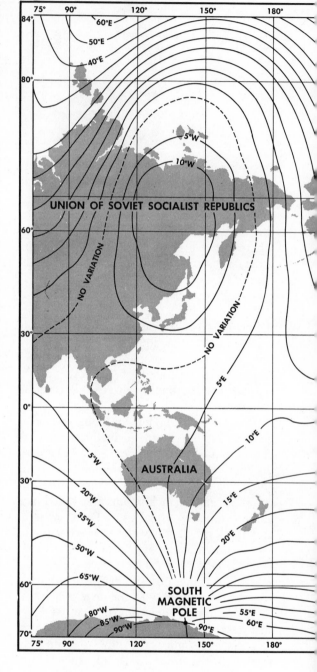

magnetic needle pointed 11° east of north in 1580 and 24° west of north in 1812. Since that time the needle point has shifted eastward and now points to about 10° west of north. All this indicates that this particular secular variation will complete a cycle in about five hundred years. The cycle of secular change varies from one place to another. Efforts have been made to predict such cycles on the basis of theoretical studies, just as astronomers predict eclipses of the sun and moon. It is now recognized, however, that because of the many unknown factors involved, there is as yet no basis for predictions of secular change. The fact is that secular variations have not only puzzled scientists for many years but are still an unsolved mystery.

It has been found that as the earth revolves around the sun during the year, there are corresponding fluctuations in the earth's magnetic field. The maximum variations, or crests, occur during the equinoctial months of March and September, when the sun crosses the equator in its apparent yearly journey through the heavens. (See the article The Face of the Sky in Volume 1.) The minimum variations, or troughs, come in the solstitial months of June and December, when the sun is farthest from the equator in that same yearly journey.

The presence of magnetic-ore deposits brings about anomalies, or irregularities, in the magnetic field of the earth. Such irregularities do not greatly alter the over-all picture of the whole field. They make it possible, however, to locate deposits of magnetic ores in a given area. Aerial surveys of the area are made with a magnetometer, an instrument for measuring the intensity and direction of magnetic forces. By examining the findings of such surveys,

prospectors can determine the extent and depth of magnetic-ore deposits. In some cases, soil and rocks are only slightly magnetic, and there are only minor anomalies in the earth's magnetic field.

Other variations in the earth's magnetism are caused by disturbances known as magnetic storms. These frequently occur simultaneously over the whole globe; they

Adapted from chart supplied by U.S. Naval Oceanographic Office

are much more violent in the polar regions because of the nearness of the earth's magnetic poles. There is not a regular cycle of quiet and disturbed days; an old disturbance may die out and a new one may occur at any time. Generally any marked disturbance in the magnetic field reappears in several successive months before it permanently disappears.

One of the most important factors in bringing about these magnetic storms is the existence of numberless electrified particles that stream out from the sun. The earth's lines of magnetic force, extending far out into space, entrap these charged particles, which spiral around the lines of magnetic force. Since these lines are steepest in the polar regions, the electrified particles penetrate most deeply in the earth's atmosphere in these areas and cause the natural displays called polar lights, or auroras (see Index, under Auroras). These result from the resistance offered to the electrified particles by the earth's atmosphere — a resistance that makes the particles glow. Polar lights are known as the aurora borealis (northern lights) when they occur in the Northern Hemisphere and the aurora borealis (southern lights) when they occur in the Southern Hemisphere.

It has been discovered quite recently that the earth's magnetic field is responsible for the formation of a vast zone of radiation surrounding the earth. This zone is called the Van Allen radiation belt and is described elsewhere (see Index). It is made up of charged particles (from the sun and beyond) captured by the magnetic

field of the earth. Some authorities think that the particles causing auroras may come from the Van Allen belt.

The space near the earth is filled with a stream of charged particles from the sun known as the "solar wind." Satellite explorations have shown that the solar wind distorts the earth's magnetic field, which thus forms a long "tail" on the side of the earth away from the sun.

Observations in the United States and in various European countries have shown that there is a very close connection between sunspot activity and disturbances in the earth's magnetism. When the sunspots are the most active, there are the greatest variations in the earth's magnetic field and the most brilliant displays of polar lights.

Cosmic rays from outer space also contribute to magnetic variations. (See the article The Cosmic Rays, in Volume 8.)

Thus far we have dealt with the effects of magnetism and with its numerous applications. The question now arises: what is the ultimate cause of magnetic fields of force and of polarity? Thus far the scientists have not been able to give a definite answer. It is quite generally agreed that magnetism results from the orderly arrangement or interaction of particles of matter within magnetic materials. According to one theory the molecules in such substances are tiny magnets. When they are all jumbled together within a given substance, pointing every which way, the magnetic forces involved cancel each other and the substance is not a magnet. But if the wee molecule-magnets are lined up so that all their north poles point in one direction and all their south poles in the opposite direction, the substance becomes a magnet with a north pole at one end and a south pole at the other.

Other scientists believe that the basic units in magnetic phenomena are not molecules but much smaller particles — the electrons that revolve about the nuclei of atoms and that also spin about their own axes. According to this theory, the manner in which the electrons revolve and rotate accounts for the magnetic effects.

ELECTRICAL PARTICLES FROM SUN

POLAR LIGHTS, PRODUCED BY FRICTION AS ELECTRICAL PARTICLES ENTER EARTH'S ATMOSPHERE

SUN

The atmosphere's resistance to electrical particles coming from the sun causes polar lights.

See also Vol. 10, p. 281: "Magnetism."

FUN WITH CHEMISTRY

A Topsy-turvy
Chemical-Magic Session

BY NELSON F.
BEELER

1. The fountain that starts spouting for no good reason.

WE SHALL assume that you have gone over the chemistry chapters of the "Projects and Experiments" section in Volume 4 and that you have already carried out the projects and experiments listed there. You are now ready to put on a chemical-magic show. It will be unusual because you are going to play the part of an idiotic chemist who has no idea how his chemical magic is going to turn out. In fact, everything he tries to demonstrate will seem to work in reverse.

Of course, for any kind of magic show you must keep up a running fire of talk, or "patter." This serves to draw the attention of the audience from your preparations and to make them think what you want them to think. Part of the fun of a magic performance is working up your "patter."

In the following pages, we present a routine consisting of a number of tricks. You will find, in the case of each trick, a description of what your audience will see and some little indication of the "patter" that might be used. Then there will be an explanation of how to set up the trick (in advance of the actual performance, of course) and a brief account of the chemistry involved.

The self-starting fountain

Begin by telling your audience that there is nothing to fear from these demonstrations, as no reaction can take place until you are ready for it. While you continue to talk in this vein, move a bottle from one end of the table to the center. Keep assuring your audience that you will let them know just what is going to happen in each one of your demonstrations. As you are delivering this "patter," the bottle you have just set in the center of the table will begin to spout like a fountain all by itself (Figure 1). You will appear to be embarrassed; you will tell the onlookers that you are sure you will be able to think of some way to make the fountain stop spouting. While you are deep in thought, the fountain stops all by itself. Quickly take away the offending bottle and go on with the next demonstration on the program.

The bottle (Figure 2) is a kind of miniature fire extinguisher. The first thing to do is to fit a single-hole stopper to the bottle. Then a medicine dropper with the rubber bulb removed is forced through the stopper from the underside so

2. How to prepare the self-starting fountain described on the preceding page. Details are given in the text.

that the tip of the dropper is just beneath the top opening of the stopper. The bottle contains a solution of baking soda and water; the level of the solution is about halfway up the medicine dropper. A small open vial of vinegar is supported inside the bottle by means of a piece of stiff wire held in place by the stopper (Figure 2). The bottle should be covered with black paper so that the audience will not be able to see the inside arrangements.

If you tilt the bottle as you move it, the vinegar will spill out into the soda solution. The soda and vinegar will then react to produce carbon-dioxide gas, which will drive out the soda solution through the medicine dropper in a fine jet. When the solution level drops below the dropper, the fountain will stop playing. The soda solution is harmless; all you have to do is to clean up the mess with a sponge before you go on to the next act.

A powder that bursts into flame

"Liquids seem to be a little undependable," you will say. "Solid materials are more reliable." Pick up a stoppered test tube from a rack and say: "I would now like to show you a really dependable powder." Let the audience see it in the bottom of the test tube. "First," you will say, "I shall pour out the powder onto the table here. When all the powder has been transferred to the table, we shall try a little experiment." But no sooner has the powder begun to pour out from the test tube when it will burst into flame (Figure 3).

The powder is a finely divided form of lead, called pyrophoric lead. To make it, add a solution of tartaric acid to a solu-

3. As the idiotic chemist pours out a "dependable powder" from a test tube, the powder bursts into flame.

4. To make the "dependable powder," heat some lead acetate in a Pyrex test tube, which is held with tongs.

tion of lead acetate. Lead tartrate is precipitated. Filter it and let it dry in the
air. Transfer the precipitate to a Pyrex
test tube, held with tongs, and heat the
tube, but not too strongly. (Hold the mouth
of the tube away from you, as in Figure 4.)
The lead tartrate is decomposed, fine particles of lead resulting. Stopper the tube
when it cools. Hold it three or four feet
above a cookie sheet or sheet of aluminum
foil. Then unstopper the tube and sprinkle
the contents onto the sheet. The lead particles will ignite as they come in contact
with the air. For the best results, prepare
the lead shortly before using it.

The magician produces
an unexpected sausage

You will now tell your audience in a
self-important manner: "I should like to
call to your attention the fact that many
chemical reactions require the addition of
heat. To demonstrate this, I shall heat a
liquid in a beaker placed over a heat source
[a spirit lamp or Bunsen burner]. By heating the beaker gently, I shall control the reaction so that it will proceed very gradually." Continue heating the beaker as you
discuss further the control you have over
this chemical reaction. Suddenly a large
sausagelike growth will emerge from the
mouth of the beaker (Figure 5).

The beaker contains paranitroaniline
to the depth of an inch. A small amount
of concentrated sulfuric acid is added to
make a paste. (CAUTION: Be careful not
to splash any of the acid onto your skin, as
it can produce burns. If you do spill any
on yourself, flush it off immediately with
plenty of water.) When you heat the paste,
you will produce a plastic material (the
"sausage"), which is bulky as well as lightweight because it is filled with air bubbles.

When is a liquid
not a liquid?

Next pick up from the table a flask
containing a liquid. Tell your audience
that you would like them to pass the flask
from hand to hand to observe that the liquid
in it is clear and colorless. "You need not
be afraid," you will add, "that the liquid will

undergo any change while you are passing it
around because, as you can see, I am not doing anything to it." But, strangely enough,
as the flask is passing from hand to hand,
the liquid in it begins to "freeze." In a
short time, the material in the bottle is completely solid, and the bottle and its contents
have become quite hot, though not uncom-
fortably so (Figure 6).

The trick is done best with sodium-
acetate crystals. Place the crystals just as
they come from the reagent jar in a clean
flask. Put the flask in a large container of
water; heat the water and let it boil until
the crystals have completely melted. Cover

5. The idiotic chemist pours liquid in a beaker (A) and
lights a spirit lamp under it (B). Result: a sausage (C).

the mouth of the flask with a piece of aluminum foil to keep dust particles from falling
in. Allow the flask to cool slowly, being
careful not to move it. The contents will
stay liquid; they make up what is called a
supersaturated solution (see Index). Just
before handing the flask around, drop in a
tiny crystal of sodium acetate; be sure that
your audience does not see you do so. The
whole liquid will then begin to crystallize.

Photographer's hypo (sodium thiosulfate) can be used for this trick. It is easier to get, but its action is not so dependable. To prepare the hypo solution, add the crystals to hot water until no more will dissolve. Filter the hot solution through a small bit of absorbent cotton; be sure that no solid crystals remain. Then allow the hypo solution to cool.

Whether your flask contains sodium acetate or hypo solution, you can use the contents again for the same kind of demonstration. Simply heat the flask, and then let the solution cool slowly.

6. A flask that contains a liquid is passed around. The liquid in the flask begins to "freeze" and soon is a solid.

The not-quite-so-
colorless water

"As you all know, water is a colorless liquid. Here is some." Proceed to pour water from a pitcher into a clean drinking glass and show that it is indeed colorless. "I am going to show you," you will add, "that the shape of the container has nothing to do with the color of the water." To prove your point, pour some water from the same pitcher into a wineglass. To everyone's surprise (and yours, too!), the liquid becomes wine-colored. Next, pour the contents of both glasses and the pitcher into a milk bottle. Slowly the liquid in the bottle will turn to "milk" (Figure 7).

The "water" is actually very dilute hydrochloric acid; the solution is prepared by adding about fifteen drops of concentrated hydrochloric acid to a quart of water. Add several drops of the indicator phenolphthalein to the acid in the pitcher. The color of the indicator is not affected by the acid; hence the "water" in the pitcher remains colorless. The wineglass contains a very small amount of sodium-hydroxide solution, a base. This neutralizes the acid, and the solution will become red in color. The milk bottle has a small amount of hypo solution * in it. The excess acid from the pitcher breaks this material down and produces a suspension of finely divided sulfur, which looks like milk.

You will have to practice this trick to get just the right amount of acid and base, but once you have found the proper quantities to use, it is easy to work the demonstration successfully each time.

Some more
"colorless water"

"I don't know just what happened," you will remark, "but I still insist that water remains colorless, no matter what the shape of the container is. Let us try again." To be sure of the results this time, you discard the pitcher, drinking glass, wineglass and bottle you used in the last demonstration, and you use a new set of these containers. You add about the same amount of water from the pitcher to each of the two glasses and the milk bottle. This time you get a red liquid in the drinking glass, a white one in the wineglass and a blue one in the milk bottle. Apparently, the water will not stay colorless, no matter what you do. Admit defeat and go on to the next demonstration.

For this second "colorless-water" demonstration, the solution in the pitcher is sodium hydroxide. The drinking glass contains a few drops of phenolphthalein solution; the wineglass, a little lead-acetate solution; the milk bottle, a small amount of copper-sulfate solution. The red color in the drinking glass is due to the indicator it contains; you will recall that this indicator is red to bases, such as sodium hydroxide. The "water" in the wine glass is white because of the formation of white lead hydroxide. The liquid in the milk bottle turns blue as copper hydroxide is formed. A piece of black friction tape wrapped around

* To produce the solution, use about a half teaspoonful of hypo crystals and just enough water to dissolve them.

7. The idiotic chemist pours water into a drinking glass (A); the water undergoes no change. It becomes wine-colored when it is poured into a wineglass (B). When it is poured into a milk bottle, it turns into "milk" (C).

the bottom of the milk bottle will hide the copper-sulfate solution in the bottom. In each case, pour in just enough sodium hydroxide from the pitcher to make each color appear in turn.

Patriotic fireproofing

You are now ready to demonstrate the All-American Method for Fireproofing Paper. A piece of nearly white paper is attached to a line by means of clothespins or paper clips (Figure 8). Using an insect spray gun, you proceed to wet the paper. You explain that you are fireproofing it and you discuss the value of the process. As you continue to talk and to work the gun, an American flag appears on the paper.

The paper has been treated with two reagents made up in fairly concentrated solutions. The chemicals can be swabbed onto the paper with a piece of absorbent cotton wrapped around a wooden splint. The stripes that will later be red are put on the paper with potassium thiocyanate (sometimes called sulfocyanate). The blue background for the stars is made with potassium ferrocyanide. (Do not use potassium ferricyanide, which will not produce a blue color.) The white stripes and stars that will appear on the American flag will represent untreated paper, of course. The paper is allowed to dry thoroughly. At even a short distance, the audience will not be able to see that the paper has been treated since both of the chemicals you have used leave fairly colorless traces.

The spray gun contains a concentrated solution of ferric (Iron III) chloride. The iron compound in the spray reacts with one chemical on the paper to produce red ferric thiocyanate and with the other chemical to produce blue ferric ferrocyanide. Be sure to use as fine a spray as possible in order to keep the colors from running into the white parts of the flag.

A startling blow-up

Here is how you can produce a startling flare-up and a loud explosion quite easily and safely. Prepare your audience by showing them a can with a press-on cover. Light a candle stub and set it upright inside the can; then tell the onlookers that you

8. Our chemist tries to fireproof a piece of paper by spraying it (A). An American flag appears on it (B).

9. What happens when the idiotic chemist tries to extinguish a lighted candle in a can by blowing into the can.

FUNNEL FILLED WITH LYCOPODIUM POWDER AND TILTED —

10. Cutaway drawing of the can in Figure 9, showing the tilted position of the funnel used in the demonstration.

propose to blow out the candle. Replace the cover and blow forcibly into a rubber tube which protrudes from the bottom of the can. The top will fly off with a loud bang and a high flame will spring up from the can (Figure 9). Apparently your plan to blow out the candle backfired.

The can is prepared as in Figure 10. The candle can be made to stand upright in the bottom of the can if you put a little molten candle wax on a small piece of cardboard and set the candle in position on the wax. The small funnel is set in the can with its wide part uppermost and its narrow neck protruding through a hole punched in the bottom of the can (Figure 10). About a tablespoonful of lycopodium powder is poured into the funnel before the show begins. Lycopodium powder is a collection of spores from the lycopodium plant, a species of club moss. It would be advisable to dry the lycopodium powder on a cookie sheet placed in the oven just before you are going to use it, since it works best if it is very, very dry. The funnel must be tipped toward the candle so that the powder will be blown directly into the candle flame and not into the space alongside it.

When you blow forcibly into the can, the lycopodium powder will be distributed throughout the interior of the can in the form of a finely divided cloud of dust. The candle ignites the dust nearest it. The flame then spreads quickly throughout the whole interior because there is a great deal of air present compared to the amount of combustible material. The heat resulting from this rapid burning causes the air in the can to expand and forces off the cover. There is no danger from this demonstration if you will continue to blow into the can until the flame dies out, which it will do very quickly. Dust explosions of this sort occur once in a while in coal mines where there is a good deal of dust and also in places where flour or sugar is stored. In places such as these, extreme care must be taken to prevent open flames or sparks from igniting the dust.

Flour is sometimes used in this demonstration instead of lycopodium powder. It does not work so well and should be used only if the powder is not available.

You can have a little fun with your audience by offering to repeat the dust explosion for them. Tell them to watch the can very carefully this time. As they are concentrating on the can, a tremendous bang is heard — a bang that does not seem to proceed from the can at all. If you have prepared the scene well, the onlookers will just about jump from their chairs.

Actually, there is nothing chemical about this particular "explosion"; it is produced by a broom hidden from view behind the table. You are to hold the broom near the end of the handle with one hand, thus leaving the other hand free for pointing at the can and in other ways diverting the attention of your audience. Place your foot on the straw part of the broom. When you let go of the handle, it will strike the floor with a resounding whack. Since your audience is tense, waiting for the explosion in the can to go off, this bang will really startle them.

The blazing handkerchief that does not burn

After everyone has recovered from the effects of the double "explosion," you are ready to talk about flames and the chemistry of oxidation. Say that you will demonstrate the chemistry of flames by burning up your pocket handkerchief. Take your handkerchief from your pocket and dip it

The final touches

It is about time to bring your routine to an end, so you proceed to wash your hands with water and a little soap, thanking your audience for having been so attentive. You rinse your hands in clear water and wipe them on a towel. Both your hands and the towel will become a dark blue.

The apparently clear rinse water is really a solution of ferric chloride. The towel has previously been dipped in potassium ferrocyanide solution and has been allowed to dry. The reaction between the two chem-

11. The chemist dips his handkerchief in a solution and squeezes it to get rid of some of the liquid (A). Then he holds the handkerchief with a pair of tongs and sets fire to it (B). The handkerchief will be undamaged (C).

in a solution which is on the table in front of you. Squeeze the cloth to get rid of some of the liquid. Then hold the handkerchief with a pair of tongs and light it with a match. It will catch fire readily enough; keep on waving it back and forth until the flame dies out (Figure 11). To the surprise of everyone in the audience, the handkerchief will be undamaged.

The solution is made from equal parts of rubbing alcohol and water. It will be the alcohol and not the cloth that will catch fire; and it will burn with such a cool flame that the cloth will not become hot enough to char or catch fire itself. It might be well to try the solution on a piece of cloth before the demonstration. If the flame does not last as long as you would like, add a little more alcohol to the solution and try again.

icals produces a blue ferric ferrocyanide. This can be removed from your hands easily with a little household ammonia and water later on.

As a grand finale, touch a match to a piece of heavy cardboard that is hanging behind the lecture table. The written words "That's all" will be seen to burn themselves slowly into the cardboard (Figure 12).

The words have been written previously on the cardboard with a "pen" consisting of a swab of cotton on a stick and with a saturated water solution of potassium nitrate as the ink. Be sure that each letter of the writing is connected to the next one. When you touch a match to the first letter, the fire will continue to burn along the entire set of words. The reason is that the potassium nitrate is an excellent oxida-

12. When a match is touched to a "blank" piece of heavy cardboard, the written words "That's all" appear on the cardboard.

tion agent; it provides a quantity of oxygen sufficient to support combustion. It is used as one of the ingredients of gunpowder for this reason.

Precautions
to be taken

All the above demonstrations can be carried out safely. You should remember, however, that in many of them you are dealing with flames. You should be prepared to take care of any fire that might start. Have a large piece of heavy cardboard ready to set upon anything that continues to blaze longer than you want it to. It would be a good idea, too, to keep two large pails, one containing sand and the other water, under the table, ready for every emergency.

The routine we have given you above will be successful only if you practice each one of the demonstrations until you are letter-perfect in it. It goes without saying that you must know at all times what you are doing and why you are doing it. You must be a pretty alert chemist to give the "idiotic chemist" routine effectively.

13. The formidable-looking salt-making machine that is supposed to transform sawdust or sand into pure salt.

An encore — the
salt-making machine

If an encore is called for, prepare your masterpiece — a salt-making machine. Connect up, in any way you please, the glassware and rubber tubing you have used in the previous demonstrations; the only requirement is that the apparatus should look as complicated as possible. It would be a good idea to set a Bunsen burner or a spirit lamp under a beaker containing water somewhere in the assembly. At one end of the apparatus there is to be a big glass jar, with the bottom covered with sawdust or sand to a depth of three or four inches. Attach a string to a salt shaker containing salt; bury the shaker in the sawdust (or sand), letting the end of the string hang over the rim of the jar. At the end of the apparatus nearer the audience, set a flat plate with tubing dipping into it. Figure 13 gives you some idea of the way in which the salt-making machine might be set up.

Explain to your audience, as you are arranging the equipment, that you are going to make salt from the sawdust (or sand) in the glass jar. "As the salt is prepared," you will add, "it will drop into the flat plate here. I will invite you to taste it so that you will see it is real salt." Start the equipment working. It will look particularly impressive if you can heat some water and bring it to a boil. At the climax of the operation, pull up the salt shaker by the string attached to it from the big jar at the end of the salt-making machine, and sprinkle some salt on the flat plate in front of your audience. Then make your getaway!

Actually, this device will function only if salt from the shaker hidden in the can is sprinkled on the plate!

L— SAWDUST

MAMMALS IN THE WATER

Fishlike Creatures That Suckle Their Young

SEVERAL times in the long history of the vertebrates, or back-boned animals, species that once lived on land have invaded the seas. The marine turtles and the crocodilians (the crocodiles and their kin), descendants of land-dwelling reptiles, are now perfectly at home in the water. Many types of birds have also become specialized for this mode of life; among them are the penguins, auks, cormorants and loons. Various mammals, too, including the otters, seals and walruses, are at home in aquatic surroundings. The most highly specialized of the marine mammals, however, are the manatees, dugongs, whales, dolphins and porpoises, with which we shall deal in this chapter.

The manatees and dugongs belong to the order of the Sirenia; the whales, dolphins and porpoises, to the order of the Cetacea. Although the two groups have quite different ancestry, they are similarly specialized for the way of life that they have adopted. They have developed tapering, streamlined bodies with which they can move easily through the water in swimming and diving. Their forelegs have been greatly modified, having become well-developed flippers, used for steering. These mammals have lost all traces of external hind legs. The hind end now terminates in a horizontally flattened tail, which gives the propulsive thrust in swimming. The Sirenia and Cetacea have extremely short necks and little if any body hair. In spite of their many fishlike characteristics, however, they are true mammals, for they are warm-blooded, placental (see Index under Placenta) and suckle the young.

The Cetacea became marine mammals quite early in the history of mammalian evolution. In all probability, their ances-tors were primitive land carnivores, called creodonts. The primitive whales known as zeuglodonts swam in the sea some 45,000,-000 years ago. The nostrils of these animals had already started their migration toward the top part of the head (that is where the nostrils of modern whales are located); their hind legs had already disappeared. Their bodies were considerably slimmer than those of modern whales, so that they must have looked a great deal like sea serpents. Like the marine reptiles of previous times, the zeuglodonts had elongated jaws; their teeth were like those of early land-dwelling flesh eaters. They were quite large — up to 70 feet in length.

Today there are a number of species of Cetacea, as we shall see. Some are comparatively small; others are among the largest of all living animals. One species — the blue, or sulphur-bottom, whale — is the largest animal that has ever existed upon the earth, as far as we know; it reaches 100 feet in length and weighs up to 150 tons. Its proportions are far more massive than those of the bulkiest dinosaurs that lived in the Age of Reptiles.

The manatees and dugongs are probably descended from land-dwelling, vegetation-eating mammals that also numbered the elephants among their descendants. The modern Sirenia, which are also known as sea cows, feed on vegetation along ocean coasts or in rivers. Their heads are not at all fishlike, like those of whales. They have heavy, bristly jowls with nostrils set at the apex of a triangular-shaped muzzle. The nostrils are fitted with valves that can be closed in order to keep out water when the animal dives below the surface. The tail of the manatee is rounded; that of the dugong is crescent-shaped.

Manatees and dugongs swim through the water by moving the tail and front flippers up and down. However, the tail and flippers undulate out of phase; that is, they do not move up and down at the same time. The animals may remain under water for some time — as much as sixteen minutes in the case of the manatee.

Both the dugong and manatee have tough, leathery skin. The brain is small. The eyes are tiny; there are no external ears and the sense of smell is limited but not absent as is true with the whales. Manatees lack front teeth entirely as adults, but have a number of molar teeth that are continually replaced from the hind end of each tooth row. In the dugongs, there are only a few peglike crushing teeth, and the lower jaw carries a horny pad; the males also possess a front pair of upper tusks formed from the incisor teeth. Aquatic plants are digested in the sirenian's complex stomach; the intestine is extremely long. Young dugongs and manatees are born in the water; they are nursed at the mother's teats located high on her chest.

It is thought that some, at least, of the fanciful legends of mermaids — creatures with a woman's body above the waist and a fish's tail — may have been based on the appearance of the sirenians. Certainly these ungainly looking animals could never have been mistaken for human beings at close range. If they were seen from a distance, however, this fancied resemblance would not be so farfetched, for the sirenians frequently stand erect in the water, supported by their tails. Their heads are often draped with loosened vegetation resembling long hair; they suckle their young in an almost human fashion.

The American manatee (genus *Trichechus*) inhabits the Atlantic coast of the Americas from Florida, around the Caribbean, to the mouths of the Amazon and Orinoco rivers. The animal is not found at sea but may occur in island lagoons as much as eighty miles from the nearest

N. Y. Zool. Soc.

Captive manatees in an aquarium. These amiable creatures browse on plants along sea coasts and up rivers.

mainland coast. This slow-moving and amiable creature has been unforgivably slaughtered almost to the point of extinction. Fortunately, efforts have been made to protect manatees in Florida so that they may not become entirely exterminated in that area. Another species of manatee lives along the coast of West Africa; it may ascend large rivers for over a hundred miles.

Manatees are able to live equally well in fresh, brackish and salt water. They travel in small bands and remain near shore, feeding on various aquatic plants. The upper lip of the manatee is split down the middle, and the two halves, which are strongly muscled, work against one another in cropping plants. The front flippers are used to stuff the vegetable material into the mouth; the food is then chewed with deliberation. If the animals are disturbed, they sink out of sight and swim away under water.

A single young manatee is born after a gestation period of about 150 days. The young is born in the water, but immediately after birth, the mother carries the little animal on her back, completely out of the water, for some 45 minutes. Then she gradually submerges the newborn during the following two-hour period.

The dugong (*Dugong*) inhabits the waters along the coasts of the Indian Ocean, from central East Africa to Indonesia and northern Australia. It may grow to a length of ten feet, exceeding the manatee by a good two feet. Unlike the manatee, the dugong is almost strictly marine and thus does not ascend rivers very far. Dugongs are sluggish animals, drifting with the tide back and forth in shallow waters where they feed. They crop seaweeds and other aquatic vegetation by wrapping the whole, extended upper lip around the material, pressing it against the lower lip and pulling it away. Apparently they do not use their flippers in feeding. Though formerly found in large herds, extensive, ruthless hunting has greatly thinned out the numbers of dugongs. Like the manatees, they are defenseless against man; dugongs, however, have been seen driving

sharks away by butting the fish with their heads.

Whales occur in all oceans and seas

There are about a hundred known species of whales, which comprise two main groups. One group — the whalebone, or baleen, whales — includes the right whales, rorquals (blue, fin and humpback whales) and gray whales. In the other group — the toothed whales — we find the sperm whales, beaked whales, white whales, dolphins and porpoises. The largest cetacean, as we have mentioned, is the blue whale; some of the porpoises and dolphins do not exceed much more than 5 or 6 feet in length. Whales occur in all open seas and oceans; some live in tropical rivers; and one species, the Chinese lake dolphin, inhabits the Tung Ting Lake in Hunan Province, China, 600 miles up the Yangtse River. Many cetaceans migrate long distances between subpolar latitudes and tropical waters.

Both small and large whales are capable of swimming at a steady speed of 15 to 20 knots. Sudden bursts of higher speeds are made in capturing food or escaping danger. A whale swims by straight up and down movements of its tail, which makes up the hinder third of the body. The tail is divided into the tail fin, or flukes, and the tail proper, a solid cone of large muscles and straplike sinews. When the cetacean begins the downstroke of the tail, the tail is at its greatest angle to the trunk, and the flukes are horizontal. As the tail moves down, the flukes are bent upward; and as the tail continues downward, the flukes gradually reach a horizontal position again. During the upstroke, as the tail moves upward, the flukes first bend downward and then again straighten to the horizontal at the end of the upstroke. The effect of moving the inclined plane of the flukes up and down is to provide a thrust, driving the animal forward. The front flippers stabilize the whale.

All whales can remain under water for considerable periods; the Greenland right whale and the bottlenose whale seem to

NORTH ATLANTIC RIGHT WHALE.

BLUE WHALE.

FINBACK WHALE.

WHALES AND THEIR KIN

Whales, dolphins and porpoises, which belong to the order Cetacea, are marine animals and look like fishes. They are really mammals, however. They are warm-blooded, breathe air through lungs, bring forth living young and suckle their offspring. Their ancestors lived on land many millions of years ago. On these two pages we show some well-known members of the order.

Amer. Mus. of Nat. Hist.

SOWERBY WHALE.

SPERM WHALE.

HUMPBACK WHALE.

BOTTLENOSE WHALE.

ATLANTIC KILLER.

COMMON DOLPHIN.

GRAMPUS.

HARBOR PORPOISE.

WHITE WHALE.

hold honors, submerging for 80 and 120 minutes respectively. The sperm whale, which may stay under for some 75 minutes, can sound to a depth of 3,000 to 5,000 feet. The cetaceans are capable of such feats because of special adaptations of the respiratory and circulatory systems. The nostrils, which form the blow hole, are on top of the head, and the nasal, or air, passages go directly to the lungs without joining the throat. The very elastic and extensible lungs are quickly filled with large volumes of air when the animal comes to the surface. Special networks of blood vessels throughout the body store up an extra supply of oxygen. When a dive is made, valves close the nostrils; the heartbeat slows down and oxygen is conserved by the shunting away of blood from the non-vital centers of the body.

Under the paper-thin, hairless skin of the whale lies a thick layer of fibrous tissue, which is impregnated with oil; this is known as blubber. A poor conductor of heat, blubber partially insulates the warm-blooded whale from the cold water in which it swims; but in spite of this blubber layer, most whales when at rest lose heat more rapidly than they produce it and therefore swim to keep warm. The blubber probably serves also as a food reservoir, a function supported by the fact that baleen whales have a much reduced blubber layer in winter when they eat very little. Blubber also reduces the specific gravity of the whale and probably forms an elastic covering that allows for changes in volume during deep dives.

The whale's brain is larger than that of any other animal. The sense of smell is poor or absent; the eyes are small, but under-water vision is fairly good. A whale's sense of hearing is acute, a fact that is probably correlated with the phenomenon of sound production by the animals. For example, the bottle-nosed dolphin whistles, barks and makes a snapping sound with its jaws; the white whale produces high-pitched whistles and squeals, ticking and clucking sounds and noises suggesting mewing, chirping, trilling and bell-like notes; other whales also whistle and bellow. The sig-

nificance of these sounds is not yet understood. Some of them are probably means of communicating between individuals of the same species. Since many whales form herds, called gams, the production of sounds may keep a school of these animals together. Furthermore, whales may use echo-sounding to locate obstacles in much the same way as bats do (see Index under Bats); this would be especially important for deep-diving cetaceans.

During the mating season, male and female whales swim side by side, rub and nuzzle one another, give each other resounding blows with their flippers and jump clear of the water, falling back with a great splash. Normally only one young is produced after a gestation period that varies from about 1 year for the sperm and fin whales to 180 days for the porpoises. At the end of the gestation period, delivery of the young from the female's womb is rapid; the infant swims from birth and must come to the surface to breathe in the first few seconds after its emergence. Within the first 24 hours, the new-born whale begins to nurse from its mother's mammary glands, which are situated in a pocket on the rear belly and are enclosed in a compressor muscle. Nursing by the infant is very brief. The mother, swimming slowly, turns on her side; as the infant touches the nipple of the mammary gland, milk is squirted into its mouth by a contraction of the muscle surrounding this gland. The milk is rich in mineral elements (which are essential for growth of the skeleton), proteins and fats. The mother blue whale, for example, gives about 200 pounds of this rich nourishment every day to her infant, which measures 20 feet in length and weighs 2 tons. On this diet the young grows rapidly. Young cetaceans nurse from 2 to 7 months after birth. Sexual maturity is reached by most whales in their third to fifth year.

The baleen whales are clearly distinguished from the toothed whales in their manner of feeding. Baleen whales lack teeth but possess sheets of a horny material, called baleen, that hang down from the upper jaw on either side of the roof of the mouth from front to back. Each sheet of baleen is fringed along the edge that faces down into the mouth. The mouth is immense, for the jaws make up a third of the length of the whale's body. The lower jaw forms a hoop that supports a huge pouch. When the mouth is closed, the rows of baleen sheets hang down into this pouch. The lips curve upward on each side of the mouth. When the baleen whale feeds, it moves through the water with its mouth open, taking in huge quantities of the shrimplike krill and other forms of plankton (see Index). This food is swept up against the matted surfaces of the fringed baleen sheets. The whale closes its mouth and raises its tongue against the palate. Water is forced out between the baleen sheets and the loose lips, and the filtered and unchewed food organisms are pushed back by the tongue and swallowed, entering a four-

ing even the largest whales; bay dolphins feed exclusively on water plants and vegetable matter washed down from the land.

Most toothed whales are active, fast-swimming mammals; many, such as the dolphins and porpoises, possess a fin on the back. The boutu, a porpoiselike creature of the Amazon Basin, has front flippers with much flexibility in the fingers. By using these flippers, the animal can lumber over various obstacles.

Perhaps the most impressive of toothed whales is the sperm whale, which grows to a length of 60 feet. It has an enormous square snout, filled with spermaceti. This substance is highly important to the whale; together with the thick layer of blubber and the oil-containing humps along its back, it seems to cushion and protect the vital organs of the whale from the effects of the excessive pressure at great depths.

A catch of baleen whales being towed by a whaling vessel to the factory ship for processing. The whales are inflated with air; as a result, they float. Modern whaling methods are extremely efficient.

chambered stomach where they are slowly digested. Baleen whales will also eat small fish, in addition to plankton organisms.

The toothed whales may possess many peglike teeth in both jaws, or have teeth in only the upper or lower jaw, or have very few teeth or lack teeth entirely. Many are active predators, feeding on fish and squids. Killer whales are fierce and cunning hunters, moving in packs and attack-

Unfortunately for the whale, the same substances so vital to its deep-sea life are greatly prized by man. Because of ruthless whaling ventures, the sperm whale, and other whale species as well, face extinction. Many international agreements have been made to limit the whaling catch and protect failing species, but they are difficult to enforce, and the sperm whale and others are in great danger. Modern whaling is done on a mass scale. The mother factory ship, in which the whales are processed, is accompanied by a fleet of smaller boats. The whole group may remain at sea for months at a time.

The sperm whale is found mainly in the southern oceans, but it ranges to subarctic and subantarctic waters. It is a fair swimmer, cruising along at four knots and capable of three times that speed if necessary. After a dive that may last an hour, the whale surfaces and blows a great cloud of spray from its blowhole. This water is not taken in by the whale's mouth, but is given off as water vapor by the blood in the whale's lungs and is condensed there as it accumulates under great pressure

Since a whale has lungs for breathing air, it may seem odd that a whale will die when cast up on land. The reason is that the great weight of the whale, no longer supported by water, crushes the lungs and causes the big animal to suffocate. Why, however, do whales and other cetaceans ever become stranded? Dead specimens may float ashore, of course. As for cetaceans found stranded while still alive, in many cases their bodies show evidences of serious infectious diseases. Either the sick animals drift ashore, or else they deliberately swim onto the land in a strange sort of reaction to their illness. Occasionally whole schools of whales are found stranded in what would appear to be an attempt at mass suicide. In some instances, whales have been known to swim ashore in order to escape the attacks of man.

Like all toothed whales, the sperm whale feeds on sea animals much larger than the tiny crustaceans and mollusks that serve as food for the baleen whales. If the marine animal that swallowed Jonah (according to the Bible story) was indeed a whale, it must have been a sperm whale, since it alone has a gullet big enough to swallow a man whole. There is no scientific evidence that the sperm whale is a man-eater.

The sperm whale's ordinary food and hereditary enemy is the giant squid. Whalers have occasionally witnessed duels to the death between these two monsters of the sea. Probably the most spectacular duels

of this sort take place in the natural lair of the squids, far below the surface of the sea. The stomachs of sperm whales are often found to contain the bodies of squids six or more feet long, with tentacles up to ten or fifteen feet in length. The hard, indigestible inner shell of the squid is responsible for the formation of ambergris in the sperm whale's intestine. Ambergris is a dark, sticky, ill-smelling substance, which is disgorged usually only by sick whales. It is found in large or small lumps floating on the sea or cast on shore. When it hardens it has a sweetish odor. This substance is rare and costly too, for it is used in making expensive perfumes.

Sperm whales are dark in color, sometimes black. The great white sperm whale described in MOBY-DICK, by the American novelist Herman Melville, was an albino, a great rarity. In the winter of 1951, an albino whale was caught and killed by Norwegian whalers off the coast of Peru. This was the first albino-whale catch to be recorded since the account of the legendary white whale in Melville's novel, which was published in the year 1851.

The pygmy sperm whale is the smallest member of the sperm-whale family. Though it is called a pygmy, this mammal, which averages about thirteen feet in length, is not exactly an aquarium pet. The most unusual feature of this relatively rare animal is the proportional size of the young. The calves are generally more than half as long as their parents at birth.

Sperm whale are members of the superfamily Physeteroidea (true, or blower, whales), one of the three subdivisions of the toothed whales. This superfamily also includes the curious beaked whales. The cowfish (which is neither a cow nor a fish!) is a beaked whale. It derives its name from the deep sound that it emits, suggesting the lowing of a cow. The bottle-nosed (or bottlenose) whale, so called because of the shape of its head, is the most important beaked whale, commercially; it is hunted for its spermaceti. It is the most dangerous of all whales to hunt, for it can sound to a depth of three thousand feet in two minutes when struck by a harpoon.

A bottle-nosed dolphin taking a between-meals snack. Dolphins rank with the more intelligent animals, they have been trained to retrieve various objects, to pull a surfboard and even to jump through a hoop.

The name Delphinoidea (dolphinlike cetaceans) is given to the second superfamily of the toothed whales. Some are called whales, some dolphins and some porpoises. The narwhal, a native of Arctic and North American waters, is twenty feet long and has one tooth: a nine-foot ivory tusk sticking out in front of its upper jaw.

The ferocious killer whale, found in every ocean, is actually a gigantic dolphin. It is the only cetacean that feeds on warm-blooded animals, including its own kin. This bloodthirsty mammal reaches a length of thirty feet and travels in small schools. It attacks almost any animal, including the largest whales, tearing out huge chunks of flesh with its powerful jaws.

Most dolphins, however, are milder-tempered and run in large schools. Averaging six to ten feet in length, the majority have long beaks and a dorsal fin. The most often seen is the friendly bottle-nosed dolphin. The common dolphin frequently accompanies ships at sea and gracefully leaps over the waves. Some have been clocked at thirty knots. The true porpoises belong to the dolphin group, but have round heads and measure four to six feet in length. The harbor porpoise is found in the shore waters of the Atlantic and Pacific.

The dolphins, especially the bottle-nosed variety, are noted for their great intelligence, apparently greater than that of the apes and perhaps even rivaling that of man. These animals have been taught to perform all kinds of complex acts. They communicate with each other by high-pitched or ultrasonic noises, which scientists are attempting to decode with the idea of understanding or even "talking" to these cetaceans. Dolphins themselves seem to mimic human speech in the presence of people. Like the whales mentioned above, they navigate by means of sonarlike emissions of high-frequency sound waves. They locate enemies, prey or underwater obstacles by the echoes produced as these sound waves bounce off objects back to the dolphins' ears.

The river dolphins constitute the third superfamily of toothed whales; they are a waning group. They include the La Plata and Amazon dolphins of South America and the Ganges River dolphin.

See also Vol. 10, p. 275: "Mammals."

ACCIDENT PREVENTION IN THE HOME

Safety Rules for All Members of the Family

BY GLADYS J. WARD

GENERALLY we think of the home as a place of refuge, where the members of the family are safe from the thousand-and-one dangers that confront us on the highways and byways. And yet, like so many popular ideas, this one does not hold water. The average home is one of the most dangerous places in the world; within its walls lurk the hazards of broken bones, electric shock, burns, poisoning and a host of other dangers. In a recent year, 35,000 Americans lost their lives because of accidents in their own homes. Over 5,000,000 more were hurt, and of these 140,000 suffered permanent injury. A great many of the tragedies happened to small children.

The majority of accidents at home are due to carelessness; they are caused in the main by articles that are out of place or in need of repair. That means that the majority of accidents are preventable. We should seek out all possible sources of accidents and should work out a systematic plan for avoiding them.

Fires and explosions

Fire is a useful servant; it may also become a ferocious enemy. Under control, in a furnace or stove, it keeps our buildings warm and cooks our food. But when fire gets out of hand, it is a dangerous foe. It strikes quickly, spreads rapidly and may cause injury or death.

Three things — fuel, heat and oxygen — are necessary to start a fire. The fuel may be the coal or oil or gas used for heating purposes; or it may be an inflammable cleaning fluid, or waste paper stored in a basement or attic. The heat may be provided by a lighted gas burner or match or an overheated electric wire. The oxygen is always available, since roughly one-fifth of the air is made up of this gas.

We can do nothing, of course, about eliminating oxygen in the home, since we need it for breathing purposes. But we should see to it that temperatures high enough to cause fires are restricted to our cooking and heating units; we should see to it, also, that potential fuels, other than those used for heating and cooking, are kept away from extreme heat.

More dangerous fires start in the basement than anywhere else, since the furnace and the hot-water heater are usually placed there. Hence we should regularly and carefully inspect our heating equipment. Furnaces should be installed at a safe distance from wooden partitions, beams or ceilings, and furnace ducts should be at least one inch away from these. A pipe passing through a wall or floor should be encased in a metal tube an inch larger in diameter than the pipe; this tube should be provided with tight metal caps at either side of the wall or floor.

The house heating system should be large enough to heat the home comfortably. A heater that is too small may be a hazard because it may be necessary to overfire the furnace in cold weather. The heating system should be equipped with ample safety controls. Each boiler should have a device limiting the temperature of the water to a safe point. For a gas-fired boiler the principal control is the gas pilot safety device, which shuts off the gas supply if the pilot light is not burning. For oil furnaces there is a safety combustion control, which prevents the continuous pumping of oil when the flame fails to ignite. It is hardly necessary to point out how dangerous it is to let your cellar be flooded with highly combustible fuel oil.

The illuminating gas used in cooking ranges, and in certain heating units, is highly explosive. If it escapes from the range or from a leaky pipe it may set the stage for a grim disaster, for the slightest spark will explode it. Should there be the faintest odor of unburned gas anywhere in the house, put out all flames. Never strike a match in order to locate the leak; use a flashlight. Open the windows wide; then call your gas company if you can not locate the source of the smell.

on the gas and lighting the match. Keep a watchful eye on any pots or kettles containing a liquid that is about to come to a boil. If it should boil over and put out the flame, gas would be set free. If such a thing happens, turn off the gas immediately and open the windows for a few minutes before relighting the burner. Never hang window curtains too near the range, since the draft from an open window might blow them on the flame.

Fire may sometimes break out when a house is struck by lightning. Carefully installed lightning rods on the house and near-by buildings will help to prevent fires by grounding the electricity during storms.

PRINCIPAL TYPES OF HOME ACCIDENT FATALITIES IN 1961

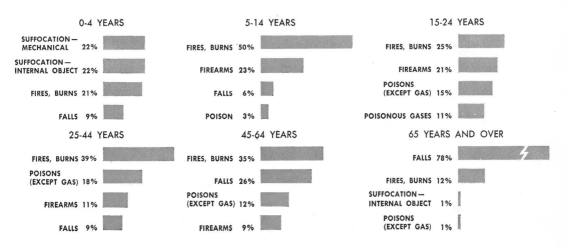

Note: These figures were compiled by the National Safety Council.

Sometimes the pilot light on a kitchen range becomes blocked up; it then goes out, allowing gas to escape. Clean the pilot light carefully, using a fine wire about the size of a hairpin. Burner cocks that become loose should be repaired or replaced at once, to avoid leaks. There is always the danger, too, that one may turn on a cock without noticing it.

Keep the surface and oven burners on gas and kerosene ranges clean and free of burned food. Light the gas oven according to the manufacturer's directions. Open the oven door to let air in before turning

If a television antenna has been installed on your roof, be sure that it has been properly grounded.

Misused or faulty electrical equipment is another common cause of fire. The trouble may come from electric wires that are exposed to a heavier current than they can safely carry; as a result, they become overheated. Fuses are inserted in each electric circuit to prevent such an occurrence. Each fuse generally consists of a strip of a bismuth alloy, with a remarkably low melting point. When the current becomes too strong for the wires, the heat causes the alloy to melt and thus breaks the circuit.

If a fuse blows (melts) on a given circuit, it may simply mean that you have been using too many pieces of electrical equipment at the same time. But if the fuse on this circuit blows again and again, it provides a warning that you should not ignore. Have a competent electrician check your wiring system; he may find it advisable to install heavier wiring or to add a circuit or two to the ones you already have.

Always have the wiring system checked before buying heavy electrical equipment. You may find it necessary to install special heavy-duty wire for the electric range, clothes dryer and ironing machine. Use electrical appliances and cords according to the written directions that accompany the equipment. Light sockets are made for lighting purposes; appliances such as irons should be plugged into appliance outlets — never into light sockets. When disconnecting any appliance, pull on the plug, never on the cord.

Worn-out cords can also lead to trouble. It is a dangerous practice to run cords under rugs, over radiators or through door jambs, since this causes undue wear. Promptly repair or replace frayed cords.

Inflammable liquids are a constant fire hazard

Inflammable liquids like gasoline, kerosene, oils, paint and turpentine are a constant fire hazard. Of course we should never under any circumstances store gasoline inside a house. If we must keep kerosene cans there, we should be sure that they are tightly closed, clearly labeled and stored far away from all sources of heat. Avoid the dangerous practice of using kerosene to start or kindle a fire in a stove or furnace. Kerosene will start a fire quickly, it is true; but you may find yourself with a much bigger fire on your hands than you bargained for.

Among the inflammable liquids that cause explosions are various dry-cleaning fluids. Keep such fluids far away from any open flame or source of heat. Open the windows wide when you clean a gar-

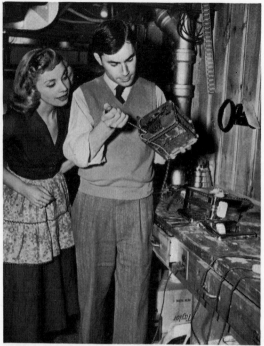

National Board of Fire Underwriters

This home handyman, repairing a toaster, may unwittingly remove safeguards provided by the manufacturer to prevent overheating and shock. Let an expert do the work.

ment, or, better still, do your dry cleaning out-of-doors. Never smoke or have lighted cigarettes around while the cleaning is going on. Keep the container of the fluid tightly sealed when it is not in use. Children should not be permitted to use cleaning fluids.

If you polish furniture or apply stain with an oil or wax that is inflammable, be sure that there is no flame near by. Use only a little at a time and rub it in well. Any oily cloths that are to be kept even a short time should be stored in tightly covered metal containers away from fire and heat.

A fireplace in a home is a joy for everyone if it is used properly; but it may also present a serious fire hazard. To prevent sparks from sputtering kindling or logs from igniting objects within the room, you should set a sturdy wire screen across the opening of the fireplace as soon as a fire is lighted. Do not permit children to play near the screen; they may knock it down and forget to replace it. Before you go to bed, be sure that the fire has been put out;

keep the screen in place as an added precaution. Sometimes sparks from a fireplace may issue from the chimney and set fire to the shingles of the roof. A spark arrester — a screen set across the opening of the chimney — will help to prevent such fires. So will the use of shingles made of a non-inflammable material like asbestos.

The Christmas tree is a symbol of good cheer; it is also a real fire hazard. Never set lighted wax candles on the branches; use electric bulbs that have adequate wiring. Do not decorate the tree with objects made of paper, cotton or similar materials; candy canes, oranges, nuts and apples make just as colorful ornaments and they are infinitely safer. Bear in mind, too, that the longer the tree remains in the house, the more it dries out; and the more it dries out, the more of a fire hazard it is.

Smoking has caused many a disastrous fire. The smoker should never put a lighted cigar or cigarette on a table or bureau top. He may be careful to have the lighted end protrude beyond the edge; he may intend to pick up the cigar or cigarette in just a minute or two. But

American Mutual Liability Insurance Co.

Tossing oily or greasy rags into a stack of papers and boxes invites trouble. The rags may ignite spontaneously and set the boxes and perhaps the house on fire.

suppose he forgets to do so? Smoking in bed is also dangerous. Many a tragedy has resulted when a smoker dozed off.

We have already spoken of fires starting from waste materials left about the house — stacks of old paper, oily rags, rubbish and wooden boxes in the attic or basement. Materials like greasy and oily cloths may catch fire even without an external agent, like a match or a spark; they may ignite from spontaneous combustion. Here is what happens. The inflammable materials, the oil or the grease, contained in the rags, gradually undergo oxidation — that is, they gradually combine with the oxygen of the air even at ordinary room temperature. As a result of oxidation heat is released. The oily or greasy cloths retain a good deal of this heat, and the remaining oil or grease combines more readily than before with the oxygen of the air. This raises the temperature still more, and oxidation goes on at a more rapid rate. At last the temperature is so high that the materials burst into flame. Good housekeeping will help to prevent fires of this kind. We should keep attics, basements and closets cleared of any rubbish that might form such a fire trap. We should burn all greasy or oily cloths, and all cloths used to wipe paint from our hands, unless we provide a closed receptacle for them.

Here are a few more suggestions. Use fire-resistant materials as much as possible for curtains, draperies, upholstered furniture and covers for ironing boards. Glass-fiber materials are ideal in this respect. Keep matches in a metal container with a tightly closed top and set it high enough so that the children will not be able to reach it. The metal container will also keep mice and rats from nibbling at the matches and possibly causing them to burst into flame.

Suppose that, in spite of all your precautions, fire should break out. You should always be well prepared for such an emergency. Keep fire escapes clear of obstacles such as flowerpots or boxes. Be sure that every door leading out-of-doors can easily be opened from the inside at all times. If you live in a large house, familiarize yourself with all the exits that could be used when fire breaks out, so that if flames block one exit, you may at once make for another. It might be well to have family drills, so that each person may know what to do and where to go in case of fire.

Automatic sprinkling systems, which release a spray of water when the temperature rises above a certain level, are efficient but are too costly for the average home. On the other hand small fire extinguishers are not expensive and they are effective if you catch a fire in the early stages. When you choose a fire extinguisher, be sure that you will be able to have it recharged in your own town. Have it inspected regularly to see that it is filled and ready for use. If your home has more than one story it would be well to provide extinguishers for each floor.

Falls

A bad spill may cause painful bruises or broken bones; a particularly serious tumble may prove fatal. A number of different conditions and practices may be responsible for falls; we should be on our guard against them all.

Many bad falls take place on staircases. Harmless-looking rugs at the top and bottom of stairs are responsible for many a "tail spin." Either remove such rugs or else anchor them with a non-slip device. Children should be trained never to leave objects on stairs; adults, too, might do well to keep this in mind.

Staircases are doubly perilous in the dark. Install convenient light switches at both the top and the bottom of each stairway in the house, including the basement stairs; outside stairs should also be effectively lighted. As an added safety measure, it would be well to paint the last step in the basement white.

The staircase should be carefully guarded in homes where there are very young children. In such homes, gates at the head and the foot of open stairways are a must; but remember that they give no protection at all unless they are kept closed at all times except when an adult or older child is about to go up or down. Children, even older children, should never be permitted to slide down the banisters.

Those who are having new homes built should keep all these facts in mind. Of course one way of avoiding the problem of stairs is to build a one-story house, without a basement. If stairs are installed, there should be no "winders" or circular stairs. The risers should be not more than seven and a half inches high; six and a half inches would be better. The width of the tread or step plus the nosing or edge should be at least eleven and a half inches. One sturdy handrail or, better still, two should be provided.

A good ladder is an asset; but if it is wobbly, topheavy, worn out or placed unsafely, it is a hazard that requires your prompt attention. Be sure that your ladder can safely support your weight; be sure that you never leave it in a place where somebody can stumble on it. Above all, never use makeshift ladders made up of chairs, boxes or anything else that happens to be near at hand.

The best way to avoid a fall in walking over a slippery floor or sidewalk is to remove its slippery coating. If you spill liquid or drop fat or peelings upon the floor, clean the floor immediately. Ice on steps, porch or walk should be covered with sand, ashes or rock salt as soon as possible.

If you have to grope your way in the darkness in a room, because the switch or pull cord is set far within it, you may run the risk of tripping over a toy wagon or some blocks. Try to place switches near the doors so that you can turn on the light before actually entering the rooms or just as you enter them. In any case, keep passageways clear within the room.

There have been many jokes about the person who slips on a bar of soap in the bathtub and falls with a resounding crash or splash, but that situation is funny only in cartoons. Many a fall will be prevented if the bathtub or shower has a secure grab-rail within easy reach of the bather. A rubber mat placed under the shower will also be helpful in preventing a bad fall.

How not to use a ladder! You should keep both feet on the rungs while working. Never use a shutter, window sill or other projection as an extra rung, for broken bones or fatal injury may result from such carelessness.

Inspect your yard regularly. Holes in the ground should be refilled promptly with dirt. Loose wire and boards bristling with nails should be removed. Garden tools like rakes and hoes should be kept in their proper storage place and not left in the path of the next passer-by, who may be you!

When you have checked all your equipment and surroundings, you must take still other precautions against accident. Try to avoid extreme fatigue. A tired person is particularly likely to fall; if he is not only tired but in a hurry as well, the chances of a fall are even greater. Absentmindedness is another potential cause of injury. Daydreaming is harmless when you are basking in the sun in your backyard; it is downright dangerous when you work on a high perch like a stepladder.

Burns and scalds

Among the most painful of injuries are those caused by burns or scalds. Such injuries may result, of course, when fire breaks out in the house; but they may also come about in many other ways. They may be caused when you upset pots and pans, containing hot liquids, because they have been left too near the edge of a table or because their handles protrude beyond the edge of the kitchen range. The remedy is obvious enough. Set hot coffee pots well back from the edge of the table; turn the handles of saucepans and other containers away from the edge of the stove.

Keep thick pot holders within easy reach near the range and use them in handling hot utensils on the range and in the oven. When broiling meat avoid too hot a flame; you may be spattered with burning fat when you open the oven door. If you use a cook stove, never let it become overheated. Be careful when you carry a pot or pail full of scalding water.

Pressure saucepans and cookers greatly reduce the time necessary for cooking foods, but since they contain live steam under considerable pressure, they may cause face-scarring burns if you open them prematurely. Some pressure pans can not be opened at all until all the pressure has been removed, thus insuring a large degree of safety. The most reliable rule to apply here is to follow the directions given by the manufacturer.

Electric shock

The current that runs through the electric wires in our homes does not exceed 125 volts. Since it takes from 1,800 to 2,000 volts to kill a condemned prisoner in the electric chair, the danger of electrocution in the home may seem very slight. It is true that if the average person comes in contact with the house current he will probably receive a disagreeable shock and no more, *provided that his body is dry.* The reason is that the human body normally has a high degree of resistance to the electric current. However, this degree of resistance depends upon a number of factors. If the skin is dry, the resistance is

from five to twenty times as great as when the skin is wet. If a person standing in a bathtub full of water touches a defective electric fixture, he may well receive a fatal shock. Even a comparatively mild shock may prove fatal to a person with a weak heart or in a generally weakened condition. We should therefore avoid all contact with the house electric current.

We have already discussed the matter of keeping electrical equipment in good working order. Here are some further suggestions. No wall outlet should be placed within reach of the bathtub or washboard or kitchen sink — the places where water is made available to members of the family. Unfortunately, in some houses that is just where wall outlets are located. In such cases, remember that you should never touch either the outlet or any equipment connected with it with wet hands. Above all, never touch anything connected with the electric current of your house while you are in the bathtub.

Many outlets are only slightly above floor levels, so that childish fingers can probe their dangerous depths with hairpins or similar objects. It would be well to provide all such outlets with guards, which permit access to the socket holes only when a plug is to be inserted.

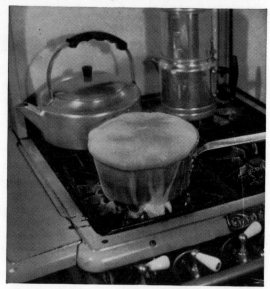

American Mutual Liability Insurance Co.

Household gas may be hazardous. Do not allow liquids to boil over and put out the flame, for gas will escape.

If you wish to repair a worn-out electric cord, be sure that the appliance is disconnected. Many a homeowner has absentmindedly snipped a cord above the frayed part without bothering to disconnect it, with most unhappy results. It is best to leave complicated repair jobs to a competent electrician.

Poisons and poisonous gases

One way of preventing accidents caused by poison would be to keep all poisonous materials out of the house. But poisons like iodine or ammonia or sodium arsenite may serve a useful purpose; they may guard us against infection or cleanse our garments or keep vermin out of the house. They are not the only possible sources of poison; certain medicines or drugs may be most harmful if taken in too large doses.

The important thing is to see to it that no member of the family swallows poisons, either because he mistakes them for something else or else because he is too young to know better. We should clearly label all bottles and other containers of antiseptics, medicines, insecticides and the like and keep them in a cabinet high above the reach of young children. As an added measure of precaution, it would be well to keep the cabinet locked.

It has been suggested that if pins are inserted in the corks of each bottle containing poison, anyone reaching for such a bottle in the dark will be forcibly reminded of its contents. Some people may feel, however, that this is a rather drastic measure, and they will be content with the less painful precautions noted above.

As we have seen, illuminating gas is a serious fire hazard. It is just as dangerous if it is breathed in considerable quantities. A leak in the gas pipe or an open gas cock will flood the house in time, if the windows and doors are closed, with enough gas to cause unconsciousness or death. So when we keep our gas apparatus in good working condition, we are guarding against a double danger.

Even when the gas stove is properly lighted, it can be a source of danger, for the flame uses up oxygen. Every winter

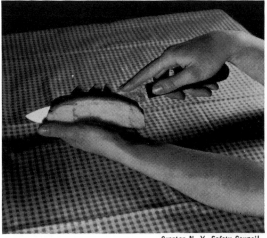

If you handle a knife as shown above, you will be lucky to avoid injuring your hand. Cutting strokes should always be made away from your hand, rather than toward it.

we read of people meeting death by asphyxiation because they tried to keep warm by lighting gas ovens and closing all windows. Remember that a kitchen range is *not* a heating unit. If your house is cold, bundle up in warm clothing or get into bed or visit a neighbor.

Poisonous gas fumes are sometimes given off by heating units that have become caked with soot or in which combustion is imperfect. Have your heating unit checked and cleaned by a competent service man at the start of each heating season.

Cuts and scratches

Pins or needles that are left lying on the floor or upon a chair or sofa have resulted in many scratches and infections. The writer recalls a case in which a careless person dropped a needle on a dining-room rug and left it lying there. A young girl, running barefoot over the rug, ran the needle into her foot. The foot became badly infected and required the doctor's care. It is best to do all your sewing in a special room set aside for that purpose. After you have finished sewing, put all your sewing implements — needles, pins, scissors and so on — back where they belong; and do it *at once.*

Knives, forks and other sharp tools misused or used in haste are responsible for many injuries, minor and severe. Sharp knives must be used carefully and stored safely. When using a knife, make cutting strokes away from your hand, rather than toward it, whenever it is possible to do so. Wash and dry knives separately, and store them in a knife rack out of reach of childish fingers. Children should never be permitted to use knives until they are old enough to handle them safely. Never use the sharp edge of a knife to pry open a jar. Scissors should be handled with care by adults and kept out of reach of young children.

Since so much of our food comes in cans, it is important to be able to open these containers safely. Select a can-opener that leaves no jagged edges to cut the user. An excellent type is the revolving-motion opener, which folds the sharp edges underneath. Avoid haste in opening cans equipped with a flat key for removing a metal band. Turn slowly so as to prevent breaking the band and handle the sharp edges of the band carefully.

Safeguarding young children

We can reason with adults and older children; we can win their co-operation in preventing accidents. But the very young can not co-operate in this way and therefore we should take particular pains to safeguard them.

One of the most dangerous places for little children is the kitchen. They should be kept out of this room as much as possible; if they are permitted to enter it, they should be watched every minute of the time. Needless to say, the mother should keep young children away from hot stoves or cooking ranges, and from all moving kitchen equipment, such as washing machines, clothes wringers, electric mixers and food choppers.

Play pens will protect children from many hazards while the mother is busy. For safe sleep, the baby crib with closely spaced slats will help prevent falls. So will low chairs for young children.

Since the serious business of the very young is play, we should be particularly careful about the toys that we put into their hands. Toys should be strongly built,

with smooth surfaces and rounded corners. Metal toys should have no sharp point; edges should be rolled. Never give a toy so small that it can be swallowed. Rag dolls or stuffed animals are safe toys, *provided* they are washable and that they do not have eyes made of glass or pins.

Are you appalled by the long list of accidents that can happen to you or to a member of your family? Yet no accident need result in most homes if each member of the family will co-operate fully in the task of removing all hazards that may endanger young and old alike.

National Board of Fire Underwriters

Violating two safety rules. The handle of the percolator should not protrude beyond the edge of the range; the little girl should not be allowed to stay so near it.

ELECTROMAGNETIC RADIATION

Waves of Energy That Fill the Universe

BY JAMES STOKLEY

IF YOU stand in front of a campfire, even though you do not actually touch the flames, something that is emitted from the blazing wood makes itself felt on your face or hands. Out in the noonday sun, on a summer's day, you get the same sensation of warmth. You know that if you stay out in the sun too long you will get sunburned, possibly painfully.

You listen to the radio or watch television. So do thousands of others, all hearing or watching the same program. Something is sent out from the transmitting station; the receiver picks up this something and converts it into the particular program that you hear or see.

These are all examples of the process called radiation, whereby energy is carried across space. Ordinarily the energy travels outward from its source, spreading equally in all directions like the radii of a circle; hence the name.

The most familiar kind of radiation is visible light, which makes it possible for us to see the world about us. Long ago men were puzzled as to just what light was, and even today we do not have the final answer. Some believed in the corpuscular theory. They held that the sun, the flame of a candle and all other luminous bodies give off tiny particles, or corpuscles, which fall upon an object in their path, bounce off and are detected when they hit the eyes. Others thought that light is something like the waves that are formed in a pond when you drop in a stone. These travel outward on the surface of the water; if they hit some solid obstruction, they are reflected — that is, a new series of waves appears.

One of the basic discoveries about light came in the year 1666 when the celebrated English scientist Sir Isaac Newton held a glass prism over a small hole in a window shutter, through which a beam of sunlight entered the room. The result, instead of a spot of white light, was a band of colors — a spectrum — red at one end, violet at the other. Thus he showed that what we ordinarily call white light is a mixture of colors. (Six are now generally accepted as the principal colors — red, orange, yellow, green, blue and violet.) Newton held up a second prism, which was turned in the opposite direction, and let the band of colors fall upon it; the light that finally emerged was white once more. He had taken white light apart and put it back together again.

Although Sir Isaac never expressed a very positive opinion as to the nature of light, he leaned toward the corpuscular theory. His high position in science did much to maintain it, even though in 1690 a Dutch physicist, Christian Huygens, published a well thought out wave theory, which later became widely accepted. According to this theory in its modern form, light is made up of waves, and their length determines the color. The longest — about 40,000 to the inch — produce the light we call red, while the shortest, which are about 1/70,-000 of an inch in length, produce violet. In between are the wave lengths of the other colors of the visible spectrum.

About the beginning of the nineteenth century, scientists found that this spectrum represents only the range of radiation that the eye can see, and that beyond both ends there are other rays, which are invisible.

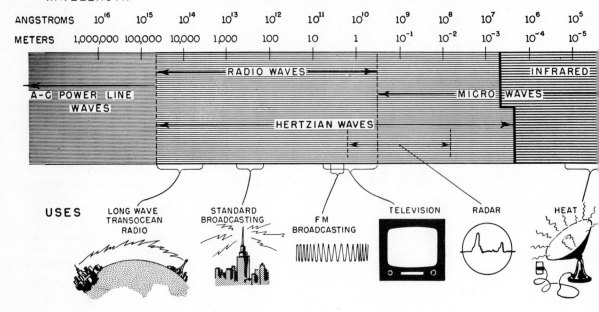

WAVELENGTH

ANGSTROMS	10^{16}	10^{15}	10^{14}	10^{13}	10^{12}	10^{11}	10^{10}	10^{9}	10^{8}	10^{7}	10^{6}	10^{5}
METERS	1,000,000	100,000	10,000	1,000	100	10	1	10^{-1}	10^{-2}	10^{-3}	10^{-4}	10^{-5}

RADIO WAVES — INFRARED — A-C POWER LINE WAVES — MICRO WAVES — HERTZIAN WAVES

USES — LONG WAVE TRANSOCEAN RADIO — STANDARD BROADCASTING — FM BROADCASTING — TELEVISION — RADAR — HEAT

The first discovery of this sort was made by the English astronomer Sir William Herschel, already famous as the discoverer of the planet Uranus. In 1800, just as Newton had done, he put a prism in front of an opening through which sunlight was shining and obtained a spectrum. Then he placed several thermometers at the various colors, to see which would produce the greatest heating effect. Of all the visible parts, the red light made the temperature go up the most. Then Herschel placed one of the thermometers beyond the red end of the spectrum; the mercury went up even higher, clearly showing that invisible heat rays were present.

In this way Herschel demonstrated the existence of what we now call infrared rays. ("Infra" means "below"; the infrared rays have a lower frequency than the red rays.) He performed a whole series of experiments with these heat rays and discovered that he could reflect them with mirrors and focus them with lenses, just as visible light is reflected and focused. He also found that these rays are emitted from a bed of hot coals in a fireplace, as well as from the sun.

A year later (in 1801) a German physicist, Johann Wilhelm Ritter, discovered that there was also something at the other end of the spectrum. This did not cause heating, but was capable of producing chemical effects. Ritter knew that the white compound called silver chloride turns black when exposed to light; he put some of this substance in line with a solar spectrum, out beyond the violet part, in a place where no visible light was shining. The silver chloride blackened even more rapidly than it did in the region where the various colors could be seen.

Detecting ultraviolet rays by fluorescence

Thus ultraviolet rays were discovered. ("Ultra" means "beyond.") These rays could also be focused and reflected; but they did not penetrate glass very well. By 1852, the English physicist Sir George Stokes found that the ultraviolet rays could pass through quartz quite easily. So he made a spectrum-producing device out of quartz lenses and prisms. With the light from an electric spark, he could produce an ultraviolet spectrum ranging to a wave length about half that which produces the deepest violet light. To detect these invisible rays, Stokes made use of fluorescence. This is an effect shown by certain chemicals: when ultraviolet rays fall on them, they shine with visible light.

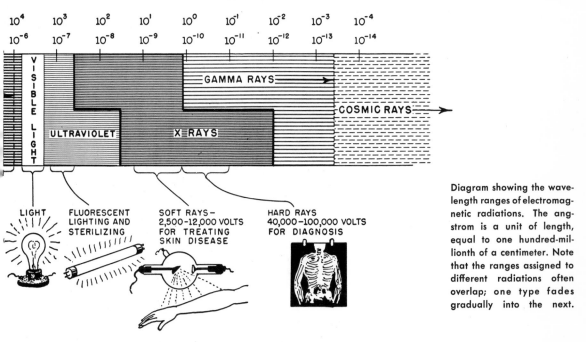

| 10^4 | 10^3 | 10^2 | 10^1 | 10^0 | 10^1 | 10^2 | 10^{-3} | 10^{-4} |
| 10^{-6} | 10^{-7} | 10^{-8} | 10^{-9} | 10^{-10} | 10^{-11} | 10^{-12} | 10^{-13} | 10^{-14} |

VISIBLE LIGHT

GAMMA RAYS

COSMIC RAYS

ULTRAVIOLET

X RAYS

LIGHT

FLUORESCENT LIGHTING AND STERILIZING

SOFT RAYS— 2,500-12,000 VOLTS FOR TREATING SKIN DISEASE

HARD RAYS 40,000-100,000 VOLTS FOR DIAGNOSIS

Diagram showing the wavelength ranges of electromagnetic radiations. The angstrom is a unit of length, equal to one hundred-millionth of a centimeter. Note that the ranges assigned to different radiations often overlap; one type fades gradually into the next.

Since silver chloride and similar substances darken when exposed to either visible or invisible light, plates coated with these substances can be used to photograph the invisible spectrum. With refinements in this method, it was possible to extend the study of the spectrum far into the ultraviolet region. Special improved plates were used in a spectrograph from which air had been evacuated, so as to avoid the absorbing effect of the air upon ultraviolet waves.

While some photographic materials are sensitive to infrared, they do not record rays far beyond the visible spectrum; other methods must be used, therefore, in studying these rays. Some of the most fundamental work on the infrared region was done by an American, Samuel P. Langley, who for years was secretary of the Smithsonian Institution, in Washington. To study infrared rays, Langley invented an electrical device called the bolometer (ray-measurer). With the bolometer, which detects and measures small quantities of radiant heat, he studied the infrared spectrum of the sun well beyond the wave lengths of visible light.

Later, with the bolometer and other even more efficient detectors, scientists found out that still longer waves are given off from earthly sources that do not even

have to be what we commonly call "hot." Infrared rays are emitted, though rather feebly, from a glass of ice water, for example, in a long range of wave lengths, with the maximum at about 1/2500 of an inch. If the water is boiling, the emission is stronger, with the maximum wave length now slightly shorter. For still hotter objects, the total amount of radiation given off increases, and the maximum wave length becomes shorter and shorter. This is in accordance with the so-called displacement law discovered by the German physicist Wilhelm Wien in 1893. According to this law, the product of the wave length at which a radiating body gives off the greatest energy and the absolute temperature (see Index) of the body is a constant.

The first clue that there might be additional waves, still longer than those of the infrared, came from the Scottish physicist James Clerk Maxwell. In 1864 he published a series of papers dealing with the nature of light, and showed, theoretically, that it is a movement of electrical and magnetic waves; he reached the conclusion that these waves could extend far beyond the infrared. One of his suggestions was that a vibrating electrical charge could set up such waves, and that they would travel through space at the speed of light — more than 186,000 miles per second.

Perhaps the first person to produce such waves experimentally was Elihu Thomson, a brilliant young science teacher at the Philadelphia Central High School. In 1871, while experimenting with high-voltage electrical sparks which could jump across a gap of several inches, he connected one of the terminals, through which the electrical discharge passed, to a water pipe, the other terminal to a metal table top. While the sparks were jumping, he found that he could go to distant parts of the building, hold a knife blade near a metal object and draw sparks from it. After some other experiments, a few years later, he realized that he had confirmed Maxwell's prediction. The energy that produced the sparks at the knife point was transmitted from the original spark by waves that traveled through space.

As sometimes happens in scientific history, Thomson's experiments were almost entirely ignored. In 1887 Heinrich Hertz in Germany obtained similar effects with what was essentially the same equipment. The world acclaimed the German scientist, and the radiation that was produced came to be known as hertzian waves. They are now generally called radio waves.

Using radio waves
to send messages

Various people realized that these waves might make it possible to send messages between distant points, without any wires to carry them. The first to succeed was a young Italian engineer, Guglielmo Marconi. After some preliminary experiments in which he sent signals across a vegetable patch near his home, he improved his equipment and finally, on December 12, 1901, sent the letter "S" in the Morse telegraphic code across the Atlantic Ocean from England to Newfoundland. From this humble beginning came such developments as television, radio broadcasting and radar.

The waves used in broadcasting are about 1,000 feet in length. Still longer ones, as much as a mile in length, are some-times used in transmitting radio messages across the oceans. Certain waves, many miles long, are emitted from the power lines over which alternating electrical currents are transmitted. This equipment is designed, of course, to deliver electrical power; the waves are a sort of by-product.

The range of wave lengths of radiation has been extended, therefore, from those of the shortest ultraviolet to others a million million times as long. What of the other end of the spectrum? Are there any rays shorter than the ultraviolet?

Here again Germany enters our story. In November of 1895, Professor Wilhelm Konrad Roentgen, at the University of Wuerzburg, discovered that some new kind of ray was given off from a Crookes tube, an evacuated glass bulb in which an electrical discharge was produced. This ray caused some materials to glow by fluores-

A fluorescent sun lamp, suspended from the ceiling of a pigpen, subjects hogs inside to ultraviolet radiation.
Westinghouse

Sometimes infrared rays are used to detect alterations in paintings. When a painting by Il Tintoretto—The Doge Alvise Mocenigo Presented to the Redeemer (above)—was photographed by infrared rays, they brought out the figure of an angel hovering over the kneeling Doge. Il Tintoretto had changed his mind about the composition of his masterpiece.

cence; it could also be recorded by its effect on a photographic plate. The most striking characteristic of the new rays was that they could pass through many solid materials — wood, paper and even human flesh; with the rays one could see and photograph the bones in one's body. Roentgen gave the name of X rays to the newly discovered and mysterious emanations, because in science X is the symbol of the unknown.

Finally it turned out that X rays — or roentgen rays, as they are also called — are radiations with wave lengths even shorter than those of ultraviolet. Their wave length depends on the voltage of the electricity used to create them; the higher the voltage, the shorter the length. For 100,000-volt X rays, most of the radiation has a wave length of about 1/1,380,000,-000 of an inch, or about 1/21,400 of that of the shortest visible light.

With some of the large atom smashers that are used by physicists, X rays of hundreds of millions of volts energy are produced, and their wave lengths are still shorter. Beyond these are certain radia- tions that occur in nature; these are associated with the cosmic rays that rain upon us from outer space.

All the radiations that we have been discussing — light, ultraviolet rays, infrared rays, X rays and the rest — are known as electromagnetic radiations. They have received this name because they are sent out into space as the result of periodic variations (variations occurring at regular intervals) in electric and magnetic fields. They are all transmitted at the same speed — 186,282 miles per second. The complete range of wave lengths of these radia-

Photos, General Electric

Modern radar height-finding apparatus. Radio waves of different lengths are used in radar.

Common dog flea under the X-ray microscope. This device magnifies up to 1,500 diameters.

Using X rays to fluoroscope blueberries packed in boxes, in order to make sure that no foreign substances are present.

tions is known as the electromagnetic spectrum. (See table on pages 200-01.) The known electromagnetic spectrum extends from the cosmic rays, with wave lengths so tiny that some two trillion would have to be lined up to equal an inch, all the way up to alternating-current power waves, more than a billion billion times as long.

The quantum theory of light

So far we have been discussing the wavelike properties of light and similar radiation. The wave theory of light, which, as we have seen, had been originally proposed by Huygens, had won wide acceptance in the nineteenth century. However, about 1900 the work of Max Planck, in Germany, and later that of Niels Bohr, in Denmark, showed that there were some effects that the wave theory could not explain. Apparently, at least in certain respects, light acts as if it were a stream of tiny corpuscles of energy called photons. A photon is the smallest amount of light energy possible. Many other radiations, especially those that come from excited atoms, seem to show the same property: radiant energy is emitted and absorbed in separate, particlelike units, or quanta. These ideas of Planck and Bohr were eventually united in a revolutionary theory of atomic structure. However, the overwhelming weight of experiment still seemed to uphold the wave nature of light. Indeed, it was said that one had to believe the wave theory on Monday, Wednesday and Friday, and the quantum theory on Tuesday, Thursday and Saturday.

The wave mechanics theory

A compromise was introduced about 1925, as a result of the work of a French physicist, Louis de Broglie, and an Austrian, Erwin Schroedinger. They originated the theory of wave mechanics. According to this theory, all forms of matter and energy have both wavelike and particlelike qualities, but the two aspects never appear together under the same conditions. All "particles" have waves associated with them, whose wave lengths depend on the mass and velocity of the "particle." The bodies of our familiar world, such as a bullet fired from a gun, have relatively huge masses and low velocities, and their associated waves are therefore too small to be detected. But an electron, which is one of the "particles" of which atoms are made, has an infinitesimal mass and moves with a velocity close to the speed of light; the wave length associated with the electron is therefore great enough to measure.

Beams of electrons, and many other elementary "particles," have been diffracted to produce interference patterns just like those of a conventional wave. From these patterns, the wave length of the electron is measured and is found to agree with the theoretical prediction of wave mechanics. Therefore, the seemingly paradoxical ideas of Schroedinger and De Broglie have been generally accepted by science.

How an atom generates waves of light

For an atom to generate waves of light, changes must take place in its structure. An atom consists of a positively charged nucleus, around which are moving negative electrons; from one in the case of hydrogen to more than a hundred in the case of the heaviest element known. Normally, these electrons move in certain regions, or orbits, but when energy is absorbed they can be shifted to other orbits, farther away from the nucleus. Scientifically, they are said to be shifted to a higher energy level. Sometimes electrons may be removed completely; then the electrically unbalanced atom is said to be ionized.

After an electron has been thus shifted or removed, it tends to return to its former position; when it does, energy is given off in the form of radiation. Visible light, as well as the nearby ultraviolet and infrared, is a result of transitions of the outer electrons in atoms and molecules, while those of the inner electrons in atoms give rise to very short ultraviolet rays and to X rays. Gamma rays, still shorter in length, which come from radioactive materials, are a result of changes of energy state in the nucleus itself. In the case of the longer infrared rays, the atoms are not affected; vibrations and rotations of the molecules, consisting of a number of atoms, are responsible for the radiations.

The many uses of X rays

Let us examine some of the applications of radiation, starting at the short-wave end. So far cosmic rays have not been used by man; indeed it is only comparatively recently, with the greatest of atom smashers operating at energies of billions of volts, that some of their effects have been duplicated for the first time in the laboratory. But X rays have found wide application. The enormous penetrating power of fifteen- to twenty-million-volt rays, which are produced by several commercial devices, have been utilized in the X-ray examination of very thick metal parts. Steel materials from eight to ten inches thick can be examined with one- and two-million-volt radiation. X rays of this same energy range are also used in treating cancer. Properly controlled, they do more damage to the cancer than to the healthy tissue.

For more general medical use, as in finding the place where a bone has been fractured, rays of about 100,000 volts may be used; these also serve in industry. X rays have been employed to analyze the structure of matter. A beam of X rays, passed through a crystal in which the atoms are arranged in regular layers, is scattered by the atoms and forms a pattern of spots, characteristic of the particular kind of crystal, on a photographic film. This is called X-ray diffraction.

The longest-wave X rays overlap into the shortest of the ultraviolet waves. One of the chief uses that man has found for the ultraviolet is in fluorescent lighting, which has now become widespread. Inside these familar tubular lamps, an electrical discharge produces ultraviolet rays, which shine on the special material used to line the tube. The invisible rays are thus turned into visible light by the process of fluorescence. It is the ultraviolet part of sunlight that produces sunburn, in addition to forming vitamin D in the body and preventing the disease called rickets. Ultraviolet rays can also be used to kill germs; lamps producing these rays are employed in medical treatment.

The uses of rays of visible light are obvious enough; one can readily imagine what the world would be like without light. It will be remembered that in the Biblical story of the creation, one of God's earliest acts was the creation of light.

Next above the light waves in the electromagnetic spectrum are those of the infrared — the heat rays. Any incandescent lamp gives off these rays in copious amounts. There are special heat lamps in which the proportion of visible light is reduced, while that of infrared is increased. Such lamps are employed for drying purposes. For example, after an automobile body is painted, it is often run through a tunnel in which it is exposed to the rays from a battery of heat lamps; as a result it dries in minutes. The drying process would take much longer with other methods.

Microwaves and chemical research

The shortest radio waves, which overlap the region of the longest infrared, are often known as microwaves. One use is in chemical research — in the study of the structure of molecules. Some gaseous molecules are able to absorb these tiny waves, and the energy the molecules acquire will start them spinning, much as the blades of a windmill turn in a breeze. The windmill can turn rapidly or slowly, or at any speed between; the molecule, on the other hand, can absorb only certain well-defined amounts of energy, and none that are intermediate between these. The amounts in question depend on the weights and arrangements of the atoms that make up the molecule. When the rotational energy that a molecule absorbs from microwaves is determined, it is possible to calculate the relative locations of the atoms in the molecule.

Radio waves of various lengths, down to the microwaves, are used in radar. This development makes it possible to detect ships and airplanes at night and through fog, and to determine their exact direction and distance. With radar, navigators of ships and airplanes can "view" clearly the objects and geographical features around them under adverse conditions of visibility. All this is done by sending out a short pulse of radiation; when it hits the distant target it is reflected and the echo is picked up. Even though radio waves travel nearly a thousand feet in a millionth of a second, electronic circuits determine accurately the time it takes for the echo to return, and thus give the distance. Radar pulses have even been bounced off the moon, at a distance of some 240,000 miles, and the echo has been detected and measured.

Radio waves emitted from various celestial objects have opened up a new field of research into the heavenly bodies (including many that cannot be detected by other means) and have given rise to the science known as radio astronomy. (See Index.) By studying the radio waves coming to us from outer space, radio astronomers have demonstrated, for example, the presence of clouds of hydrogen gas between the stars. The hydrogen atoms in such clouds can have two different formations; they switch back and forth between one and the other, emitting waves about eight inches in length as they do so.

Of course, the most familiar uses of radio waves are in the fields of communication: broadcasting, telecasting and radio telegraphy and telephony between ships and across continents or oceans. All these developments represent the work of thousands of scientists and engineers in many countries since that day in December 1901 when Marconi with great effort first managed to get the three dots of the letter "S" across the Atlantic.

Scientists are still at work upon the radiations that fill the universe. The result of these researches, in the centuries to come, will probably be even more fantastic than the recent developments.

See also Vol. 10, p. 280: "General Works."

Monitors in a television studio watch a baseball game as it is pictured by different cameras at a ball park. The best pictures are routed to transmitters which send them, in the form of radio waves, to TV sets in our homes.

Con. Edison

Buttons of past generations.   France, eighteenth century: upper left, left center, upper right, right center.   France, nineteenth century: lower left.   England, eighteenth century: lower center. Holland, nineteenth century: upper center.   Place of origin uncertain, eighteenth century: lower right.

HOW BUTTONS ARE MADE

A Survey of a Flourishing Industry

TO THE average person, a button is a rather insignificant item. The word is sometimes used figuratively, indeed, to mean "something of little value," as in the phrase "I don't care a button for what he says." Yet buttons are among the most useful attachments on garments, particularly men's garments, and the button industry is a flourishing one. In a recent year, the value of its products was $58,916,000.

Buttonlike disks or knobs were used as ornaments thousands of years ago, but for a long time it did not occur to people that they could use these ornaments to fasten their clothing. It is believed that primitive man used thorns and sinews for that purpose. Later, such civilized people as the Egyptians, the Greeks and the Romans fastened their garments with pins, brooches and buckles as well as with buttons.

Some very ancient buttons were discovered by the English Egyptologist Sir Flanders Petrie (1853-1942) a number of years ago in a tomb in Coptos, in Upper Egypt. One of them went back to 2500 B.C. A hole had been pierced through a projection on the back of this button, thus forming a shank, or eye. The thread by which the button would be attached to a garment would undoubtedly be passed through this eye.

Buttons were first used in Western Europe about the thirteenth century A.D. In a manuscript that was written not later than the year 1300, there is a reference to a hero who wore buttons "from his elbow to his hand." We cannot tell whether these buttons were employed for decoration or as fasteners. In the course of time, however, buttons served both purposes. In the fourteenth century, they were used lavishly on fashionable attire. They rather lost their vogue for a time, but in the sixteenth century they became more fashionable than ever. They were worn by both sexes.

In the days of Charles I of England, in the first half of the seventeenth century, buttons attached to large handkerchiefs were much in style. Tastes had become extravagant; we find frequent mention of buttons made of diamonds and precious stones. A generation later, Louis XIV, the "Sun King" of France, is said to have had a positive mania for buttons.

By the eighteenth century, button making had become a flourishing industry in France, Germany, England and other European countries. Buttons were made of a variety of materials, including gold, silver, brass, pewter, wood, bone, glass, leather and tortoise shell. They were sometimes covered with velvet or silk cloth.

The first buttons made in America were of metal. A German immigrant, Caspar Wistar, began to manufacture brass buttons in Philadelphia in 1750; it is said that he guaranteed each one for seven years! Within a few years, several firms in New England were also producing buttons. The total production was small, however. In the American Revolution (1775-83), many of the buttons used on the uniforms of American soldiers had to be imported from France.

Button imports in the United States were cut off during the War of 1812 as a result of the British blockade. Aaron Benedict, a button maker of Waterbury, Connecticut, profited by the emergency. He bought all the brass pots and pans that he could and rolled the metal in his own rolling mill; then he made buttons of it. After the war, the American metal-button industry made rapid progress.

About the middle of the nineteenth century, the Frenchman Emile Bassot devised a method for making buttons from the softened horns and hoofs of cattle. The vegetable-ivory button was developed in Austria at about the same time. It was manufactured from the tagua nut, the fruit of the tagua palm, found near the west coast of South America, from southern Panama to northern Peru. Tagua nuts could be readily sawed, carved and turned in lathes in a great variety of sizes and shapes.

Pearl buttons won great popularity in the last half of the nineteenth century. The first buttons of this type were made from the shells of pearl oysters; they became known as ocean-pearl buttons. In 1891, the pearl-button industry in the United States received a great impetus because of the discovery, in the Mississippi River, of mussels whose shells could be made into buttons. Because of the abundance of suitable shells in its vicinity, Muscatine, Iowa, was selected as the site of the first factory in the United States devoted to the manufacture of pearl buttons from mussel shells. Many other factories were established in the years that followed.

In the present century, buttons made of various plastics have come to the fore. Plastics, as we point out elsewhere (see Index), are synthetic materials that can be molded or pressed into a desired shape. They lend themselves excellently to mass production; and there is a minimum of waste. Today more buttons are produced from plastics than from any other material. They can be made to resemble vegetable-ivory, pearl and horn buttons so closely that only an expert can tell the difference between the real and synthetic articles. As a result, they are taking over the markets formerly served by natural products.

**The manufacture
of plastic buttons**

Certain plastic materials, such as Bakelite and Plaskon, are made into buttons by the process known as compression molding. The manufacturer receives the plastic material in the form of a dry powder. This powder is converted into preforms, or pellets, each of which is about the size of a finished button. The preforms are molded by compression in cavity dies. The buttons are then tumbled in a revolving machine to remove excess material; finally, they are filed, drilled and polished.

A process called injection molding is used to manufacture buttons from cellulose-acetate plastics, such as Tenite. The plastic material, in powder form, is dumped into a hopper in the injection-molding machine. It then goes into a heating chamber, where it acquires the consistency of paste. A piston pushes it out of the heating chamber through a nozzle; from the nozzle it is squirted into a mold. This has a number of cavities, each large enough to contain material for one button. The cavities are connected with each other by little channels. The plastic paste runs along these channels and into the cavities.

When it has hardened, the contents of the mold are ejected. We now have a number of buttons connected by little stems (the plastic material that has remained in the channels). The stems are broken off from the buttons by means of buffing machines; they are then reground and used as materials for other buttons.

Celluloid buttons are made in various ways. In one process, blanks (pieces about the size of the finished buttons) are cut from large rods. These blanks are sometimes placed in holders, which are called chucks, and then turned; sometimes the buttons are held stationary while a revolving blade shapes them. In making die-pressed celluloid buttons, round disks are cut from celluloid sheets and are pressed into shape by means of dies. Twisted celluloid buttons are made from thin rods.

A favorite plastic material for buttons is Galalith. This trade name, which comes from two Greek words meaning "milk stone," is quite appropriate, for Galalith is produced by the action of formaldehyde on milk casein, producing an insoluble, tough, hornlike substance. It is interesting to note that Galalith was created by two German scientists, Wilhelm Krische

COMPRESSION MOLDING

Powdered plastic, upper left, the material from which many buttons are made. Button-size pellets or preforms, upper right, ready for compression molding. Molded buttons, lower left, before excess material is removed. Finished buttons, filed, drilled and polished, lower left.

A pellet-making machine of the same type as that used in making various kinds of pills, such as aspirin. Here, dry powdered Bakelite or Plaskon, plastic material, is formed into button-size preforms on the machine. At left, preforms are expelled automatically from machine.

INJECTION MOLDING

Merit Plastics

Injection molding is accomplished in a very different way from compression molding. At the right of the picture you can see a pattern of holes that are part of the stationary button mold. A movable mold is brought up against the stationary one to fashion the buttons.

"Trees" of button shapes, in branch formation, after they have been removed from the ejector unit of the injection mold. The stems will be broken off the buttons in a buffing machine and will be reground later for material to be used in the making of still other buttons.

and Adolph Spitteler, who were trying to develop a composition material to replace slate for blackboards.

Galalith is mixed with coloring matter and various other ingredients. The mixture is then fed into a machine that operates on the general principle of a meat grinder. When the mixture comes out of this machine, it is in the form of plastic rods. Sheets of plastic are sometimes made from these rods by pressing in heated presses. Disks are sliced from the rods or punched from the sheets; they are then hardened in formaldehyde. The disks are turned, carved, drilled and polished. Galalith makes a sturdy, hornlike kind of button.

Buttons from other materials

Pearl buttons are used in considerable quantities for shirts and undergarments. Shells for ocean-pearl buttons come principally from the waters around Australia and the East Indies. The shells are soaked in water for several days to make them less brittle. Then they are cut into blanks by tubular saws that revolve at high speed. The blanks are split lengthwise two or three times, depending on how thick the finished button is to be. The back of each blank is ground flat or else is rounded under an emery wheel. After the completion

of the grinding process, the blanks are placed in chucks on an automatic pattern machine. As each blank is carried around the machine, it is processed by a succession of tools. These shape it into the desired pattern, round its edges and drill it with two or four holes. The button is put in a barrel of acid to give it luster and is then tumbled in a barrel of sawdust. Fresh-water pearls are manufactured like the ocean-pearl variety, except for the fact that the blanks are not split.

Most of the nuts that are used for vegetable-ivory buttons come from Panama, Colombia and Ecuador. The nuts are first dried under intense heat in order to crack their shells; then the shells are broken off by means of rolling in a metal drum. The nuts are now cut by circular saws into slabs, which are dried in kilns until all moisture has been removed. Blanks are cut from the slabs, turned on lathes and drilled. The buttons that are to have a solid color are dyed in vats. To produce a mottled effect, various color shades are sprayed upon the buttons through a series of stencils; then the buttons are dipped in vats. Sometimes vegetable-ivory buttons are embossed — that is, ornamented with raised work. Vegetable-ivory buttons are used principally on men's suits, army shirts and women's fine tailored clothing.

The evolution of pearl buttons from fresh-water mussel shells to the exquisite finished product.

A native boy, standing beside a tagua palm, proudly displays a sliced fruit from the tree. The cross section of the large husk shows the egg-shaped nuts from which vegetable-ivory buttons are made.

Metal buttons are used mostly for military uniforms and work clothes and as ornaments for women's coats and dresses. They are produced mostly from rolled sheet brass. Circular blanks are first punched out of the brass. An automatic machine then depresses the center of each button and forms the edge. The holes are also punched by machinery. When shanks are used, they are formed of wire by a separate machine, which cuts off the pieces and bends them into loops of the required form. After these are soldered on, the buttons are trimmed on a lathe. They are then finished by gilding or burnishing.

Fancy metal buttons are sometimes manufactured from so-called white metal, which has a tin base and is alloyed with copper and antimony. The metal is heated until it is molten; it is then poured into rubber molds. After being molded, the buttons are plated with gold, silver or copper.

Horn buttons are now made chiefly from cows' hoofs, ground to a powder and mixed with color ingredients and water. Since the hoofs contain natural glue, no binding material is added. The mixture is poured into dies containing about a hundred cavities. The dies are heated and then they are chilled. After the buttons are removed from the dies, they are filed, drilled and polished. Bone buttons are generally made from the shinbones of cattle. They are used chiefly on undergarments or the inside flaps of garments, where the buttons will not be visible. First, the bones are softened by soaking; then they are cut into slabs by circular saws. Automatic machines cut buttons from the slabs, turn them and then drill them as desired.

Covered buttons are generally manufactured by covering metal parts with the same textile materials as those from which the garment itself has been made.

The unit of measurement for buttons

The unit of measurement for buttons is the line; there are 40 lines to the inch. For example, a 30-line button is ¾ of an inch in diameter; a 20-line button has a diameter of ½ inch.

A homemade sundial, used for a project in this article. The triangular piece which casts the shadow is known as the gnomon.

All photos, Kellner Associates—D. Krueger

ASTRONOMY ACTIVITIES

Investigating the Motions of Our Home, the Earth

BY NORMAN D. ANDERSON

THE professional astronomer uses both optical and radio telescopes, plus countless other pieces of equipment, in his work. Even without such devices, it is possible to make a number of interesting astronomical observations and to carry out various projects and experiments that will illustrate basic ideas in astronomy. In the following pages, we shall give some idea of what can be done even by a beginner without elaborate equipment. Let us begin with the rotation of our home, the earth.

The rotation of the earth

You can easily observe the daily motions of the sun, moon, planets and stars across the sky from east to west. You can also photograph stars in the northern sky as they appear to circle the North Star.* Until the time of the astronomer Nicolaus Copernicus (1473–1543), most men interpreted these observations as evidence that the celestial objects revolved around a stationary earth. We now explain these same observations with a theory, or model, of a solar system with the sun at the center. In our present model, the earth spins on its axis, completing one rotation each twenty-four hours.

The flattening of the earth at the poles. The earth is not a perfect sphere; it is

---

*Directions for making such photographs are included in the article Observing the Heavens, in Volume 6.

slightly flattened at the poles and it bulges a little at the equator. This has resulted from its rotation. According to a widely held theory, while the earth was still in a molten state, its spin caused particles to be forced outward from its axis. The particles were piled up least of all at the poles and most of all at the equator. By the time a solid crust had formed at the surface of the sphere, it had become slightly distorted. We know that the distortion exists because the earth's diameter is 7,927 miles at the equator and only 7,900 miles from pole to pole (Figure 1).

You can show how the flattening of the earth results from rotation by setting up a piece of equipment in your home workshop or in the school laboratory. You will need a long and short stick and a spool (Tinker Toys will work very well), plus a strip of heavy paper, $\frac{3}{4}$ inch wide and approximately 12 inches long. Assemble these pieces as shown in Figure 2. The lower ends of the paper strip should be secured to the spool, and a hole should be made in the top of the paper loop so that it is free to slide up and down on the stick.

Place the device in a hand drill, as shown, and set it to rotating rapidly. The circular loop will then be flattened into the shape of an ellipse. The flattening will be much more pronounced than that of the earth; but it will be based on the same general principle. It is interesting to note that the planet Jupiter is also flattened at the poles and has a bulge at the equator. In this case, the distortion is readily visible through a telescope of suitable power. We will later investigate one effect of the earth's equatorial bulge on its motions.

The Coriolis effect. The earth's rotation also brings about what is called the

1. Left: by measuring the earth's diameter at the equator and from pole to pole, we can tell that the earth is flattened at the poles.

7,927 MILES

7,900 MILES

STICK
SPOOL
HAND DRILL

A B

2. Right: rotation causes a circular loop of paper (A) to become an ellipse (B).

GULF STREAM

3. The Gulf Stream is deflected toward the east because of the Coriolis effect.

4. A merry-go-round can be used to give a striking demonstration of the Coriolis effect. The arrow marks the direction in which the merry-go-round is rotating; the dotted line shows how the ball curves.

Coriolis effect, named after the French engineer Daniel Coriolis. It can be defined as the deflection of a moving object from a north or south path because of the rotation of the earth. For example, air and water currents moving northward in the northern hemisphere are deflected toward the east. The Gulf Stream in the Atlantic Ocean is an excellent example of this phenomenon (Figure 3). The shift to the east can be explained by considering the velocities at which objects at different latitudes are moving as a result of the earth's rotation. At the earth's equator, an object is moving eastward at a speed of over 1,000 miles per hour. At the latitude of Chicago this eastward motion is about 800 miles per hour. At the North Pole, it takes twenty-four hours to complete a single rotation.

To demonstrate motions similar to those involved in the Coriolis effect, you will need a small ball, a merry-go-round, such as you would find in a playground, and the help of a friend. Seat yourself on the merry-go-round and ask your friend to stand a few feet away from it. Start the merry-go-round turning; then throw the ball to your friend when he is directly opposite you (Figure 4). The ball will appear to curve. Reverse the direction in which the merry-go-round is turning. In what direction does the ball now curve?

At the time the ball left your hand, it had at least two motions — one in the direction in which the merry-go-round was rotating (that is, eastward or westward) and another in the direction you threw the ball. The result — a curve ball! Actually, since the ball will also be affected by the force of gravity, you will have a curve ball with a drop.

The precession of the earth. One end of the axis of the spinning earth points toward Polaris, the North Star. Very careful

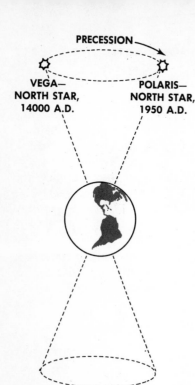

PRECESSION

VEGA—
NORTH STAR,
14000 A.D.

POLARIS—
NORTH STAR,
1950 A.D.

5. Left: the earth's axis traces out a circle in the sky —a motion called precession.

A   B

PRECESSION

DIRECTION OF GRAVITY

6. Demonstrating precession with a toy gyroscope. A: winding up the gyroscope. B: as the gyroscope spins, its upper end traces out a circle.

observations made over a period of several years reveal that the axis of the earth is slowly tracing out a circle in the sky — one complete revolution about every 26,000 years (Figure 5). This motion, called precession, results in a number of things of interest to the astronomer. Because of it, in about 12,000 years Vega instead of Polaris will be our North Star.

You can illustrate precession with a spinning toy gyroscope. Set it on a table with its axis vertical; the axis will continue to point straight up. If, however, you set the gyroscope on the table with the axis tipped, the upper end will slowly trace out a circle (Figure 6). Gravity is the force that causes the tilted gyroscope to precess. In the case of the earth, precession is chiefly due to the moon's gravitational pull on the equatorial bulge of the earth, as our planet rotates.

The revolution of the earth around the sun

The earth completes an elliptical orbit around the sun in one year—approximately 365¼ days.* The earth makes this yearly revolution with its axis tipped, at an angle of 23½ degrees, relative to the perpendic-

ular to the plane of its path around the sun. Study Figure 7. It is important for you to note that the earth's axis points in the same direction throughout the year.

The following project will help you visualize sun-earth relationships as they appear from outside of our solar system. All that is needed is a globe (mounted on a base), a dark room and a source of light — a slide projector, flashlight or small electric lamp with the shade removed. A convenient source of light is an electric light bulb of low wattage (15 watts, say), set in the socket of an extension cord. The globe should be at least six inches in diameter and should clearly show the earth's geographical features.

If an ordinary globe is not available, an inexpensive toy bank globe can be adapted for use in this experiment. Remove the base from the globe and drill a hole through each pole on the globe. Next prepare a base from a block of wood ¾ inch by 6 inches by 8 inches. Drill a hole in the base at an angle of 23½ degrees (Figure 8). The diameter of the hole is to be just large enough so that the stick to be used in mounting the globe will fit tightly. Slide the globe onto the stick, placing a spool between the globe and the base.

Set the source of light, which is to represent our sun, in the central part of a darkened room. It can be placed on a table or perhaps on the floor. It is to be at the center of a circle 6 feet in diameter (in-

* Actually the ellipse described by the earth as it revolves around the sun is very nearly a circle. Diagrams in which the elliptical nature of the orbit is clearly shown have been purposely distorted.

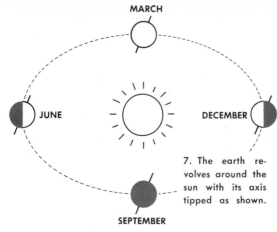

7. The earth revolves around the sun with its axis tipped as shown.

dicated by the dotted lines in Figure 9); this circle is to represent the earth's orbit.* Set the globe in the position for December, as indicated in Figure 9. The center of the light source is to be level with the center of the globe; the axis of the globe is to point away from the source of light, as shown. This represents the relative positions of the earth and sun in the month of December, at the beginning of winter. To show the relative positions in March, set the globe in the position labeled March in Figure 9.

*Presented on this scale, the orbit appears as a circle rather than as an ellipse.

Several other months — January, February, June and September — are indicated in the figure. Note that the axis is to continue to point in the same direction throughout the experiment. You should be able to position the globe correctly for any month of the year. For example, for January the globe should be set on its supposed orbit one third of the way to its March position.

Set out the globe in the appropriate position for the month in which you are working on this project. Slowly rotate the globe while observing it directly from above. Can you follow your home town or state, as it moves through the zones of light and darkness? (Note that 15° of rotation — that is, 15° of longitude — corresponds to one hour of time.) Can you predict the number of hours of daylight for your home town during the different months of the year? How many hours of darkness would there be for a person whose home is on the equator? Can you explain the phenomenon referred to as the "midnight sun" (that is to say, when the sun is above the horizon at midnight)?

In addition to determining the hours of daylight and darkness at a given location

HOLE TO BE DRILLED IN BASE AT ANGLE OF 23½°

23½° A   B

¾" x 6" x 8" WOOD BASE

8. How to prepare the toy bank globe that will represent the earth, as described in the text. A: the stick has been inserted in a hole in the base. B: a spool and the globe have been slid onto the stick.

MARCH   FEBRUARY

JANUARY

JUNE

SOURCE OF LIGHT

DECEMBER

9. How the globe, mounted at an angle, is used to demonstrate the effects of the orbit of the earth around the sun.

SEPTEMBER

10. The angle at which sunlight strikes the earth has an important bearing on the seasons.

11. The temperature of the sand in pans A and B (see the text on this page) is affected by the angle at which the sun's rays strike the pans. Pan A has been placed horizontally. Pan B has been propped up in such a way that the rays of the sun strike it directly.

12. A globe mounted on a cardboard ring can be used for interesting observations.

with your globe, you can also estimate the angle at which the sunlight strikes the earth during the four seasons. To an observer in North America, during what month does the sunlight appear to be coming almost straight down?

Some of this information can be used in explaining the seasons that we have on earth. A location having more hours of daylight than of darkness tends to be warmer than if the opposite is true. Why? The angle at which the sunlight strikes the earth's surface is also important (see Figure 10). This can be demonstrated by placing two pans of sand in the sunlight as shown in Figure 11. One of the pans is to receive the sunlight at a slant; the other is to be set at an angle, as shown, so that the rays of the sun are perpendicular to the surface of the sand. Place a thermometer in each pan of sand and record the temperature every 10 or 15 minutes. (Use the same kind of pan, sand and thermometer.) Which pan will become hotter, and why?

A globe can serve for other interesting observations. First remove the base of the globe, if any. Prepare a cardboard ring, an inch wide and four inches in diameter and set the globe upon it (Figure 12) in direct sunlight. The most dramatic results can be obtained by using a beam of sunlight entering a partially darkened room. Position the globe so that your home town is uppermost on it and the north pole of the globe is pointing due north. The illuminated part

of the globe will correspond to the part of the earth having daylight at the time of your observation. Can you determine what locations are having sunrise and sunset? What is the approximate time of sunrise and sunset for your location on the day of your observations? (Remember that 15° of longitude corresponds to one hour of time.)

How to use our knowledge of the earth's movements

Once one has developed an understanding of the earth's movements within the solar system, it is possible to apply this knowledge to the solution of certain problems. Finding the latitude and longitude of your home town would represent two problems of this kind.*

How to determine latitude. One way of finding out at what latitude you are (that is, without consulting a map) is to measure the altitude of the sun. There are various ways of doing so. If you measure the length of the shadow cast by a vertical stick of known height, you can calculate the angle, using the mathematics of trigonometry. (See Figure 13.)

If you do not know trigonometry, you can make an approximate direct measurement of the sun's altitude with the device shown in Figure 14. It consists of a 180° protractor, attached to a soda straw by means of Scotch tape. A string with a pa-

---

* *Editor's note*: For definitions of latitude and longitude, see the Index.

13. How to find the altitude of the sun by trigonometry. *a* represents a stick 4 inches high; *b*, the 6-inch shadow cast by the stick; *c*, a straight line drawn from the top of the stick to the end of the shadow. Angle *A* represents the altitude of the sun. The tangent of angle *A* (tan *A*) = $a/b = 4/6 = .666$. To find the number of degrees in the angle, we consult a table of trigonometric functions and find that *A* is 33° 41'.

14. How to measure the altitude of the sun with the device described in the text.

per clip fastened to the end is attached to the middle of the protractor, also with Scotch tape.

Hold a piece of white paper or cardboard a few inches from the lower end of the straw and point the straw at the sun. Caution: *Do not look directly at the sun without the protection of a special filter or goggles.* Make the necessary vertical and horizontal adjustments till the end of the shadow cast by the protractor on the paper or cardboard is a ring surrounding a light area. Record the protractor reading (starting from the "O" mark nearer the sun) at the point through which the string passes.* Subtract 90° from this reading and you will have the sun's altitude. Can you tell why this subtraction is necessary? To help you answer this question, note what the reading is when the straw is in a horizontal position.

You are now ready to find your latitude. Your task will be simple if you set about it on the first day of spring (about March 21) or the first day of autumn (about September 23). On these days, the sun appears to be directly overhead (that is, at an altitude of 90°) at noon to an observer at the earth's equator. Measure the altitude of the sun above the southern horizon at noon, subtract the number of degrees in this measurement from 90° and you will have the latitude of the place where you are taking the observation. If you were at the equator, the altitude of the sun would be 90°; the latitude would be $90° - 90° = 0°$. If you were at Chicago, Illinois, the altitude of the sun would be 48°; the latitude would be $90° - 48° = 42°$. You can check your own latitude figure by consulting a map.

If you wish to determine your latitude on some day other than the first day of spring or autumn, you must take into account the sun's declination. This represents the number of degrees the sun appears to be north or south of the equator. During the fall and winter, the sun appears to be

*There is another "O" mark, of course, at the other end of the protractor.

a certain number of degrees (varying according to the date) south of the equator. This number must be added to the measured altitude of the sun. During the spring and summer, the sun appears to be a certain number of degrees north of the equator. In this case the number must be subtracted from the sun's altitude. The amount to be added or subtracted for a given date can be obtained from Table 1, on the next page.

Here is how to use the table. First determine the sun's altitude, using the protractor device. Either add to or subtract from this figure the one given in Table 1 for the date on which you are taking the observation. Then subtract the result from 90° and you will have the latitude. For dates not listed in the table, use the figure given for the nearest date listed.

Let us consider an example. A person in New York City measures the altitude of the sun at noon on February 17 and finds it to be 37°. Consulting Table 1, he notes

TO BE ADDED TO SUN'S ALTITUDE				TO BE SUBTRACTED FROM SUN'S ALTITUDE			
Date	Degrees	Date	Degrees	Date	Degrees	Date	Degrees
Sept. 24	0	Jan. 1	23	March 21	0	July 2	23
Oct. 3	4	" 5	23	" 31	4	" 6	23
" 10	6	" 11	22	Apr. 6	6	" 13	22
" 13	7	" 18	21	" 10	8	" 21	21
" 24	11	" 20	20	" 20	11	" 23	20
" 29	13	" 30	18	" 23	12	Aug. 2	18
Nov. 3	15	Feb. 2	17	May 1	15	" 5	17
" 10	17	" 9	15	" 8	17	" 13	15
" 13	18	" 17	12	" 11	18	" 21	12
" 23	20	" 19	12	" 22	20	" 24	11
" 25	21	March 1	8	" 23	20	Sept. 3	8
Dec. 3	22	" 5	6	June 1	22	" 7	6
" 8	23	" 11	4	" 7	23	" 13	4
" 12	23	" 21	0	" 11	23	" 24	0
" 22	23½			" 22	23½		

that since his observation was made on February 17, he must add 12° to this figure. $37° + 12° = 49°$. Subtracting 49° from 90°, he gets 41° as the latitude of New York City.

Another method of finding your latitude involves measuring the altitude of Polaris, the North Star. An observer's latitude is equal to the altitude of Polaris.

Apparent solar time and mean solar time. In order to determine one's longitude, it is necessary to find out the difference between apparent solar time and mean solar time for a given date. Let us see what is meant by these two kinds of time.

As everybody knows, the day is made up of twenty-four hours and it is based on the rotation of the earth or the apparent daily movement of the sun around the earth. When the sun is at its highest point in the heavens or, as an astronomer would say, when it is at the meridian,* it is 12:00 o'clock noon as indicated on a sundial. Will the 12:00 o'clock reading of the sundial correspond to the hour as given on your watch or clock?

If you construct the sundial shown in Figure 15, you will be able to find the answer to your question. The gnomon, or triangular piece that casts the shadow, should be made so that the angle that its upper edge will form with the base will be equal to your latitude. The base should be level; this can be done with a carpenter's level.

* The meridian of a given place is the great circle passing through the poles and the zenith (see Index) of that place.

The gnomon should point due north; to line it up properly, sight along its upper edge to the North Star. Once the sundial has been correctly positioned, do not move it.

When the sun is at the meridian (at its highest point in the sky), the shadow cast by the gnomon will point due north. This is the time when the reading of your dial will be 12:00 o'clock. It is called apparent solar time, because it is based on the apparent movement of the sun around the earth. What time will it be on your watch? (Be sure that your watch is running correctly.) The chances are that the time as given on your watch will be either before or after 12:00 noon as recorded on the sundial. If you take a series of readings over a long period of time, your watch will record a wide range of deviations from apparent solar time.

Imagine the difficulties we would get into if we measured the length of one day as the time between two successive appearances of the sun at the meridian (12:00 noon apparent solar time). We would have days of varying length ranging from 23 hours, 45 minutes, to 24 hours, 15 minutes. With days of varying length, we would have to reset all of our watches and clocks every 24 hours!

In order to have days of uniform length, we base our time system on the average length of time between one appearance of the sun at the meridian and the next appearance. This is called mean solar time because it is based on a mean (average) sun.

15. Sundial set up in accordance with the instructions given in the text. The angle that the upper edge of the gnomon forms with the base is 41°, representing the latitude of New York City, where the sundial was put up. The photo was taken on October 1 at the time when the sun was at the meridian (that is, at its highest point in the sky). This represents 12:00 noon apparent solar time. The watch lying on the sundial base shows the mean solar time—10 minutes after 12. For an explanation of the difference in time, see the text and Table 2.

Table 2   **EQUATION OF TIME**

Mean solar noon (12:00 noon on your watch) plus or minus the values given below gives the time of apparent solar noon (noon on the sundial).

Date	Equ. (in minutes)	Date	Equ. (in minutes)
Jan. 1	−3	July 19	−6
" 3	−4	" 27	−6⅓
" 5	−5	Aug. 5	−6
" 7	−6	" 13	−5
" 9	−7	" 18	−4
" 12	−8	" 22	−3
" 15	−9	" 26	−2
" 18	−10	" 29	−1
" 21	−11	Sept. 2	0
" 24	−12	" 5	+1
" 29	−13	" 8	+2
Feb. 4	−14	" 11	+3
" 12	−14⅓	" 14	+4
" 20	−14	" 17	+5
" 24	−13½	" 19	+6
" 27	−13	" 22	+7
Mar. 4	−12	" 25	+8
" 8	−11	" 28	+9
" 12	−10	Oct. 1	+10
" 16	−9	" 4	+11
" 20	−8	" 7	+12
" 23	−7	" 11	+13
" 26	−6	" 15	+14
" 29	−5	" 20	+15
Apr. 2	−4	" 27	+16
" 5	−3	Nov. 4	+16⅓
" 8	−2	" 11	+16
" 12	−1	" 18	+15
" 16	0	" 22	+14
" 20	+1	" 26	+13
" 25	+2	" 29	+12
May 2	+3	Dec. 1	+11
" 7	+3½	" 4	+10
" 15	+3¾	" 7	+9
" 23	+3½	" 9	+8
" 28	+3	" 11	+7
June 4	+2	" 13	+6
" 10	+1	" 16	+5
" 15	0	" 18	+4
" 19	−1	" 20	+3
" 24	−2	" 22	+2
" 29	−3	" 24	+1
July 4	−4	" 26	0
" 10	−5	" 28	−1
" 14	−5½	" 30	−2

Astronomers use the term "equation of time" to represent the difference between the time of apparent solar noon (sundial time) and the time of mean solar noon (watch time). Some values for the equation of time are given in Table 2. These values are to be added to your watch time or subtracted from your watch time in order to find apparent solar time.

How to determine longitude. You are now ready to find the longitude of the place where you live. You will have to note what progress the sun is making in its apparent journey around the earth and you will also have to apply the equation of time.

The sun covers 360° in 24 hours every time it makes a circuit of the earth. Therefore it covers 15 degrees (360° ÷ 24°) every hour. On the basis of the sun's apparent journey, the world is divided into 24 time zones, each having a width of 15 degrees of longitude. The time as indicated by a watch or clock is the same for any place within a given time zone. If it is 3:45 P.M. in town A in a given zone, it is 3:45 P.M. in town B in the same zone. As one moves westward from one time zone to the other, one must move one's watch back an hour.

There are four time zones in all in the continental United States (not including Alaska). There is the Eastern Time Zone, extending theoretically 7½° on either side of 75° west longitude, which is the center of the zone; the Central Time Zone, centered about 90° west longitude; the Mountain Time Zone, centered about 105° west longitude; and the Pacific Time Zone, centered about 120° west longitude. 75°, 90°, 105° and 120° are called standard meridians; so are 135° west longitude, 150° west longitude and the rest.

At all locations at 75° west longitude, when the mean time is 12:00 noon, apparent solar time may range from about 16:00 minutes after 12:00 to 14:00 minutes before 12:00, depending upon the day of the year, as indicated in Table 2. For example, on September 19, when mean solar time is 12:00, apparent solar time comes 6 minutes later: that is, at 12:06 P.M.

The farther west we go, the later the apparent solar time will come with respect to the standard time (mean solar time) for a given time zone. Each degree of longitude that the sun travels corresponds to 4 minutes of time (one hour, or 60 minutes, divided by 15°). Hence, at one degree west of 75° west longitude — that is, at 76° west longitude — apparent solar time would come 4 minutes later than at 75° west longitude. On September 19, therefore, apparent solar time would come at 12:10 P.M.

Now suppose an observer at Columbus, Ohio, which is in the Eastern Time Zone, finds the shadow on his sundial pointing directly north at 12:38 E. S. T. (Eastern Standard Time) on September 19. The apparent solar time (when the sundial shadow points due north) at 75° west longitude for September 19, as we have seen, corresponds to 12:06 watch time (mean solar time). The difference between our Columbus observer's apparent time and that at 75° west longitude is 32 minutes (12:38 minus 12:06). Since 4 minutes of time corresponds to one degree of longitude, 32 minutes of time would correspond to 32 ÷ 4 degrees, or 8 degrees, of longitude. Hence Columbus, Ohio, is at 75° + 8°, or 83°, west longitude.*

* Theoretically, Columbus should be in the Central Time Zone, centered about 90° west longitude, since it is within 7½ degrees of that mark. However the actual boundaries of a time zone do not always coincide exactly with the halfway mark between standard meridians (i.e., 75°, 90°, 105°, and so on). In the United States, Time-Zone boundaries are established by the Interstate Commerce Commission.

On the same day — September 19 — an observer at Boston, Massachusetts, which is also in the Eastern Time Zone, notes that the shadow of his sundial points due north at 11:50 A.M. He calculates, using the same procedure as the Columbus observer, that at 75° west longitude, when mean solar time is 12:00 noon, apparent solar time corresponds to 12:06 P.M., mean solar time. He knows that he must be east of 75° west longitude, since the apparent solar time is earlier than at 75°. The difference between the apparent solar time at 75° west longitude (12:06 P.M.) and apparent solar time at Boston (11:50 A.M.) is 16 minutes. 16 ÷ 4 = 4. Therefore, Boston must be at 4 degrees east of 75° west longitude: that is, at 71° west longitude.

On the basis of all these observations, can you sum up the rules for determining longitude when one is west of a given standard meridian? When one is east of a standard meridian? You can apply these rules to find out the longitude of your home town, checking the result you get by consulting a map. Make your observations at different times of the year, and see if you get the same result in January, say, as in April or in October.

If you have found the irregular motions of the earth to be intriguing, you may want to carry out other investigations. The following books will provide ideas for additional projects and experiments in this field:

MAE and IRA FREEMAN, *Fun with Astronomy;* Random House, New York, 1957. — Contains directions for projects and experiments in astronomy.

D. S. HALACY, JR., *Fun with the Sun;* Macmillan Co., New York, 1959. — Solar-energy projects for the layman.

J. ALLEN HYNEK and NORMAN D. ANDERSON ("Astronomy Activities" author), *Challenge of the Universe;* Scholastic Book Services, Inc., New York, 1962. (Also available in cloth binding from McGraw-Hill Book Co., New York.) — A casebook of astrophysics and celestial mechanics, plus a section of projects and experiments.

THE MOTIONS OF THE STARS

Apparent and Real Movement in Space

FOR many centuries, the stars were known as the fixed stars because they did not seem to change their relative positions in the heavens. They were contrasted by early astronomers with the planets. The latter could be seen to follow definite paths in the skies with reference to other heavenly bodies and therefore they were called "wanderers." (The literal meaning of the Greek word *planetes,* from which "planet" is derived, is "wandering.")

If the individual stars did not change their relative positions, they did apparently move around the earth, which was thought of as a fixed body set in the center of the universe. The different constellations and other star groups rose and set just as the sun did. They had to be looked for in different places in the heavens according to the time of day and also the season. These apparent motions of the stars have been known and recorded ever since the heavenly bodies were first studied.

The rising and setting of the stars and their positions in the skies have, from time immemorial, caused certain star groups to be associated with various events of human life. Thus the ancient Greeks began their navigation season when the Pleiades were first seen to climb above the horizon before sunrise in the month of May. To them, consequently, the Pleiades were the "sailing stars." Other peoples associated these stars with the planting season.

Chaucer and other medieval writers often used astronomical terms, based on apparent star motions, in referring to the time and season. This practice shows that in the Middle Ages the motions of the stars were not only the concern of special stu-

dents but were familiar to educated people in general. The men of the medieval period marveled at the wonderfully consistent patterns the stars formed as they wheeled majestically through the skies. No wonder that even learned men thought that these glittering celestial bodies were closely linked with human destinies.

The Copernican theory, which was advanced by the Polish astronomer Nicolaus Copernicus (see Index) in the sixteenth century, dispelled the old belief that the earth stood fixed in the center of the heavens. Copernicus pointed out that the earth revolved around the sun and that it held no more exalted place in the scheme of things than did Venus, or Mercury, or Mars or the other planets. Astronomers came to realize that the revolution of the stars around the earth was only apparent. It was an optical illusion, based on the rotation of the earth about its axis.

Yet modern science has shown that the stars in our galaxy (the only ones that can be made out individually even with the most powerful telescopes) actually move, so that they gradually change their positions with respect to one another. The British astronomer Edmund Halley, after whom perhaps the most famous of all comets was named, was the first to call attention to these individual motions of stars. He reported that the stars Arcturus and Sirius were both definitely south of the positions noted by the Alexandrian astronomer Ptolemy in the second century A.D.* With the introduction, in the nineteenth century,

---

* These positions were given in Ptolemy's *Great Composition,* which is better known as the *Almagest* (the name given to it by the Arabs).

of the photographic method for determining star positions, astronomers have been able to measure the individual motions of many thousands of stars.

The study of these motions is one of the most difficult branches of astronomy. There are several reasons for this. In the first place, the distances between stars are so immense that one can make out changes in their relative positions only with the most precise instruments and the most painstaking methods. Another problem is the lack of a reliable frame of reference in measuring stellar motion. Since we live on the planet earth, we have to use it as a reference point. Obviously, it is not very satisfactory for this purpose. Not only does it make its annual journey around the sun, but the entire solar system, as we shall see, is also moving constantly through the skies. Despite all obstacles, however, astronomers have made a great deal of progress in analyzing the different types of stellar motion.

The arrow in the photograph below points to Barnard's star. The arrow in the right-hand photograph points to the same star. Note the evident shift in position with respect to the other stars in the vicinity. Barnard's star has a greater proper motion than any other star.

The proper motions of stars

We determine the position of a star in the heavens at a given time by observing its right ascension and its declination. The right ascension of a star is its east-west position along the celestial equator.* The star's declination is its position north or south of the celestial equator. We explain these two terms in greater detail elsewhere in THE BOOK OF POPULAR SCIENCE. (See Index, under the entries Declination; Right Ascension.)

When we take observations of a star's right ascension and declination over a period of years, we find that its position gradually shifts. To a certain extent, this change is only apparent. It is partly due to precession (the wobbling of the earth on its axis), which causes apparent changes in the locations of all the stars in the skies. It is also due, to a certain extent, to aberration. This is caused by the changing direction of the earth as it revolves around the sun and the resulting apparent change in speed with respect to a given

* This is the extension of the earth's equator into space until it touches the imaginary outer limit of the heavens.

star. All the stars in a given region are equally affected by precession and aberration. The changes in position that result from these phenomena are known as common motions. After astronomers take precession and aberration into account, there still remain certain individual motions that can be traced in the heavens. These are called proper motions, because they are proper to (characteristic of) given stars.

We may define proper motion as the apparent motion of a star across the sky, with relation to neighboring stars. It is given in seconds of arc. To understand what this means, we must think of the heavens as a hollow sphere, with the celestial bodies appearing on its inner surface. Any two objects in the sky are to be thought of as lying on a circle passing through the center of the hollow sphere and bound by the inner surface of the sphere. Each circle is divided into 360 units, called degrees of arc. The distance between the two heavenly objects mentioned above is expressed in degrees (°) of arc, if the distance is considerable. Smaller distances are measured in minutes (′) or seconds (″) of arc. There are sixty minutes in a degree and sixty seconds in a minute. The proper mo-

tions of stars are so small in all cases that they are given, as we pointed out, in seconds of arc.

We determine proper motion by comparing star catalogues compiled at widely separated periods of time, or by examining photographs made with the same telescope at intervals of several years. The change in the alignment of a given star with respect to other stars in its vicinity will represent its proper motion.

The star with the greatest proper motion known to us is Barnard's star, which was discovered photographically by the American astronomer Edward E. Barnard at the Yerkes Observatory in 1916. This faint tenth-magnitude star,* which is in the constellation Ophiuchus, has a proper motion of 10.3″ a year. The annual proper motion of Kapteyn's star (ninth magni-

* "Magnitude," in this case, is a measure of brightness. In the catalogues of the ancient astronomers, the stars were grouped in six classes, called magnitudes, on the basis of their brightness. The first magnitude was assigned to the brightest stars, the second to the next brightest and the sixth and last to those just visible with the naked eye. (Of course, there were no telescopes in those days.) Our system is based on this classification, though with certain modifications. For one thing, with our powerful telescopes we have extended the scale of magnitudes; we can make out stars of magnitude 23. The scale is such that if one star is five magnitudes brighter than another, it is a hundred times as bright. Certain stars have been found to be brighter than first magnitude; these stars are assigned negative magnitudes. Sirius, for example, is of magnitude −1.52.

Both photos, Yerkes Observatory

tude) is 8.7"; of Groombridge 1830 (sixth magnitude), 7.04". It is interesting to note that the stars with the greatest proper motion are faint stars which, like Barnard's star, can be made out only with the telescope. The only bright stars with a proper motion of more than 2" a year are Alpha Centauri (3.7") and Arcturus (2.3"). These motions are so slow that it takes hundreds of years before the change of position of the star with relation to its neighbors can be made out with the naked eye.

The radial
motions of stars

Stars not only move across the heavens, as seen from the earth, but they also move toward us or away from us. They may move at an angle (other than a right angle) to our line of sight, or they may travel directly along the line of sight. In either case, motion toward or away from the earth is involved. It is called radial motion and it can be detected by means of the spectroscope. This device, described elsewhere in THE BOOK OF POPULAR SCIENCE (see Index), analyzes the colors of the spectrum. Those in the visible spectrum range from violet to red. If a star is approaching the earth, all the lines of its spectrum shift toward the violet end. If it is speeding away from the earth, the lines of the spectrum shift toward the red. Thus we can determine whether a star is traveling toward the earth or away from it; by analyzing the amount of the shift in the spectrum, we can determine the velocity of its motion.

Radial velocity is indicated in kilometers per second (km/sec). When the number of kilometers is preceded by a plus sign, it indicates that the star is moving away from us; the radial velocity is then said to be positive. A minus sign before the number of kilometers shows that a star is coming toward us; the radial velocity is said to be negative. For example, when we say that the radial velocity of Van Maanen's star is + 240 km/sec, we mean that it is receding from the earth at the rate of 240 kilometers per second. The radial velocity of Helsingfors 956 is − 325 km/sec; this means that the star is coming toward us at the rate of 325 kilometers per second.

The space
motions of stars

Most stars have both proper and radial motions: that is, they are moving across our line of vision and at the same time they are receding from the earth or coming nearer to it. Hence we must know a star's proper motion and its radial motion before we can determine its actual motion in space — its space motion, as it is sometimes called. But to find out the space motion of a star, it does not suffice to know its proper and radial motions; we must also know how far distant it is from us.

To show the importance of distance in calculating the actual motion of a body in space, let us consider the flight of a jet plane across our range of vision. If the plane is only a few hundred feet above the

The double star called Krueger 60 is made up of a pair of stars that describe distinct orbits around each other — orbits that can be made out with the telescope. The three photographs at the left show different stages in the orbital motion of Krueger 60.

Yerkes Observatory

surface of the earth, it will zoom past us in a matter of seconds. Suppose that the plane flies at the same speed at an altitude of five thousand feet. In that case, it will move across our range of vision much more slowly. The "proper motion" of the plane for a given period of time when it is near the surface of the earth is much greater than its "proper motion" at a considerable height.

The factor of distance from the earth is just as important in analyzing the velocity of stars and the distance they cover in space in a given time. If the proper motion of two stars, *A* and *B,* is the same and if *A* is much nearer to us than *B,* the distance actually traversed by *B* in a year, say, will be greater; so will its velocity.*

Fortunately, it is possible to determine the distances of stars with considerable accuracy. In the case of certain stars, we can determine distance from the earth by working out the parallax (see Index). In other cases, indirect methods are used.

Once we know the proper motion of a star, its radial motion and its distance, we can determine its space motion. It is expressed in kilometers per second. Among the stars with the most rapid space motion are BeB1366 (425 km/sec); Groombridge 1830 (348 km/sec); Kapteyn's star (287 km/sec); and Van Maanen's star (247 km/sec).

* To have large proper motion, a star must not only be comparatively close to the earth but it must also be moving rapidly. Some stars that are relatively near us have a small proper motion. Sirius, with an annual proper motion of only 1.38", is a good example.

The space motion of the sun

The sun, traveling through space with its retinue of planets, asteroids, comets, meteors and other members of its family, has a space motion of its own. The determination of this motion is difficult because we upon the earth share in it, and also because the stars that might serve as frames of reference are moving in varying directions and at varying speeds. However, in spite of the apparent confusion of these motions, astronomers have been able to determine the sun's space motion with considerable accuracy.

In 1783, the great German-English astronomer Sir William Herschel, taking into account the proper motions of thirteen reference stars, came to the conclusion that the sun was moving toward a point in the constellation Hercules. He called this point the "apex of the sun's way." Since he did not know the distances of these stars and their radial velocities, he was unable to give even an approximate idea of how rapidly the sun was moving through space.

In the course of time, the proper motions of more and more stars became known to astronomers and they acquired more information about stellar radial velocities and distances. Hence it became possible not only to map out the sun's course in the heavens but also to determine its velocity. Today it is generally agreed that the sun and its satellites are moving at the rate of about 12 miles a second in the general direction of a star in Hercules — Mu Herculis. In comparison with other stars, the space motion of the sun is quite slow. As we shall see, in addition to its space motion, the sun is carried, together with all the other stars in our galaxy, around the center of the galaxy.

Star groups with common space motion

There are certain groups of stars whose members move through space at equal speeds and follow parallel courses. In 1915, Lewis Boss, an American astronomer, discovered what came to be known as the Taurus moving cluster. The stars making up the group (they are now known to be about a hundred in number) were seen to move at the same velocity and along paths that seemed to converge at a point somewhat east of Alpha Orionis. This apparent convergence is really an effect of perspective — an effect that we see in parallel railroad tracks that apparently merge in the distant horizon. Actually, the stars of the Taurus moving cluster follow a parallel course. Some of the stars now within the cluster are probably interlopers, which do not share in the motion of the cluster as a whole. In time, these stars will no longer form part of the group.

Another group of stars with common space motion is the so-called Ursa Major (Great Bear) group, which includes five of the seven stars that make up the Big Dipper. The group also includes Sirius, Alpha Coronae, Beta Aurigae, Delta Leonis and Beta Eridani, which are found scattered in the heavens. The Ursa Major group is moving toward a point southwest of Altair, the brightest star in the constellation Aquila. There are other moving groups of stars in the constellations Perseus, Orion, Scorpius and Centaurus. The stars that make up the Pleiades, in the constellation Taurus, constitute still another group of stars with common space motion.

The orbital motions of stars

Certain stars, occurring in pairs, show a different type of motion, called orbital motion: they describe distinct orbits around one another.* If they can be made out with the telescope, they are known as visual binaries. On page 229, we show three such visual binaries — Mu (μ) Draconis, 70 Ophiuchi and 61 Cygni. Other well-known ones are Krueger 60, Alpha Centauri and Castor.

Certain star pairs are too far away to be seen as separate stars even when viewed through powerful telescopes. In such cases, the orbital motions can sometimes be made out by the use of the spectroscope. Unless the orbit of such a pair is at right angles to the line of sight, the revolving stars alternately approach the earth and recede from it. Their orbital motion can be detected by analyzing the shift toward the violet or toward the red of the spectrum, as described previously. Star pairs whose orbital motion is revealed in this way are called spectroscopic binaries. Among them are Mizar (Zeta Ursa Majoris), Spica (Alpha Virginis) and Beta Aurigae.

In certain cases, we can detect orbital motion because two stars periodically eclipse one another. Such stars are called eclipsing binaries. They include Algol (the "Demon Star"), UX Ursae Majoris, Epsilon Aurigae, Zeta Aurigae, Y Cygni and GL Carinae.

The number of star pairs displaying orbital motions is very great. A great many stars which were once thought to be single stars are really binaries with orbital motion. Among them are Sirius and Barnard's star.

Orbital motion is not limited to star pairs; it is also found in the more or less spherical groups of stars called globular clusters. There are over a hundred of them in our own galaxy and they are undoubtedly to be found in other galaxies. Each globular cluster contains many thousands of stars, which are in particularly dense swarms toward the center. We can make out only the brightest stars in each cluster even with our most powerful telescopes.

---

* Not all star pairs in the skies display orbital motion. Two stars that appear close together when viewed through the telescope may simply happen to lie in the same general direction; they may have nothing else in common. Such stars are called optical pairs.

Astronomers agree that the stars that make up a globular cluster move in orbits about the cluster's center of gravity. Very little is known about the orbits of the individual stars of such a group. It is evident, however, that these orbits must lie in different planes, to account for the spherical shape of the cluster as a whole.

The rotation of stars about the galactic center

In addition to the different kinds of stellar motion that we have already mentioned, the stars in our galaxy are all moving about its center. This is called the galactic rotation. Of course, our own star, the sun, takes part in this type of movement; it travels at the rate of about 120 miles per second as it circles the center of the galaxy. Its circuit is completed in something like 200,000,000 years, a period of time sometimes known as the cosmic year. (The ordinary year, of course, is the time taken by the earth to make a single circuit of the sun.)

The speed of rotation of the stars around the center of the galaxy depends upon their distance from it; the closer they are to it, the more rapidly they revolve. Since the sun is located about two-thirds of the way from the center of the galaxy to its outer edge, its rotational movement is slow compared to that of the innermost stars. *See also Vol. 10, p. 267: "General Works."*

Visual binaries — μ (Mu) Draconis, 70 Ophiuchi and 61 Cygni — in two different stages of their orbital motion. Visual binaries are orbiting star pairs that can be made out with the telescope.

Yerkes Observatory

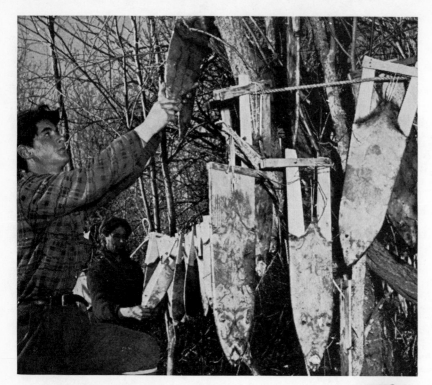

Canadian fur trapper hanging a muskrat pelt on a stretcher to dry. The animals are usually skinned the same day they are caught.

"Fleshing" a sealskin (removing the flesh) is a familiar task to this Eskimo woman from one of the small islands in James Bay.

An Eskimo of the Belcher Islands, in Hudson Bay, trades furs for provisions of a store operated by the Hudson's Bay Company.

Photos, Nat. Film Board

THE FASHIONING
OF LEATHER AND FURS

From Animal Pelts to Valuable Industrial Materials

BY KENNETH E. BELL

A FINE pair of shoes, a sturdy briefcase or piece of luggage, a costly mink wrap or stole, a richly ornamented saddle, an exquisite morocco bookbinding — all these articles and numberless others are products of two of the oldest industries known to man. For the conversion of animal pelts into leather and into furs goes back to the early days of recorded history.

Animal skin, which yields such varied products, is a living tissue, with its own system of blood vessels, nerves and glands. In the outer layer, called the epidermis, we find great numbers of hairs growing in little depressions in the skin. The part of the skin beneath the hair roots is made up of a vast number of matted fiber bundles. This skin layer is known as the corium; it is the part that is converted into leather. Corium is made up largely of collagen, a gelatinlike protein; it also contains fats, carbohydrates, mineral matter and water.

In the pages that follow we shall describe in turn the processing of leather and of furs from animal pelts.

THE PROCESSING OF LEATHER

In the Boston Art Museum there is a beautiful coat of white antelope that was made in Egypt some five thousand years ago. Evidently the Egyptians were skilled workers in leather at that early period. The ancient Hebrews also made numerous articles of leather. The Greeks, Romans and Anglo-Saxons used leather for body armor, shields and bowstrings, as well as for gloves, belts, shoes (or sandals) and clothing. Parchment, prepared from sheepskin, was used for manuscripts long before the birth of Christ.

During the Middle Ages workers in leather formed powerful trade guilds. Apprenticeship was long, and stern measures were taken to ensure the quality of work turned out by guild members. Medieval craftsmen produced many useful and ornamental leather articles: shoes, buff jerkins, belts, gloves, scabbards, inkhorns, caskets and the like.

Methods of preparing leather changed little for centuries thereafter. Since the equipment required was relatively simple, tanning was essentially a home industry. Toward the end of the eighteenth century, however, the Industrial Revolution brought about a great change. Ingenious machines were invented and new techniques were developed; large factories gradually replaced small establishments.

Today leather ranks as a highly important industrial material. Yet, curiously enough, most leather is a by-product, derived from the skins of animals, such as cattle and sheep, that are killed chiefly for their meat value.

Like every other industry, the leather business has its own special vocabulary. The word "hide" refers to large, heavy skins. "Skin" generally applies to smaller and more delicate skins, like those of calves, sheep, goats and kids; however, the word sometimes refers to all animal pelts. When we speak of the "grain" of a skin we have in mind the outer or hair surface; the term "flesh" refers to the inner surface. Most leathers are finished on the grain surface, because this can stand the greatest amount of abrasion and wear. In cases where a softer texture is desired, the skins are finished on the flesh side; skins

Ancient Egyptian tanners preparing hides.

prepared in this way are called suèdes. The name "suède" comes from the French word for Sweden; it is thought that the process of finishing skins on the flesh side originated in that country.

The leathers used today are divided into two groups — upper leather and sole leather. The term "upper leather" applies primarily to leathers used for shoe uppers; but it also includes lightweight leathers used for gloves, bookbinding and so on. Sole leather serves as sole and heel material for shoes and for other heavy-duty materials, such as industrial belting, harness, luggage and upholstery.

Upper leathers come chiefly from calf-skins (the skins of calves), kips (the skins of somewhat older cattle) and the lighter weight hides of fully grown cattle. Sheep-skins are also used as upper leather; so are the skins of goats, pigs, kids, kangaroos, antelopes, ostriches, alligators, lizards and snakes. Sole leather is made almost exclusively from heavyweight cattle hides; however, the hides of buffaloes, horses and other large animals are sometimes used.

Skins are sprinkled with salt or immersed in brine (water saturated with salt) within a short time after the animals are killed. This process preserves the skins by partially dehydrating them (freeing them from water) and by killing certain bacteria. The salting process, however, does not preserve the skins indefinitely; they spoil if they are not used within a few years. After salting, the skins are made up into bundles for the tanneries; or if they are destined for foreign markets they are packed in large casks.

The tanner begins by cleaning the skins thoroughly. They are put in soaking vats — wooden boxes containing cold, clean water — or in water-filled pits. The soaking process takes from one to seven days, during which the salt is dissolved, the dirt is loosened and the skin is restored to a soft condition. Next, the skins are usually rinsed to remove the loosened dirt.

Most skins or hides have flesh or fat adhering to the flesh side as a result of imperfect flaying. Such materials prevent the chemicals used in later operations from penetrating uniformly. Hence they are removed at this point by a fleshing machine, consisting of spiral knives set in a revolving cylinder. This machine leaves a comparatively smooth surface; any flesh still remaining is removed by a knife.

The next step is unhairing, or removing the hair. The skins are placed in vats containing a solution of slaked lime to which other chemicals, such as sodium sulfide, are added. The purpose of liming, or treating with lime, is to loosen the outer layer of skin in which the hair is embedded so that the hair may be easily removed. After from two to seven days, the skin is removed from the vat and is fed into an unhairing machine. This is quite similar in construction to the fleshing machine; only in this case the knife edges are dull, and it is the hair side of the skin that comes in contact with the knives. The squeezing action of the dull knives removes practically all the hair and its roots. The skins are then carefully inspected; any hair that still remains is pulled out by hand.

In order to remove the lime used in the unhairing process, upper leathers are placed in a bating bath — a solution containing an extract of pancreatic glands and an ammonia compound. The bating bath removes most of the lime; it also dissolves certain proteins, making the skin soft and pliable. After bating, the skins are placed in a solution containing common salt and sulfuric acid — a process called pickling.

Sheepskin is unhaired, limed, bated and pickled before it is sent to the tannery.

Sole leathers are generally placed in a lactic-acid bath after liming instead of in a bating bath. The lactic acid does not remove as much of the hide substance as the bating bath — sole leather, of course, must be as heavy and thick as possible.

For thousands of years all hides were converted into leather by the process called vegetable tanning. This method is still used in the preparation of sole leather. It is based on the fact that tannin, a bitter ingredient found in vegetation, will combine with the proteins of the skin, forming a chemical compound that resists decay. The tannin used in vegetable tanning is derived chiefly from the bark of the oak, hemlock and mimosa, from the wood of the quebracho tree, from acorns and from the abnormal growths, called galls, found on oak trees. Hemlock and oak bark

In this big lime vat, the hides are carefully processed for the removal of the hair.

Cattle hides are split into top cowhide and split leather in this "splitting machine."

Photos, Les Cooper

liquors and extracts are used more than any other tanning preparations.

Before tanning, the hides that are to be used for sole leather are cut into two parts, called sides. They are placed in pits containing weak solutions of tannins and are kept in slow, constant agitation by a rocker mechanism. This flexes the hides so that the tannins can penetrate more rapidly; it also keeps stirring the tannin solution. Next the hides are placed in pits containing high concentrations of tannins. Often, ground tannin extract is dusted directly on the surface of the hides. It takes up to two months for leather to be completely tanned by the vegetable tanning process.

Most upper leathers are prepared by a different method, called chrome tanning. The essential ingredient in this process is chromium — the metal used for bathroom faucets and automobile grill work. Before chromium can be used for tanning, it

These hides are drying under infrared lamps after dyes have been applied.

Conner-Geddes

must first be dissolved in acid to form the compound known as basic chromium sulfate. The skins are placed in revolving drums, or cylinders, which contain the tanning solution. The drums are usually raised several feet above the floor so that, when the tanning process is completed, the skins can be dumped into wooden boxes set under the drums. Leather can be tanned by the chromium compound in less than twenty-four hours.

Vegetable tanned leathers are brownish in color, while those that are chrome tanned are greenish blue. (Of course this is before the dyeing process.) You can sometimes see these colors when you examine the cut edges of finished leather articles.

For white leathers alum is used in place of the chromium compound. In other cases formaldehyde or rare metals, such as zirconium, are employed. Chamois is tanned by the process called chamoising. In this, oil is rubbed into hides or skins that are stretched out on a frame.

Many cattle hides are split by a machine into two parts after tanning: a grain split and a flesh split. The grain split is commonly used for shoe uppers; the flesh split serves for gloves, shoe tongues and medium-grade luggage.

The skins are now ready to be dyed. Some important tanners' dyes are made from the wood of certain trees; others are aniline colors, created by chemists from coal tar. Leather may be colored, with either natural or synthetic dyes, to any shade of the rainbow that happens to be fashionable. Lubricants like cod oil, neat's-foot oil or castor oil are generally added to the coloring solution. The coloring operation is carried out in drums similar to those used in chrome tanning.

When skins are removed from the drums, they are dripping wet. They are first put in machines that wring out most of the moisture and are then placed in driers. Most modern tanneries employ conveyer driers; the skins are carried on conveyers through drying chambers in which the temperature and humidity are carefully regulated. By the time they have dried out, the skins have become stiff; they are now softened in machines that flex the fibers.

The finishing processes come next. In the case of upper leather, solutions containing casein, synthetic resins or lacquers are applied to the grain surface. This is done either by means of spray guns or by seasoning machines, in which a rotating brush applies the finishing solution to the grain surface. Sole leather is finished by applying wax emulsion to the grain together with some filling material. A varnish of linseed oil is used to finish patent leather.

Leather is polished by lustering or burnishing machines in which cylinders of glass or metal rub or compress the surface. Ironing machines, like those found in laundries, are sometimes used for this purpose; in other cases machines operated by hydraulic pressure give the desired luster.

Any desired pattern can be imprinted on the surface of leather by means of engraved plates applied by hydraulic pressure. For instance, skins can be given an ostrich print so that they resemble genuine ostrich in appearance. Such skins are never sold as genuine ostrich skins; they are called ostrich printed skins.

Special effects can be obtained by applying gold leaf or by stenciling. Vegetable tanned leather can be tooled so as to produce the designs one sees in saddles, or wallets or book covers. Such work is usually done by craftsmen who make leather articles and not by tanners.

Finished leather is sorted by experts who grade it according to appearance, feel and freedom from defects. The individual skins are then passed through an ingenious machine that measures their area and records the measurement. Finally the skins are made up in bundles for shipment.

Today about 85 per cent of the leather processed by tanneries is used for shoes. Genuine leather shoes are attractive in appearance and durable; they are comfortable, too, for air permeates the fiber substance of the leather so that the foot can breathe. Leather has literally hundreds of other uses. It is a favorite material for

jackets, belts, gloves, luggage, bookbindings, harnesses, saddles and upholstery. Power is often transmitted from motors to machines by means of leather belting. Leather washers are often used in pumps where, unseen and unattended, they withstand hundreds of thousands of flexings and give years of service.

Leather is not the only product of the processing of skins and hides, for the material that is trimmed off is processed into valuable by-products. The flesh is converted into gelatin, used as a food and also in photography. The hair goes into the manufacture of felts, carpets and rug anchors; it serves as a binding material in plaster or wallboard and for insulating purposes. Large quantities of oils and greases are recovered from hides and skins and are converted into soaps, beauty creams and lubricants. Other types of leather scrap, because of their high nitrogen content, make valuable fertilizers.

Plastic materials are often used today in such articles as shoe soles and heels, ladies' bags, belts, briefcases and upholstery. Yet the demand for genuine leather articles is still great.

HOW ANIMAL PELTS ARE CONVERTED INTO FURS

It is probable that prehistoric men made garments out of the furs of animals long before the first written records appeared. The Chinese held furs in great esteem as early as 1,500 years before the birth of Christ; the Egyptians seized them as tribute; the Phoenicians traded in them.

Greek and Roman writers often referred to the use of furs. In ancient times the fur-trading center of the world was the great plain of Armenia, called the Plain of Taurus.

In Medieval Europe, furs were worn by all classes of society. The nobility and

Canadian mink ranch. Many striking new varieties of mink have been developed in ranches like this one.

Fur Trade Journal

the higher clergy wore expensive Russian sable, vair and gray squirrel; they often bordered their cloth garments with beaver, fox and other furs. Lesser folk satisfied themselves with such furs as rabbit, cat, sheep and lamb. In England the wearing of ermine was restricted to royalty by King Edward III (reigned 1327–77). This beautiful white fur also came to be part of the insignia of judges; as a result the name ermine became a symbol of the judge's office. In those days furs were obtained chiefly from northern and central Europe.

The modern age of the fur trade began with the discovery of America. The quest for fur-bearing animals was a powerful spur to the exploration of Canada by the French. The Hudson's Bay Company entered upon the scene in the last part of the seventeenth century; in time its trading posts extended from the east coast to the west and northward as far as the Arctic Ocean. The fur trade became fabulously lucrative; John Jacob Astor, for example, laid the foundations of the Astor family fortune by trading in furs at the turn of the nineteenth century.

Today furs are as popular as ever, at least among the feminine part of the population. As in the Middle Ages, costly furs, like precious gems, are often held to be the badge of wealth. But furs are not restricted to any one class of society; people of modest means can buy attractive and serviceable furs at prices they can afford.

The heaviest, thickest fur is generally found on animals living in regions that are very cold for at least part of the year; naturally such animals need more protection against cold than those living in warmer climates. An animal's coat is at its best in midwinter; the fur is not only heavier but it is also silkier, finer, more lustrous and of better color.

The most valuable furs today come from North America and Siberia. North America supplies beaver, mink, skunk, raccoon, various kinds of foxes and other furs; northern Europe and Siberia yield ermine, wolf, bear, badger, kolinsky, mink, marten and Russian sable. Furs also come from other regions of the world. Thus

Nat. Film Board

Inspecting and tagging choice beaver pelts flown in from Amos, in Quebec.

China provides kid, goat, lamb and marmot; Australia, rabbit, opossum, red fox and wallaby; South America, skunk, chinchilla and nutria.

In general, fur-bearing animals are taken by trappers in the wilds by means of snares or traps; this method is preferred to shooting, which would damage the pelts. The skin is removed from the carcass as soon as possible after the animal is killed. It is lightly tacked out on boards, with the fur side outward, and permitted to dry. All raw skins are subjected to this drying process with the exception of sealskin, which is salted. The pelts are collected by dealers or large companies and are then sold, generally at auction, in New York, St. Louis, London, Leipzig or other world fur markets. The prices paid depend on the rarity and beauty of the pelts as well as on the fashion demands of the season.

An increasing number of pelts now come from animals raised on farms or ranches; these animals include foxes, sables, minks, beavers, skunks, raccoons and chinchillas. The furs of animals raised on farms are free from the scars that are acquired in the wilds through fighting. Moreover, the scientific breeding of animals for their furs has resulted in the development of striking new varieties. Mink, for example, is now available in a great number of beautiful shades.

The pelts of true fur-bearing animals have a double coat of hair. There is a soft, silky undercoat of fur fibers, called the pelage; from this there protrude straight and rather coarse hairs known as overhairs or guard hairs. In nature, guard hairs serve to shed water and to protect the fur fibers, which provide most of the warmth. The guard hairs of certain fur-bearing animals, like the seal and the beaver, are plucked in the course of manufacturing; in other cases the guard hair is retained.

Nat. Film Board

Workers carefully cutting and matching furs in a large Winnipeg factory.

We can give only a very general account of the methods of dressing and dyeing furs, since furriers jealously guard their trade secrets. This much is certain: costly furs, like sables, chinchilla, ermine and mink, are still largely processed by hand. First, fat is scraped off the pelts by dull-edged knives; then the pelts are soaked. Next comes the fleshing operation; a skilled worker removes the flesh from the underside of the skin with a razor-sharp knife. The pelt is then put in a pickle solution, containing alum, or a bite, consisting of either hydrochloric acid, or sulfuric acid plus salt. The furs are now carefully lubricated with natural oils. They are often dyed black or brown or any other desired color.

After being dyed, the pelts are dried and stretched; certain types are plucked or sheared. The sheen, or luster, of furs is improved by tumbling them in drums together with hardwood chips or sawdust. They may also be run through combing machines, where wire bristles or combs straighten out the fibers.

Certain furs are pointed in order to improve their appearance — that is, overhairs are inserted in the fur by hand. For example, to produce the fur called pointed fox, the fox pelt is dyed black and the silver hairs of a badger are inserted. Each hair is generally attached directly to the surface of the skin by means of a tiny blob of cement.

This is only the barest outline of the dressing and dyeing processes; there may be as many as a hundred different operations in the case of certain furs. In dressing inexpensive furs, ingenious machines cut down the time required.

There are over a hundred different kinds of furs in the fur trade; we name and describe some of the more important ones in the table on the next page. These furs are made into coats, wraps, jackets, capes, scarves, stoles and muffs. They are also used as linings for cloth garments and gloves as well as for trimmings of women's millinery, cloth garments and slippers.

Synthetic furs have appeared on the market in recent years. In some cases plastic filaments of different colors are applied to a base of shorn sheepskin to produce cheap imitations of costly furs. In other cases "furs" are made of various woven materials, both synthetic and natural. They may imitate broadtail, chinchilla, ermine and other expensive furs; or else they may have exaggerated markings, and they may be dyed in all sorts of fantastic colors. These synthetic products are not quite so warm as real furs.

See also Vol. 10, p. 283: "Furs."

LIST OF IMPORTANT FURS

BADGER. Pale, fluffy fur, with long silky guard hairs. Best quality comes from western Canada. Guard hairs are often plucked out and used to point other furs.

BEAVER. Untreated peltry has ugly guard hairs, which are plucked; thick underfur is sheared. Fine beaver skin is bluish brown, with silvery belly. Canada is largest producer of beaver.

BROADTAIL. Pelt of a baby Persian or karakul lamb. No curl; watered pattern.

CHINCHILLA. Animal lives in Andes (Peru, Chile, Bolivia). Fur is delicate; lustrous slate blue in color. Chinchilla farming is carried on in North America.

CIVET. True civet lives in southeastern Asia. In fur trade, "civet" usually refers to coat of little spotted skunk of North America; animal is black with white markings.

CONY, see Rabbit.

ERMINE. A weasel, which changes from brown in summer to white in winter; in far north may stay white all year. Southwestern Siberia supplies most beautiful ermine.

FISHER. Dark, blue-brown peltry, with long guard hairs and full underfur. Eastern Canada produces best skins.

FITCH. Animal is a wild ferret; member of weasel family. Best yellow fitch comes from central Europe; best white fitch, from Siberia.

FOX. Red fox is one of the most important furs. Black, silver and cross fox are color variations of red. North America and Kamchatka Peninsula, in eastern Asia, produce finest red fox. White and blue fox are color variations of Arctic fox. Platinum silver fox was first discovered in Norway in 1935.

HARE. Used to imitate white fox, Alaska seal and other furs.

HUDSON SEAL. Muskrat, in which guard hairs are plucked, underfur is sheared and skin is dyed black to resemble Alaska seal. Most muskrat skins treated in this way come from eastern Ontario and around Great Lakes.

KARAKUL LAMB. Flatter and more open curl than Persian lamb. Best comes from Kirghiz region, western Asia.

KOLINSKY. Name given to China mink; see Mink.

KRIMMER. Trade name for lamb pelt; mixture of gray with some white and black; open curl. Best source is Circassian lambs of Caucasus.

LEOPARD. Somali leopard, from Somaliland, is choicest. Himalayas, mountains of China and jungles of Africa and India yield fine furs.

LYNX. Long and silky guard hairs and fur fibers; most valuable natural color is blue-gray. Hudson Bay region and Alaska produce best skins.

MARMOT. Finest skins come from Mongolia and Central China. Usually dyed to imitate mink; is then called mink-dyed marmot.

MARTEN. Beautiful full-haired fur with fine guard hairs and silky texture. Canadian marten is often called Hudson Bay sable; Baum marten, which comes from Europe, resembles Siberian sable.

Stone marten, also from Europe, is the most durable.

MINK. Best peltries from North America. Mink farming is important in the United States and Canada. Blue-brown is most desired color; silver-blue and snow white are being bred. China mink is yellow; Japanese mink is yellow-brown. Both are always dyed.

MOUTON. Trade name for skins from fine wool sheep. Usually dyed to imitate beaver or Alaska seal.

MUSKRAT. Huge quantities of this skin, supplied mostly by North America, are used in the trade. Skins may be used in natural brown color, but are often dyed or blended to resemble more expensive furs.

NUTRIA. Native to South America; introduced into North America and Europe. Long, ugly guard hairs are plucked. Best quality underfur is dark bluish brown.

OCELOT. Central and South America produce most of skins. Tawny, with black, brown and white oblong spots.

OPOSSUM. Skins obtained chiefly from North America and Australia. Generally is dyed brown, blue or black, and may be used to imitate skunk, a more expensive fur.

OTTER. Peltries obtained from all continents except Australia. Fur is short, lustrous and dark brown.

PERSIAN LAMB. Covering of animal is not woolly, but silky, with tight, lustrous curls. Usually dyed black; some natural grays and browns are also used. Comes from Persia and east of Caspian Sea; best quality produced in region around Bukhara.

PONY. Finest skins come from Poland and Russia; flat short-haired pelt is usually dyed.

RABBIT (Cony). Caught everywhere; peltries used in North American trade come mostly from Australia and New Zealand. Used chiefly to imitate other furs.

RACCOON. Caught from southern Canada to Gulf of Mexico. Best quality is silvery, with thick gray-brown underfur. Sometimes sheared to imitate beaver.

SABLE. A choice fur. Peltries come chiefly from Siberia; some from northern Canada. Finest peltries—dark bluish brown—are caught northeast of Lake Baikal.

SEAL. Obtained mostly from Pribilof Islands, off Alaskan coast. Fur is soft, short, fine and thick; is dyed black or brown.

SKUNK. Most desirable peltries are dark smoky black; poor qualities are dyed black. Minnesota is chief source of supply.

SQUIRREL. Europe and Asia are largest producers. Best skins are steely blue and full-furred. Inferior skins are dyed.

WEASEL. In fur trade means American animal closely allied to ermine. Fur is soft, lustrous, with thick brown underfur. Inferior skins may be bleached or dyed.

MATHEMATICS OF STATISTICS

Collecting, Organizing, Analyzing and Presenting Numerical Data

BY F. JOE CROSSWHITE

HAVE you ever noticed how much of the information we receive comes to us through numbers? Particularly since the coming of age of electronic computers, more and more kinds of information are being coded, processed and presented numerically. On any given day, we can expect to see numerical presentations of weather information, the stock market, political polls, business transactions, census data, government operations and many other types of data.

In most instances, the numerical information in its original form would be difficult to interpret. For this reason, the information is usually organized, summarized and presented to us in a form that can be more readily interpreted. Frequently this is accomplished by reducing the numerical data to a table or graph or by reporting one number (such as the average) to represent an entire set of numbers.* The process by which numerical data are collected and eventually presented in a usable and understandable form is an important part of the mathematical science of statistics.

Statistics is important not only for communication; it also provides a basis for decision-making. The government makes extensive use of statistics in estimating its budget needs and setting its tax rates. Statistics enables manufacturers to compare production processes when they seek to improve their products or increase their profits. Store managers may rely upon statistical analyses to determine the items they stock. Scientists employ statistics in comparing the effects of critical variables upon their experiments. Insurance companies rise and fall on the accuracy of their statistical predictions. Engineers base the design of highways and bridges upon statistical studies of materials and traffic. School officials may modify their curricula on the basis of statistical analyses of student achievements and needs. The list of such decision-making uses of statistics is almost endless.

The collection
of data

The science of statistics involves a variety of tasks. Even the seemingly simple business of collecting numerical data requires careful study. Obviously the conclusions of a statistical study can be no more reliable than the figures upon which they are based. The statistician must be sure that the data he collects are *accurate*, *relevant* to the problem being studied and *representative* of the problem. Invalid conclusions drawn from statistical evidence are often due to inadequacies in the data collected.** Although we cannot go into the matter of data collection in detail, its importance is so great that we should be at least aware of some of the problems involved.

First, the *population* to be studied must be well-defined. What do we mean by "population" here? To the statistician, it may consist of a set of cities, or automobiles, or books or even scientific experiments. In fact, the population for a statistical study might be any set of objects having a common characteristic to which a number might be assigned. Of course, the population selected must supply the appropriate numerical data for the problem being studied. If the population of a statistical study is not well-defined or is not representative of the problem being studied, the results of the study will be difficult to interpret or apply. For example, surveys of the voting preferences of high school students would be of questionable value in predicting the results of an election, since few high-school students can vote.

Once the population has been identified, the particular characteristics to be studied must be represented numerically. Sometimes the numerical data are already available in recorded form. For example, if you wanted to study the rainfall in your city over the past year, you could probably obtain the needed data from your local weather bureau. (In this case, the population might be defined as the set of days in the year.) Sometimes the numerical data may be obtained by a simple counting process. You might be interested, for example, in a study of the books in a school library. This project would involve counting the number of volumes devoted to each of several subjects.

More often, the data for a statistical study are obtained by *measuring* some common characteristic of the population being studied. If the population were a set of scientific experiments, the scientist might be concerned with such characteristics as time, temperature, volume and mass. In each instance, he would need to use a suitable measuring instrument to assign a number to the characteristic.

In some cases, no measuring instrument is available and the investigator must create

---

* *Editor's note*: A "set" in mathematics is a collection of objects. See Index, under Sets (mathematical), theory of.

** Many interesting examples of the "misuse" of statistics can be found in the delightful little book called *How to Lie with Statistics*, by Darrell Huff, published by W. W. Norton and Co., Inc., New York, 1954.

TABLE I	16	18	16	14	12	13	18
	19	12	17	15	16	14	16
Thirty-Five Scores on a Spelling Test	14	16	20	16	17	15	15
	16	15	14	18	15	16	13
	17	13	16	17	15	19	17

his own measuring device. For this purpose, he may construct an examination. This then becomes the instrument that enables him to assign a number to measure student achievement. As with any other measuring instrument, accuracy is a prime consideration. The investigator would need to know how well the number assigned represents the true value of the characteristic being measured: in this case, student achievement.

The ultimate value of a statistical study depends to a large extent upon the quality of the measuring instrument that is employed. For this reason, the construction and evaluation of such an instrument is often a critical task in a statistical study.

Sometimes it is possible to obtain numerical data about each member of a population that is being studied. When this is true, the data are completely representative of the population, and the task of the statistician is to *describe* the numerical data obtained. This branch of statistics is called *descriptive statistics.*

Often it is necessary or practical to collect data only for a *sample* of the population and to make *statistical inferences* about the population itself. An inference is a conclusion about the unknown based upon something that is known. A statistical inference, of course, is one based upon statistical data. When data are available only for a sample, the sample represents the known and the population the unknown. Any subset of a population would constitute a sample, but statistical inferences are valid only when the sample is representative of the population. Many techniques are employed by statisticians to insure that the samples they select are representative.

When each member of the population has an equal chance of being chosen, we have what is called a *random sample.* This is usually assumed to be representative of the population. In some special problems, the statistician uses a *stratified sample,* which insures that specific segments of the study population are represented in the sample. The process of identifying a representative sample is a critical task in many statistical studies. In the examples that follow, we will assume that the samples used are representative of the populations from which they have been selected.

Let me summarize the above remarks about collecting data by considering the following example. Suppose that the population being studied is the set of students in a given grade. If each of these students was assigned to an English class by a random process, the English class would constitute a representative sample of the population. If you were to measure the height, weight or age of each student in the class, or record his score on a particular test or count the number of people in his family, you would obtain a set of numbers. These numbers could then become the data for a statistical study.

TABLE II	
Frequency Distribution of Spelling Scores	
Score	Frequency
20	1
19	2
18	3
17	5
16	9
15	6
14	4
13	3
12	2
	n = 35

Note: "n" stands for the number of scores.

TABLE III	
Grouped Frequency Table of 200 Spelling Scores	
Interval	Frequency
23-25	8
20-22	19
17-19	44
14-16	60
11-13	40
8-10	21
5- 7	8
	n = 200

The data could be used to describe the English class (the sample). They could also be used to make *estimates* or *inferences* about the total set of students in the grade (the population).

Organizing the data

Once data have been collected, they must be arranged in some systematic order before a useful interpretation can be made or conclusions drawn. Sometimes a simple table or graph can be quite helpful as a. first step toward the statistical analysis of numeri cal data.

The numerical data presented in Table I are scores obtained by thirty-five students in a spelling test. Each score represents the number of words that have been spelled correctly by a given student. In this case, the word "score" is used in its usual sense. However, regardless of the nature of the numerical data, statisticians often use the term *raw score* to indicate the individual numbers obtained as a basis for a statistical study.

It is difficult to make any useful interpretation of the data in Table I. The simplest way of organizing these data would be to arrange the scores in numerical order. It is common to record only the different raw scores (in this case, 16, 18, 14 and so on) and to note the *frequency* with which each score occurs. Table II is a frequency

table presenting the same data that appear in Table I.

Even a cursory examination of Table II permits some elementary interpretation of the data. We can easily observe the highest and lowest scores (20 and 12) and the most frequent score (16). We can even begin to have some feeling for the way the scores seem to cluster about a central point.

Further clarification of the data may be obtained by translating Table II into a graphical form. Figure 1 is a common type of graph used to present frequency distributions. The numbers below the horizontal line represent scores; the numbers at the left represent the frequency distribution — that is, the number of times each score occurs. This is a frequency graph.

The frequency polygon shown in Figure 2 is based on the same idea. In this case, we may consider that lines have been drawn perpendicular to the scores on the bottom line and to the frequencies at the left. A point indicates the intersection of a score line and a frequency line; thus we have a point where the score 12 and the frequency number 2 meet. The points are connected by straight lines. A line is drawn in each case between the point representing the lowest score and the score immediately preceding on the horizontal line; also between the point representing the highest score and the score immediately following on the horizontal line.

An examination of these two graphs will reveal exactly the same information available in Table II. For some people, the graphical form is easier to interpret than the tabular form. In particular, the tendency of scores to cluster around a central point becomes more apparent when the data are presented pictorially.

In many statistical studies, the number of different raw scores obtained is so large that it becomes cumbersome to work with all the different scores. In these cases, it is common to condense the data by grouping the raw scores into *class intervals*. Instead of considering each score individually, we combine a certain number of adjacent scores to form an interval. Thus we would combine the individual scores 23, 24 and 25 to form the interval 23-25. Intervals are treated in much the same way as we would treat individual raw scores.

A grouped frequency table, based on intervals, is shown in Table III. It presents scores made by 200 students in the same spelling test for which thirty-five scores were reported in Table I. We could think of the data in Table I as representing the scores of one of six randomly assigned English classes whose total scores are reported in Table III.

When the number of possible raw scores is large, the grouping of data into appropriate intervals enables the investigator to

work with a manageable number. (The seven intervals in Table III may reflect as many as three times that number of different raw scores.) At the same time, this grouping method has the disadvantage of obscuring individual scores. Thus only one score may be represented in the interval 23-25, while all three scores might be represented in another interval. We have to ignore this consideration when working with class intervals. Once the data have been compressed by grouping, in all subsequent analysis and computation, we must treat individual scores as if they were evenly distributed throughout the interval to which they belong.

Graphical representations of grouped frequency tables are very similar to those presented earlier for ungrouped data. One special kind of graph, the *frequency histogram*, is worthy of note. To construct a histogram from Table III, as in Figure 3, the frequency of scores in each interval is represented by a rectangle with its center at the mid-point of the interval, its height equal to the frequency and its width equal to the width of the interval — with a difference.

Here it is necessary to distinguish between *score* limits and *real* limits. When an interval is identified as 14-16, the limits reported are called score limits. They identify the lowest score and highest score that belong to the same interval. For purposes of mathematical treatment and graphical representation, it is common to use the real

1. Frequency graph of data in Table II on preceding page.

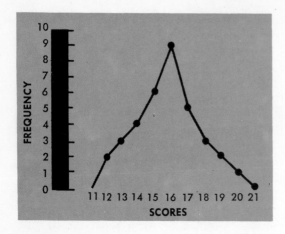

2. Frequency polygon based on data given in Table II.

limits 13.5-16.5 to identify this same interval. The interval is represented as extending halfway to the scores immediately preceding and following. Such an interpretation is consistent with the way we usually report measurements. For example, if we were measuring to the nearer foot, any measurement between 13 feet, 6 inches and 14 feet, 6 inches would be reported as 14 feet.

Analyzing
the data

Tables and graphs can help us obtain considerable understanding of a set of scores. However, for many purposes, it is more de-

3. Frequency histogram of data in Table III on page 242.

sirable to try to represent the set of scores by a single number. When selecting a single number to represent a whole set of numbers, the first thing we usually think of is the average. As we noted earlier, the scores we have been examining seem to cluster around a central point. It is this point of central tendency which statisticians identify when they report an average score. In statistics, there are several types of averages. Three are common in statistical analysis—the mode, the median and the mean. Each is called a measure of central tendency. For the data with which we have been working in this article, the mode, median and mean are close together. This is not always the case; they may be appreciably different.

The *mode* is quite easily identified from a frequency table or frequency graph. It is the score that occurs most frequently—in a sense, the most popular score. In the ungrouped data presented above, we have already noted that the most frequent score is 16. (This can be determined from Table II, Figure 1 or Figure 2.) Thus 16 is the mode of this set of scores. In the grouped data, the *crude mode* would be identified as the midpoint of the interval with the highest frequency. From either Table III or Figure 3, we can see that the interval of highest frequency is 14-16; hence 15 would be the crude mode of this distribution since it is the midpoint of the interval. Since individual

4. In the graph of this distr. on there are two scores—5 an 25—that have the highest frequency. Compare it with the graph shown in Figure 5, on the following page.

scores have been obscured, we cannot be sure that it is actually the most frequent individual score, but it is our best estimate of the most frequent score.

The *median* is the middle score in a set of scores. If we examine the set of scores in Table II, we see that the median is 16. (If there had been an even number of scores, the median would have been reported as a figure that is half way between the two middle scores.)

Since the second set of data, presented in Table III and Figure 3, has been condensed by grouping, we cannot work with individual scores and must find a new procedure for identifying the median. From Table III, we find that the middle score must fall in the interval 14-16. Since only 69 scores out of the total number of 200 fall below this interval, we know that 31 of the 60 scores in the interval 14-16 must also be below the median. Since for grouped data we must assume that scores are evenly distributed within an interval, we will assume that the median lies 31/60 of the width of the interval above its lowest boundary. 31/60 × 3 (the number of scores in the interval) = 93/60 = 1.5+. We add this number to the left end point of the interval 14-16. We noted previously that this point is 13.5 since an interval begins and ends halfway between two scores. Hence we have 13.5 + 1.5 = 15. The median, then, is 15 for the second set of data.

The *mean* is the most commonly used measure of central tendency and is the average most of us think of first. It is found by dividing the sum of all the individual scores by the number of scores in the set. This calculation can be shortened when a frequency table is available if we multiply each score by its frequency and then find the sum. From Table II, for example, we would perform the following calculation*: $(20 \cdot 1) +$ $(19 \cdot 2) + (18 \cdot 3) + (17 \cdot 5) + (16 \cdot 9) +$ $(15 \cdot 6) + (14 \cdot 4) + (13 \cdot 3) + (12 \cdot 2)$ divided by 35 = 550 divided by 35 = 15.7. 15.7 is the mean.

When computing the mean for grouped data, we assume that the scores in any interval are evenly distributed. We multiply the value of the midpoint of each interval by the frequency, and we divide the sum of the resulting number by the total number of scores. In the case of the grouped data in Table III, we could compute the mean thus: $(24 \cdot 8) +$ $(21 \cdot 19) + (18 \cdot 44) + (15 \cdot 60) + (12 \cdot 40)$ $+ (9 \cdot 21) + (6 \cdot 8)$ divided by 200 = 3,000 divided by 200 = 15.

The calculation of the mean can be simplified by using more advanced methods. These are mathematically equivalent to the above calculations.

The mode is used less frequently than either the median or the mean. It is useful only when we want to identify the number

* *Editor's note*: The symbol "·" in this calculation is equivalent to "times."

5. In the distribution graph here, the mean (15) and the range (20) are identical with those shown in Figure 4 on the preceding page. But the distributions are different.

occurring most frequently in a set of numbers. As a matter of fact, if the mode is to be truly meaningful, one number in a set must occur quite a bit more frequently than any other number in the set. The advantage of the mode is that, like the median, it is easy to identify and understand. But the term "mode" is sometimes ambiguous because there may be more than one score with the "highest frequency" (see Figure 4). Also the mode is not too reliable as an indication of central tendency because the most popular score is not always near the center of a given distribution.

The chief advantage of the median is that it is not affected by extreme scores. The "average" income in a community, for example, is often more accurately reflected by the median than the mean because the value of the median is not influenced by a few very high or very low incomes. The idea of the median is closely related to the concept of percentiles — a type of "score" students receive on certain standard tests in school. The median corresponds to the 50th percentile. Other percentiles can also be used in connection with tests; they are valuable as a basis for comparing individual scores with other scores in a distribution.

For most purposes, the mean is the best measure of central tendency. It is the only one of the three measures that depends upon the numerical value of each score in a distribution. It is a reliable indicator of "central

tendency" because it always identifies the "balancing point" or "center of gravity" in the distribution. Since the mean lends itself better to mathematical computation, it is more suitable for deriving other statistical measures. For example, the means of two sets of data can be used to compute a mean for the combined set of data. This cannot be done with the mode or the median.

However, the mean can give us information only about the central point in a distribution. To understand a set of scores more fully, we also need to know how the scores spread out around this central point. For this reason, statisticians develop measures of *dispersion* or *variability*.

The simplest measure of distribution is the range, which is defined as the difference between the highest and lowest scores in a distribution. The range of spelling scores reported in Table II is easily identified; we simply subtract the lowest score (12) from the highest score (20). Since the range is sensitive only to the two extreme scores in a distribution, it is not considered a very satisfactory measure of dispersion. Its weakness is dramatized in the two distributions whose graphs are presented in Figures 4 and 5. Both the mean (15) and the range (20) are identical for these two distributions; yet the distributions are obviously different.

As with the median and the mode, the weakness of the range is that it does not take into account the numerical value of each score. A natural measure of dispersion involving every score is the average difference between the individual scores and their mean. As we have seen, the mean serves as a "balancing point" for a distribution. Hence we can measure the deviations from the mean in terms of positive and negative differences. Deviations from the mean in one direction would be positive; in the other, negative.

Since the mean is the "balancing point" or "center of gravity" for a distribution, the sum of the deviations from the mean is 0. (This is because some of the differences are positive and others are negative.) That is why we must employ the mathematical notion of *absolute value* to treat the deviations from the mean as distances without regard to direction — that is, without indicating whether they are positive or negative. The average of the absolute values of the differences between individual scores and the mean is called the *mean deviation* and is a simple and accurate measure of dispersion. For the distribution pictured in Figure 4, the calculation of the mean deviation would appear as follows: $15 \cdot |5 - 15|* + 10 \cdot |10 - 15| + 5 \cdot |15 - 15| + 10 \cdot |20 - 15| + 15 \cdot |25 - 15|$ divided by 55 (frequency). It would be equal to $15 \cdot 10 + 10 \cdot 5 + 5 \cdot 0 + 10 \cdot 5 + 15 \cdot 10$ divided by 55. This would give us

$$\frac{400}{55} \approx ** 7.3$$

A similar calculation for the distribution in Figure 5 would yield a mean deviation of 4.0. Thus greater dispersion is indicated for the figure in Figure 4.

The use of absolute values presents mathematical difficulties which can be avoided by using another measure. The positive and negative signs that led to the introduction of absolute values could also have been eliminated by squaring the deviations from the mean, since the square of a positive or negative number is always positive. Such a procedure preserves the descriptive qualities of the mean deviation while providing a measure that is easier to handle mathematically. Hence statisticians prefer to use the standard deviation (indicated by the symbol "σ") as a measure of dispersion. The standard deviation is defined as the square root of the average squared deviation from the mean. Thus to calculate the standard deviation, we first find the average of the squares of the deviations. This number is called the *variance*. Suppose we wished to find the variance and standard deviation (σ) for the data in Table II. We would obtain the variance thus: $(20 - 15.7)^2 + 2(19 - 15.7)^2 + ...3(13 - 15.7)^2 + 2(12 - 15.7)^2$ divided by 35 (total number of scores.) This would be equal to 128.15 divided by $35 \approx 3.66$. The variance then is 3.66. We would then have

$$\sigma = \sqrt{\text{variance}} = \sqrt{3.66} \approx 1.9$$

Similar calculations would yield a standard deviation of 4.2 for the data in Table III. If we compare these two measures of dispersion, we see that the scores in Table II (the sample) are not so "spread out" as the scores in Table III (the population).

Interpreting the data

Together, the mean and the standard deviation give us a reasonably clear picture of a distribution, because they describe both its central tendency and its dispersion. Sometimes, if we know the general nature of the distribution, we need only these two numbers to reconstruct the distribution. For example, many sets of measurements have the *normal* distribution shown in Figure 6.

When a set of numbers "fits" such a standard distribution, we can determine approximately how many of the numbers fall within a given distance of the mean. For the normal distribution, approximately two-thirds of the scores fall within one standard deviation of the mean. Thus, given the mean (15) and the standard deviation (4.2) for the set of spelling scores in Table III, we could "predict" that approximately two-thirds of the scores would be between 10.8 and 19.2.

---

* *Editor's note*: The numerals 5 and 15 are enclosed between absolute value signs (| |). These signs must be used. They indicate that we are to consider the "distance" between the score and the mean without regard to direction.

** *Editor's note*: The symbol "$\approx$" stands for "is approximately equal to."

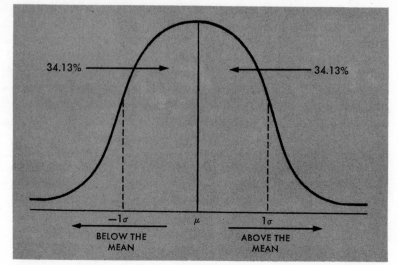

34.13% ⟶   ⟵ 34.13%

−1σ   μ   1σ

BELOW THE
MEAN

ABOVE THE
MEAN

6. A normal distribution curve. The symbol "μ" stands for the mean; "σ" stands for standard deviation. For explanation, see the text on pages 245 and 247.

Since the distribution is actually given in Table III, we see that 144 of the 200 scores actually *do* fall in this interval. The "prediction" is fairly accurate since the number of scores is relatively large and they do "fit" the normal distribution.

The knowledge of such general models for distribution coupled with the laws of probability form the basis of predictive statistics. Both statistics and probability have to do with distributions and it is upon this common focus that we capitalize in predictive statistics. In probability, the sample space (population) is known and we predict the composition of a set of outcomes (sample). In statistical inference, the sample (set of outcomes) is known, and we infer the composition of the population (sample space.) Thus predictive statistics, also called statistical inference, can actually be thought of as an application of the laws of probability in reverse.

If we could be certain that the distribution of scores in a sample reflected exactly the distribution of scores in the population from which it was chosen, statistical inferences would be exact and simple to make. But even when a population is known, probability theory tells us that samples will not always be the same. The best we can hope for is that, if the sample is large enough and is carefully chosen, the sample characteristics will closely approximate those of the parent population.

Suppose we had only the data recorded in Table II and wished to estimate the mean spelling score for all the English classes. Our best estimate would be the mean obtained for the sample: 15.7. But knowing that samples vary, we would hedge on this estimate. We would give a *confidence interval* within which we would expect the true mean of the population to fall. By assuming the total set of spelling scores to be normally distributed and applying basic laws of probability, we could determine that there is 95 per cent chance that the population mean falls in a given interval with its center at 15.7. The 95 per cent is a measure of the confidence or reliability we can place in our interval estimate. It means that 95 of every 100 populations from which a sample with the given characteristics might be chosen would have a mean within the determined interval. Because of the uncertainties involved in sampling, such an interval estimate, accompanied by a statement of the degree of confidence we can place in the estimate, is preferable to a single number approximation.

The process of establishing confidence intervals permits us to test hypotheses about a population. Modifications of this process permit us to make statistical comparisons of two samples drawn from the same population, to compare a sample to a known population or to infer other characteristics of an unknown population.

AN INTRODUCTION
TO OPTICS

Some Striking Effects of Light and How They Serve Man

BY J. H. RUSH

MEN of science have realized for years that light is a form of radiant energy. Light, X rays, radio waves and gamma rays are all electromagnetic radiations. They are so called because they are sent out into space as a result of variations in electric and magnetic fields.

Not so many years ago, scientists were quite sure that light and other radiant energy consisted of electromagnetic waves rippling through space. They distinguished sharply between the wave character of radiation and the particle character of matter. Today the picture is not so clear. In some respects, at least, light and other radiations behave like streams of particles. What is even stranger, perhaps, electrons and other very small particles sometimes behave like waves.

The peculiar dual nature of radiation and of material particles is the subject matter of wave mechanics. It would take a great deal of space to explain this theory, even nonmathematically. It is perhaps enough to say here that neither radiation nor material particles ever exhibit both wave and particle characteristics at the same time. In transit — that is, as it moves from place to place — light behaves like a system of waves. It has a fixed speed in empty space; its wave lengths can be measured by a variety of methods. In many ways its behavior is entirely consistent with the theory that it is an electromagnetic wave disturbance. But in its emission from electrons in an atom and in its absorption or other reaction with atoms in its path, light behaves more like a stream of very small particles of energy — photons.

The old argument over the nature of light seems to have ended in a draw. Instead of saying that light (or any other kind of radiation) consists of waves or particles, physicists recognize that it behaves like waves in certain respects and like particles in others.

The speed of light plays an important part in astronomical and physical research. It is extremely important, therefore, to measure it as accurately as possible. For nearly three centuries scientists have gradually refined and improved their techniques, until now the speed of light is known to within about one part in a hundred thousand. It is very nearly 299,792 kilometers, or 186,281 miles, per second.

Strictly speaking, light means any radiation whose wave lengths excite a sensation of brightness, or illumination, in the retina of the eye. These wave lengths range from about $16/1,000,000$ of an inch to $30/1,000,000$ of an inch. Certain types of radiation — ultraviolet light and infrared light — are similar to visible light, though their wave lengths are somewhat shorter or longer than those of the visible range. In the following pages we will use the word "light" in the sense of all wave lengths that behave similarly to those that excite vision.

What happens when
light encounters matter

When light encounters some form or other of matter, it behaves in different ways. For example, when it strikes an opaque object (one that does not transmit light), the object casts a shadow. Much of the early argument as to whether light is made up of waves or particles hinged on observations of shadows.

If light consists of a shower of flying particles, those striking an opaque barrier in their path would be stopped. Other particles would miss the edge of the barrier, as shown in Figure 1a. If the latter struck a screen set beyond the obstacle, a geometrically sharp shadow would appear on the screen. That is apparently just what happens. In this respect light seems to

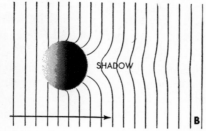

SHADOW

SHADOW

A

B

1. Shadow formation. In A we assume that light consists of particles; in B, that it has a wavelike nature.

act unlike waves of water or sound, which bend around obstacles. That is why Sir Isaac Newton and other thinkers came to the conclusion that light does not consist of waves, but of tiny flying particles.

Careful observation, however, shows that light *does* bend around obstacles (Figure 1b). Short waves of any kind bend less than long ones, and light waves are very short indeed. Yet under special conditions this bending of light at edges — a phenomenon called diffraction — produces striking effects. A certain amount of light makes its way into the shadow area. Ordinarily it is not noticeable. However, in the case of a small ball or disk, all the light diffracted around the edge crosses at the center of the shadow, and a bright spot appears. Immediately outside the shadow cast by the sharp edge, the light is broken up into a series of bands, or fringes, that alternate in intensity.

When light falls on a material barrier, some of it is reflected; it bounces back from the surface, like a ball from a floor. If the material is not quite opaque, some of the light is transmitted through it at reduced speed. In its course it is refracted, or bent. Usually a large portion of the light is absorbed in the material. It disappears as light, and its energy is changed into other forms.

The most common effect of absorption is the change of light energy into heat. The rapidly oscillating electric and magnetic fields involved in the light wave set the electrons in the material to vibrating. As a result, all the molecules of the material vibrate more energetically and the material becomes hotter. To understand why this is so, one must bear in mind that heat is simply the kinetic energy, or energy of motion, of the molecules of a substance. The more vigorously its molecules vibrate, the hotter the substance is.

Light energy is not always transformed directly into heat. If it strikes a clean metal surface in a vacuum, the light energizes some electrons so violently that they jump out of the metal and fly through the adjacent space. This so-called photoelectric effect is used in television cameras and many other electric-eye devices. (See Index, under Photoelectric cells.) Light also causes chemical changes in many substances. It can bleach various dyes, or cause intense irritation of the skin or produce subtle changes in the silver chloride of a photographic film. From the human standpoint, the most important photochemical effect of light takes place in a substance in the retina of the eye, called visual purple. This pigment is partially bleached by light, and the chemical change that takes place is an essential part of the visual process.

Light affects matter chiefly by acting upon the outer electrons in atoms. When light energy sets the electrons dancing, each electron acts like a tiny radio antenna, radiating back part of the energy it has received. Some of this reradiated light goes back in the direction from which the light originally came; it is reflected energy.

In describing what happens when light strikes a surface, we shall have occasion to speak of rays and beams of light; rays will be represented by arrows in our diagrams. We must think of a ray as representing the direction in which a wave front is advancing. A bundle of rays is called a beam.

When light is transmitted through space, the waves spread out at equal speed in all directions from the source, as shown in Figure 2. By the time a wave of light from a point on the sun reaches the earth, some 93,000,000 miles away, the part of the wave that strikes a surface such as a mirror or a pavement is only very slightly curved. To all intents and purposes the

wave front is a straight line and the rays of light are parallel to each other (Figure 3).

The light rays that fall upon a surface are called incident rays. (*Incidere* in Latin means "to fall upon.") If the rays strike a surface perpendicularly, they are reflected straight back. Figure 4 shows what happens when they fall obliquely upon the surface. AB is the incident ray, which strikes the surface at B. BC represents the ray after it has bounced back from the surface, as a reflected ray. Let us draw a line, BD, at right angles to the surface at the point B. This perpendicular is called the normal. The angle ABD (or I), formed by the incident ray and the normal, is the angle of incidence. The reflected ray and the normal form another angle, CBD (or R), which is known as the angle of reflection. The angle of incidence is always equal to the angle of reflection; the incident ray, reflected ray and normal, all lie in the same plane. This statement is the law of reflection.

If the entire reflecting surface is very smooth, regular reflection takes place — that is, light is reflected in a regular, orderly way. The surface need not be flat; but if it is curved, the curve must be smooth and gradual. If such a smooth surface, flat or curved, is capable of reflecting most of the light that falls on it, it is called a mirror (Figure 5).

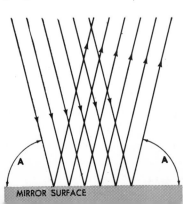

In Fig. 4, extreme left, we see light striking an ordinary surface and reflected from it. Angle I is the angle of incidence; angle R, the angle of reflection. The other drawing (Fig. 5) shows light being reflected from a mirror surface.

6. When light strikes a rough surface, made up of many tiny smooth surfaces, it is reflected in many directions.

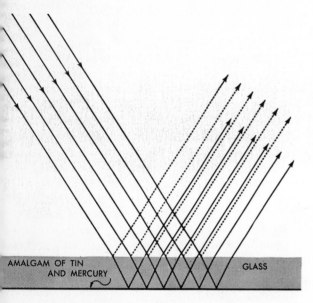

AMALGAM OF TIN AND MERCURY   GLASS

7. Light that strikes an ordinary mirror of plate glass is reflected from the coating on the back of the glass.

8. Light reflected from a precision mirror is reflected from a metal film on the front surface of the mirror.

GLASS   SILVER OR ALUMINUM FILM

Mirrors are scarce in nature. Most objects would absorb too much light to be good mirrors, even if they were smooth; and comparatively few are smooth. Dirt, stones, leaves, wood, hair, skin — nearly all common materials have surfaces that are very rough and irregular, from the "atom's-eye view" of a light wave. We may think of such a surface as made up of a great number of very small smooth surfaces (Figure 6). Light is reflected from each small surface element according to the law of reflection, but the rays from the various elements go off in many different directions. The reflected light is diffused, or scattered. This process is called diffuse reflection.

Our visual judgment of the textures of different surfaces depends mainly upon the degree of diffuseness of the light they reflect. Consider, for example, the difference in appearance between a piece of black velvet and one of polished black marble or obsidian, or between a good mirror and a slab of plaster of Paris.

Good mirrors are relatively hard to make. Not only must the surface be smooth to within a few millionths of an inch; it must also absorb no more than a few per cent of the incident light. With a few special exceptions, metals are by far the best mirror surfaces. Why? Metals conduct electricity, and that means that their electrons are not bound to their respective atoms so strongly as in the nonmetals. Consequently, the electrons in metals have more freedom to vibrate in unison with the incoming light waves, and to reradiate the energy they absorb. In nonmetals, more of the absorbed energy is trapped as heat. Except for gold, silver and copper, metals are rarely found uncombined with other elements. That is why natural mirrors are scarce.

Ordinary household mirrors are made of plate glass coated on the back with an amalgam of tin foil and mercury, which is painted black to protect it. The metal film itself is the mirror; the glass serves only to shape the film and protect it (Figure 7). Such a mirror is very durable, but it is not satisfactory for a telescope or any other precision optical instrument. For such exacting purposes, a piece of plate glass is so irregular that it may be compared to a plowed field. The front surface of the glass in an ordinary mirror reflects enough light itself to produce an undesirable secondary image.

Glass for a precision mirror must be ground and polished to near-perfect smoothness. A thin layer of metal — usually aluminum — must then be evaporated in a vacuum onto the front surface of the glass. The glass itself merely supports the metal film (Figure 8). Such a mirror reflects up to 95 per cent of the light that falls upon it.

Most substances absorb practically all the light they receive before it penetrates to any appreciable distance. Such substances are said to be opaque. A few natural substances (besides gases) and many more artificial ones are transparent. They permit substantial fractions of light to penetrate through moderate thicknesses of material. All substances absorb some light energy; transparency is only relative. Good optical glass will transmit more than 99 per cent of the light entering a plate one inch thick; but such transparency is uncommon.

The light that strikes transparent substances usually is a mixture of all the different wave lengths that we see as white light. Transparent materials absorb some wave lengths more than others. Since different wave lengths cause different sensations of color to arise in the brain, very few transparent materials appear colorless in transmitted light. Ordinary glass favors the green wave lengths slightly; it is practically opaque in the ultraviolet region. A thin film of silver, such as is used on some mirrors, is quite opaque to visible light, but is transparent in the ultraviolet range.

Some materials allow light to pass through, but they scatter and diffuse it. Such a material is called translucent; its effect can be compared to that of diffuse reflection. Opal glass and certain kinds of paper are very familiar examples of translucent substances.

9. A column of marching men would change direction as it passed from a smooth parade ground to a rough field. On the plowed field the men could not march so rapidly.

When an incident ray of light enters a transparent substance at some angle other than the perpendicular, or normal, to the surface, its direction is changed. This effect is called refraction (bending). The ray whose course has been changed in this way is known as a refracted ray. Refraction takes place because the speed of light in a vacuum (or in air, which in this case amounts to nearly the same thing) is greater than in water, say, or glass.

To illustrate the principle involved in refraction, let us suppose that a column of marching men crosses the boundary between a smooth parade ground and a plowed field at an angle, as in Figure 9. They cannot march as rapidly on the rough ground as they can on smooth terrain. In each rank the men who first reach the rough ground slow down while those to their left gain on them. As a result of this difference in marching speed, the direction of march of the column is changed.

10. This diagram shows how a wave of light is refracted. Details about refraction are given on this page.

In Figure 10 we apply this principle to the refraction of light. The rays AA' indicate the direction of a train of light waves advancing in air and approaching the surface of a transparent material SS. The speed of light in this material is less than the speed of light in air. As the advancing wave front reaches the position CD, the part near C enters the material and is slowed down. The portions of the front nearer D continue to advance in air at their former speed. As a result, the advancing wave front swings toward the normal, or perpendicular.

By the time the wave front at D has reached the surface at E, traveling the distance *a,* the light that entered at C has traveled a lesser distance, *b,* to the point F. Other points of the wave front will have traveled intermediate distances, so that the new wave front in the transparent substance will be EF. Note that the angle between the refracted ray and the normal NN (angle R), called the angle of refraction, is smaller than the angle of incidence (angle I). A ray will be turned toward the normal when its velocity is reduced; it will be turned away from the normal when the velocity is increased. This happens, for example, when light passes from water into air.

The ratio of the speed of light in air * to the speed of light in a given substance is called the index of refraction of that substance. The index of refraction can be defined more exactly as the ratio of the sine of the angle of incidence to the sine of the angle of refraction. Let us see what this means. In Figure 11 a ray of light strikes the surface of a transparent substance — say, water — so as to form the angle of incidence I. It is then refracted; the angle of refraction is R. We mark off equal distances AC and BC on the incident ray and the refracted ray. Then we draw perpendiculars AD and EB to the normal NN. ADC and ECB are two right-angled triangles, with equal hypotenuses.

The sine of any angle of a right-angled triangle is the ratio of the side opposite that angle to the hypotenuse. The sine of angle I, therefore, is AD/AC; the sine of angle R is EB/CB. Since the index of refraction is the ratio of the sine of the angle of incidence (I) to the sine of the angle of refraction (R), it is

$$\frac{AD/AC}{EB/CB}$$

The hypotenuse AC is equal to the hypotenuse CB; therefore the index of refraction is AD/EB.

The sines for all angles up to 90° are given in trigonometric tables. Once we know the angle of incidence and the angle of refraction as a ray of light strikes and then penetrates a given substance, it is a simple matter to find the sines of the two angles and to determine the index of refraction. The index of refraction of water is about 4/3, or 1.3; that of common glass is about 3/2, or 1.5.

We saw that when light passes obliquely from a transparent substance into air, the rays bend away from the normal. This may result in the effect called total internal reflection. In Figure 12, the ray

* As we have seen, the speed of light in a vacuum is practically the same as its speed in air.

of light A passes through glass and is bent away from the normal as it moves through air (as A′). In this case, the angle of incidence is I^1; the angle of refraction is R^1. If the angle of incidence is increased, the angle of refraction will be increased even more, proportionately, and the refracted ray will be closer to the surface of the glass.

When incident ray B passes through the glass, the angle of refraction (R^2) as it penetrates the air (as B′) is 90°; the ray will graze the surface of the glass, as shown. Angle I^2, formed by the incident ray B and the normal, is called the critical angle. If the critical angle is exceeded, the ray does not leave the glass at all but is totally reflected from the surface.

11. How to find the index of refraction of a transparent substance. Details are given on the preceding page.

12. Total internal reflection: ray C is reflected from the surface of the glass as C′. See pages 254 and 255.

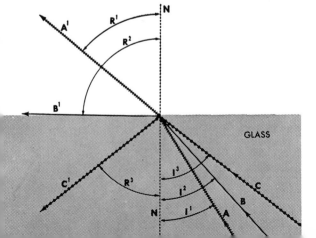

This happens, for example, when ray C passes through the glass, forming the angle of incidence I^3, which is greater than the critical angle I^2. The ray is reflected from the surface (as C′), following the law of reflection.

The critical angle depends on the index of refraction on either side of the boundary surface. It is about 41° for a glass-air boundary, and about 49° for water-air. Total reflection can occur only in the medium that has the higher index of refraction.

The effects we have been describing apply to light of one particular wave length. Light is usually made up of many wave lengths, which are not refracted uniformly. Nearly all transparent materials refract short waves more than long ones. This effect is the basis of the most common type of spectroscope, in which a refracting prism is used to separate the wave lengths that make up light. (See Index, under Spectroscopes.)

Refraction effects may be used to identify small samples of mineral crystals. This is done by immersing them in a succession of liquids, each with a different refractive index. A transparent crystal or other material is visible in air mainly because it refracts light passing through it; it also reflects some of the incident light. It is visible for the same reasons in liquids that have a different index of refraction from its own. Suppose, however, that the crystal is placed in a transparent liquid whose index of refraction is identical with that of the crystal. The light rays will then pass through both liquid and crystal without reflection or refraction and the crystal practically disappears. An imitation diamond of ordinary flint glass vanishes in carbon disulfide, while a real diamond continues to sparkle in the liquid.

How images are formed

The simplest way to form an optical image is to allow light from a glowing or illuminated object to pass through a pinhole and to let it fall on a white screen. Some light will be diffracted from the edge

OBJECT — PINHOLE — LIGHT RAYS — IMAGE — p — q

13. Light from an illuminated object passes through a pinhole and falls on a white screen. In this way an inverted image of the man's head is formed on the screen.

14. In the most familiar type of mirror, which has a flat surface, a virtual, or apparent, but reversed image is produced.

of the pinhole. Most of it, however, will pass through the hole and will form an inverted image on the screen. We show how such an image is produced in Figure 13. Light from the bottom of the head passes through the pinhole and forms the top of the inverted image on the screen. Rays from the top are directed by the pinhole to the corresponding part of the image. Of course light is spreading in all directions from the illuminated object, but the pinhole allows only the light traveling in certain definite directions to reach the screen.

An important factor in any image-forming system is its magnification. This term means the ratio of any dimension — height or width, for example — of the image to the corresponding dimension of the object. In a pinhole system, such as is shown in Figure 13, the magnification is the ratio of the image distance q to the object distance p. These distances can be made whatever one likes.

To obtain a brighter image than the pinhole permits, we need a device that will collect a substantial quantity of the light radiating from an object. The mirror offers such a device.

The most familiar type of mirror is the plane mirror, which has a flat, or plane, surface. Figure 14 shows a typical mirror of this kind. Light coming from a series of points on the object is reflected

by the mirror to the eye as shown, creating the illusion of coming from a corresponding series of points behind the mirror. As a result, a virtual, or apparent, reversed image is formed. It is the same size as the object itself and is at the same distance behind the mirror as the object is in front of it. The image is reversed from left to right. The plane mirror is the only optical device that is capable of forming a completely accurate image (in reverse, of course) of an object of appreciable size.

Some mirrors are curved. Such mirrors generally form part of the surface of a sphere. In Figure 15 we show a concave spherical mirror. The center of the sphere of which the mirror forms a part is called the center of curvature. The line passing through the middle of the mirror and the center of curvature is the principal axis.

Most spherical mirrors are relatively flat. This means that the diameter of the mirror is small compared with the radius of curvature — any straight line drawn from the center of curvature to the surface of the mirror. In concave mirrors of this type the rays of light parallel to the principal axis will pass through or very near a common point after they have been reflected from the mirror surface. This point (F in Figure 16) is called the principal focus; it is on the principal axis, half way between the center of curvature and the surface of the mirror. It is known as a real focus because the rays of light actually pass through it. We can show that this is so by placing a piece of paper at the focus of a concave mirror upon which sunlight is falling. The rays converging at the focus will soon cause the paper to burst into flames.

Not all the rays parallel to the axis of a concave spherical mirror meet exactly at the principal focus. This failure of the rays to converge at a single point is called spherical aberration (see Figure 17). Spherical aberration is comparatively small when the mirror is almost flat; it is larger when the mirror is more rounded. This effect can be remedied by making the curve of the mirror a paraboloid instead of a sphere (Figure 18). This figure is commonly used in searchlights, automobile headlights and various other devices. Large mirrors used in telescopes are usually paraboloids.

Some spherical mirrors use the convex side of a spherical surface (Figure 19). In this case, parallel rays diverge from the surface when they are reflected. However, they all seem to come from a single point behind the mirror (F in the diagram). This is called a virtual (apparent) focus, because the rays do not actually converge at this point but only appear to do so. If one exposed a convex mirror to sunlight and placed a piece of paper at the virtual focus, nothing would happen to the paper.

If all the rays that struck the surface of a spherical mirror were parallel to the principal axis, they would not produce an image of appreciable size. The reason is that they would all really meet (concave mirror) or apparently meet (convex mirror) at about the same place. Actually, however, many of the rays are not parallel to the principal axis. As a result, they produce an appreciable image.

The images produced by concave spherical mirrors may be smaller or larger than the objects; they may be virtual or real. As in the case of the plane mirror, an image is virtual if the light rays only seem to form it after they are reflected from the

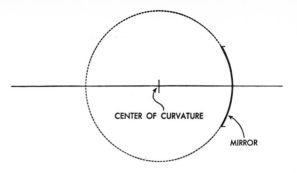

15. A concave spherical mirror, part of the surface of a sphere whose center is called the center of curvature.

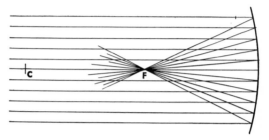

16. The light rays that are reflected from the surface of a concave mirror pass through the principal focus, F.

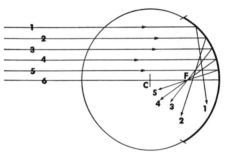

17. Spherical aberration, which is explained in the text.

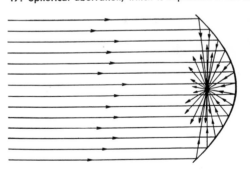

18. Spherical aberration can be remedied by making the curve of a mirror a paraboloid rather than a sphere.

19. Some spherical mirrors use the convex side of a spherical surface. The virtual (apparent) focus is F.

20. If an object is placed at the center of curvature of a mirror that has a concave surface, the image is real, inverted and also of the same size as the object.

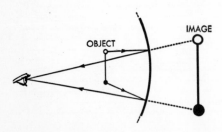

21. When an object is placed between the principal focus and the mirror, a virtual, erect image, larger than the object, will appear — and apparently behind the mirror.

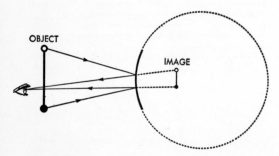

22. The image in a convex spherical mirror is virtual, erect instead of inverted, and smaller than the object.

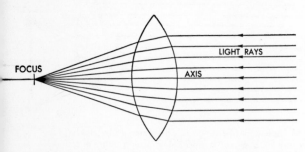

23. A converging lens. Rays parallel to the principal axis are bent so that they meet at the principal focus.

24. A diverging lens. Rays parallel to the principal axis seem to meet at the virtual principal focus, F.

mirror surface. The image is real if it is actually produced by the rays. Both types of images look the same; however, a real image can be thrown on a screen, while a virtual one cannot. A real image is an actual convergence, or concentration, of light; a virtual image is an optical illusion.

If an object is placed at the center of curvature of a concave mirror, the image is real, inverted and the same size as the object (Figure 20). The image is also real and inverted if the object is placed farther away from the mirror than the center of the curvature; in this case, however, the image will be smaller than the object. It will dwindle to a point as the object is moved to a very great distance from the center of curvature.

Suppose we place the object between the center of curvature and the principal focus. The image will still be real and inverted but it will be larger than the object. We could also put the object between the principal focus and the mirror; in that case a virtual, erect image, larger than the object, would appear apparently behind the mirror (Figure 21). This is what happens when one uses a concave shaving mirror. One sees an erect image of one's face larger than life.

Convex spherical mirrors can produce only virtual images, which seem to be located behind the mirror. These images are erect (not inverted) and smaller than the object (Figure 22). Small convex mirrors are sometimes fastened outside a car near the windshield to bring into the driver's view cars that are approaching him from behind.

So far we have been dealing with images formed by mirrors. They can also be produced by lenses. A lens is a piece of transparent material, such as glass, shaped in such a way that it intercepts rays of light from an object and bends them by refraction so that they meet at a common focus. A simple lens has two opposite regular surfaces, which are generally spherical; in some cases, however, one surface may be a plane.

There are two chief kinds of lenses — converging and diverging. A converging

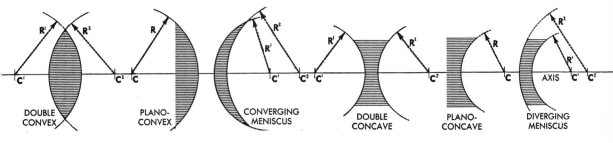

DOUBLE CONVEX   PLANO-CONVEX   CONVERGING MENISCUS   DOUBLE CONCAVE   PLANO-CONCAVE   DIVERGING MENISCUS

25. Six important types of lenses are illustrated above. The first three — the double convex, the plano-convex and the converging meniscus — are converging lenses. The last three — the double concave, the plano-concave and the diverging meniscus — are diverging lenses. C stands for "center of curvature"; R stands for "radius."

lens is thicker at the center than at the edges. Light rays parallel to the axis converge, or meet, at a point beyond the lens (Figure 23). This point is the principal focus. A diverging lens is thicker at the edges than at the center. When light rays parallel to the principal axis pass through the lens, they are spread apart. In this case the rays seem to come from a virtual focus on the same side of the lens as the light source (Figure 24). This point, F, is the principal focus. In both converging and diverging lenses, the distance from the principal focus to the lens is called the focal length. The focal length depends on both the index of refraction of the material and the curvatures of the two surfaces of the lens.

In Figure 25 we show some common types of converging and diverging lenses.

Note that in each case the principal axis is a straight line drawn through the centers of curvature of the two spherical surfaces. If one surface is plane, the principal axis passes from the center of curvature to the center of the lens.

The relationship between the object and the image formed by a converging lens is much the same as in a concave mirror of the same focal length. The only difference is that since light passes through the lens, real images are formed on the side opposite the incoming light, while virtual images are formed on the side from which the light comes. As in the mirror, the nature of the image will depend upon the distance of the object from the lens (Figure 26). Diverging lenses produce much the same type of image as convex mirrors; the image is virtual, erect and

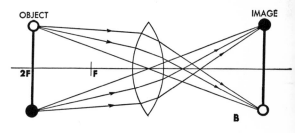

26. Converging lenses. A, object beyond twice focal distance — image inverted, real and smaller than the object. B, object at twice focal distance — image real, inverted and same size as object. C, object at focus — no image. D, object between focus and lens — the image is erect, virtual and larger than the object.

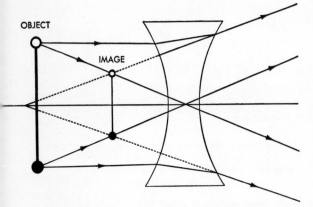

OBJECT

IMAGE

27. Diverging lenses produce very much the same type of images as those produced by convex mirrors. The images are virtual, erect and smaller than the objects. The only difference is that the virtual images are behind the mirror while they are in front of the diverging lens.

smaller than the object. The only difference is that the virtual image is behind the mirror, while it is in front of the lens (Figure *27*).

Optical images except those formed by plane mirrors are distorted to a greater or lesser extent as a result of various defects. We have already mentioned spherical aberration in spherical mirrors; this defect occurs also in lenses. Another defect found in mirrors and lenses is astigmatism. In this case rays that come to a lens or mirror from a point far from the principal axis do not meet at a common point of the image. A blurred effect is produced. Astigmatism in lenses can be corrected by using several lens elements. This arrangement is found in the expensive camera lenses called anastigmats.

Chromatic aberration is a familiar type of lens defect. The index of refraction depends upon wave length. Hence any simple single-element lens will focus short-wave light nearer to the lens than it will longer-wave light. This chromatic aberration causes serious blurring and confusion in the image in an instrument of any power. It is usually reduced to a tolerable level by a two- or three-element combination called an achromatic lens. The principle of this correction is somewhat complicated. It depends upon the use of two or three different kinds of glass to bring all

wave lengths approximately to the same focus without lessening the over-all power of the lens combination.

Some familiar optical instruments

A number of devices, called optical instruments, are based on the refraction or reflection of light. Here is a brief survey of a few of the better known ones.

One of the most familiar optical instruments of any complexity is the camera. Basically this familiar device is a converging lens arranged to form a real image on a piece of sensitive photographic film. Usually the image is smaller than the object, but this is not always the case. The lens and the film are mounted in a light-tight box, and a shutter is provided for opening and closing the lens opening, thus governing the amount of exposure the

THREE FAMILIAR OPTICAL INSTRUMENTS

EYEPIECE LENS

OBJECTIVE LENS

OBJECT

CONDENSER

SECOND IMAGE

INCOMING LIGHT RAYS

film receives. In most cameras it is possible to vary the distance from lens to film so as to bring nearby or distant objects into sharp focus in the picture. In most cameras, too, an adjustable mask, called an iris diaphragm, is set in front of the lens; it controls the size of the aperture through which the light passes. We describe cameras in detail in The Versatile Art of Photography, in Volume 9.

A projector is simply a camera in reverse. If a transparent photograph or drawing is placed in the film position in a camera and strongly illuminated, an image will be projected on a screen placed at the normal object position in front of the camera. This is the principle of the photographic enlarger, the slide and motion-picture projector and other such devices. Opaque objects, such as pictures in books, can be projected if suitably illuminated.

The simple magnifier, commonly called a magnifying glass, is a converging lens used to view an object placed nearer to the lens than its principal focus. Under these conditions the eye sees a magnified virtual image, as in Figure 26d. This is a very convenient arrangement because the image is upright. For low-power work, up to magnifications of three or four times, a single lens element works acceptably as a magnifier. For more power, however, it is necessary to use a more complicated lens to correct the chromatic and other aberrations that cannot be avoided in the simpler instrument. The eyepiece of a telescope or microscope is a high-quality simple magnifier, used to view a real image formed by other optical elements — lenses or mirrors or both.

The compound microscope is used to obtain high magnifications — up to sev-

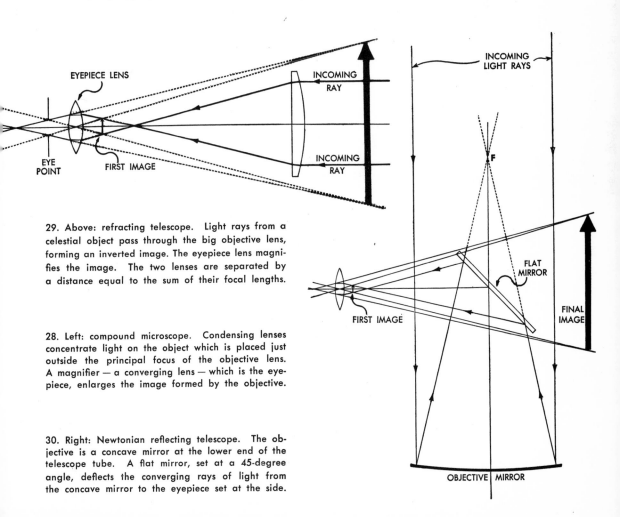

29. Above: refracting telescope. Light rays from a celestial object pass through the big objective lens, forming an inverted image. The eyepiece lens magnifies the image. The two lenses are separated by a distance equal to the sum of their focal lengths.

28. Left: compound microscope. Condensing lenses concentrate light on the object which is placed just outside the principal focus of the objective lens. A magnifier — a converging lens — which is the eyepiece, enlarges the image formed by the objective.

30. Right: Newtonian reflecting telescope. The objective is a concave mirror at the lower end of the telescope tube. A flat mirror, set at a 45-degree angle, deflects the converging rays of light from the concave mirror to the eyepiece set at the side.

eral thousand times — of very small objects. In principle it is very simple, as Figure 28 shows. Condensing lenses concentrate light on the object, which is placed just outside the principal focus of a small converging lens, called the objective. This objective forms a magnified real image of the object a few inches away. Since this image, which is inverted, is still quite small, a magnifier (consisting of another converging lens) is used as an eyepiece to produce a further enlarged virtual image of the first image.

Although the principle of the microscope is simple, its actual construction is one of the most difficult accomplishments in optics. Since it is designed to view very small objects, the objective lens must be on a similarly small scale. The problem of controlling image defects, especially spherical aberration, is a serious one. The result is that high-powered-microscope objectives are quite complicated, consisting in some cases of as many as ten separate lens elements.

The oldest optical instrument of any complexity is the astronomical refracting telescope (Figure 29). As originally devised by Galileo, the instrument used a diverging lens as an eyepiece. However this system, which still serves in cheap opera glasses, has serious defects. The arrangement shown in the diagram is almost universally used in refracting telescopes.

The optical relationships in this instrument are beautifully simple. When properly adjusted for a normal eye, the real image formed by the objective lies at the principal focus of this lens. If the principal focus of the eyepiece is brought to this same point, the observer sees the final virtual image projected to a great distance. It may be noted that the question so often asked of astronomers: "What is the magnifying power of your telescope?" is meaningless. The magnifying power depends on the eyepiece in use at any particular time; it is simply the ratio of the focal length of the objective to that of the eyepiece.

The reflecting telescope (Figure 30) substitutes a concave mirror for the objective lens. This arrangement leads to some difficulties in design, since the light bends back on itself and some means must be found to bring the image out of the incoming beam. This is done in the Newtonian reflector, shown in Figure 30, by means of a flat mirror, set at an angle of 45° to the optical axis of the mirror. Mirrors are free from chromatic aberration, which plagues the objective lenses of all refractors. Another advantage is that they can be made in much larger sizes than lenses. However astigmatism and certain other image defects are more of a problem than in refracting telescopes.

The eye as an image-forming device

The eyes of animals are image-forming devices. The eyes of human beings and other mammals, as well as those of most other highly developed species, are similar in principle to the ordinary camera. They use a small lens that forms an inverted real image on the sensitive film of the retina. The retina then relays information on light intensities to the brain. The eye has an iris diaphragm to control the amount of light entering the organ. Instead of varying the lens-to-film distance in order to focus for various ranges, the eye makes this adjustment by varying the curvature, and consequently the focal length, of the lens itself. Thus it performs a feat that would be quite impractical with artificial optical materials.

At least one living species has long since appropriated the simplest image-forming device — the pinhole. The eye of the pearly nautilus is merely a hollow, enclosed cup with a small hole leading to the exterior. On the inside facing the hole there is a primitive retina. The compound eyes of insects are rather complicated versions of the same principle; they consist of a great number of narrow tubes pointing in different directions. Each tube "sees" a tiny portion of the environment; all the tubes together build up a picture somewhat on the principle of a halftone print or a television screen.

See also Vol. 10, p. 281: "Light and Illumination."

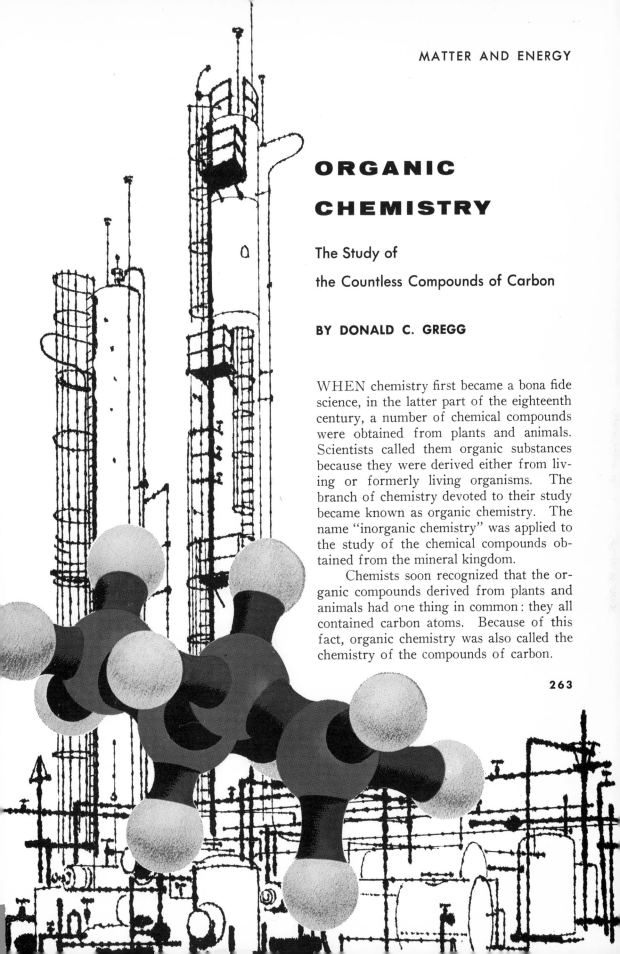

ORGANIC CHEMISTRY

The Study of
the Countless Compounds of Carbon

BY DONALD C. GREGG

WHEN chemistry first became a bona fide science, in the latter part of the eighteenth century, a number of chemical compounds were obtained from plants and animals. Scientists called them organic substances because they were derived either from living or formerly living organisms. The branch of chemistry devoted to their study became known as organic chemistry. The name "inorganic chemistry" was applied to the study of the chemical compounds obtained from the mineral kingdom.

Chemists soon recognized that the organic compounds derived from plants and animals had one thing in common: they all contained carbon atoms. Because of this fact, organic chemistry was also called the chemistry of the compounds of carbon.

263

The early chemists spent most of their time studying the acids, bases and salts; they were interested chiefly in the substances obtained from, or related to, the mineral kingdom. It was much easier to work with such inorganic compounds, since most of them were soluble in water or in the common acids. Usually their reactions were quite rapid. It was not too difficult to understand these reactions, or at least to explain them logically by using the theories that were then believed to be correct. Chemists could prepare many inorganic compounds by using very simple methods.

Organic compounds seemed to be quite different in nature and behavior. Many of them reacted with most common inorganic substances very slowly, or not at all. Heat played an important part in the preparation of inorganic compounds, but it usually caused organic compounds to decompose. As we pointed out, chemists could make inorganic compounds in the laboratory; but apparently it was impossible to create an organic compound. Chemists wondered how such compounds were produced in plants and animals.

The Swedish scientist Joens Jakob Berzelius was one of the foremost authorities in chemistry in the nineteenth century. This learned man made no effort to explain the behavior of the organic compounds. He simply stated that since they were derived from plant or animal organisms, their formation was probably due to some "vital force," a force totally lacking in inorganic material. It would be impossible for man, he maintained, to duplicate this "vital force"; hence nobody would ever be able to prepare an organic compound.

In 1828, a young German chemist, Friedrich Woehler, succeeded in doing what Berzelius had declared was impossible. He heated an inorganic compound, ammonium cyanate, and produced urea, an organic compound that occurs in urine. Chemists now began to doubt the existence of Berzelius' "vital force"; they theorized that perhaps other organic compounds might be prepared in the laboratory.

In the years that followed, chemists succeeded in producing many such compounds. More and more researchers devoted themselves to organic chemistry, and

In 1828, the brilliant young German chemist Friedrich Woehler produced the first synthetic, or man-made, organic compound. By heating an inorganic compound, ammonium cyanate, he produced urea, an organic compound found in urine. From Woehler's remarkable achievement stem the innumerable modern applications of synthetic organic compounds. They are used, among other things, for drugs, perfumes, dyes and a host of plastic materials.

the number of synthetic (man-made) compounds mounted steadily. In a few decades they far outnumbered the inorganic compounds. We have traced the history of this development in the chapter Science and Progress I, in Volume 5.

Today we know that the basic laws that govern the formation and behavior of inorganic compounds also apply to the compounds of carbon.* However, we still study organic compounds separately for several reasons. For one thing, carbon atoms have the capacity (which is almost unique) of producing chains and rings of atoms as they combine with each other and with other atoms.** Then too, the organic compounds as a group are much less stable than the inorganic, so that chemists must use different techniques in working with them.

Why do we still call the compounds of carbon "organic" when we realize that many of them are man-made and not found in any living organism? The chief reason is that the compounds derived from nature and those produced in the laboratory are closely related to one another chemically. It has always seemed best, therefore, to give the name of organic compounds to *all* the compounds of carbon (except the few we have indicated in the first footnote of this article), whether they are of natural origin or produced in the laboratory.

Hundreds of these compounds are synthesized or discovered every year. It would be impossible to overemphasize their importance. Plants and animals are composed mostly of organic compounds; so is most human food, derived directly or indirectly from living things. Many fabrics are produced from organic materials (such as wool, cotton and linen) obtained from plants or animals. Many, too, consist of synthetic organic materials (rayon, nylon, Dacron and the like), developed in the laboratory in an attempt to duplicate natural fibers or to improve upon them. Plastics, rubber, paper and wood are all organic substances. Petroleum, from which we

* Not all carbon compounds are organic. The carbon oxides, carbonates and cyanides are considered to be inorganic.

** Alternating silicon and oxygen atoms also form a network of atoms when attached to various organic groups. The resulting compounds are called silicones (see Index).

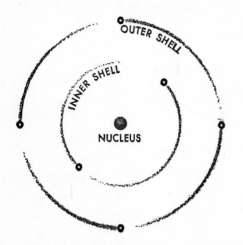

Highly simplified diagram of carbon atom. Its six electrons revolve around the nucleus in two shells. The inner shell has only two electrons; the outer one has four.

obtain fuels and many industrial products, is a mixture of carbon compounds. So is coal tar, which yields drugs, perfumes, flavorings and other useful products.

The structure
of the carbon atom

In other articles * we have pointed out that each atom has a certain number of negatively charged particles called electrons, revolving around a central core in a number of shells. There are two such shells in the carbon atom; the first one has two electrons and the second has four. Only the electrons in the outer shell are involved in chemical changes.

This shell, with its four electrons, is not filled to capacity; there is room for four more. The carbon atom can share electrons with other atoms in order to fill up the gap — a type of combination called covalence (see Index). When a carbon atom combines with four hydrogen atoms, sharing four pairs of electrons, we say it has a covalence, or combining power, of four.** There are so very few cases in which a carbon atom has a covalence of three that we may leave them out of con-

* Inside the Atom, Volume 1; How Atoms Combine, Volume 3.
** Covalence may be expressed in terms of hydrogen, since this element always has a covalence of one and never more. Other atoms may have different covalences.

sideration for the purposes of this article. We shall assume that in all simple organic compounds, such as we shall take up, each carbon atom has four covalent bonds.

In order to have a clear idea of the carbon atom, we may picture the four valence electrons as being equidistant from each other and from the nucleus of the atom. We can visualize this best if we think of them as located at the corners of a regular tetrahedron,* as shown at the bottom of this column. Of course, it must always be remembered that electrons are in constant movement in space. However, for our purposes the tetrahedral arrangement is a reasonable representation.

The simplest organic compound is methane, in which one atom of carbon (C) is combined with four atoms of hydrogen (H). The formula for this compound is CH_4.** A formula such as this is called compositional; it indicates the kinds and numbers of atoms in a compound.

A space model of CH_4 is shown in the left-hand diagram on the next page. Four electrons, each from a hydrogen atom, which has but one electron, have been added to the outer shell of the carbon atom. This shell, therefore, now has its full quota of electrons — that is, eight.

* A regular tetrahedron is a figure or solid with four faces, consisting of equal triangles — triangles whose sides are all equal.
** A small figure after and near the bottom of a chemical symbol, such as C or H, indicates the number of atoms. If no figure is added, the number 1 is understood.

VALENCE ELECTRON

NUCLEUS

At the bottom of column 2, we give a simplified projection of this model; a carbon atom is shown linked to four hydrogen atoms. This is not a true representation, of course; for one thing, it is two-dimensional, while a real molecule has three dimensions. However, chemists represent organic compounds in this simple manner because it is convenient and gives at least some idea of the actual three-dimensional structure. Such pictures of the way in which atoms are joined together are called structural formulas.

The methane, or paraffin, series of hydrocarbons

Methane, CH_4, is called a hydrocarbon because it is made up only of atoms of hydrogen and carbon. There are a great number of other hydrocarbons, all containing only carbon and hydrogen atoms. They occur as gases, liquids or solids. They are found in the gases formed by heating coal or wood in a closed vessel. Petroleum and natural gas are made up almost entirely of hydrocarbons.

Methane is a member of the so-called methane series of hydrocarbons. Each compound in the series has the general formula C_nH_{2n+2}. If there is only one carbon atom in a compound of the methane series, n is equal to 1; if there are two carbon atoms, n is equal to 2 and so on. In the case of methane, for example, since there is only one carbon atom, n equals 1. Substituting 1 for n in the formula C_nH_{2n+2}, we have $C_1H_{2\times1+2}$, or CH_4. In the hydrocarbons of the methane series, the quota of electrons for the outer shells of the carbon atoms is filled; hence these atoms cannot take on any more hydrogen atoms. In other words, they are "saturated" with hydrogen atoms; for this reason they are called saturated hydrocarbons.

The compounds of the methane series are sometimes known as paraffin hydrocarbons. The word paraffin comes from the Latin *parum affinis,* meaning "having very little affinity." The name paraffin hydrocarbons is quite appropriate, since the compounds of the methane series have little affinity with other atoms: that is, little tendency to join them in chemical combinations. The members of the methane series are also called alkanes.

Methane, the first of the methane series, is a gas occurring in natural gas. It is sometimes called marsh gas because it is found in marshes, where it is formed by the decay of vegetable matter. Sometimes it collects in coal mines; miners call it fire damp. When methane is mixed with the oxygen contained in air, it is explosive; many disastrous accidents in mines have been due to the ignition of such a mixture. Methane is a common source of hydrogen; it is also used in the manufacture of carbon black.

ELECTRON OF HYDROGEN ATOM

On column 2 of the preceding page, we give a space model of a carbon atom. The model shows the nucleus and the outer shell; the inner shell is not indicated, since it does not take part in chemical reactions. Note that the four outer electrons of the carbon atom are represented as equidistant from the nucleus and from each other. In the left-hand diagram on this page, we show a carbon atom combined with four hydrogen atoms to form the compound methane (CH_4). Four electrons, each from a hydrogen atom, have been added to the carbon atom. Right: two-dimensional structural formula for the methane atom.

ETHANE   *n*-BUTANE

In these diagrams of ethane and *n*-butane molecules, each black
sphere represents a carbon atom; each white one, a hydrogen atom.

The second member of the methane series is ethane, which has the compositional formula C_2H_6. It is a colorless, odorless gas, found in coal gas and natural gas. Its structural formula is as follows:

$$\begin{array}{c} \text{H} \quad \text{H} \\ | \quad | \\ \text{H---C---C---H} \\ | \quad | \\ \text{H} \quad \text{H} \end{array}$$

Each link in the above formula, of course, indicates a covalent bond. Whenever we write a structural formula such as this, we must check it to make sure that the four covalent bonds of the carbon atom are accounted for. Note that in each case a carbon atom is linked to three hydrogen atoms and also to the other carbon atom.

The structural formula shown above can also be written as CH_3CH_3. This is called a simplified structural formula. It indicates that a carbon atom (C), which is connected to three hydrogen atoms (H_3), is linked to another carbon atom (C), also connected to three hydrogen atoms (H_3).

Propane is the third member of the methane series; it has the compositional formula C_3H_8 and the structural formula:

$$\begin{array}{c} \text{H} \quad \text{H} \quad \text{H} \\ | \quad | \quad | \\ \text{H---C---C---C---H} \\ | \quad | \quad | \\ \text{H} \quad \text{H} \quad \text{H} \end{array}$$

The simplified structural formula of propane is $CH_3CH_2CH_3$. This means that a carbon atom (C), connected to three hydrogen atoms (H_3), is linked to another carbon atom (C), joined to two hydrogen atoms (H_2); the second carbon atom is linked in its turn to a third one (C), joined to three hydrogen atoms (H_3). Compressed propane is used as a fuel gas.

The fourth member of the methane series is butane, with the empirical formula C_4H_{10}. Since we have so many building blocks, in the form of atoms, to work with in butane, we might suspect that the different carbon and hydrogen atoms can be combined in more than one way. Actually this is the case. One structure has the normal straight-chain form:

$$\begin{array}{c} \text{H} \quad \text{H} \quad \text{H} \quad \text{H} \\ | \quad | \quad | \quad | \\ \text{H---C---C---C---C---H} \\ | \quad | \quad | \quad | \\ \text{H} \quad \text{H} \quad \text{H} \quad \text{H} \end{array}$$

The other has a chain of three carbon atoms, with a carbon attached to the middle carbon of the chain as follows:

$$\begin{array}{c} \text{H} \qquad \text{H} \qquad \text{H} \\ | \qquad | \qquad | \\ \text{H---C}\text{------}\text{C}\text{------}\text{C---H} \\ | \qquad | \qquad | \\ \text{H} \quad \text{H---C---H} \quad \text{H} \\ | \\ \text{H} \end{array}$$

This forms what is called a branched-chain configuration; it shows a chain with a branch leading from one part of it.

The two butane structures shown above represent two different compounds, each having the compositional formula C_4H_{10}. The compound with the straight-chain structure is called normal butane or *n*-butane; the branched-chain compound is known as isobutane. They have different physical properties and chemical behavior. *n*-butane is a major source of butadiene, the principal chemical in some kinds of synthetic rubber; isobutane is used in the manufacture of certain superior grades of motor fuel.

Two or more compounds with the same compositional formula but with dif-

ferent structural formulas are called isomers. n-butane is the straight-chain isomer
of butane; isobutane, the branched-chain
isomer. There are only two isomers in the
case of butane; as we shall see, other compounds have a great many. The existence
of isomers is a common and significant
phenomenon in chemistry.

In the fifth member of the methane
series — pentane — five carbon atoms are
combined with twelve hydrogen atoms; the
compositional formula is C_5H_{12}. There
are three different isomers of pentane, each
with a different structural formula: n-
pentane, isopentane and neopentane. Here
are the structural formulas:

a) n-pentane

b) Isopentane

c) Neopentane

Other members of the methane series
include hexane (C_6H_{14}), heptane (C_7H_{16})
and octane (C_8H_{18}). The number of possible isomers increases as the number of
carbon atoms in the molecule increases.
For $C_{10}H_{22}$ there are at least 75 possible
isomers; for $C_{20}H_{42}$, at least 366,319. Only
a few of the latter are known. Obviously,
because of the existence of isomers, the
number of possible organic compounds
reaches almost astronomical proportions.

The lighter members of the methane
series of hydrocarbons, containing less than
five carbons per molecule, are gases. Those
having from five to fifteen carbons are
usually liquids; those with more than fifteen carbons are solids.

The paraffins are constituents of
natural gas and petroleum. Natural gas
is mostly methane with some of the other
gaseous paraffin hydrocarbons. Crude oil
consists of a mixture of many different
liquid and solid hydrocarbons. In gasoline,
there is also a mixture of hydrocarbons,
generally ranging from C_6H_{14} to $C_{12}H_{26}$.
The yield of gasoline from a given amount
of crude oil may be increased by building
up hydrocarbons containing less than six
carbons to produce molecules with from
six to twelve carbons. It can also be increased by breaking down the hydrocarbons
that have more than twelve carbon atoms.
The latter process is known as "cracking."

Pure paraffin hydrocarbons are colorless, almost odorless and inflammable.
They are very insoluble in water and they
do not form ions in water solutions. When
they undergo complete combustion, they
yield only carbon dioxide (CO_2) and
water. It is rather difficult, however, to
bring about this type of combustion; hence
carbon and carbon monoxide are often produced in addition to carbon dioxide and
water. For example, when gasoline is
burned in the motor of a car, carbon may
be deposited in the cylinders and carbon
monoxide (CO), a poisonous gas, may
issue from the exhaust pipe.

Certain saturated hydrocarbons have a
ring structure. We can form such a structure by joining the ends of a chain together,
provided there are at least three carbon
atoms. Cyclopropane, with the compositional formula C_3H_6, is a good example of
a ring formation. This substance, which
is used as an inhalation anesthetic, has the
following structural formula:

Saturated hydrocarbons with a ring structure are called cycloparaffins. Cyclobutane
(C_4H_8), cyclopentane (C_5H_{10}) and cyclo-
hexane (C_6H_{12}) are well-known cycloparaffins.

The unsaturated hydrocarbons

In all the carbon compounds we have discussed thus far, there is only one bond between any two carbon atoms. There is more than one such bond in certain hydrocarbons. For instance, in the substance called ethylene, C_2H_4, there are two links between the two carbon atoms in its molecule, as the structural formula shows:

$$\begin{array}{cc} H & H \\ | & | \\ H-C\!=\!C-H \end{array}$$

When there is more than one bond between carbon atoms, the molecule is not saturated since other atoms could be added to it.

For example, instead of the double carbon link in ethylene, we might substitute a pair of hydrogen atoms, enclosed in squares in the following formula:

$$\begin{array}{cc} H & H \\ | & | \\ H-C-C-H \\ | & | \\ \boxed{H} & \boxed{H} \end{array}$$

This is exactly what happens when ethylene is treated with hydrogen gas and a suitable catalyst. You will note that the new substance that is produced in this reaction is ethane gas (C_2H_6).

Substances such as ethylene, in which carbon atoms are joined by double bonds, are called unsaturated, because they are capable of taking up more hydrogen atoms (and other atoms as well). They are quite reactive.

In some unsaturated hydrocarbons, there are three bonds between carbon atoms. To give a familiar example, acetylene (C_2H_2) has the following structural formula:

$$H-C\!\equiv\!C-H$$

Acetylene is widely used for oxyacetylene welding and cutting and in the preparation of many important organic compounds, such as acetic acid and acetone. It is the first member of a series of hydrocarbons with triple bonds between carbon atoms — the acetylene series.

The unsaturated hydrocarbons play an important part in the rubber industry and many others. The basic unit of rubber is isoprene (C_5H_8), an unsaturated hydrocarbon with the following structure

$$\begin{array}{cccc} H & & H & H \\ | & & | & | \\ -C & -C\!=\!C-C- \\ | & | & | \\ H & H-C-H & H \\ & | & \\ & H & \end{array}$$

Rubber is a polymer; this means that it is made up of a great number of identical small units. This is how two of the many isoprene units in rubber would be linked:

$$\begin{array}{ccccccc} H & & H & H & H & & H & H \\ | & & | & | & | & & | & | \\ -C & -C\!=\!C-C-C & -C\!=\!C-C- \\ | & | & | & | & | & | \\ H & H-C-H & H & H & H-C-H & H \\ & | & & & | & \\ & H & & & H & \end{array}$$

<u>Isoprene unit</u>   <u>Isoprene unit</u>

OXYACETYLENE

ISOPRENE

METHYL CHLORIDE

ETHYL CHLORIDE
ETHYL BROMIDE

Some derivatives of the paraffin hydrocarbons

The alkyl halides. The alkyl halides are simple compounds derived from the paraffin hydrocarbons. In them, a halogen * atom takes the place of a hydrogen atom. If a chlorine atom (Cl) is substituted for a hydrogen atom (H) in methane, CH_4, we obtain the alkyl halide known as methyl chloride, CH_3Cl, as the following structural formulas show:

Methane   Methyl chloride

Methyl chloride has been used pretty extensively as a refrigerant.

Two other familiar alkyl halides are ethyl chloride (C_2H_5Cl) and ethyl bromide (C_2H_5Br):

Ethyl chloride   Ethyl bromide

Both these substances have been used as anesthetics.

The typical alkyl halide is quite reactive, as the halogen atom in its molecule is held rather loosely. This atom may be removed completely or it may be replaced by certain atoms or groups of atoms.

* The halogens are chlorine, bromine, iodine, fluorine and astatine. They are so called because they form salts when they react with metals. (*Hals* is the Greek word for "salt.")

The alcohols and ethers. In the compounds called alcohols, a hydroxyl group, OH, or more than one such group, is substituted for one of the hydrogen atoms in a paraffin hydrocarbon. When a hydrogen atom of methane (CH_4) is replaced in this way, we have methyl alcohol (CH_3OH):

Methane   Methyl alcohol

Methyl alcohol, often known as wood alcohol, can be made by the destructive distillation of wood; it can also be prepared from water gas, consisting of carbon monoxide and hydrogen ($CO + H_2$). Methyl alcohol is a colorless liquid with an odor suggesting that of wine. When taken internally, it can bring about blindness or cause death. Methyl alcohol is used to denature ethyl alcohol (grain alcohol), making it unfit for human consumption. It is also useful as a solvent in the manufacture of varnishes and shellacs. Quantities are employed in the preparation of formaldehyde, a preservative and disinfectant.

The hydrocarbon ethane (C_2H_6), as we have seen, has the structural formula

Replacing a hydrogen atom in this molecule by a hydroxyl group, OH, we have ethyl alcohol (C_2H_5OH), or common alcohol, with the structural formula

Ethyl alcohol, also called grain alcohol, is produced by the fermentation of sugars, and is an ingredient in alcoholic beverages and many medicinal preparations. It has many important industrial uses. Among other things, it is an important solvent in the preparation of varnishes, shellacs and enamels.

In some alcohols, two or more hydroxyl (OH) groups are attached to carbon atoms. An alcohol with two such groups is called dihydric. Ethylene glycol, $C_2H_4(OH)_2$, is a typical dihydric alcohol; it has the following molecular structure:

It is used as an antifreeze in automobile radiators and as a solvent.

The alcohol glycerol, or glycerine, $C_3H_5(OH)_3$, has three OH groups:

This substance is a useful solvent and serves in the manufacture of nitroglycerin and dynamite.

RUBBING ALCOHOL

ALCOHOLIC BEVERAGES

The ethers are obtained by eliminating water from alcohols. The most common ether is diethyl ether, $(C_2H_5)_2O$, with the structural formula

$$H-\overset{\overset{\displaystyle H}{|}}{\underset{\underset{\displaystyle H}{|}}{C}}-\overset{\overset{\displaystyle H}{|}}{\underset{\underset{\displaystyle H}{|}}{C}}-O-\overset{\overset{\displaystyle H}{|}}{\underset{\underset{\displaystyle H}{|}}{C}}-\overset{\overset{\displaystyle H}{|}}{\underset{\underset{\displaystyle H}{|}}{C}}-H$$

It may be prepared from ethyl alcohol, with concentrated sulfuric acid serving as the dehydrating (water-removing) agent. Diethyl ether serves as an anesthetic.

The aldehydes, ketones and organic acids. When simple alcohols are oxidized (combined with oxygen), aldehydes, ketones or organic acids are produced.

The aldehydes contain the group $-\overset{\overset{\displaystyle H}{|}}{C}=O$. A simple aldehyde is formaldehyde (HCHO), which can be prepared by passing the vapor of methyl alcohol over a heated metal catalyst. The structural formula of formaldehyde is

$$H-\overset{\overset{\displaystyle H}{|}}{C}=O$$

Formaldehyde, a gas, is used in the manufacture of plastics, dyes and drugs. When it is dissolved in water, this most useful compound serves as a potent disinfectant and antiseptic.

In the ketones, we always find the group $-\overset{\overset{\displaystyle O}{||}}{C}-$. Dimethyl ketone, or acetone, $(CH_3)_2CO$, is the most important of the ketones; it is widely used as a solvent. Its structural formula is

$$H-\overset{\overset{\displaystyle H}{|}}{\underset{\underset{\displaystyle H}{|}}{C}}-\overset{\overset{\displaystyle O}{||}}{C}-\overset{\overset{\displaystyle H}{|}}{\underset{\underset{\displaystyle H}{|}}{C}}-H$$

Organic acids contain the group $O=\overset{|}{C}-OH$. The simplest of these acids is formic acid (CH_2O_2). The name is derived from the Latin word *formica,* meaning "ant"; the acid was formerly prepared by distilling red ants. A much more effective method of preparation is to oxidize methyl alcohol in the presence of a platinum catalyst. Formic acid is a colorless liquid with an unpleasant odor; it is used, among other things, to dye cloth. The structural formula of the acid is

$$O=\overset{\overset{\displaystyle }{}}{\underset{\underset{\displaystyle H}{|}}{C}}-OH$$

Other important organic acids are lactic acid, tartaric acid, oleic acid and stearic acid.

The esters. The esters are the most important derivatives of the organic acids. They are prepared by heating an organic acid with an alcohol in the presence of a small quantity of concentrated sulfuric acid. (Esters can also be prepared from inorganic acids.) For example, when acetic acid reacts with ethyl alcohol, it forms an ester called ethyl acetate ($CH_3CO_2C_2H_5$). This substance is used in synthesizing various organic compounds. Its molecular structure is

$$H-\overset{\overset{\displaystyle H}{|}}{\underset{\underset{\displaystyle H}{|}}{C}}-\overset{\overset{\displaystyle O}{||}}{C}-O-\overset{\overset{\displaystyle H}{|}}{\underset{\underset{\displaystyle H}{|}}{C}}-\overset{\overset{\displaystyle H}{|}}{\underset{\underset{\displaystyle H}{|}}{C}}-H$$

ANTIFREEZE

NITROGLYCERIN

BAKELITE

FORMICA

NYLON

PHENOLIC PLASTIC

The aromatic hydrocarbons

Chemists were able to obtain certain hydrocarbons in large quantities by the distillation of coal tar long before petroleum became available in vast amounts. Since these coal-tar hydrocarbons had rather marked odors, in contrast to the practically odorless paraffins, they received the name of aromatic hydrocarbons. They have since become exceedingly important in industry and medicine. They are used in the manufacture of explosives, synthetic dyes, perfumes, photographic developers, drugs and many other products.

The simplest aromatic hydrocarbon is benzene, C_6H_6. This substance was first obtained by Michael Faraday by the distillation of coal. For a number of years chemists were puzzled about the structure of the benzene molecule; they wondered how six atoms of carbon could be combined with six atoms of hydrogen. The German chemist August Friedrich Kekule solved the problem.* He pointed out that the six carbons formed a ring, with single bonds between carbon atoms alternating with double bonds, as follows:

*It is said that the solution came to him in a dream. We give this interesting story in the article Science and Progress I, in Volume 5.

Since Kekule's structure is actually inadequate, organic chemists generally represent the benzene molecule as a hexagon:

In derivatives of benzene, one or more of the hydrogen atoms are replaced by other atoms or groups. To indicate the structural formulas of such derivatives, a hexagon may be used, with the substituted group at one of the corners. For example, chlorobenzene, C_6H_5Cl, can be represented either by the complete structural formula or by a hexagon, with a chlorine atom (Cl) at a corner, as follows:

FUELS

COAL OIL

PERFUMES

PHARMACEUTICALS

PHOTOGRAPHIC SUPPLIES

A well-known aromatic carbon is trinitrotoluene, $C_6H_2(CH_3)(NO_2)_3$, popularly known as TNT, and used as an explosive in peace and war. It has the structural formula

$$CH_3$$

or

Molecular structure of alanine, one of the amino acids.

CH_3, a radical, or inseparable group, known as methyl, has replaced one of the hydrogens in the benzene ring. Three other hydrogens have been replaced by NO_2, the nitro group.

Some organic compounds found in living matter

The processes of life take place in a jellylike substance, the protoplasm, which is found in all living cells. It is made up mostly of water (85 to 90 per cent). It also contains a small percentage of minerals and 10 per cent or more of the organic substances known as proteins, fats and carbohydrates. Let us examine briefly the chemical structure of these substances.

The proteins. The proteins are among the most complex of all molecules; their molecular weights * sometimes come to many millions. The human body has hundreds of different proteins, with special structures that enable them to perform different tasks. All these proteins contain nitrogen, carbon, hydrogen and oxygen, and often various other elements, including iron, sulfur, copper and phosphorus.

Proteins can be broken down chemically into substances called amino acids. There are a number of different kinds of such acids; all contain an amino group, $-NH_2$, consisting of nitrogen and hydro-

gen, and also a carboxyl group, $-COOH$, made up of carbon, oxygen and hydrogen. The simplest amino acid is glycine, $CH_2(NH_2)COOH$, with the structural formula:

More than twenty amino acids in all have been obtained by breaking down plant and animal proteins. We list them in the article Basic Food Elements, in Volume 4. It is believed that the proteins consist of long chains of these acids, stretched out in zigzag form, or coiled in a spiral or compactly folded together.

The fats. The natural fats are made up of carbon, hydrogen and oxygen atoms. They are esters of the alcohol glycerol and a fatty organic acid.* Among the fatty acids are palmitic and stearic acids, which are saturated, and oleic and linoleic acids, which are not. The saturated fatty acids yield solids (at ordinary temperatures), when they react with glycerol; the unsaturated ones, liquids. Generally the fats occurring in nature are mixtures of solid and liquid fats. For example, the solid fats palmitin (from palmitic acid) and stearin (from stearic acid) make up about two-

---

* The molecular weight of a molecule is the sum of the weights of the atoms of which the molecule consists. The molecular weight of water (H_2O) is 18; of carbon dioxide (CO_2), 44; of glucose ($C_6H_{12}O_6$), 180.

* We have pointed out that esters result from the reaction of an alcohol and an acid.

fifths of hog lard; about three-fifths of it is a liquid fat, olein (from oleic acid).

The carbohydrates. The carbohydrates contain three chemical elements — carbon, hydrogen and oxygen. The general formula for all of them is $C_xH_{2y}O_y$. In the case of the carbohydrates d-glucose, x is equal to 6 and so is y. Hence the compositional formula for this compound is $C_6H_{12}O_6$. Note that in every carbohydrate there are always twice as many hydrogen atoms as there are oxygen atoms, just as in the water molecule (H_2O). The d-glucose molecule has the following structure:

$$
\begin{array}{c}
H \\
| \\
H-C-O-H \\
| \\
H-C-O-H \\
| \\
H-C-O-H \\
| \\
H-C-O-H \\
| \\
H-C-O-H \\
| \\
H-C=O
\end{array}
$$

The carbohydrates are called saccharides (compounds made up of sugars). The simplest are the monosaccharides, which are also known as the simple sugars.

a disaccharide, or double saccharide. The general formula for this type is $C_{12}H_{22}O_{11}$. The three most important disaccharides are sucrose (table sugar), lactose (milk sugar) and maltose (malt sugar).

The more complex carbohydrates are known as polysaccharides; they are made up of combinations of monosaccharides and their molecules are very large. They include starch, glycogen and cellulose, all of which have the general formula ($C_6H_{10}O_5$). The polysaccharide starch is found chiefly in the seeds or tubers of plants and serves as a food reserve. Glycogen occurs principally in the internal organs and blood of animals; it furnishes most of the fuel required for cellular activity. Cellulose forms the cell walls and woody structure of plants. We discuss starch, glycogen and cellulose in detail in several other chapters of THE BOOK OF POPULAR SCIENCE. (See the entries Starches, Glycogen and Cellulose, in the Index.)

In this short article we have been able to give only the briefest sort of introduction to the vast field of organic chemistry. However, you have learned something about the significance of molecular structure and the intimate relationships existing

It is believed that proteins consist of long chains of amino acids.

Glucose, mentioned above, is a monosaccharide; so are fructose and galactose, which have the same compositional formula as glucose — $C_6H_{12}O_6$. When two monosaccharides combine chemically, they form

between organic compounds. If you would like to know more about this fascinating subject, you will find ample material in the books we list in Volume 10, page 280, under the heading "Organic Chemistry."

THE WORLD OF COLOR

Effects Produced by Different Wave Lengths of Light

BY J. H. RUSH

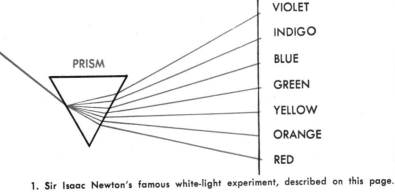

SUNLIGHT

PRISM

VIOLET
INDIGO
BLUE
GREEN
YELLOW
ORANGE
RED

1. Sir Isaac Newton's famous white-light experiment, described on this page.

THE perception of color adds greatly to our knowledge of the world around us, and is also a never ending source of pleasure. It causes us to appreciate fully the beauty of a sunset, the striking hues of autumn foliage or the manifold colors of the rainbow. Men have been keenly aware of color since the early times, as countless writings attest. Yet its nature remained a complete mystery until the seventeenth century. Sir Isaac Newton's classic experiments in 1666 yielded the first clues to its physical basis.

Newton admitted a narrow beam of sunlight into a darkened room through a very small hole in a window shutter. When he placed a triangular glass prism in the beam, the light falling on a normally white screen appeared as a series of colors (Figure 1). This is because light is refracted in passing through a prism; in other words, its path is bent away from the original direction. This effect had long been known, but Newton's experiments showed that different colors are bent through different angles. Red is bent least; then, in order, orange, yellow, green, blue, indigo and violet. To Newton it seemed evident that these colors must be derived from the white sunlight. To prove this point, he used a second prism to bend the colored rays back to their original path. When the rays were recombined in this way, they produced white light.

Much later, when Thomas Young and other investigators established that light is a wave disturbance, they found that color is related to the wave length of light. Waves of light are not directly visible, as are the crests and troughs of waves on water; but they can be demonstrated by indirect methods.

Light is one of many different kinds of electromagnetic radiations — disturbances that travel through the universe in the form of waves.* (See the article Electromagnetic Radiation, in Volume 7.) These radiations all travel at a fixed speed of about 186,300 miles per second in free space. They show an indefinitely long range of wave lengths. Lightning generates waves that may be several miles long; the waves of gamma rays emitted from radioactive materials may be less than $\frac{2}{100,000,000,000}$ of an inch in length.

Scientists express very small distances in units called angstroms. An angstrom is equal to $\frac{1}{100,000,000}$ of a centimeter, or about $\frac{1}{254,000,000}$ of an inch. The wave lengths of visible light range from about 7,500 angstroms (about $\frac{30}{1,000,000}$ of an inch) in the red end to 4,000 angstroms (about $\frac{16}{1,000,000}$ of an inch) in the violet end. Electromagnetic waves in this range excite certain nerve endings in the retina of the eye. The impulses transmitted to the brain by these nerves give rise to sensations of light and color. We shall consider this process later in more detail.

A wave length of light is not a color; rather, it is related to a sensation of color. Different wave lengths excite different color sensations. The sensations can be produced without the agency of light. If you have reasonably good visual imagination, you can "see" colors at will by closing your eyes and imagining them. You can generate the sensation of color by pressing gently on your closed eyes. A blow on the forehead may cause you to "see stars."

How colors are isolated by refraction

We pointed out that a ray of light is refracted, or bent, as it passes through a prism. It is always refracted whenever it crosses the boundary between air (or a vacuum) and a transparent substance, except when it strikes the substance at right angles.** The paths of the different wave lengths of light will diverge within the

---

* Light and the other kinds of radiation behave like particles in certain respects.

** We discuss refraction in the article An Introduction to Optics, in this volume.

2. How light is refracted and reflected (once) when it strikes a water droplet that is floating in the air. The path of only one wave length is shown.

3. How two wave lengths of light, corresponding to two different colors, are refracted and reflected (once) upon striking a raindrop. Note their effect upon the eye of an observer at ground level.

4. The light that produces a rainbow's outer bow is reflected twice inside water droplets. In this drawing we show the path of a single wave length.

5. How a two-bow rainbow appears to an observer.

substance, because each wave length is bent at a different angle. This divergence is the basis of many natural phenomena and is applied by man in various ways.

A familiar example of color dispersion by refraction (and also by reflection) is the rainbow. This phenomenon is produced as sunlight strikes water droplets floating freely in the air. The droplets are nearly spherical. The sunlight that strikes them is refracted and reflected in such a way that the observer sees a huge arc extending above the horizon and showing the full range of color. A rainbow generally shows a bright primary, or inner, bow and a fainter secondary, or outer, bow.

The rays of light that produce the inner bow are refracted in water droplets, reflected once at the internal surface and then refracted again on emerging (Figure 2). Since the different wave lengths of sunlight are refracted differently, they follow different paths within a given drop and also as they emerge from it. Figure 3 shows how two wave lengths of light — those corresponding to violet and red — are refracted from a drop.

An observer can see color only from certain raindrops. In each case a given wave length of light, refracted and reflected from a drop, must strike the observer's eye. This happens only if the ray striking the drop and the emerging wave length that strikes the eye form the appropriate angle (A in Figure 2). The angle in question ranges from about 42° for red to 40° for violet. The observer will obtain the sensation of color from a vast number of drops, which from his viewpoint form an arc in the sky. The different colors of the inner bow follow one another in order from the outer part of the arc to the inner part, red being outermost.

The secondary, or outer, bow of the rainbow is formed by light that has been reflected twice inside each droplet (Figure 4). The order of colors is reversed from that of the primary bow and the colors are fainter. The two bows will appear to an observer as in Figure 5. Theoretically a third bow can be produced by

three internal reflections. However the third bow is rarely, if ever, intense enough to be visible.

The effects called halos and sundogs are produced quite similarly by the refraction of sunlight or moonlight in ice crystals high in the atmosphere. These colored rings or spots occur at definite angles from the sun or moon; they result from somewhat more complex optical processes than those that produce the rainbow.

The dispersion of wave lengths by a prism of glass (or other material) is the basis of one of the most useful instruments of science — the spectroscope. A familiar form of prism spectroscope is shown in Figure 6. Basically it is simply a prism of the type used by Newton, plus various accessories. The first section of the instrument is the collimator. This consists of a tube with a slit at one end and a lens at the other. The slit limits the width of the entering beam, so that the final images in different wave lengths will be narrow and will not overlap. The lens of the collimator bends the rays of light so that the rays from any point on the slit are all parallel as they enter the prism.

As the prism disperses the light, wave lengths are sent off in different directions. The lens on the other side of the prism brings each beam of parallel rays to focus again, forming a sharp image of the slit in each wave length. These slit images are viewed through a magnifying eyepiece; the second lens and the eyepiece form a small telescope. Figure 7 shows a side view of this type of spectroscope. The telescope, which can be swung around on a vertical axis, can be focused on different wave lengths of light.

There are various other kinds of spectroscopes. In the instrument called the spectrograph, the spectral images are focused on film and are photographed; the photographic records they produce are known as spectrograms. The prism is not the only device used to disperse the different wave lengths of light. The diffraction grating, described later, serves the same purpose; it is superior in certain respects to the prism spectroscope.

Characteristics of
sources of light

The band of colors, or wave lengths, produced by a spectroscope is called a spectrum. All wave lengths are present in white light. Its spectrum forms a continuous, unbroken spread of color from the longest visible waves of red light to the shortest visible waves of violet. This is called a continuous emission spectrum (see page 284a). Incandescent solid or liquid substances, or even gases under unusual conditions, radiate white light and show a spectrum of this kind. Sunlight is essentially white; but its spectrum is interrupted by thousands of narrow dark lines, representing missing wave lengths (page 284a). As we shall see, these wave lengths have been absorbed by atoms in the sun's atmosphere. The sun's spectrum is called an absorption spectrum.

When a gas at low pressure is heated or excited by electrical discharge, it shows a different kind of spectrum. The molecules of the gas will always radiate certain sharply defined wave lengths, just as each string of a musical instrument "radiates" (that is, produces by vibration) its characteristic tone. This kind of radiation appears in the spectroscope as a bright-line spectrum — a series of isolated sharp images of the slit (page 284a). Each of the images represents a different wave length.

Even iron and other metals, normally solids, emit bright-line spectra in the vapor state. The vapors of the chemical elements and of many compounds can be identified by the characteristic wave lengths they radiate. Sodium vapor, for example, emits only two wave lengths in the visible spectrum: these are in the yellow-orange region. They are only six angstroms apart, and are easily mistaken for a single line in a small instrument.

The wave lengths of the bright sodium lines match those of two strong dark lines in the spectrum of the sun (page 284a). This is why. Any relatively cool vapor absorbs exactly the same wave lengths of light that it radiates when it is hotter. The region outside the brilliant white photosphere of the sun is cool, compared to the photosphere itself. Therefore the sodium vapor in this outer region absorbs its characteristic wave lengths out of the continuous spectrum radiated from the sun's dense interior. Instead of bright lines of sodium the sun's spectrum shows dark lines of this element. Other dark lines in the solar spectrum similarly reveal the presence of other elements in the sun.

Many substances radiate visible light even when cool and in the solid or liquid state if they are excited by other radiation. Such substances are said to be fluorescent. (Materials that store the exciting energy and reradiate it visibly later are said to be phosphorescent.) Zinc sulfide glows yellow under blue or ultraviolet light or X rays; barium platinocyanide glows blue. Mix these two materials, and you get a fluorescence that approaches white light.

6. Above: diagram of a simple prism spectroscope, as seen from above. It consists of a prism and several accessories.

7. Right: side view of the prism spectroscope shown in Figure 6. The telescope can be swung around on a vertical axis.

This principle is used in fluorescent lamps. A glass tube is coated inside with a mixture of substances known as phosphors that emit a great number of wave lengths when they are excited. The total effect of these wave lengths on the eye is similar to that of white light. The tube is filled with mercury vapor at low pressure. When the vapor is excited by a high-voltage discharge, it radiates strongly in the violet and ultraviolet regions. These radiations bring about visible fluorescence in the coating on the glass.

Effects of interference, diffraction and polarization

Bubbles of nearly colorless soap solution develop brilliant colors before they break. Similar colors appear in cracked glass or ice, or on the surface of very old glass, or in insect wings, or in oil films on water, or in light viewed through a window screen or through one's eyelashes. All of these color effects are caused by the interference of light waves and by a related effect called diffraction.

Interference can be illustrated by a familiar example, illustrated in Figure 8. When a motor boat cuts through calm water, it throws out a series of waves that run off at an angle from the bow. These waves move across the water at a definite speed. If two boats cruise on parallel courses some distance apart, their bow waves meet and cross each other. As they do so, they interfere. If crests on both waves pass a certain point at the same time, the water at this point rises to twice the height of one wave. This effect is called construction interference, or reinforcement. At an adjacent point, a crest of one set of waves arrives simultaneously with the trough of another set, and the two cancel each other. This is destruction interference. If the two wave motions interfere with one another in this way, the water at the said point will hardly be disturbed. As a result of reinforcement and destructive interference, the water between the two boats will show a checkerboard pattern — smooth at some points and with up-and-down motion at others.

8. Waves produced by the boats show an interference pattern. The water is choppy where crests or troughs intersect each other; quiet where crests intersect troughs.

Such interference effects are commonplace in the case of light waves. Let us see what happens when light is reflected from a thin film, such as the wall of a soap bubble (Figure 9). When light encounters a surface of transparent material, such as this, most of it goes on through; but a small fraction of its energy is reflected. We see a soap bubble, therefore, partly by light that is reflected back to us from the outside surface of the watery film. But some of the light is reflected from the second, inside surface also, and most of this light also comes back to our eyes. What we then see depends on the degree of interference that takes place between these two reflected beams of light. It will depend on the wave length of the light and the thickness of the bubble film.

In certain instances the two reflected wave trains for a given wave length will be in phase: that is, their positive crests will coincide and so will their negative crests * (Figure 10). The film will then appear bright in the color corresponding to that wave length because of what is known as constructive interference. The reflected wave trains for another wave length will be out of step, and will cancel one another as a result of destructive interference (Figure 11). The film will then appear dark as far as this particular wave length of light is concerned.

Usually we see a soap bubble film in white light, which presents the entire visible range from red to violet. Since the

* A wave of light can be represented as having a positive and negative crest, corresponding to the crest and trough of a wave of water.

wave lengths differ, the film cannot cancel or reinforce all colors at once. If the thickness of the film is such that one wave length will be canceled, another wave length will be partially reinforced. The colors that are reinforced and that are therefore visible will change continually as the film grows thinner by evaporation.

An air space between two surfaces of glass, ice, mica or other transparent material behaves much the same as a water film in air. If two such surfaces meet at an angle, the thickness of the air gap between them will vary along the wedge that is formed (Figure 12). If light passes through, one color and then another is reinforced. The colors of the spectrum are repeated along the wedge like a series of rainbows. Exceedingly small distances can be measured by instruments that depend on slight changes in the width of the air gap and the consequent shifts of the colored fringes.

The phenomenon called diffraction is basically an interference effect. A wide, uninterrupted wave front moves forward without appreciable change of form. If the wave is interrupted, however, by an opaque edge or a narrow obstacle, the light bends around the obstacle into the shadow zone. Light and dark fringes then develop outside the edge of the shadow. When white light is diffracted in this way, differences in wave lengths lead to color effects as in other cases of interference.

Diffraction effects ordinarily become noticeable only when light passes through very small openings or around very narrow obstacles. A very common and beautiful demonstration is the appearance of the moon through a door screen or window screen. Four bright streaks of light appear to radiate from the round globe, parallel to the horizontal and vertical wires of the screen. These streaks appear nearly white when seen with the naked eye. But a binocular or a small telescope will reveal that the streaks consist of a series of white-light spectra, in which the sequence from violet to red is repeated over and over again. This principle is applied in the diffraction-grating spectroscope (Figure 13). The diffraction grating used in this instrument consists of a surface of glass on which many thousands of fine grooves have been ruled; there are generally several thousand evenly spaced grooves to the inch. When white light strikes the diffraction grating, a series of continuous spectra is produced.

Striking color effects can be produced when certain objects are viewed in plane-polarized light. To understand what this kind of light is, it must be pointed out that light does not vibrate in the direction in which it travels, but at right angles to that direction. It vibrates in all possible directions perpendicular to the ray — up and down, sideways, obliquely (Figure 14).

Suppose we let a beam of white light pass through a thin plate cut from a crystal of the mineral called tourmaline. If the beam is directed to a screen after it passes through the tourmaline plate, the

9. When light encounters the transparent soap-bubble film, most of it goes through the film, but a small fraction of its energy is reflected.

10. The two reflected beams of light for the wave length corresponding to violet, below, are in step; hence the film will show a bright violet color.

11. Here the reflected beams for the wave length corresponding to red are out of step. As a result the soap-bubble film will show no red at all.

RAY OF SUNLIGHT

VIOLET

RED

AIR

SOAP BUBBLE FILM

light will appear practically unaltered. Yet a definite change in its character has taken place. The tourmaline plate has permitted only the vibrations in a single plane to pass through (Figure 15). Let us now put a second tourmaline plate behind the first. This second plate can be set in such a way that light vibrating in one plane will pass through both plates and will appear on the screen (Figure 16A). If we now turn the second plate 90°, the light vibrations in the single plane can no longer pass through and no light at all will fall on the screen (Figure 16B).

When vibrations of light can vibrate only in a single plane as in Figures 15 and 16A, we say that the light has been plane-polarized. The plate that polarizes the light is called the polarizer; the second plate, which serves to analyze the light, is called the analyzer.

If we put a flake of mica between the plates, a series of beautiful spectral colors will appear on the screen. This is due to variations in the thickness of the crystal and in the wave lengths of light that pass through it. Various other transparent crystalline substances will show similar effects in plane-polarized light. If glass or transparent plastic is stretched or compressed, the stresses set up in this way alter its structure. When plane-polarized light is passed through it, colored fringes will appear.

Why is the sky blue? Why is the setting sun red? Why is deep water blue or green? The cause in each case is the scattering of light — a diffraction effect. Dust particles and even the molecules of atmospheric gases interrupt the wave fronts of sunlight advancing into the atmosphere. The light that was advancing in a straight line from the sun to the earth is dispersed; tiny new wave fronts develop in all directions. In a word, the light is scattered.

Like all diffraction and interference effects, the resulting color patterns depend on wave length. A given obstacle "looks bigger" to a short wave of violet light than it does to the longer red; therefore, the effect of the obstacle on the violet wave will be more drastic. Consequently,

violet light is scattered most, blue somewhat less and green, yellow and orange still less, in that order. Red is affected least of all.

The sky generally looks blue because the short blue waves are scattered more than the longer waves of red light. It is true that the violet waves are dispersed even more than the blue. However, the sky does not appear violet because the sun is relatively weak in violet light. Besides, the eye is less sensitive to violet light than to blue. Deep water appears blue for the same reason. However, impurities in the water often absorb the blue, and green becomes the predominant tint. The sky looks red near the horizon because at that angle, the path through the atmosphere is long and traverses much low-flying dust. As a result the bluer light is effectively scattered out of the direct beam before it can be observed by the viewer.

Twilight is also the result of the light scattered by particles and molecules in the atmosphere. Were it not for this scattering, we would be in darkness as soon as the sun went below the horizon.

The selective absorption of wave lengths of light

A white dress, red roses, green leaves, brown paint, blue enamel, a black diamond — each of these terms implies that a definite color is associated with a particular kind of stuff? How do such colors arise?

First, let us see what we mean by "black" and "white." We have already

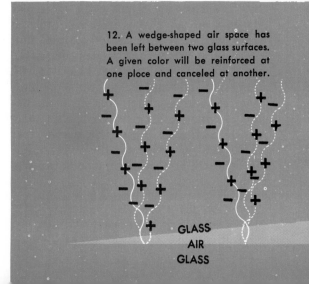

12. A wedge-shaped air space has been left between two glass surfaces. A given color will be reinforced at one place and canceled at another.

GLASS
AIR
GLASS

ELECTRODE →

SLIT

FOCUSING
LENS

COLLIMATING
LENS

SAMPLE

CONCAVE GRATING

ELECTRODE →

13. The chemical composition of a given sample can be analyzed by a diffraction-grating spectroscope.

pointed out that white light is a mixture of all visible wave lengths of light. Obviously, when an opaque object * reflects all wave lengths equally well, it will appear white in white light. Surfaces that reflect all wave lengths weakly will look gray; extreme gray merges into black. A truly black surface would be one that absorbed all the light falling upon it, reflecting none whatsoever. Actually there is no absolutely black surface.

If an opaque object absorbs certain wave lengths and reflects others, we see a blend of the colors that it reflects. A red rose absorbs violet, blue, green and yellow wave lengths much more strongly than it does red. Blue enamel absorbs red and other longer waves and reflects blue and perhaps some green. If an object absorbs wave lengths at both ends of the spectrum — violet and red — and reflects the middle lengths, we see yellow-green.

The apparent color of an opaque object depends upon the quality of the light that falls upon it. Suppose the molecular structure of a substance is such that it can reflect only blue light. If it is illuminated by white light, it will absorb all wave lengths except that of blue. It will reflect blue light and will appear to be blue. If a blue beam of light falls upon the object, the beam will be reflected; the object will still look blue. Suppose, however, that we direct a red light upon the object. The red light will be absorbed. The object will

* A substance is opaque if no light can pass through it. A transparent substance transmits light freely so that objects on the other side can be clearly seen. A translucent substance also lets light pass through it; but it diffuses the light in such a way that objects on the other side cannot be seen clearly.

reflect no color at all; therefore, it will appear to be black.

It is a sensible precaution to take a piece of fabric to the front door of a store that does not have daylight illumination to see how the fabric will look in white light. Any amateur photographer knows that daylight and the light of a tungsten lamp differ greatly in color values they give objects. A special filter or special film must be used to equalize the rendering of color in these two kinds of illumination.

Visual judgments of color are very rough. They tell only the predominant behavior at the surface of an opaque object. Only the spectroscope can reveal just what the object really does with the light that falls upon it. Frequently the actual color pattern is quite complex.

What happens when light passes through a colored transparent or translucent substance? Some wave lengths are absorbed as they pass through the material; those that emerge in perceptible strength determine the color (Figure 17). The absorption pattern is complex; it varies according to the material. For example, if cellophane in a certain shade of green is folded and refolded and viewed against a strong white light (such as that from a photoflood lamp), the green color gradually darkens as the number of folds increases. After the cellophane has been folded fifteen or twenty times, the light that comes through will no longer be green but deep red.

The spectroscope would show why this mystifying color change occurs. The dye in the cellophane is only relatively

Spectrum of incandescent light, produced by a 4-by-4-inch Bausch and Lomb diffraction grating.

the world of
COLOR

Light is a form of energy, traveling through the universe in waves. The wave lengths of visible light range from rather less than 4,000 angstroms to more than 7,000. (An angstrom is 1/100,000,000 of a centimeter.) The waves of light in this range excite certain nerve endings in the retina of the eye. Impulses are transmitted by these nerves to the brain; here they give rise to sensations of color. Here we show some interesting color phenomena.

284-a

When light from a given light source is broken up by the instrument called the spectroscope into different wave lengths, the resulting color combination is called a spectrum. Below are some spectra.

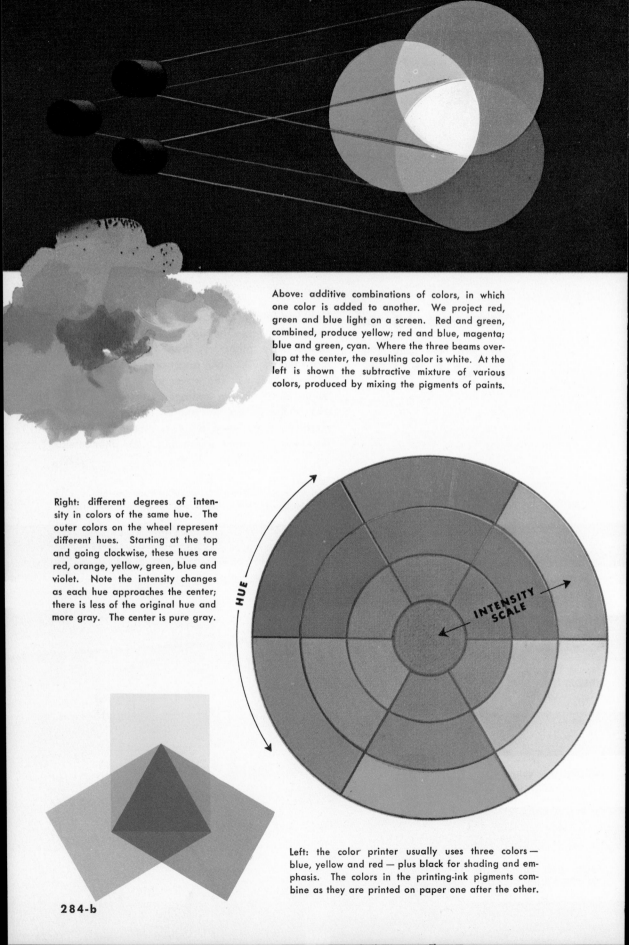

Above: additive combinations of colors, in which one color is added to another. We project red, green and blue light on a screen. Red and green, combined, produce yellow; red and blue, magenta; blue and green, cyan. Where the three beams overlap at the center, the resulting color is white. At the left is shown the subtractive mixture of various colors, produced by mixing the pigments of paints.

Right: different degrees of intensity in colors of the same hue. The outer colors on the wheel represent different hues. Starting at the top and going clockwise, these hues are red, orange, yellow, green, blue and violet. Note the intensity changes as each hue approaches the center; there is less of the original hue and more gray. The center is pure gray.

HUE

INTENSITY SCALE

Left: the color printer usually uses three colors — blue, yellow and red — plus black for shading and emphasis. The colors in the printing-ink pigments combine as they are printed on paper one after the other.

How white light is transformed to produce a series of striking color patterns. (1) Upper left: a full-scale replica of a bolt has been made out of a plastic called photoelectric Fosterite. The bolt has been heated and subjected to tension; the stress pattern that has been produced is preserved as the plastic cools. The bolt is sliced; when it is viewed in polarized light, the stresses that have been brought about show up as a definite color pattern. Note the vivid colors at the points of greatest tension. (2) Upper right: the closely spaced ridges on a phonograph record convert white light into colors through diffraction. (3) Lower left: every color of the spectrum is produced as light strikes cut-glass carvings, acting as prisms. (4) Lower right: color patterns brought about by interference as white light strikes an oil slick that has been spread on a black asphalt pavement.

#1 — Albert Fenn. #2, 3 and 4 — Andreas Feininger. LIFE © Time, Inc.

1 **2** **3** **4**

THE PSYCHOLOGY OF COLOR

Identical colors may appear to be quite different when they are seen against different backgrounds. Here is a good way to test the keenness of your color perception. The six lettered circles shown at the left are also given, in different order, at the right; here they are indicated by numbers. Try to match the lettered colors on the left with the numbered colors on the right. Then check your answers against the correct pairings, which are printed here upside down:

A-2; B-6; C-5; D-4; E-3; F-1.

CONTRAST

CONTRAST

The colors used for the lettering in the two panels are identical. Note how faint the lettering in the left-hand panel appears, because the background is so light in color. The lettering in the other panel is far more legible, because it contrasts sharply with the background.

The five circles, above, are apparently different in color. As a matter of fact, these "different" colors are identical in hue, value and intensity. The apparent differences between them are due entirely to the fact that we view them against five different backgrounds.

Under very strong illumination, fix your gaze on the lowest right-hand star in the flag for fifteen seconds. Then look at a blank piece of paper. The flag will now appear in its proper colors. This effect is due to retinal fatigue, discussed in considerable detail in this article.

transparent to green. It is even more transparent to deep red than to green — that is, it permits a greater percentage of the red light to pass through. But the eye is not very sensitive to deep red, and so it responds to the green instead of to the red. When enough thicknesses of cellophane have been provided, the absorption of the green light becomes so much greater than the absorption of the red that the eye at last perceives red as the predominant wave length.

Color mixing:
lights and pigments

We know that when wave lengths of roughly equal intensities from all regions of the spectrum are combined, they give the color sensation of white light. Curiously enough, however, by mixing certain color pairs, we can deceive the eye into believing that the entire spectrum is present. Blue and yellow are one such pair; red and cyan (bluish green) are another. The colors in a pair of this kind may consist of light from very narrow portions of the white-light spectrum. Yet, if the wave lengths and intensities are properly balanced, the total impression they give is the same that we would get from viewing the whole spectrum of light.

Obviously there is more to the perception of color than the simple matter of wave lengths in the spectrum. As a matter of fact, this very complexity makes the task of the artist or dyer easier than it would be if every color had to correspond to a definite wave length. Two colors can match perfectly, as far as the eye can see, and yet appear altogether different in the spectroscope. Because of the flexibility of color sensation, it has been difficult to develop a science of *color*, as distinguished from a purely physical science of *wave length*.

The most familiar approach to the analysis of color is based on a set of three primary colors. Many different three-color combinations can produce the sensation of white light when they are superimposed. Red, green and blue are often chosen; they can be used as the basis of

a color wheel, which will show the relationship between the primary and secondary colors (Figure 18). When two primary colors, such as red and green, are combined, they give a secondary color. Red and green light produce yellow; blue and green give cyan; blue and red yield magenta, a shade of reddish purple. Each secondary color produced by the mixing of two primaries lies half way between them on the color wheel. For example, we saw

14. Ray of unpolarized light. The light vibrates in all possible directions in a plane at right angles to the ray.

15. The plate permits only light vibrations in a single plane to pass through; the light has been plane-polarized.

16. In A, below, plane-polarized light passes through both plates and appears on the screen. In B, plane-polarized light passes through the first plate but is stopped by the second; it does not appear on the screen.

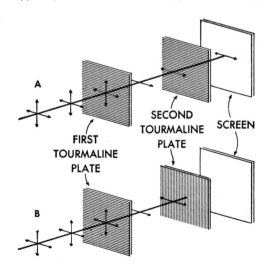

that red and green produce yellow; therefore, yellow lies half way between red and green on the wheel. There is an infinite variety of intermediate hues between adjacent primary and secondary colors.

It is interesting to note that the secondary color magenta is not a spectral color: that is, it does not correspond to any wave length in the white-light spectrum. It is produced when we bend the spectrum back on itself, so to speak, allowing the red and violet ends to overlap.

Each primary color on the wheel is opposite the secondary formed by the mixture of the other two primaries. The colors in such a primary-secondary pair are called complementary; when they are combined, they produce white. Green and magenta are complementary; so are red and cyan; so are blue and yellow.

The color relations we have been discussing apply only to *additive* mixtures of colored lights, in which one color is *added* to another. This kind of color mixing must be distinguished from the process of *subtractive* combination. In this process, blended colors *subtract* from white light the colors that they cannot reflect.

Let us examine the difference between the two processes. To illustrate the additive process we project yellow and blue light onto the same area of a white screen. We add one color (yellow) to the other (blue); both colors are reflected and the eye registers the combination as white light. When we mix yellow and blue paints, we are using the subtractive process. The resulting mixture, as any child who has dabbled in water colors knows, is green, not white.

To understand why subtractive combination produces this result, we must point out that paint contains coloring ingredients called pigments. These are finely divided particles of a substance that absorbs certain wave lengths and reflects others. Pigments do not absorb or reflect sharply defined regions of the spectrum. Yellow pigment absorbs violet and blue light almost completely; but it reflects some green and red, together with the yellow that it reflects most strongly. Similarly, blue ab-

sorbs practically all the red and yellow but reflects some green and violet, as well as blue. When yellow pigment and blue pigment are mixed and exposed to white light, each is free to absorb any light not absorbed by the other. The only region of the spectrum that is not fully absorbed by either pigment in this case is green. Therefore the mixture of yellow and blue pigments gives green.

Subtractive color mixing is the basis of color printing. The color printer applies his colors one at a time. Usually he uses three colors — blue, yellow and red — plus black for shading and emphasis. Each of four printing plates carries those details of the picture that appear in one of these colors; the plate is rolled with ink of that color and printed. When the four colors are printed on the paper one after the other, in exact register, the colors of the pigments combine subtractively and reproduce approximately the colors of the original.

We discuss the subtractive method of mixing colors, as applied to photography, in the article called The Versatile Art of Photography, in Volume 9.

The classification and measurement of color

Everyone recognizes that a word such as "yellow," or "green" or "blue" is not enough by itself to describe a color impression adequately. We commonly use the terms "strong," "rich," "pale," "weak," "dark" and "light" in our efforts to describe variations of colors. It is possible to analyze color impressions more accurately by giving three qualities or characteristics: hue, saturation and brightness.

Hue is the spectral characteristic of a color; in other words, it corresponds to a definite wave length of the spectrum. What of colors, such as magenta, that do not appear in the spectrum? In such cases, the hue represents the value obtained by the additive mixing of two spectral colors, representing two definite wave lengths of light. When we say that something is red, or green or yellow, we refer to its hue. No amount of shading or thinning can

17. All wave lengths of light except that for red are absorbed in the transparent object above. The wave length for red passes through; the object appears red.

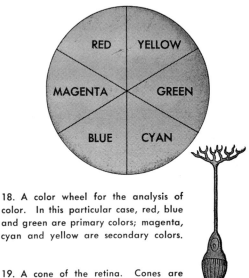

18. A color wheel for the analysis of color. In this particular case, red, blue and green are primary colors; magenta, cyan and yellow are secondary colors.

19. A cone of the retina. Cones are cells responsible for the appreciation of color and the perception of fine details.

turn red into green. Hue is really the fundamental quality of color sensation.

Saturation (sometimes called intensity) expresses the quality that we commonly call richness or strength of color. Suppose we project a beam of red light from the spectrum onto a white screen. The color we see is saturated. All of the light that comes to the eye from the screen is capable of exciting the sensation of red. Now, suppose we project a beam of white light onto the same spot as the red. The color is now diluted, paler; it is a combination of red sensation and the general sense of illumination that we call white. By varying the intensities of the white and red beams, we can get any degree of saturation. In handling pigments, adding white or gray to a hue is equivalent to adding white light. This results in a decrease in saturation.

Brightness (lightness, brilliance, intensity or value) is a measure of the ef-

fectiveness with which an object reflects light. A brightly colored object is one that reflects or transmits a large fraction of the light falling on it, so that it appears brilliant, or luminous. We can demonstrate brightness by projecting a spectral color onto a series of screens of various shades of gray. The brightness of the resulting color will vary according to the reflecting qualities of these gray shades. On a white screen, which reflects the greatest possible amount of light, the brightness of the color would be at its maximum. A black screen would not reflect any light; the brightness would be zero.

To provide a basis for comparing and cataloguing color samples, several systems of classification have been developed. All depend upon the fact that a color can be uniquely classified, provided its hue, saturation and brightness are specified. One of the systems is the Munsell color atlas, giving colored samples of different hues and various degrees of saturation and of brightness for each hue. The intervals between the successive hues, saturations and brightnesses are small enough so that they form a practically continuous series.

If a textile merchant orders a fabric of a color corresponding to a particular Munsell specification, he will have a good idea of what the material will look like. A system such as the Munsell color atlas cannot, however, be absolutely precise. In the first place, the same kind of light source must be used to illuminate both the Munsell standard and the sample that is to be compared with it. This requirement is very important, as we have already noted. Daylight and tungsten lamps, for example, give radically different impressions of some color samples, particularly mixtures that involve green or blue. Differences in texture of the colored surfaces also affect the color sensation one obtains from them. Perhaps the most troublesome factor in color standardization is the human element. Few people would agree exactly on a match of two colors. At least one person in twenty would disagree violently with the majority, and he would not necessarily be color-blind.

The Munsell atlas and other catalogue systems depend upon the matching and identification of colors in terms of the color sensation they arouse, and not in terms of their wave lengths. For many purposes, a more accurate standard is desirable. Instruments called colorimeters have been developed to measure color properties according to wave lengths of light. One type of colorimeter uses an ingenious approach, based on the hue, saturation and brightness of the sample. A spectroscope selects the wave length that matches the sample hue. An auxiliary beam of white light is then added to the hue and its intensity is adjusted to match the saturation of the sample. Finally the brightness of the combination is adjusted to match the brightness of the sample. In this way the three fac-

of puzzling details must be accounted for; that is why, even today, no theory of color vision is completely satisfactory. Most scientists agree, however, upon one basic approach to this problem. This approach was suggested by Thomas Young and developed by the distinguished German physicist and physiologist Hermann von Helmholtz a century ago.

According to the Young-Helmholtz theory, the cones * in the retina of the eye are of three types. One type is most sensitive to the red region of the spectrum (that is, the wave lengths corresponding to the red region). Another is particularly sensitive to the green region, a third to the blue-violet (see Figure 20). Each type of cone is sensitive to a wide range of other wave lengths. For this reason, as the dia-

20. Chart illustrating the Young-Helmholtz theory of color vision, described on this page. According to this theory, the cones in the retina are of three types. The first is most sensitive to the red region of the spectrum; the second, to the green region; the third, to the blue. Each type is also sensitive to a wide range of other wave lengths. The figures in the chart show the wave lengths in microns. (A micron is a thousandth of a millimeter.) Increasing distance from the base line indicates increasing intensity of sensation.

tors of color are related to the white-light spectrum.

Of course, no measurement means anything unless the standard to which it relates is accurate and consistent. It is useless to refer a color sample to a white-light spectrum if the reference light is not really white, according to an agreed standard. Much of the work of colorimetry, or color measurement, has gone into specifying and developing stable, reproducible illumination sources.

A theory of color vision

Many attempts have been made to explain the perception of colors. A number

gram shows, the sensitivity curves overlap. The red-sensitive cones respond not only to red, but also, though less strongly, to orange, yellow and green. The green-sensitive elements respond also in some degree throughout the range from red to blue; the blue-sensitive cones respond also to violet and green.

Light of almost any single wave length must excite at least two sets of cone-elements to some extent, because of their overlapping ranges of sensitivity. We pointed out that light from the red and green regions of the spectrum, received

* Cones are curiously shaped cells (see Figure 19) that are responsible for the appreciation of color and also for the perception of fine details in the image that is focused on the retina. See Index, under Rods and cones of eye.

as a single impression, is perceived as yellow. If we accept the three-color theory, yellow is a composite sensation that can be produced by stimulation of both the red-sensitive and green-sensitive cones by wave lengths near their points of maximum sensitivity. We also know that a single wave length in the spectrum between the red and green also produces the sensation of yellow. In the diagram we note that the yellow region of the spectrum is situated where the red and green response curves cross.

If all three sets of retinal cones are equally stimulated, the resulting sensation is that of white light. Two or more isolated wave lengths can produce the white-light sensory response if they are so located that they cross the sensitivity curves at equal heights. Suppose color sensation

21. The Benham disk (above) is mounted on a spindle piercing the center. If the disk is spun, colors appear.

is produced by two wave lengths of light. One of these, say, is yellow, which intersects the red and green curves at B (in Figure 20). The other wave length is a shade of blue that intersects the blue curve at about the same height (at A). These two wave lengths will combine to produce the sensation of white light.

There is nothing in the structure of the retina to support or refute the three-color theory of color vision. All the color-sensitive cones look alike under the microscope. The theory has not successfully explained some details of color sensation; however, it is supported by many bits of indirect evidence. One of the most interesting of these is retinal fatigue.

If you stare fixedly for at least fifteen seconds at a colored pattern, so that the colored image is held on a definite region of the retina, and then close your eyes or look steadily at a white surface, you will see the pattern in its complementary color. This seems to be due to the fact that exposure to a red pattern, for example, produces an effect similar to fatigue in the retina or the brain and reduces the sensitivity to red. Then, when you expose the retina to white light, green- and blue-green-sensitive cones in the fatigued area respond more strongly than the recently exposed red-sensitive cones. The resulting color sensation is that of the white-light spectrum with the red region removed — that is, cyan, the color that is complementary to red.

Color blindness affords further evidence for the three-color theory. A person with green color blindness, for example, responds to various light stimuli as if the green-sensitive curve in Figure 20 were missing. Other types of color blindness are just as consistent. It is as if one or more of the response curves shown in Figure 20 were lacking.

Oculists' charts for detecting color blindness make use of this principle. A chart of this kind is composed of a field of many small colored spots. The pigments in these spots all look alike to a person with normal vision; but the spectral colors they reflect are so chosen that certain spots look different from the others to one who is color-blind. These "peculiar" spots are arranged to form numerals or other symbols, and the person being tested is asked to read what he sees. From his response, the oculist knows immediately what elements of color vision he lacks.*

The device known as the Benham disk (Figure 21) demonstrates the color-response characteristics of the retina. It consists of a black semicircle and a white one with four sets of black arcs marked on it. The disk can be made of cardboard and mounted on a toothpick piercing the center of the disk. When the latter is spun

* Editor's note: For a different theory of color perception, see The Land Theory of Color Vision, in Volume 8.

like a top, colors appear. They are different for the four sets of arcs shown in the diagram, and they change with the direction or speed of rotation. These color sensations are not fully understood. Evidently they depend upon differences in the promptness with which the three sets of color-sensitive retinal cones respond to light stimuli.

The psychology of color perception

The visual effects we have been discussing depend upon stimuli affecting the retina and other structures of the eye. Many subtler peculiarities of color vision involve the complex processes by which visual sensations are interpreted in the brain. Among them are harmony or discord of colors, the effects of adjacent colored areas on each other and the influence of colors upon emotional moods.

Most people are aware that certain combinations of colors are pleasing, while others are distinctly displeasing or even painful to one of artistic sensibilities. The harmonious blending of colors is a fine art, which is based on certain definite principles and practices.

As in any kind of artistic composition, colors must give an effect of clear relationship and unity of purpose. Whatever colors are used, one color must clearly dominate. The others must relate themselves to the dominant color, but must not compete with it. The simplest harmonious effects depend upon the colors that have something in common. They may be different shades or tints of the same hue, or they may be neighboring hues on the color wheel. Red and yellow might clash by too much contrast. However, an intermediate orange will blend with either, or even unite all three colors harmoniously.

One of the strongest color discords occurs when highly saturated complementary colors compete with each other. We have already pointed out that the afterimage of any color in the retina is its complementary color. This fact may have something to do with the peculiarly unpleasant effect when complementaries are combined. Each is in a sense the negative of the other. However, if one complementary is subdued by reducing its saturation or brightness, it serves to enhance the other complementary, rather than to compete with it.

Subdued colors nearly always harmonize because no single color stands out strongly enough to dominate or rival the others. Compositions of this type are monotonous, however. The recent trend in clothing and decoration has been toward the more difficult but much more positive harmonious blends of bright hues.

Colors influence each other strongly by contrast, especially when they are adjacent to one another. Such contrasts usually follow the principle of black-and-white contrast effects. For instance, a small gray circle on a white background appears distinctly darker than the same circle on a background of black. In much the same way, a color generally appears lighter in contrast to a dark shade than to a light tint, regardless of the contrasting hue. Such effects are obviously important in clothing design and interior decoration, as well as in painting.

Color can deceive the eyes in many ways. A white wall seems nearer than the same wall painted a dark shade. Red seems nearer than blue; this effect seems to depend upon the way in which the eye accommodates to radically different wave lengths.

Certain more or less definite emotional effects are produced by colors. Green is restful; red exciting and disturbing. These two colors have long served for traffic signals. Green indicates that an automobile driver can safely proceed; red, that it would be dangerous to go forward. Our emotional reactions to these two colors may be based on the reassuring green of grass and trees and the alarming color of arterial blood; but this is mere guesswork. Blue is a "cool" color; do we think of blue water in this connection? It is favorable to sleep; but it can also be depressing. We say that we are "feeling blue" when we are unhappy; "blue songs" are sad.

See also Vol. 10, p. 280: "Color."

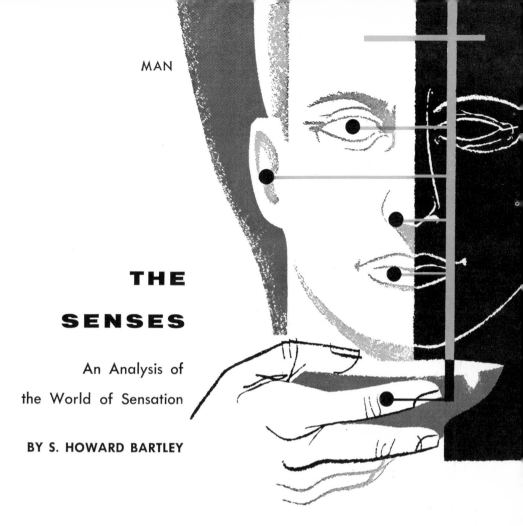

MAN

THE

SENSES

An Analysis of
the World of Sensation

BY S. HOWARD BARTLEY

FOR centuries it was accepted as self evident that there are five senses: vision, hearing, touch, taste and smell. We now realize that this list is quite inadequate. Besides the five senses it includes, there are senses of pressure, pain, heat and cold; there is a sense of balance and a muscle sense. They all function through certain specialized organs called sense organs. Some of them are more or less modified nerve endings. Others — especially the eyes and ears — are comparatively large and very complex structures.

When scientists want to find out about the senses, their experiments follow a pretty definite course. First, they try to find out the tiniest stimulus that will affect a sense organ so as to result in a conscious experience, or sensation. The stimulus that will just suffice to do this is called the threshold amount, or simply threshold. There are many kinds of thresholds. For example, there are thresholds for red, green and other color sensations, a threshold for touch and a threshold for pain.

The researcher is also concerned with the variations in the strengths of stimuli that will bring about just-noticeable differences in sensations. These just-noticeable differences, also called J.N.D.'s, represent the number of perceptible steps into which a range of sensations can be divided. If there are 60 J.N.D.'s in a band of gray tapering from white to black, it means that to the person looking at the band, there are 60 perceptible grays. It is also important, in studying the senses, to find out how the strength, amount and duration of a stimulus compare with the sensation that the stimulus produces.

The sense
of vision

The sense of vision is one of the most versatile of all. It supplies us with information about objects at very close range,

CUTAWAY DIAGRAM OF EYE

SCLEROTIC COAT
CHOROID COAT
RETINA
IRIS
LENS
AQUEOUS HUMOR
IRIS
VITREOUS HUMOR
OPTIC NERVE

EYEBALL AND EYE MUSCLES

OBLIQUE UPPER MUSCLE

STRAIGHT UPPER MUSCLE
PULLEY

STRAIGHT EXTERNAL MUSCLE

STRAIGHT INTERNAL MUSCLE

STRAIGHT LOWER MUSCLE

OBLIQUE LOWER MUSCLE

LAYERS OF RETINA

PIGMENT LAYER
RODS AND CONES
BIPOLAR CELLS
GANGLION CELLS
NERVE FIBER LAYER

at a great distance and at an infinite number of distances between these two extremes. We become aware of these objects through the sense organ known as the eye. Rays of light pass through a transparent part of the eyeball, penetrate through the inner part of the eye, and fall upon a layer of sensitive tissue — the retina. As a result impulses arise, and these impulses are carried by way of nerve fibers to the brain. Here the impulses give rise to the sensation of sight.

The eye, which is enclosed in a bony cavity called the socket, is more or less spherical in shape and is about an inch in diameter. It can be turned in different directions by six muscles, attached at one end to the eyeball and at the other end to the wall of the socket. The eyeball wall, which encloses the liquid and semiliquid interior sections, is made up of three layers. The outermost one is the tough sclerotic coat, which protects the delicate inner structures of the eye. We can see part of this coat; it is what we call the white of the eye. In front there is a circular, transparent area, called the cornea. The outer surface of the sclerotic coat is lubricated by tear fluid, secreted by the lachrymal gland. From the eye surface the fluid passes into small tubes — the lachrymal ducts — and from these into the nose. Protection for the outer surface of the eye is provided by the eyelids. These useful structures close as a result of reflex action when something is about to touch the eye.

The middle layer of the eye wall is known as the choroid coat. It carries a multitude of small blood vessels, which extend throughout the inner part of the eyeball except in front, where there is a hole, called the pupil of the eye. Surrounding the pupil is a circular band, called the iris; it gives the eye its color. The third and innermost layer — the retina — lines most of the eyeball interior (but not the front part). This tissue, as we have observed, converts the energy of light waves into nerve impulses, which are sent to the brain.

The retina consists of several layers, of which the most important are the rods and cones, the bipolar cells and the ganglion cells. The rods and cones are curiously shaped nerve cells (see diagram) that are sensitive to light. Impulses arise in them when they are struck by light rays. As a result other impulses are set up in the bipolar cells. These impulses are then transmitted to the brain by way of the fibers of the ganglion cells. The fibers make up a cablelike bundle, called the optic nerve, which issues from the back of the eye.

The rods are sensitive to far smaller amounts of light than the cones; they are responsible for vision in dim light. Cones are particularly concerned with the perception of fine detail and of color. The rods are sensitive to light because of a chemical reaction brought about by the light rays that enter the eye. The outer part of the rods contains a red pigment called visual purple, or rhodopsin. When acted upon by light, it decomposes into a substance called retinene and then into vitamin A and a protein. The vitamin A and the protein are later reconverted into visual purple. A certain amount of vitamin A is lost in the process. This loss must be made good by fresh stores of vitamin A, supplied through the circulation. If a person's diet is lacking in this vitamin, he will not be able to see well in dim light — a condition called night blindness. It is believed that much the same kind of chemical reaction takes place in the cones.

Rods and cones are not uniformly distributed throughout the retina. A small region in the center, called the *fovea centralis,* contains only cones; this region is concerned with acute vision. The cones are distributed more and more sparsely toward the edge of the retina, while the relative number of rods increases. We see clearest in daylight by using the center of the eye — the *fovea centralis;* at night, by using a region somewhat to the side. We are blind at all times to objects that cast their images only on the part of the retina where the optic nerve leaves the eye. There are no rods and cones in that part of the retina, which is called the optic disc. This results in a blind spot in the field of vision.

We can demonstrate the existence of the blind spot by a simple experiment, illustrated in the diagram on this page. Close your left eye and look at the cross in the diagram, holding the page close to your eye. Gradually move the page away from the eye. At a distance of about ten inches, the black spot beside the cross will become invisible. The reason is that the image of the spot will be formed on the part of the retina where there are no rods or cones — the optic disc.

Thus far we have described the wall of the eye, with its three layers — the sclerotic coat, the choroid coat and the retina. Let us now examine the internal structure of the organ. A short distance behind the cornea is the elastic crystalline lens, which focuses the light rays entering the eye. The lens, which is supported by a hammock-like ligament, is transparent in the case of a healthy eye. Sometimes it becomes clouded — a condition called cataract. In the commonest type of cataract — senile cataract, generally found in persons over fifty years of age — vision is gradually lost as the condition develops. To restore sight, the lens is removed and special glasses are provided to take its place. In other types of cataract the cloudiness may disappear more or less completely in time. This is particularly true in the case of cataract caused by perforation of the lens, due to injury.

The interior of the eyeball is divided by the crystalline lens and its supporting structures into two chambers. The one in front of the lens is filled with a watery solution called aqueous humor. The other chamber, occupying the space between the lens and the retina, is much larger. It contains a jellylike substance called vitreous humor.

In the article An Introduction to Optics, in this volume, we pointed out that light comes to us in a series of waves. Different wave lengths excite different sensations of color when they strike the retina. The eye is not equally sensitive to light rays of all wave lengths. Certain rays will not result in any sensation of vision; these are the ultraviolet and infrared rays.

We see objects because waves of light are reflected from them and enter the eye. The organ of vision has often been compared to a camera. In the camera, light reflected from an object passes through a lens, is focused on a film at the back of the camera and forms a small image. In the eye, reflected light passes through the crystalline lens and is brought to a focus on the light-sensitive retina. An adjustable diaphragm in the camera increases or decreases the amount of light that reaches the film. In the eye this sort of adjustment is made by the iris. Its opening can be made wider or narrower by means of muscles radiating from the inner rim of the iris.

Rays of light from a distant point are brought to a focus closer to the camera lens than rays reflected from nearby objects. To cause these dissimilar rays to be focused sharply on the film, the camera lens must

FIXATION POINT

OPTIC DISC
FOVEA

We see most clearly in daylight by focusing on a small pit, or fovea, in the retina. At all times we are blind to objects that cast their images on the optic disc, the part of the retina where the optic nerve leaves the eye. The existence of the blind spot can be demonstrated by a simple experiment, utilizing the cross and circle shown below and described in detail on this page.

be moved nearer to the film or farther away from it, as the case may be. In the case of the eye the proper adjustment is made by changing the shape of the lens, which is an elastic body. This is done by means of tiny muscles within the eyeball. In the diagram we show how the lens adjusts for far and near vision. The process of changing the shape of the lens in this way is called accommodation.

The lens of the eye produces an inverted image in the retina. (See the diagram on this page.) This image is interpreted in the brain in such a way that it appears erect. For example, when the lower part of the retina is stimulated by light rays reflected from a given object, it seems to us that the object is in the upper part of the field of vision. If we put on glasses which focus the incoming rays in such a way that upright images appear in the retina, everything seems topsy-turvy at first. In time, however, we learn to make the correct interpretation. If we remove the glasses and let inverted images be formed on the retina, we must learn all over again how to interpret the images.

The eye is able to adapt to the various levels of light that one meets in everyday life, except to such extreme intensities as those of the sun or of arc lights. There is a striking example of this faculty of adaptation when we enter a movie theater from broad daylight. At first, little is visible; soon, however, darkness gives way to dim illumination, which enables us to find our way to a seat.

In the article The World of Color, in this volume, we tell how the different sensations of color are interpreted in the brain. We also deal with the interesting phenomenon called color blindness.

It is important for our sense of vision to tell us where objects are. This is called localization. When we try to decide where an object is, our decision will depend upon *what* we think the object is. For instance, if you saw an illuminated white rectangular area in a dark room, you might consider it to be a movie screen; in that case, it would seem to be a number of feet away. Suppose you thought of it as a blank filing

card; the bright rectangular area might seem to be only inches from your eyes. In a case such as this, the observer does not have to analyze the situation at length in order to place an object. He makes an instant judgment as to what the object is, and he sees it at what he considers the appropriate distance.

If one object is partly covered by another, the covered one will appear to be farther away. This is called overlay. Elevation is another factor. Objects lying higher in the field of sight generally appear

How the lens, which is an elastic body, accommodates — that is, changes its shape — for far and near vision.

farther away than lower-lying ones. This effect is sometimes reversed; in that case the higher object seems nearer. Relative size also helps to localize objects; smaller ones seem farther away. Relative brightness is still another factor in determining apparent location. Usually the brighter of two otherwise similar objects seems to be nearer. An object appears to move toward the observer when it is made brighter, and to recede when it is dimmed.

Still another important factor in the localization of objects is parallax. This effect is obtained as one moves past objects or simply moves one's head. Certain objects will seem to stand still; others will

Rays from distant objects come to a focus in front of the retina.

seem to move in the direction opposite the observer's motion. The "still" objects will appear to lie beyond those that "move." For example, suppose the train on which one is riding moves past a telephone pole and a building. The pole will apparently move in a direction opposite that in which the train is moving, but the building will stand relatively still. The building will seem to be farther away.

The fact that we have binocular vision — that is, vision through two eyes — helps us to perceive depth. Each eye gets a somewhat different view of a given object, particularly at close range. When the two retinal images are interpreted together in the brain, we have a clear three-dimensional view. The depth of an object is not so clearly perceived when we look at it through one eye.

The interpretation of objects in the brain may not correspond to their actual appearance. In that case there will be a series of optical illusions. A number of such illusions are shown on the next page.

The vision of certain persons is limited or defective. The crystalline lens may refract rays of light effectively enough, but the retina is either farther away from the lens than in a normal eye or nearer to the lens. In such cases special artificial lenses, spherically curved, must be prepared in order to provide normal vision. These lenses may be set in spectacle frames or may be applied directly to the eyeball in the form of contact lenses (see Index).

In the condition called myopia, or nearsightedness, the eyeball is longer than it would be in normal eyes. When light rays are reflected from objects near to the eye, they focus properly on the retina. Distant rays, however, come to a focus in front of the retina. To correct this defect in vision, a concave (minus) artificial lens is placed in front of the eye. It diverges rays

and makes even parallel rays from far-off objects reach the lens of the eye as if they came from nearby objects. Hence the lens focuses them on the retina and not in front of it.

In farsightedness, or hyperopia, the eyeball is shorter than it would be in normal eyes. Rays reflected from far-off objects are focused properly on the retina; rays from nearby objects are focused behind it. A convex (plus) lens is used to remedy this defect.

Certain corrective lenses are in the form of prisms; they bend incoming rays of light so that the eyes need to converge ("turn in") either more or less than without glasses to obtain the same visual results. These lenses prevent one from seeing double. Other lenses are intended to remedy the condition called astigmatism, in which light rays are brought to focus on the retina not in the form of sharp points, but as short lines. Astigmatism is due to the fact that the crystalline lens has raised or depressed areas on its surface. A person suffering from this condition must wear lenses with raised or depressed areas to compensate for corresponding defects in the crystalline lens.

In fitting glasses, sharpness of vision, or visual acuity, is an important factor. There are several standard tests for visual acuity. One of the most common is the Snellen Chart. It consists of several lines of letters of different sizes. A person with normal vision will be able to read letters farther away than the person with poor visual acuity. A person is said to have 20/20 vision if at twenty feet (the standard distance) he can read letters that a person with normal vision can read at the same distance. If at twenty feet, a person can just read letters that are so big that the normal person can read them at forty feet, the person is said to have 20/40 vision.

Rays from objects near at hand come to a focus behind the retina.

OPTICAL ILLUSIONS

Things are not always what they seem when we use our senses to obtain information about the outer world. On this page we show how the sense of vision sometimes plays us false. For example, in the figure within the circle, at the right, the outer vertical lines will sometimes seem nearer to the eye than the central vertical line; sometimes they will seem farther away. In the next figure, the two diagonals are of the same length.

The two horizontal lines forming part of the two arrows at the left are equal in length. The two curved figures under the arrows (left) are equal. In the case of the circles within circles, the inner circle of one is equal to the outer circle of the other.

The curved figure set within the radiating lines is a true circle. The two heavy vertical lines in the next figure are straight and are parallel to each other. They certainly do not appear to be so.

If the eye of an observer were at the point where the four lines converge, he would not be able to distinguish between objects A, B, C, D and E. To one standing beside the observer, the objects would seem quite different.

The sense
of hearing

When we hear sounds, we really become aware of waves of air striking our ears. The waves arise as the result of vibrations caused by a disturbance such as the ringing of a bell or the tooting of a horn. The vibrations are set off in a series of alternating compressions and rarefactions. We describe the production and transmission of sounds elsewhere (see Index, under Sound).

All the air waves in our vicinity strike our ears, but not all produce the sensation of sound. Human ears register only the vibrations ranging from about 16 a second to between 20,000 and 30,000 a second: that is, having a frequency of from 16 to 20,000-30,000 cycles per second.

The ear, in which we receive the vibrations, is divided into three compartments —the outer ear, the middle ear and the inner ear. The outer ear is made up of two parts. One is a structure of cartilage and skin, called the auricle, or pinna. The other is a short canal — the auditory canal — which penetrates the bone of the skull and is closed at the inner end by a delicate membrane — the eardrum. The auricle is the part of the ear that protrudes from the side of the head; it serves to direct sound into the ear.* The sound waves entering the auditory canal set the eardrum, at the end of the canal, into motion. It vibrates in time with the air waves.

The middle ear is a small chamber, hollowed out in the skull bone. In this chamber, there are three small bones, called

* Animals such as horses or cats can turn their ears in the direction of a sound. Man cannot. It is true that a few persons can move (wiggle) their ears somewhat. The muscles that enable them to do so are rudimentary vestiges of the muscles that once enabled man to move his ears freely.

STRUCTURE OF EAR

SEMICIRCULAR CANALS

HAMMER

ANVIL

STIRRUP

COCHLEA

OVAL WINDOW

ROUND WINDOW

MIDDLE EAR

EUSTACHIAN TUBE

AUDITORY CANAL

AURICLE

H SEEIDEN

EARDRUM

ANVIL

HAMMER

EARDRUM

STIRRUP

ossicles, which are joined together; they form a connecting link between the eardrum and the inner ear. The ossicles act as a lever system, transmitting to the inner ear the vibrations that strike the eardrum. The outermost of the three bones is attached to the eardrum; because of its shape this bone is known as the hammer. The middle bone vaguely suggests an anvil; that is what it is called. The name stirrup, applied to the innermost bone, is very apt; the resemblance to a stirrup is quite striking. These bones are sometimes given the

The outer and middle ears serve only to transmit vibrations to the inner ear, where we find the basic organ of hearing. This is contained in a spiral chamber, called the cochlea ("snail shell," in Latin), which is imbedded in bone. The cochlea makes about two and a half turns. The inner ear also contains three semicircular canals and two small sacs; these structures have to do with the sense of balance, which we shall discuss later, and not with the sense of hearing. Only the cochlea is concerned with the latter sense.

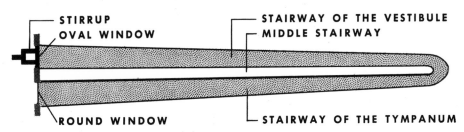

How the three tubes of the cochlea would look if they were removed from it and uncoiled.

Latin names malleus (meaning "hammer"), incus ("anvil") and stapes ("stirrup"). The footplate of the stirrup fits into an oval window, beyond which lies the inner ear; this window has a membrane stretched across it. A little below the oval window is a round window, also closed by a membrane.

A small tube, called the Eustachian tube, runs from the middle ear to the back of the nose. The middle ear connects by means of this tube with the outer air, whenever the tube is open. It opens only in the act of swallowing; whenever this takes place, air passes up the tube into the middle ear and causes the air pressure on both sides of the eardrum to be equalized. If the Eustachian tube is blocked because of a cold in the head, part of the air in the middle chamber is absorbed into the blood. There is then more pressure on the outside of the eardrum than on the inside, and the eardrum cannot vibrate freely. Sounds are imperfectly transmitted, and the person becomes slightly deaf. Infections of the middle ear may occur when organisms in the mouth or nose make their way into the middle ear by way of the Eustachian tube.

Within the cochlea is a tube which follows the windings of the "snail shell." This coiled tube is really made up of three adjacent tubes. Each of the three is called a staircase, or scala ("stairway," in Latin), because it suggests somewhat a spiral staircase. The first tube is called the stairway of the vestibule (scala vestibuli). At its base is the membrane of the oval window, to which the stirrup of the middle ear is attached. Next to the stairway of the vestibule is the middle stairway (scala media). Finally, there is the stairway of the tympanum (scala tympani), which has the round window at its base. The scala media contains a liquid called endolymph; the scala vestibuli and the scala tympani, a liquid called perilymph. Since the two outer tubes are connected with each other at the tip of the cochlea, it is evident that perilymph extends in a single channel from the oval window to the round window. In the diagram on this page, we show how the scala vestibuli, scala media and scala tympani would look if they were removed from the cochlea and were uncoiled.

The membrane separating the middle tube from the stairway of the tympanum is

ORGAN OF CORTI

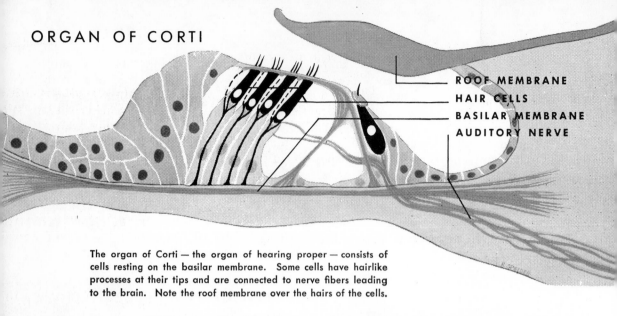

ROOF MEMBRANE
HAIR CELLS
BASILAR MEMBRANE
AUDITORY NERVE

The organ of Corti — the organ of hearing proper — consists of cells resting on the basilar membrane. Some cells have hairlike processes at their tips and are connected to nerve fibers leading to the brain. Note the roof membrane over the hairs of the cells.

known as the basilar membrane. It is made up of a great number of fine cross fibers. Upon it rest the cells that make up the organ of hearing proper — the so-called organ of Corti. Some of the cells, called hair cells, have hairlike processes at their tips. These cells are connected to nerve fibers that lead to the brain. Extending over the hairs of the cells like the eaves of a roof is a delicate membrane — the roof membrane, which can move freely.

When vibrations are transmitted to the oval window by way of the stirrup of the middle ear, the fluid in the stairway of the vestibule is alternately pushed inward and then outward again. Since the outer and inner tubes are connected at their tips, the movement of the fluid is transmitted to the round window. When the footplate of the stirrup pushes the oval window membrane inward, the membrane of the round window is moved outward. When the stirrup moves back toward the middle chamber, the movement is reversed. As a result of the to-and-fro movement, different parts of the basilar membrane are set to vibrating in turn. The hair cells resting on the vibrating part of the basilar membrane also move in unison, and impulses are generated in the appropriate nerve fibers. These impulses are transmitted to the brain.

Why does only a part of the basilar membrane vibrate at any one time? The cross fibers of the membrane increase in length; the longer ones are near the top of the spiral, the shorter ones near the bottom. Their rates of vibration depend upon their length. When a vibration of a given frequency — say, 1,500 cycles a second — is transmitted, only that part of the basilar membrane that has the same vibration rate will respond. This is called sympathetic resonance. (See Index, under Resonance.)

The sounds that are transmitted by the ear may be divided into two classes — tones and noises. Any sound having a fairly well-marked pitch is classified as a tone. Pitch is the quality of sound that enables us to classify it as higher or lower than another sound. Only if differences in pitch are clearly indicated, do we refer to sounds as tones rather than as mere noise. It is true that one type of noise — a rumble, say — may be lower than another — a rattle — but the difference between their sounds is not nearly so well defined as the difference between a C and D on a musical instrument, such as a violin or piano. Sounds vary not only in pitch but also in loudness, tone quality and duration. We analyze the different qualities of sounds in the article Musical Sounds, in Volume 5.

Sounds have the property of direction; they seem to come from somewhere. In certain cases they appear to come from the direction in which the vibrations are actually set up. But in many everyday situations the source of the sound may be a baffling mystery to the listener. A common example is the difficulty one has in locating a squeak or other noise that develops in an automobile. Many times the source of the noise cannot be discovered by listening. It may be necessary to determine the frequency range of the sound and then to test all possible sources of the squeak to see which one produces vibrations within this frequency range.

Often sounds appear to come from a plausible source (that is, from the place where we could expect them to arise), even though actually they arise elsewhere. This is one of the factors in ventriloquism. If the ventriloquist's dummy moves its lips while the lips of the ventriloquist remain motionless, the plausible source of sound would be the dummy. Therefore to us it seems that the dummy is talking and the ventriloquist is silent, even though the actual source of the sound is obvious enough if we give the matter any thought.

Sound movies and public-address systems involve ventriloquistic principles. When a movie is shown on a screen, the sound source may be located just behind the screen. Yet the sounds seem to come from a variety of plausible sources. We are not conscious of the fact that the faint sound of a trumpet in the distance originates in the same place as a "near-up" whisper uttered in a close-up. Of course this is also true of sound effects on the radio and TV.

When loud-speakers are distributed throughout a hall to transmit the voice of a speaker on a platform, the sounds you hear may come mainly from a place beside you or even behind you. This may prove to be annoying at first. In time, however, the sounds will appear to come from the plausible source — that is, from the speaker himself.

The sense of taste

The organs of taste are found chiefly on the tongue, though there are a few in other places, such as the soft palate and the epiglottis. The receptive structures for taste are called taste buds. They consist of bundles of cells, which open upon the surface of the tongue (or other area).

The cells have tufts of tiny hairs at these openings. The other ends of the cells are connected to nerve fibers leading to the brain. Substances in solution stimulate the cells through the hairs. It is important to note that unless a substance is dissolved in the mouth, it cannot be tasted. If you put a piece of lump sugar on your tongue, you will taste it only when it starts to dissolve. Ordinarily the saliva in the mouth dissolves foods sufficiently so that they can arouse the sense of taste.

There are at least four fundamental taste qualities — sweet, sour, bitter and salty. Some authorities add a fifth quality — alkaline. All other tastes result from a blending of these four (or five) and also from combinations of taste qualities with other types of sensations.

The basic taste sensations are not equally aroused in every part of the tongue's surface. The front part is particularly sensitive to sweet and salty substances. Bitter substances are tasted at the back of the tongue and also in the throat. Certain substances seem to affect more than one class of taste buds. For example, some substances may taste sweet when applied to the tip of the tongue, and bitter when applied to the back.

Taste sensations to which the different surfaces of the tongue are sensitive. A taste bud is shown at the left.

TASTE BUD

BITTER
SALT
SOUR
SWEET

The tongue is sensitive to touch, cold, heat and pain, and these sensations affect the sense of taste. Lumpy mashed potatoes do not taste quite the same as smooth mashed potatoes. It makes a difference, as far as taste is concerned, whether a food is dry or moist, soft or hard. A soda or other soft drink tastes sweeter when it is warm than when it is cold. Thresholds for saltiness, bitterness, sourness and sweetness vary with temperature, but not equally so.

Sometimes one hardly knows whether one is tasting or smelling a substance. Since the mouth and nose cavities are open to each other, particles derived from food in the mouth may ascend to the nose and stimulate the sense receptors there. This stimulation may be much more vigorous than the stimulation of the taste buds on the tongue. In such a case, taste sensations are mostly sensations of smell.

The senses of taste and smell differ greatly in the level of their thresholds. A solution of ethyl alcohol must be 24,000 times more concentrated to reach the taste threshold than to reach the threshold of smell. Only minute quantities of the gases given off from foods are needed to excite the sense of smell. That is why this sense is so often involved when we taste things. If one has a cold, and the mucous membrane of the nose is inflamed, the sense receptors of the nose will not be stimulated. The result will be that the food we eat at such a time may seem tasteless, because we cannot smell it as we chew it.

The sense of smell

The sense of smell is far more important for the lower animals than it is for man. It provides the members of many animal species with invaluable information concerning the outside world. It leads them to food, warns them of danger and helps them to select their mates. In man the sense of smell is generally quite rudimentary. There are exceptions, however. Certain primitive peoples can track down their quarry by the sense of smell. It is said that when one of the other senses is lost, the sense of smell may be developed so that it can partly compensate for the lost sense.

The cells involved in the sense of smell are in the mucous membrane of the topmost part of the nasal passages.

SITE OF
THE SENSE
OF SMELL

OLFACTORY AREA

UPPER
TURBINATE
BONE

MIDDLE
TURBINATE
BONE

LOWER
TURBINATE
BONE

We smell a substance because molecules are constantly thrown off from it in the form of vapor or dust and make their way up the nose. Very small amounts of such vapor or dust can be smelled. If only $\frac{1}{460,000,000}$ of a milligram of mercaptan, a substance smelling like garlic, is contained in a whiff of air, it can be detected. This is a remarkably small amount when we consider that a milligram is only $\frac{35}{1,000,000}$ of an ounce. However, in terms of molecules, the amount is not so small, since it contains some 21,000,000,000 molecules.

If a substance throws off a great many molecules in a short time, it will have a strong smell. This happens, for example, when gasoline fumes arise. On the other

SURFACE OF MUCOUS MEMBRANE

FILAMENTS

NERVE

Close-up of the cells involved in smell. Note the little hairs projecting above the mucous-membrane surface.

hand, a substance will have practically no odor if few molecules are emitted. This is true of most metals. However, when metals are heated to a high temperature, molecules are thrown off in quantity, and there will be a strong odor. The strength of the smell sensation does not always depend on the number of molecules a substance releases. Certain substances, such as musk, may give off a strong fragrance for years and yet remain practically unchanged in size and weight.

The organs of smell are located in the mucous membrane of the uppermost part of the nasal passages, away from the direct path of the stream of air drawn in through the nostrils. The cells involved in smell — the olfactory cells — are embedded in the mucous membrane. A long filament of protoplasm leads from each cell to the surface of the mucous membrane; tiny hairs project above this surface from the fila-

ment. A nerve fiber leads from the other end of the cell through a tiny aperture in the floor of the skull to the olfactory lobe of the brain. The surface of the mucous membrane in the olfactory area is bathed in fluid. The particles that are to be smelled must be dissolved in this fluid before the olfactory cells can be stimulated.

We pointed out that the currents of air drawn in from the nostrils do not pass directly through the olfactory area. However, particles of the odor-releasing substance are carried upward to the area by eddies that arise as the currents of cold air from the outside meet the warm air already in the nasal passages. If we want to sharpen the sense of smell as we become aware of a faint odor, we sniff vigorously — that is, we draw in short, vigorous breaths. This causes a reinforced stream of cold air to penetrate the nasal passages. The upward currents become stronger, and more molecules of the odorous substance come in contact with the olfactory area.

The sense of smell is a quickly adapting process. This means that when one is exposed to an odoriferous (odor-producing) substance for a short time, he finds the smell much less noticeable than at first or he may not even notice it any more. That is why people who have been in a room for some time are surprised when a newcomer complains, say, of the odor of stale tobacco smoke. They have become so adapted to the odor that for them it does not exist.

Various attempts have been made to classify odors, but they have not been particularly successful. About all we can do is to say that one substance smells like roses, another like garlic, and a third like almonds.

Touch and the other skin senses

When the skin is stimulated, several different sensations can be aroused — sensations of touch, pressure, heat, cold and pain. All of these, except the sensation of pain, depend on the presence of specialized sense organs at the end of nerve fibers. The nerve fibers responsible for sensations of pain have no special structures at their terminal points in the skin. The different kinds of skin receptors are shown in the diagram on this page. The receptors responsible for touch, pressure, heat and cold each respond to only one type of stimulus. The nerve endings that register sensations of pain can react to different kinds of stimulation.

The various kinds of sense receptors are not evenly distributed on the skin. It is possible to map out various spots where different types of stimuli take effect in a particular skin area. There are touch spots, heat spots, cold spots, pressure spots. Certain areas of the skin are much more sensitive than others to a given type of stimulation. For example, the finger tips are very sensitive to touch, much more so than the back of the hand. Pain fibers are found in every area; they form an extensive network.

The sense of touch. We can show the different reactions to the sense of touch in different skin areas by applying two points

point threshold is quite low for the tip of the tongue; when we let this part of the tongue pass over the teeth, a tiny cavity will be felt as a huge pit.

The skin adapts readily to the touch of an object that makes contact with it, to such an extent that the feeling of contact will soon disappear entirely unless the object is kept moving over the skin. We also need change in stimulation when we examine surfaces by touch. We must rub our fingers constantly over a substance if we are to have a good idea of its surface texture. If we put our finger tip on a piece of sandpaper and let it remain there, it will be impossible to tell whether the finger is resting on rough sandpaper or smooth glass.

The sense of pressure. If we lightly touch the skin with a rigid object, such as a matchstick, the sensation of touch will be aroused. If we press more firmly, we will experience a sensation of pressure. This is due to the stimulation of certain sense receptors, called Pacinian capsules, which

Left: skin receptors for touch, cold, warmth, pressure and pain. Only the receptor that is responsible for pain has no special structure. Right: how different sensations can be aroused by different types of skin contact.

simultaneously to the skin. When the two are very close together, they feel like a single point. As they are gradually placed farther apart, a stage will be reached at which they will just barely be felt as two points. This is called the two-point threshold. The more sensitive to touch a given area of the body surface is, the smaller the two-point threshold will be. It is much smaller on the arm than on the back, and still smaller on the finger tips. The two-

are found in the underlying tissues of the skin. As we increase the pressure, the sensation becomes duller and more pervasive. Finally, if the pressure is increased still more, there will be a sensation of pain.

The senses of heat and cold. If we are to become aware of warmth or cold, something that is at a higher or lower temperature than normal skin temperature — about 78° F. — must be applied to the skin. The sensitivity to warmth will extend to

SEMICIRCULAR CANALS

ANTERIOR CANAL
LATERAL CANAL
POSTERIOR CANAL
UTRICLE
SACCULE

CROSS SECTION OF UTRICLE

HAIR CELLS · OTOLITHS

The semicircular canals, utricle and saccule, in the ear, have to do with balance. The semicircular canals occupy different planes. One is horizontal; the second, vertical; the third vertical, at right angles to the second.

a level about 35° above 78°, or 113° F.; sensitivity to cold will extend to about 35° below 78°, or 43° F. The sensations aroused by temperatures above 113° F. and below 43° F. are identical; it is no longer possible to distinguish between heat and cold at such temperatures.

The sense of vision has quite a good deal to do with our experiences of warmth and cold. Some things look warm, others cold. Again and again we are genuinely surprised when we touch an object and find that the sense of temperature does not confirm the impression provided by the sense of sight.

The sense of pain. Pain may be caused by a rigid or sharp object pressed firmly into the skin. However, we pointed out that the nerve endings responsible for sensations of pain can react to different kinds of stimuli. Pain may be aroused by the application of an electric current, by con-

tact with chemicals, by mechanical effects, such as the cutting or tearing of tissue. It may also result when heat or cold is applied. The sensation of pain is a protective device. It warns us of possible danger to the body.

The "control senses" — balance and kinesthesia

Certain senses help us control the reactions of the body to various external stimuli. Among these "control senses" is the sense of balance or equilibrium. It is centered in certain structures of the ear — the semicircular canals and the two sacs known as the utricle and the saccule.*

The three semicircular canals are membranous tubes, filled with fluid. Each leads from the utricle, describes a half circle and then returns to the utricle. The canals

* As we shall see, it is not certain that the saccule is concerned with balance.

occupy different planes. One is horizontal; another is vertical; the third is also vertical but at right angles to the second. One end of each canal forms a swelling, called an ampulla; this contains receptor structures, from which nerve fibers lead.

The nerve endings in the ampulla are stimulated by movements of fluid in the canal. These movements arise when there is a quick turning motion of the head or of the body as a whole — as, for example, when a dancer pirouettes on one foot. Each canal is stimulated most strongly when the turning motion is in the same plane as the canal itself. The movement causes a flow of fluid into the ampulla and stimulates the receptor cells there. It produces consciousness of the rotation; it also brings about reflexes that keep the body in proper equilibrium. If the semicircular canals are diseased or destroyed, serious disturbances of balance arise.

The sac called the utricle contains tiny bodies, called otoliths, which are attached to the hairs of sensitive hair cells. When the head is tilted, the otoliths, responding to the force of gravity, pull upon the hairs of certain hair cells. As the cells are stimulated, they cause righting reflexes — that is, reflex muscular movements that tend to bring the head and body to a normal position. Seasickness and other kinds of motion sickness are probably caused by repeated stimulation of the hair cells in the utricle.

We know little about the functions of the other sac — the saccule, which is considerably smaller than the utricle. Some believe that the saccule is also concerned with the sense of balance; others think that it has to do with the sense of hearing.

Another "control sense" is kinesthesia, or the muscle sense; it has to do with the control of the muscles. Kinesthesia ("movement sensitivity," in Greek) is based on receptors in the voluntary muscles, tendons and joints. These receptors register muscular contractions or elongations; they supply information about the state of tension of the muscles and the position of the limbs. The muscle sense helps us control reflex movements. They cause the re-

flex not to "trigger off" too readily; they help sustain a reflex movement.

The muscle sense also helps us coordinate voluntary movements of the muscles. When kinesthetic impulses are lacking, muscular movements are apt to go wide of the mark. A person will often reach in the wrong direction or will bump into things or will go past objects he wishes to grasp. These ill effects vary in extent from one part of a limb to another. They are most marked at the extremities; the fingers are affected more than the wrists, and the hand more than the forearm. In all these cases, there is nothing wrong with the muscles themselves or with the nerve tracts that supply them.

The muscle sense helps us judge the weight of objects. This is because kinesthetic impulses relay to the brain the amount of effort that the muscles require to heft an object. Usually the senses of touch and sight are also involved.

**Other kinds
of sensations**

Certain sensations supply us with information about conditions in the interior of the body. There are sensations of hunger, thirst, nausea and fullness of the rectum, all of which are described in the article The Digestive Tract, in Volume 4. The sense of pain may also be experienced from within the body.

There may be acute pain when the large intestine is distended because of gas formation or when a stone obstructs the bile duct or when circulation in the heart muscle is interrupted. The inner surface of the abdominal wall is sensitive to various types of stimuli that bring about the sensation of pain. Yet apparently the nerve fibers that carry this sensation are not so widely distributed in the inner part of the body as on its outer surface. Almost any one of the internal organs can be cut or crushed or even burned without causing pain. We feel no pain when the gray matter of the cerebrum (the largest part of the brain) is cut or even removed.

For further reading see Vol. 10, p. 276:
"General Works"; "Physiology."

THE BEAR AND HIS COUSINS

Bears, Pandas, Raccoons and Others

THE bears, which include the largest modern land-dwelling carnivores, or flesh eaters, number certain quite diminutive animals among their kin. At first glance, the huge, lumbering grizzly bear, say, would seem to have little in common with the small, tree-dwelling raccoon. But a brief survey of the evolution of the carnivores will show conclusively that these two animals are really cousins.

Many of the earliest mammals were insect eaters; some of these forms merely needed to increase their size and modify their teeth a bit to become true carnivores. Consequently, as the hoofed, vegetation-eating mammals evolved, there developed a group of flesh eaters to prey upon them. These carnivores had piercing canine teeth, as well as shearing teeth, or carnassials, for cutting through tough sinews and cracking bone. Since flesh is relatively simple to digest and does not need to be vigorously chewed, the grinding molar teeth were much reduced or were completely lost in the course of time. These primitive carnivores — called creodonts by scientists — were rather slow-moving and were decidedly stupid. However, they seem to have had no trouble in coping with their equally clumsy and stupid prey.

In time the early hoofed mammals were supplanted by faster and more intelligent beasts. A carnivore that hoped to make a meal of these creatures would have to be clever enough to stalk them and speedy enough to overtake them. Of the creodonts, only one line, called the miacids, developed these qualities. The earliest miacids were about as large as weasels; they were largely tree dwellers. From the miacids developed the two modern groups of land-living carnivores. The civets, hyenas and cats comprised one group; the weasels, dogs, raccoons and bears, the other.

The dogs retained the use of some of their grinding teeth, for they were not so restricted to a diet of flesh as were some of the other carnivores, such as the cats. The raccoons, giant pandas and true bears — all descendants of primitive members of the dog family — departed still further from the carnivorous way of life.

The raccoons and their kin gradually abandoned the practice of using certain teeth to shear food, but they developed excellent grinding teeth. They added to their diet of frogs, shellfish and small mammals such food as birds' eggs, fruits, nuts and corn. The bears supplemented their meat diet with grasses, berries, fruits, seaweed (in the case of the polar bears) and roots. The grinding teeth of the bears were enlarged for chewing this vegetable matter; the shearing function of the carnassials was gradually lost.

The bears, which are found in every continent, except Australia, are divided into several distinct groups. The black bears of the United States and Canada are closely related to the great brown bears and the grizzlies. The semiaquatic polar bear, too, is closely akin to these members of the family. The honey bear of India and the Malayan sun bear, however, are more distantly related, as is the spectacled bear of South America.

All bears have heavy, long fur and stubby tails. The skeleton is massive; the limbs are strong and are furnished with powerful claws for digging and for fighting. The bear has a shuffling, flat-footed gait, called plantigrade; the sole of its foot is placed upon the ground, leaving a footprint much like that of a man.

Bears are normally slow-moving animals; yet they can break into a lumbering gallop. The black bear can run at a speed of up to twenty-five miles an hour. The big brown bear has a peculiar pacing gait. In this, first the two legs of one side are raised and brought forward together, and then the two legs of the opposite side. The brown bear will sometimes gallop for a mile or more straight up a steep slope without stopping to rest.

Usually only young grizzly and black bears climb, but older individuals, if not prevented by excess weight or large size, occasionally take to a tree. Bears climb by literally hugging the trunk or a branch with all four limbs and hitching their way upward. They carefully back down the same way. Bears will swim across swiftly flowing rivers and navigate lakes of at least five miles in width. Polar bears are excellent divers and swimmers; they have often been sighted, in polar waters, miles from the nearest land.

Bears live from sea level to high mountain country, inhabiting swamps, forests, tundras, snow fields and upland meadows. Black bears, grizzlies and brown bears confine their wanderings to a fairly restricted home range. In this area they forage for food, both by day and night, seek mates during the breeding season and spend the winter in some sheltering spot.

These bears make trails through their home ranges — trails that are followed by the same individuals for years and often used by other bears that happen to be in that particular area. Bear trails along salmon streams and in heavy forests are like any game trail that leads through dense vegetation. On the tundra, big brown bears often establish trails that consist of two parallel ruts, like the ruts of a wagon trail, but, of course, much closer together. Brown bears sometimes walk their range by stepping in the same footprints they made in the past. The result is a trail formed by a series of deep pits laid out in a zigzag pattern.

Bears let their presence be known by so-called bear trees. Often such trees stand conspicuously beside a bear trail. They are marked by smooth places where a bear has rubbed itself or by jagged wounds where the bear has clawed at the bark. Strands of hair adhere to the bark and stick to the pitch that oozes from the claw marks. Sometimes bears strip the bark from trees and scrape off the pulp that covers the wood, leaving tooth marks where the pulp has been removed.

Feeding signs also reveal the presence of bears. Ground-squirrel burrows that have been dug into and ant hills that have been scooped out show where a bear has fed and on what it has preyed. Overturned and smashed logs and rolled-over rocks are signs that a bear has been searching for ants and beetles; a patch of uprooted vegetation may mean a bear has dug for roots. Bee trees are ripped apart for their contents of both honey and bee brood. Since bears cover leftover portions of food with debris, the discovery of such a cache signifies that a bear is active in the vicinity.

Food is fairly hard to come by when snows cover the land; consequently, most bears sleep the winter through. They bed down in a sheltering cavity among rocks or in a hollow under an upturned log; if need be, a den is excavated in the side of a hill. The winter's sleep is not really hibernation, for the bear sleeps less profoundly than do true hibernators, and its body temperature remains close to normal. During this period, she-bears give birth to their tiny, undeveloped cubs. Two is the usual number, but three or four cubs are not uncommon.

The polar bear — a powerful carnivore of the Far North

Polar bears frequent ice floes, islands and coastal areas of the arctic regions. They are large, magnificent animals, the males measuring 7 to 8 feet in length and weighing 600 to 1,100 pounds; females are somewhat smaller. Polar bears are all white or yellowish white, except for their black eyes, nose pads and foot pads. Unlike other bears, only pregnant female polar bears den up during the winter. The males and barren females prowl the sea ice and open water in search of prey.

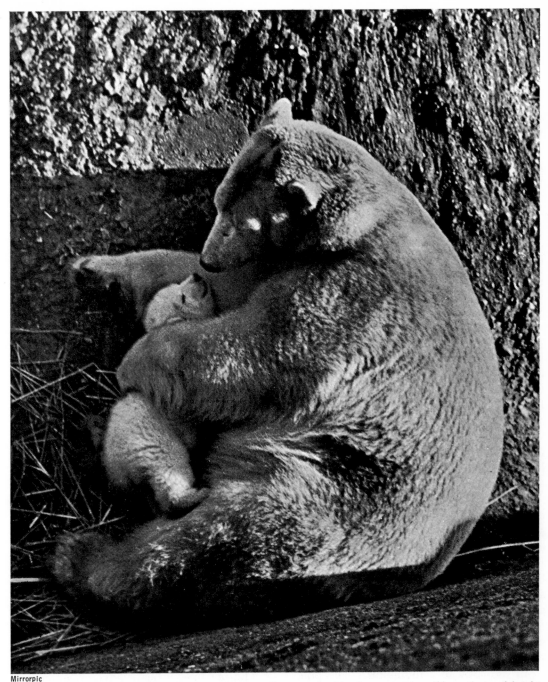

Mirrorpic

A famous polar-bear family. Brumas, an eleven-weeks-old cub, tempted by mild weather and bright sun, makes her first appearance at the London Zoo. She is held in the firm embrace of mother-bear Ivy.

Throughout the long winter, then, the female lies beneath the snow, and there brings forth her young. She must have within her system a sufficient reserve not only to support her own life during this long period, but to afford milk to her cubs as well.

These usually number two. They are born naked, blind, and helpless, unable even to wriggle a few inches to their dam's side should they be disturbed. Thus hidden in the close confinement of their snowy lair there is not much danger of their being lost in this way, of course.

The lair, dug by the female polar bear before she has her cubs, is a trim burrow in the ice or packed snow. One of these dens, which was found dug at the foot of an iceberg, tunneled downward through the ice for a short distance at an angle of something like forty-five degrees; then it angled upward for a certain space and finally terminated in an oval chamber. Lairs such as this one are temporary shelters, however, for the mother and her cubs abandon them by late February or March.

The mother polar bear is devoted to her cubs

The female polar bear has proven to be one of the most devoted of mammal mothers. She stands over her little cubs to shield them from fierce blasts of icy winds. She helps them cross open stretches of water between ice masses by towing them as they hang on to her body; sometimes she carries them on her back. There are many travelers' tales telling of the heroism displayed by mother polar bears in defense of their young against human enemies. Though mortally wounded, the mother bear will stay by her cubs and protect them to the last. If they are wounded, she will lick their wounds and try to urge them away or guard them from further harm.

The polar bear is slender of body with a long neck and a small tapering head. Its streamlined shape enables the animal to knife through the water most gracefully. It uses its front legs for swimming, while the hind limbs trail behind to function as a rudder. Oil glands in the skin oil the fur effectively so that it sheds water and keeps the body dry. A fatty layer below the skin protects against the cold, and the thick fur holds little air spaces that keep heat loss from the body to a minimum. The polar bear has broad feet, the soles of which are heavily haired to prevent slipping as the animal travels swiftly and tirelessly over the ice.

This bear shows great skill in stalking its prey. When it sees a seal basking on an ice floe close to the water's edge, the bear paddles in the water, carefully approaching the quarry. Only the bear's head appears above the surface and it resembles a bit of floating ice. If the seal rears up to look about, the hunter remains motionless, drifting. Finally the bear is near enough! It quietly sinks below the surface, swims under water the remaining distance and comes up in a thunderous thrust to knock down the prey with a heavy blow of the paw. The bear uses similar tactics to capture eider ducks and scoters that are resting on the surface of the Arctic waters. With only its eyes and nose visible, the bear swims quietly among a flock of these birds. When a bird dives in alarm, the polar bear quickly overtakes it under the water.

Sometimes the polar bear waits patiently at a hole in the ice; when a seal pokes its head up to breathe, the hunter quickly makes the kill. Water animals are not its only prey; it often tracks down caribou and the Arctic fox. It generally refrains from attacking big male walruses when they are in the water; these animals would be dangerous foes. The polar bear often feasts on the decaying remains of a beached whale, sharing the repast with others of its kind and even with foxes. The animal's sense of smell is so keen that it is said that it can scent a stranded whale, even if the carcass is covered with snow, at a distance of twenty miles.

Polar bears usually hunt alone, though the females are accompanied by their young. From May to July is the mating season, when the adult male and female travel together. Eskimos seem to be their only enemies. Polar bears have been known to live to be thirty-four years of age.

Big brown bears range over the Northern Hemisphere

The big brown bears have an extensive range over the mountainous and forested areas of the Northern Hemisphere; consequently, there are many local races of these bears, which differ from one another in color and minor characteristics. There are brown bears in the Pyrenees, the eastern Italian Alps, the Balkan Peninsula, northern Scandinavia and Finland. They occur in northern and central Asia.

The Syrian bear is a light-colored brown bear of the mountains from Turkey to Iran; the isabelline bear is native to the Himalayas; a darker race lives on Hokkaido Island, Japan, and on the Kuriles and Sakhalin Island in the Sea of Okhotsk. The big brown bears of North America inhabit the coastal regions of Alaska and adjacent islands, frequenting especially those rivers running with salmon. The closely related grizzly bears live in the Rockies through British Columbia and Alaska.

Grizzlies and brown bears are large animals that often cannot be easily told apart. They both have humps at their shoulders and their heads are massive, though the brown bear's head is larger. The claws of the brown bear are of moderate length and deeply curved; those of the grizzly are long and straight. Usually the big brown bear, which may stand almost five feet at the shoulder, has a uniformly yellowish to dark brown coat. The grizzly has a more frosted appearance due to the fact that the hairs, especially those on the back, are tipped with white. This bear's shoulder height does not often exceed three and a half feet.

Though brown bears and grizzlies eat many kinds of foods, this diet often varies with the season. A survey of what grizzlies eat shows that in the spring they dig up roots; in June and July they feed on reed grass and horsetail and, when op-portunity arises, on rabbits, young caribou and mountain sheep. In August and September they thrive on berries. Ground squirrels are eaten at any time, as are the remains of animals left by wolves.

Usually grizzlies and brown bears restrict their hunting activities to a definite territory, or home range. The home range of the Alaskan grizzly covers about sixty-five square miles. The grizzly is said to mark the boundaries of its range, as a sign to other bears, by making teeth and claw marks on trees as high as it can reach. The brown bear of Russia roams over an area of ten to thirteen square miles. Brown bears leave "scent signals" to indicate their territory by rubbing the back against a tree and leaving urine at its base.

Brown bear young, born in January or February, are only rat-size at birth. The mother transports each infant by carrying the cub with its head held in her mouth. The young develop slowly, and they are not mature, that is able to reproduce their kind, until about six years of age. These bears hear well but they have a better nose for detecting game. Since their flesh is not particularly good, their only enemy seems to be the so-called sportsman who is out to get a trophy. These animals adopt a defensive attitude toward humans. A brown bear will not attack a man unless he blocks its path or molests a she bear that is accompanied by its cubs.

N. Y. Zool. Soc.

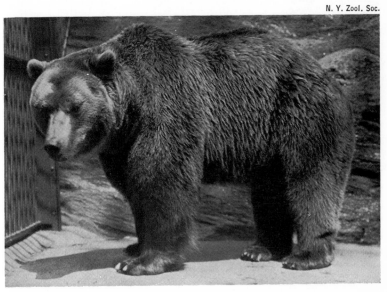

A magnificent example of the Alaskan brown bear. The big brown bears are the world's largest carnivores.

During the winter the brown bear hibernates, seeking the shelter of a tree or cave. It may scrape a hole beneath a fallen tree or it may enlarge a burrow begun by another animal. When it goes to rest, it has a large store of fat on which to live during the winter months. Instinct tells the animal when it has accumulated enough to last it through the winter. If food has been scarce during the preceding season, the bear may have to delay its winter sleep. During hibernation, only the bear's essential life functions remain in operation — respiration and circulation. All others are suspended.

In January or February, the female bear gives birth to one to four bear cubs; the number is generally two. The cubs are blind at birth and weigh about one and a half pounds. They first see the light of day in April or May when the mother bear emerges from her winter home. The cubs remain with her for the first two years of their lives.

When the bear emerges from its hibernation in the spring, it is lean and hungry after supporting itself and perhaps several cubs on the fat of its own body during the winter. It feeds voraciously at this time on both vegetation and flesh. It may even raid cattle and sheep herds.

The great brown bears of the north

In the northern parts of North America, Europe and Asia, there are a number of brown bears of great size. Many of them are local subraces, each occurring in only a very small range; they may even be restricted to a single island. For example, the famous Kadiak (or Kodiak) bears are found only in Kadiak (or Kodiak) Island off Alaska. These giant beasts may reach a length of ten feet and weigh more than 1,500 pounds. They are the largest land-living carnivores in existence. They eat both vegetation and animal food.

Another interesting local race is the Kamchatka bear of northeastern Asia. This Asian giant lives entirely on salmon that it catches while wading in a river. It does not knock the fish out of the water with its paw as many people believe. Actually the animal spears its prey on its claws and then leaves the river to eat the fish on land. The Kamchatka bear will never feed while standing in the water.

The Sitka bear is a smaller (though still very large) local race; the Yakutat and Kidder's bears on the mainland of Alaska are huge animals. All the Alaskan bears are reported to be less fierce than the grizzly, though far exceeding the latter in size. Nevertheless, the big-game hunter must be on his guard against them.

The powerful grizzly — the most dangerous of all

At one time, the grizzly bear (*Ursus horribilis*) was the scourge of North America from the badlands of Dakota to the coast of California. As time went on, large numbers of these bears were poisoned and hunted down by ranchers whose flocks they were raiding. As a result, the animal is now quite scarce. It usually reaches about six and a half feet in length and may weigh up to 1,400 pounds. Although not so large as its northern cousin, this bear is far more savage. *Ursus horribilis* is considered by many hunters to be the most dangerous of all North American wild animals. Its terrible claws are highly developed and are wielded by the grizzly with great effectiveness. Grizzlies have been known to kill full-grown bull bisons with a single blow on the neck with a paw. It is said that these bears can drag away a male wapiti weighing a thousand pounds.

The various types of American bears

There is a confusing variety in both size and coloring in the bears of North America. Consequently, naturalists differ widely in their classifications of the different species. One view holds that there are only three true species of bears in North America: the black bears; the grizzlies and brown bears; and the polar bears. According to this view, all of the other varieties are subspecies. Others describe as many as ten different species of North American bears.

The American black bear is the smallest of North American bears. It grows to a length of five or six feet and stands two to three feet at the shoulder. Its claws are comparatively short and curved. The encroachment of human civilization at one time threatened the existence of this animal over much of its territory; but laws for its protection and the bear's own resourcefulness have insured its survival. A forest and swamp dweller, the black bear inhabits much of Canada and Alaska, the eastern mountains from Maine to Florida, the Rockies and the mountains of the West Coast. In the east, the bear usually wears a coat of glossy black; in the west, however, many black bears are reddish brown and are known as cinnamon bears. There is even a creamy white variety of black bear, called Kermode's bear, living on Gribbell Island, British Columbia.

An extremely powerful animal for its size, this carnivore usually hunts, day or night, for the smaller animals such as rodents, frogs and insects. It also eats berries and roots and supplements its diet with an odd assortment of foods, including pine cones, skunk cabbage, river-clam shells, briars and wasps' nests! The nests

of bees and wasps are robbed of honey and the young insects.

Black bears are ordinarily solitary animals living in a well-defined home territory. Trees with clawed and chewed bark indicate that a bear lives in the area. Sometimes several bears congregate at a feeding ground, such as a berry patch or garbage dump. Relations among them may be peaceable but often fights take place.

The sexually mature males and females associate during the breeding season, which lasts approximately one month in June or July. After mating, the bears go their separate ways, the male having nothing to do with the raising of the family. Like other bears, black bears den up in rocky cavities, hollow trees or beds of dense foliage for a prolonged winter sleep. In late January or February, cubs are born — usually one cub to a female having her first offspring and two or three young to an older female.

The newborn cubs have a thin coat of fine hair and are blind and toothless. They are about nine inches long and weigh less than ten ounces. In March or April, when the cubs weigh four pounds, they leave the winter's den with their mother. She continues to nurse them for some time, but they also eat other foods. The cubs box and wrestle each other and engage in

Giant, or short-tailed, panda, dwelling in bamboo forests in eastern Asia. It is smaller than a black bear.

The American black bear. This animal is found in a number of forested regions of North America, north of Mexico. It climbs trees easily, travels about a great deal and is often captured and tamed. A kindred species, the Himalayan black bear, ranges from eastern Iran to the island of Formosa (Taiwan).

games of hide-and-seek. When in danger, they scurry up a tree if they cannot reach their mother. The young remain with the mother through the following winter. In the wilds, black bears probably live from twelve to fifteen years. The females are sexually mature at three years; they mate about once every two years.

In Asia, there are three species of black bears. The most widespread is the Himalayan black bear, which ranges from the eastern portion of Iran through Afghanistan, Tibet and Thailand into China and Manchuria. It is also found on the islands of Hainan and Formosa. Somewhat smaller than the American black bear, it is further distinguished by a light-colored, inverted crescent or Y-shaped patch on its chest. The hair on the neck is long, giving the animal a sort of ruff. This bear is a forest creature, living on grain, honey, roots, fruits and grasses.

The Malayan sun bear, or bruang, is a slightly smaller species restricted to the Malay peninsula and the islands east to Borneo. It has a crescent of white or orange on its chest similar to that of the Himalayan black bear. The animal is an excellent tree-climber. It has a very flexible tongue and lips, which it uses in feeding on insects and honey.

A more specialized insectivorous bear is the sloth bear of India. This creature differs from the rest of the bear family in having two less teeth than the normal quota, a long snout and a baggy, hanging lower lip. The shaggy beast lives on fruits, flowers, honey and insects; it is particularly fond of white ants, or termites, which are its natural prey. Its immensely powerful claws enable it to tear open the hills of these insects. The sloth bear's extraordinary powers of suction then come into play as it draws ants from deep within the nest by a violent intake of breath.

The spectacled bear of the Andes, in South America, is a close relative of the sun bear. It is a small, black species, ranging in the mountains from Colombia to Chile. The name is derived from the whitish, spectaclelike rings about the animal's eyes. It is the only bear in South America and the only member of the bear family found in the Southern Hemisphere. It lives primarily on fruits.

The panda is related to the raccoon

When the giant panda was first discovered in 1869 by the French missionary Armand David it was believed to be a bear with abnormal coloring because it had so many bearlike characteristics. It was classified with the bears for a long time; but as zoologists came to know more about the animal, they realized that it is more closely related to the raccoon. The giant panda reaches a length of about six feet and weighs over two hundred pounds. Like the members of the bear family, it has plantigrade feet, strong claws and a short, stumpy tail; however, it has two less teeth than the ordinary bear. In coloring, the panda is white or cream-colored, except for areas of black around its eyes, ears, legs and shoulders. The animal lives in Tibet and southwestern China at elevations of from 6,000 to 14,000 feet above sea level. Its diet is made up almost exclusively of bamboo shoots. Very few of these animals have been exhibited in zoos.

The true panda, or lesser panda, as it is more commonly known, is a bushy-tailed animal about the size of a large cat. Its back and head may be brown, red or chestnut. Black is the color of its underside, legs, feet and ears; the ears are trimmed with white. The face is white below the eyes and there are white spots above them. On the ground the true panda is slow-moving, but it is an excellent tree-climber. Like the giant panda, it lives mainly on bamboo shoots, but in captivity it will eat bread and milk, eggs and small birds. It hisses like a cat, growls like a bear and laps, at times, like a dog. Generally, however, it plunges its muzzle into water and drinks by suction, after the manner of a bear. The true panda can partially retract its claws, like a cat. The animal is a native of Asia, but formerly ranged over Europe to the British Isles, at a time when this region had a subtropical climate and was abundantly forested.

The raccoons — "washing-bears"

The German name for the raccoon is *Waschbaer,* which means "washing bear." It is derived from the fact that this little bearlike mammal washes its food before eating it whenever water is available. The raccoon is quite closely related to the bear; for one thing, like the bear, it has plantigrade feet. Raccoons have the same number of teeth as sloth bears and pandas. Internally, too, there are anatomical similarities among these animals.

The raccoon is particularly noted, perhaps, for its food-washing habits. Although not an aquatic animal, it usually lives near water. When it captures food, the raccoon carries it to the nearest water, and holding it squirrel-fashion in its front paws, dabbles it again and again in the water, before putting it in its mouth. It is interesting to note that in this operation the raccoon makes remarkable use of its fore paws as "hands"; it uses them as dexterously as most monkeys.

The common raccoon of the United States and Canada is about as big as a domestic cat, but the length of its legs and the bushiness of its coat make it appear larger. The back is highest over the hindquarters. The head is triangular; patches of black over the eyes give the face a "banditlike" appearance.

The varied diet of the raccoon

The raccoon has a varied diet. It is fond of frogs, crayfish, oysters and other shellfish; it also eats birds' eggs, poultry, mice, nuts, fruits and corn. The raccoon's appetite for ears of corn when they are young and tender arouses the particular animosity of farmers. They often hunt it down with dogs when it makes raids on their fields or chickens. The dogs drive the animal into a tree where it can easily be caught.

Raccoon attacks on chicken farms and corn fields are particularly bothersome to the farmer because these animals are so clever and so destructive. It is particularly difficult for the farmer to catch them because they seek their food only at night. In the daytime the raccoon sleeps, generally in the hollow of a tree. When it attacks chickens, the animal usually kills far more birds than it can possibly eat. Corn-field raids are equally destructive, because the raccoon not only greedily devours many ears of corn but also knocks down a number of stalks.

Raccoons find most of their food on the ground, but they generally live in hollows in trees because it is so much safer for them. They hibernate in these places of refuge in the colder parts of their range; it is in the trees that their young are born. The raccoon is quite wary, although it has relatively few enemies other than man. It is adept in climbing trees and often uses this way of escape when danger threatens. Despite man's persecution of the animal, its existence has not been threatened; in fact it is increasing in number in some areas.

Raccoons make interesting pets

When taken into captivity, young raccoons make interesting, although somewhat troublesome pets, because of their restlessness and insatiable curiosity. "Nothing," writes Godman, "can possibly exceed the domesticated raccoon in restless and mischievous curiosity if suffered to go about the house. Every chink is ransacked, every article of furniture explored, and the neglect of servants to close closet doors is sure to be followed by extensive mischief." As we have seen, the animal soaks its food in water; it also likes to play with water. A tubful should always be provided for a pet raccoon. This is one of the most playful of animals. Referring to his two raccoon pets, Godman writes: "They are frequently seen sitting on the edge of [a] tub, very busily engaged in playing with a piece of broken china, glass or a small cake of ice. When they have any substance which sinks, they both paddle with their forefeet with great eagerness until it is caught, and then it is held by one, with both paws, and rubbed between them; or a struggle ensues for possession of it. When it is dropped the same sport is renewed."

Raccoons choose as a home a hollow in a tree, which is made smooth within but which is not lined with straw or other materials. Only in the colder parts of the United States are the raccoons confined to their dens in winter. Moderate cold does not trouble them nor interfere greatly with their hunting, which in winter, in the northern states, is chiefly for mice. Three or four cubs are born in May, and by late autumn they are quite large enough to fend for themselves.

Several other animals are members of the raccoon family — the cacomistle, which dwells in well-watered woods; the kinkajou, which is quite monkeylike in appearance; and the coati, which is to be found in Central and South America.

The kinkajou, as the only member of the family that has developed a prehensile tail, is perhaps more completely at home in the trees than any of the others. The natives regard it as a type of monkey, and it has, indeed, a lemurlike appearance. But the paws are paws, not hands, and they are armed with powerful curved claws, not nails. Furthermore the dentition is unmistakably that of the raccoon family. The kinkajou, which is about as large as a small cat, eats small mammals and birds, fruit and honey. Kinkajous collect in troops. When they move through the trees, they take long leaps from bough to bough.

The cacomistle, or ring-tailed cat, ranges from Central America and Mexico to Alabama, Texas, Colorado and southern Oregon. It resembles a raccoon, but is more slender; it has a long, bushy tail, ringed in black and white. It is a dweller in the woods, making a moss-lined nest in a hollow tree. The cacomistle is a nocturnal animal; it feeds on small mammals and birds, insects and occasionally fruit.

The coati, or coatimundi, is represented by two species: the reddish brown ring-tailed coati, found in South America, and the white-nosed coati, which has white markings around its eyes and on its snout and which ranges from Mexico and Central America south to Peru. The German equivalent for coati is "proboscis bear" — an apt name for an animal with a long snout, short and sturdy limbs and a bear-like gait. (It walks on the sole of the foot, with the heel touching the ground.)

The coatis are good climbers and chase lizards among the trees. The reptiles thus pursued drop to the ground, only to find a second detachment of coatis, obviously cooperating with the hunters overhead. The coati can be tamed easily and makes a docile and interesting pet. All the members of the raccoon family, with the exception of the pandas, are to be found in North and South America.

See also Vol. 10, p. 275: "Mammals."

The eastern raccoon—
Procyon lotor lotor.

1. A striking result of wind action—a sand dune in a desolate region of Saudi Arabia.

THE WINDS AT WORK

How Wind-blown Sand and Dust Erode the Land

BY H. T. U. SMITH

WINDS rank high among the important forces that shape the surface of our planet. They erode rock materials and soil, transport the eroded material over vast areas and deposit them upon the earth. In this way they level the land here, build it up there, scoop out hollows and thus create the distinctive types of landscapes that make the earth's surface so richly varied.

One might think that the stronger the wind, the more effective it would be as an agent of erosion, transportation and deposition. This is not the case. Violent winds, such as tornadoes and hurricanes, are not particularly important as agents of geologic change. They do not come often enough, or stay long enough or cover a wide enough path to be effective. The more moderate winds that blow for hours at a stretch, time and time again through countless centuries, are far more important than are the more violent types of winds in the never-ending task of altering the surface of the earth.

As the winds erode the land, they work with two types of material — sand and dust. When the sand is carried by the wind, it drifts along close to the ground until it accumulates in the distinctive hills and ridges known as dunes. After the dunes have been formed, they too are moved by the winds. The effects of wind upon dust particles are quite different. The particles are blown high in the air and are transported rapidly and to considerable distances, sometimes traveling more than a thousand miles; finally they are deposited upon the ground. Dust is spread much thinner than wind-blown sand; it covers a much larger area.

Effects of erosion by the wind

It may be difficult to point to definite traces of erosion by the wind. Frequently the layer that has been removed is so thin and the area of removal so extensive that the noticeable effects at any one spot are slight. There are some exceptions, however. In certain desert basins in the western United States, the ground level in various limited areas has been lowered as much as fifteen feet by the blowing away of dust. In North Africa some fairly large desert basins, forming oases, have been carved out, at least partly, by the blowing away of sand and dust. In cases like these, erosion by the wind is limited to loose sand, silt and clay; in other words, the wind picks up only what other processes of erosion have made ready for it.

A special variety of wind erosion, known as sandblasting, is produced by blown sand before it is trapped to form a dune. The grains of sand act like tiny chisels, scratching and scraping whatever surface they strike. Each grain cuts a little deeper than the one before; in this way, even hard materials can be gradually ground down. Bottles and pieces of glass lying in areas of drifting sand soon lose their brightness and take on a dull, frosted appearance. If automobiles are driven in sandstorms, their paint may be worn off and their windshields frosted in a fraction of an hour. In some places where sandblasting is especially strong, wooden telephone poles are gradually worn away. They must either be protected (Figure 2) or replaced by new poles.

The effect on rocks, which naturally have been exposed to sandblasting for a longer period of time, is much greater. The larger blocks and boulders are grooved and pitted in ways not duplicated by other processes of erosion (Figure 4). If different parts of the rock are of unequal hardness, the softer parts are worn down more rapidly, leaving the harder parts standing out. Pebbles are sometimes worn down to Brazil-nut shape; one or more surfaces may become flattened. Such sandblasted rocks are called ventifacts (objects made by wind). Figure 3 shows a typical group of ventifacts. They are found in most of the areas where sand is drifting actively today, and in many other regions where wind action was once vigorous but has since been checked.

In most places, the effects of sandblasting are confined to scattered blocks

2. Protecting a telephone pole from the effects of sandblasting by means of buffer poles and a metal sheath.

All photos by the author unless otherwise indicated

and pebbles. In a few regions, however, the bedrock itself has been carved into distinctive ridges, troughs and unconnected hollows, all on a relatively small scale. This happens only where sandblasting is unusually strong, and where there is practically no rain to permit erosion by running water — a condition found in parts of southwest Africa.

Sand dune
areas of the world

The sand dunes of the world represent one of the most striking results of wind action. In the United States, dunes

3. Ventifacts, or wind-cut stones, in a striking variety of shapes. They are found in many areas of the world.

are found in a great many widely separated places. Altogether, these American dunes cover more than 40,000 square miles, or about 1½ per cent of the entire area of the country. They are far more widespread in other regions of the world; some of the dune areas in the deserts of Asia, Africa and Australia are larger than many of the American states. Smaller formations are found in many countries that do not have deserts, such as France and Germany.

There are various kinds of dunes. In some regions, such as the desert area of southern California shown in Figure 5, the dunes look like great sharp-crested waves in a vast sea of sand. Formations of this kind are called transverse dunes, because they lie athwart the direction in which the wind is blowing. They are more or less curved; each wave formation is

4. Boulders showing the remarkable grooving and pitting effects that are produced by continuous sandblasting.

generally broken up by gaps into several sections. Every dune has a steep side and a gentler slope; the steep side always faces away from the wind. The sand is blown up the more moderate slope and is dropped at the crest.

As we walk over a transverse dune, we find that the sand is loose and easily moved; our feet sink in and each step is an effort. We can climb up the gentler slope quite easily; but it is quite a different matter to scale the steep side. If the wind happens to be blowing hard, sand showers down upon us, getting into our eyes and ears and clothing. Suppose that we beat a hasty retreat to the gentle slope of the next dune. Plenty of sand is blown along here too, but it stays fairly close to the ground; only when the wind is exceptionally strong does it rise to face level.

Wind-blown sand moves in two different ways. Some grains, especially the larger ones, roll and bounce along, often forming ripples that seem to creep over the surface of the sand. Other grains, however, are swept up into the air and move along in a more or less steady stream. The harder the wind blows, the faster and higher the stream moves, and the more sand is carried. The stream flows smoothly up to the top of the dune. As soon as it passes the crest it loses momentum, drops down out of reach of the wind and is trapped behind the dunes.

As the wind blows, sand is taken from one side of the dune and added to the other; therefore, the dune as a whole advances with the wind. The advance continues as long as the wind blows in the same direction. A change in direction will cause a corresponding change in the direction in which the dune will move. If the wind entirely reverses its direction, the dune will do likewise. What was formerly the steep side will become the gentler slope, and vice versa.

Transverse dunes are found in many parts of western North America and also in the deserts of Africa and Asia (including Arabia). In many of these places, the sand waves are lofty and have long valleys, or troughs, between them. Such dunes may be hundreds of feet high, and occasionally may tower to a height of a thousand feet or more.

So far we have been dealing only with the larger transverse dunes on a continuous sea of sand. If we look at the lower right-hand corner of Figure 5, we see a series of smaller, more regular dunes quite distinctly separated from one another. These dunes are more or less crescent-shaped, with stubby horns pointing in the direction toward which the wind is blowing. Dunes such as these are called barchans (pronounced *bar'-kans*). In the photograph, some of the barchans have joined together, forming "Siamese twins" and "Siamese triplets." The more sym-

Spence Air Photos

5. Sand dunes in southeastern California. The small dunes shown in the lower right-hand corner are barchans.

metrical forms are found only where there is no crowding. Barchans are moved by the wind in much the same way as the larger sand waves; the difference is that some sand is blown around the sides as well as over the top, thus accounting for the horns.

In some places the principal forms of dunes are long, low ridges of sand that lie approximately at right angles to the trend of the sand waves, or parallel to the direction of the wind. These large formations are called longitudinal dunes. Some of the ridges are practically straight; others are slightly wavy. They range up to about thirty feet in height and a hundred feet in width; many are more than a mile long.

Both sides of these dunes have practically the same slope. The dunes are more or less covered with grass and bushes; only the crest is bare. On some dunes, even the crest is covered with vegetation; where this occurs, it means that wind action has stopped on this particular dune. There are many varieties of longitudinal dunes; they occur in true deserts and also in regions where there is scanty vegetation. In some parts of the Sahara Desert they represent the main type of

dune; they are also widespread in the deserts of Australia and India. There are interesting longitudinal dune formations in the semidesert plateau region of northeastern Arizona.

There is a fourth type of dune, made up of U-shaped ridges, largely covered with bushy vegetation. In some places bare patches, across which sand is blowing, may be seen at the bend in the U. On these so-called active dunes, there is a steep slope away from the wind, as in barchan dunes; but the horns point in a direction opposite to that of the barchans. This type of dune is found only where vegetation is present; the sides of the U are always at least partly covered with vegetation. In some places there are variations of the U shape; individual dunes have been crowded together, producing forklike or rakelike formations. Here and there U-shaped dunes are gradually being buried by oncoming sand waves, as shown in Figure 6. This means that a second series of dunes is being built up upon the older dunes. More than two generations of dunes may be formed in this manner.

U-shaped dunes and similar types are common along sandy shores and other sandy areas, where grass, bushes or trees are growing. They occur at many places in the Great Plains, east of the Rocky Mountains, where winds are strong, droughts occur frequently and the ground is very sandy. They are never found in true deserts.

In some dune areas, it is difficult to recognize any distinctive types of dune. This is especially true where the formations are largely covered with trees, as along the southern shore of Lake Michigan. From a high vantage point one sees only an irregular pattern of hills and ridges, crossed here and there by long, narrow patches of bare, drifting sand, called blowouts. Only the blowouts have a distinctive appearance; they alone show the

effects of present-day wind action. The typical blowout (Figure 7) is an elongated, troughlike zone, culminating in a broad apron of sand. The trough is formed by wind erosion — the blowing away of sand. At the end of the trough that is away from the wind, the sand generally forms a steep, high front; as more sand is blown over the top, this front gradually moves forward, burying trees and whatever other obstacles may lie before it. Blowouts gradually bring about a breakdown of older dune masses that have become static.

Irregular, grass-covered sand hills, such as those we have described, are called dead dunes; they represent masses of sand that were once shaped by the wind and were then anchored in place by the overgrowth of vegetation. Where blowouts occur, the conflict between grass and drifting sand can be seen today, although on a much smaller scale than before. In some places, the sand drifts fast enough to bury the grass and destroy it. In other areas, certain hardy kinds of grass keep growing fast enough to escape burial, and they stop the drifting sand.

Transverse dunes, barchans, longitudinal dunes and U-shaped dunes are all referred to as live, as long as they undergo the action of the wind. They can all become dead if they are invaded by vegeta-

6. Dunes along the coast of southern California. The U-shaped dunes on the landward side are being gradually overridden by the waves of sand advancing from the seaward side.

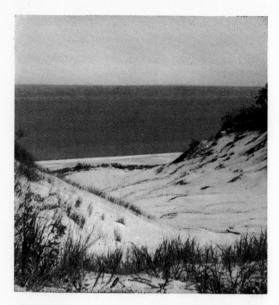

7. A blowout. Winds blowing from the lake have cut through the older dunes.

tion. As dead dunes, they will no longer be subjected to the effects of wind action. If the vegetation is destroyed, wind action may be revived, leading to various changes in the shape of the dune.

All live dunes have the property of movement, either of the entire dune or part of it. The rate of movement depends on the strength and frequency of windstorms, the constancy of wind direction and the size of the dune; the larger the dune, the slower it moves. The rates of migration (movement) range from a few feet to several hundred feet per year; the average is probably less than a hundred feet. Where strong winds blow regularly in the same direction, large dunes can override and bury whatever lies in their path; farm land, forests, roads, buildings, even entire villages may be overwhelmed. Sooner or later, however, most migrating dunes are anchored by vegetation.

Dust storms
and dust deposits

Dust storms are a vivid memory to those who lived in the Great Plains area of the United States in 1933 and in the years following. While these storms were raging, the air was filled with choking dust. Sometimes it swept forward, for all the world

like a great, high cloud with a steep front; those overtaken by such a storm would suddenly find themselves gasping amid swirling clouds of dust particles. During severe dust storms, day became as dark as night. Automobile headlights could be seen only at a distance of a few feet. Breathing was difficult; practically all outdoor activity came to a halt.

After a storm had passed, dust was left everywhere. It was a fine, powdery substance that penetrated even into tightly closed buildings. If the storm had been mild, the dust residue was only a thin, gritty film. If there had been an unusually severe storm, it left behind layers of dirt that could be removed by the shovelful.

The air would often be hazy with dust hundreds of miles from the starting point of a storm. Sometimes a thin layer of brownish dust would be deposited more than a thousand miles away from the point of origin; the layer would be particularly noticeable if it fell on snow. A typical storm, in November 1933, was traced from the Great Plains to northern New York, a distance of 1,300 miles. It traveled at an average speed of 43 miles per hour.

The amount of dust carried and deposited by a single storm was enormous. At moderate distances from the starting point, up to forty tons of dust per square mile were deposited. At greater distances, the deposits were not so heavy, of course; yet they amounted to three tons per square mile in some instances. Since the dust storms raged over tens of thousands of square miles and extended over a period of several years, the total amount of dust laid down came to millions of tons.

The dust carried in this way had been blown from farms in which the soil had become dry, powdery and bare. For a long time there had been too little rain; crops had failed to grow; the ground had been left unprotected from the wind. In many places, in a desperate attempt to start new crops, the dry ground had been broken up by farming implements into a crumbly mass. As strong winds swept over this bare, loose earth, the finer material was stirred by gusts and eddies and carried away. The coarser material was blown along the ground, scraping loose more dust for the wind to pick up. Once in the air, the dust was kept continually stirred up by swirling air currents. Only when the wind died down, or when it encountered obstacles such as buildings, was this stirring process checked; the dust then settled down gradually.

The dust storms that we have described resulted from temporary, man-made deserts. The conditions under which they occurred have been duplicated again and again in widely separated regions of the world, and have led to the devastation of immense areas.

The dust storms that have a particularly important bearing upon geologic change occur particularly in two types of environment: in true deserts and in the vicinity of glaciers.

In true deserts, there is no vegetation to protect the ground. The wind sweeps unchecked over bare earth and stirs up any fine material that is present. Severe dust storms are common; frequently the dust is blown long distances beyond the borders of the desert. Showers of reddish dust from the Sahara have long been familiar in southern Europe; they have penetrated as far north as England. One of these dust falls, in 1901, left from 3 to 31 tons of dust per square mile over an area of at least 300,000 square miles, making a total

deposit of some 2,000,000 tons in Europe alone. It is estimated that an average thickness of about 5½ inches has been added to the soil of Europe in the last 3,000 years by dust storms originating in the deserts of Africa. A similar story could be told of other deserts.

In the vicinity of glaciers, too, conditions favor the rise of dust storms. Glaciers carry much ground-up rock material scoured from their rocky channels. During the melting season, running water transports this drift along broad outwash channels away from the glacier. After the melting season, the channels become dry; they then contain large amounts of rock flour, or ground-up rock. This powdery material is easily picked up by winds blowing out from the ice, and local dust storms result. As the winds slow down away from the ice, the dust settles out, collects around vegetation and in time becomes a part of the soil. It may gradually collect to a thickness of many inches or even feet, covering the ground like a blanket. Fairly rapid deposition of this type takes place near the glaciers of Alaska and Greenland.

If a deposit of wind-blown dust is thick enough and distinctive enough to be easily recognized, it is known as loess (pronounced *loh'-ess* or *luhss*). This formation, illustrated in Figure 8, generally shows no horizontal layering or bedding; it occurs in a single vast layer. The thickness of the deposits ranges from a few feet

8. Loess formation exposed in a road cut near St. Louis, Missouri. Loess represents a thick deposit of wind-blown dust.

to more than a hundred feet; Chinese deposits are several hundred feet high in some areas. Loess sometimes forms high bluffs along the sides of valleys. When these deposits are eroded by running water, a distinctive landscape is formed; in this, nearly vertical walls alternate with flat-bottomed valleys and gulleys, forming an intricate pattern.

The dust particles of which loess is composed are well sorted; they consist of grains between $\frac{1}{16}$ and $\frac{1}{32}$ of a millimeter in diameter. Fossils found in loess are mostly the shells of land snails and the bones of land animals.

Loess deposits, dating back to the glacial period are widespread in the central and northwestern parts of the United States. Extensive loess deposits also occur in South America, Asia and Europe. In some parts of China, thousands of people live in cavelike dwellings dug into bluffs of loess. Some Chinese loess deposits show the layering that is generally associated with deposits laid down by water, thus suggesting that running water finished what the wind began.

The depositing
of volcanic ash

The eruptions of active volcanoes provide a special source of dust for the wind to move. This material, which is called volcanic ash, is blasted violently into the air. It reaches far greater heights and is present in far greater quantities than ordinary dust; it is carried farther and is deposited in thicker layers. When Katmai Volcano, in Alaska, erupted in 1912, volcanic ash fell like snow at the village of Kodiak, a hundred miles from the volcano; it covered the ground to a depth of nearly a foot. The clouds of ash were so dense that they brought almost continuous darkness for more than two days. After the ash had settled down, it was drifted like snow by the wind, and was stirred into minor dust storms.

Other regions were similarly affected. It is estimated that a mantle of ash a foot or more in thickness covered an area of 2,000 square miles; the ash mantle was a quarter of an inch or more thick over an area of more than 20,000 square miles. Some ash fell as far as 900 miles away from Katmai Volcano; the presence of volcanic dust in the air was reported from North Africa.

When the island volcano of Krakatoa, in Indonesia, exploded in 1883, volcanic ash fell inches deep nearly a thousand miles from the scene of the explosion; some ash was deposited as far away as Holland. Quantities of volcanic dust were carried around the world, causing unusually brilliant sunsets.

It has been estimated that hundreds of cubic miles of volcanic ash have been blown into the air and spread out over the earth's surface within the comparatively brief span of time covered by historical records. This, however, is but a trifling amount compared to the enormously greater volume of dust that was transported during the preceding millions of years.

A great deal of volcanic ash falls on land, remains where it fell and becomes a part of the soil. It acts as a natural fertilizer, adding chemical elements needed by growing plants. A few years after the eruption of Katmai Volcano, the grass in the vicinity grew better than ever before; the berries were larger and more abundant. In some parts of the world the soil would be very poor indeed if it were not for the repeated additions of volcanic ash.

A certain amount of ash is drifted away by the wind, or washed away by running water. Sooner or later, much of it finds its way into streams and lakes, where it forms extensive deposits. Some of these are so thick and pure that they have been exploited as a source of scouring powder and for other purposes.

Some volcanic ash falls directly into the sea; to this is added the ash that has been washed down from the land by running water. In the course of long ages such deposits have formed distinct layers of sedimentary rock, known as tuff and bentonite. Rocks of this type have been found in many places; they were formed at various periods of the earth's history.

See also Vol. 10, p. 270: "Sculpture of Land."

OBSIDIAN HYDRATION DATING

A Simple and Effective Technique

BY JOSEPH W. MICHELS

THE discovery and development of new dating techniques is a matter of great interest and importance to the archaeologist. This is especially true in the case of obsidian hydration dating. It can be applied to a wide range of archaeological problems; yet there is "do it yourself" simplicity in the method.

Obsidian is a natural glass substance that is often formed as a result of volcanic activity. Prehistoric man was struck by the naturally sharp edges produced when a piece of obsidian was fractured. With little difficulty, the prehistoric toolmaker could fashion a wide range of implements from quarried obsidian: knives, scrapers, drills, arrow and dart tips, saws, gravers and punches. The intrinsic beauty of the lustrous glass, ranging from translucent greens to opaque blacks, inspired Stone-Age artisans to fabricate personal ornaments such as nose plugs, ear-spools and pendants. The same esthetic qualities led to the use of obsidian objects in religious and ceremonial activities: elaborately flaked figurines, nonrepresentational geometrical forms and mirrors. The artisans also made large obsidian ceremonial blades, known to have been used in human-sacrifice ceremonies by at least one culture.

Wherever obsidian can be obtained through surface collection or shallow mining, the archaeologist finds evidence of its use by prehistoric man. Artifacts of this volcanic glass are to be found in the western parts of North and South America, East Africa, the Near East, New Zealand, Japan and certain parts of Central Europe.

In 1958, Irving Friedman and Robert L. Smith, both of the United States Geological Survey, were able to show that obsidian undergoes progressive alteration as water diffuses into its interior. This is the process known to chemists as hydration, or combination with water (see Index). Nonhydrated ("fresh") obsidian usually contains less than 0.3 per cent water by weight. It tends to adsorb water, forming a film of molecular thickness, from the surrounding air or soil. A process of diffusion then begins. When viewed from an ordinary light microscope, water drawn from the surface film appears to advance into the obsidian as a sharply demarcated front. The water-saturated zone that is produced is referred to as the layer or rim of hydration.

The hydrated layer contains approximately ten times more water than does the nonhydrated interior of the obsidian. The greater water content increases the density of the layer and magnifies its volume. The mechanical strains produced as a consequence throughout the hydrated layer can be recognized under polarized light. The optical phenomenon then appears as a measurable luminescent band.

The hydrated layer has a higher index of refraction (see Index) than the rest of the obsidian. Hence the boundary, or interface, between the hydrated and nonhydrated obsidian stands out sharply. The depth of hydration can be measured readily under high magnification.

Each time a freshly fractured surface is prepared on a piece of obsidian, the hydration process begins from scratch. The depth of hydration achieved in any obsidian artifact, therefore, represents the amount of time that has elapsed since the artisan made the object. It is true that differences in composition can affect the rate at which water diffuses into the interior of the volcanic glass. This is generally not an important consideration. Most obsidians are rhyolitic* and exhibit largely similar compositions. What variability does exist among rhyolitic obsidians is brought about by differences of atmos-

---

Editor's note: Rhyolite is the lava form of granite.

pheric or soil temperature. The amount of error occasioned thereby is negligible in comparison with the amount of error produced by the measuring process itself (a standard deviation of ± 0.07 micron *).

If obsidian dating is to yield absolute dates, it is necessary to establish a rate of hydration that accurately reflects the temperatures to which the artifacts have been exposed since they were originally made. Rates may be established in either of two ways. (1) The investigator may correlate hydration measurements with points along an independent scale such as is provided by radiocarbon dating (see Index). (2) He may calculate the effective temperature of the locality in which the obsidian was found. Friedman and Smith originally established seven different rates of hydration: one arctic, one subarctic, two temperate, one for coastal Ecuador and two for Egypt (reflecting the presence of two kinds of obsidian there — rhyolitic and trachytic). Since then, several other rates have been established: West Mexico, Hokkaido and Central California.

In cases where there is no known hydration rate, the obsidian hydration measurements can be used for relative dating. This means that instead of saying that an object is so many years old, we say that it is older

* *Editor's note:* A micron is a thousandth of a millimeter.

or younger than some other object. Within an archaeological site, obsidian artifacts can be put in chronological order from early to late on the basis of their micron values. The highest values are oldest; the lowest values are youngest.

The optical measurements of hydration are carried out on thin sections prepared from obsidian samples. Using a diamond-embedded continuous rim saw, the investigator makes two parallel cuts about two mm (millimeters) apart and 4 mm deep in the artifact, parallel to one or more of its surfaces. The section between these cuts is removed and ground down to about half of its original thickness. This operation is necessary in order to eliminate surface chipping produced by the saw blade during the cutting operation. Next the section is cemented to a microscope slide with cooked Canada balsam. The slide is washed and dried. Finally the section is sealed with another application of Canada balsam and a cover slip.

After cooling, the slide is examined in cross-polarized light. The investigator seeks a part of the hydration layer containing two parallel lines of minimum thickness. This indicates, it is thought, that the outer edge of the sample and the advancing surface of the hydration layer are both parallel to the optic axis of the microscope. When such a

All photos, Joseph W. Michels

A   B

Photomicrograph of the rim of hydration on a Mexican obsidian artifact from Tenango. The rim measures 4.67 microns (a micron = a thousandth of a millimeter). This would give the artifact a date of about 2879 B.C., give or take 145 years. That is, the possible dates are 3024 to 2734 B.C., a range of almost three centuries. For full explanation, see text on pages 327, 329.

region is found, contrast-enhancing adjustments are made — say, by opening or stepping down the aperture diaphragm in the optical path or through the use of filters. (See the article on Microscopes in Volume 9.)

The standard procedure has been to take two measurements at each of two widely separated parts of a sample. The mean value of the four measurements is calculated and is converted into micron units.

One of the more exciting results of hydration dating occurred recently in my study of the pre-Hispanic industry of the Valley of Mexico. This valley is a large basin, where Mexico City is located; it has an altitude of 7,000 feet. Archaeologists have been very successful in learning about the rise of civilization in this region. The history they were able to write, based on archaeological excavations, extended back to 1500 B.C. It told of the gradual transformation of a small population of horticulturalists into the magnificent civilization of the Aztecs.

A problem arose, however, when the archaeologist attempted to push his knowledge back to the era before 1500 B.C. — the so-called Food-Gathering and Incipient Agricultural Period. The evidence provided by pottery and architecture was not available for the latter period. From information gathered in other areas, archaeologists deduced that a population of nomadic hunters was being transformed into a society of horticulturalists. Thus the stage was being set for the rise of civilization.

A number of sites previously excavated had been dated on the basis of pottery and agriculture. Through a large-scale obsidian-dating program, I was able to discover that these sites contained obsidian artifacts originally manufactured before the time indicated by the evidence of pottery and agriculture. No less than 14.5 per cent of all the articles I dated fell within the Food-Gathering and Incipient Agricultural Period. Using the data, I succeeded in providing accurate dates for twelve of the sites. In two of them, over a third of the dated artifacts fell within the pre-1500 B.C. period; over a fourth of the artifacts, in the case of two other sites.

Cutting wedge from obsidian artifact to make thin section.

Grinding wedge down to prepare microslide thin section.

Coverslips are mounted on some microslide thin sections.

Measuring hydration rim with image-splitting eyepiece.

THE ORIGIN OF THE UNIVERSE

The Big-Bang and Steady-State Theories

BY GEORGE B. FIELD

DID the universe originate suddenly in an enormous primeval explosion, billions of years ago, or has it always been in process of creation, without a definite beginning or end? Exponents of the first idea, called the "big-bang theory," believe that all the matter in the cosmos once formed a compact mass, which some have likened to a huge "atom" of sorts. This mass then exploded, forming a vast fireball. In a few minutes, perhaps, matter was scattered across immense stretches of space. Today, the stars, galaxies and planets that were formed from this material still have the motion that resulted from the explosion and are speeding away from each other at tremendous velocities. The different elements developed from the primitive matter that exploded. On the other hand, followers of the continuous-creation, or "steady-state," theory, say that the universe has always been much the same for long ages, and that matter, namely hydrogen, is constantly being created, apparently from nothing. This material forms the stars and galaxies and arises more or less uniformly throughout the cosmos. In this article, we shall assess the scientific standing of the big-bang and steady-state theories in relation to the latest astronomical research.

Theories of the universe form a discipline known as cosmology. Einstein was the first truly modern cosmologist; in 1915 he completed his general theory of relativity; it was then applied to the problem of the distribution of matter in space. In 1917 it was determined mathematically that there seemed to be a more or less uniform mass of material which is precariously balanced between the attractive force of gravitation and another, unfamiliar, force of cosmic re-

pulsion, or pushing apart. In 1922, a Russian physicist came up with another solution to the problem, in which repulsion does not play a role; instead, there is an expanding universe where all particles are flying away from each other at high speeds. The expansion is constantly slowing because of the attractive force of gravity; earlier, the particles had been moving outward even faster. The expansion in this model of the universe started at a unique moment in the past (the so-called "big bang").

The big-bang theory seemed so contrary to the astronomical knowledge of the period, that at first it attracted little attention. After all, the many stars in the Milky Way galaxy do not seem to be moving away from each other, but instead to be traveling in circular orbits around its massive central region. But in 1929, Edwin Hubble, then an astronomer at the Mount Wilson Observatory, announced that the galaxies he had been observing were in fact receding from us, and from each other, at speeds of up to several thousand miles per second. These galaxies, like the Milky Way, apparently keep their internal structure intact over long periods of time; individually they are moving through space, more or less as units, or "particles." The Einstein theory could be applied to galaxies instead of to stars.

To determine the speeds of galaxies, Hubble made use of the Doppler effect.* In examining the light from the galaxies

Editor's note: The Doppler effect is the phenomenon experienced when a source of waves, such as light or sound, is moving with respect to an observer or listener. If the source *approaches* a person, the latter perceives the waves as rising in frequency: sound becomes higher-pitched or light tends toward the violet end of the spectrum. If the source is moving *away* from the person, the waves drop in frequency: sound becomes lower in pitch or light tends toward the red end of the spectrum.

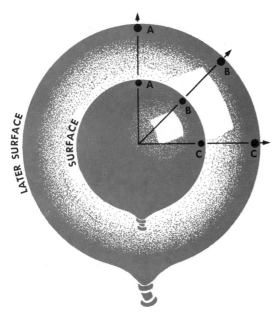

LATER SURFACE
SURFACE

Expansion of the universe according to the big-bang theory; it is compared here to a balloon undergoing inflation. The specks, A, B and C, are galaxies at "fixed" locations on the skin of the balloon. (In the real universe galaxies fill the entire space, not just the "surface.") As the balloon grows in size, the skin stretches and the distances among the specks increase, but in the same proportions as on the earlier surface. In this case, C always is twice the distance of B from A. On the later surface, C has moved twice as far from A as B.

the red — the so-called "red shift." Hubble was able to deduce the velocities of the receding galaxies from the percentage of red shift; he determined that a shift of 1 per cent toward the red corresponded to a speed of 1,860 miles per second, for example. Furthermore, the apparently fainter and therefore more distant galaxies seemed to have greater red shifts — i.e., they were traveling the fastest of all. More recent work on the problem has disclosed that there is an increase of speed of about 20 miles per second for each million light years * of distance outward into space. Thus, at a distance from earth of 3 billion light years, a galaxy is traveling as much as 60,000 miles a second.**

Such figures represent the distances and speeds of galaxies *as they appear to us now.* We see the galaxies as they looked hundreds of millions or several billion years ago, since their light has taken that long to reach the earth. Although the figure of 20 miles a second for each million light years seems to be constant, there is some reason to believe that it is changing very slowly with the passage of time.

The big-bang theory is also based on the observation that galaxies are distributed more or less uniformly throughout space, much as

spectroscopically (see Index, under Spectroscopes; Spectrum), Hubble noted that the lines were shifted out of their customary positions, toward the red end of the spectrum. He concluded that this was due to the motion of the galaxies away from the earth. Moreover, the greater the speed of recession, the greater was the shift toward

* *Editor's note:* A light year is the distance light travels in a year at 186,000 miles per second; it is about six trillion miles.

** *Editor's note:* Recent studies of quasars (see the article in Volume 5 on quasi-stellar objects) have shown that the most distant ones have speeds exceeding three-fourths the velocity of light. Even more remote and faster quasars may yet be discovered. Because of this, some astronomers are questioning the meaning of the red shift.

Schematic representation of the steady-state universe. Galaxies (starlike objects) are uniformly distributed throughout space and are not markedly different from each other. As the universe expands, new matter in the form of hydrogen is created in the space among the galaxies. This matter will come to form more stars and galaxies in time.

a cloud of particles. The physicist George Gamow has explained the expansion effect by an analogy with an inflating balloon. If one blows up a balloon that is uniformly covered with specks of paint, one sees all the specks move away from each other. If two specks, A and B, are at first one inch apart, while at the same time A and C are two inches apart, the distance AC is always twice the distance AB, because all lengths increase in the same proportion as the balloon is inflated. To keep this proportion, speck C must cover twice the distance from speck A that speck B does in the same span of time. Thus, speed is proportional to distance, as in Hubble's findings on galactic recession. The specks on the balloon, as the galaxies in space, remain uniformly distributed as expansion proceeds; no single speck or galaxy is the "center" of the expansion. As the specks or galaxies move away from each other, an observer on any one of the specks (as a man on earth in the Milky Way) would get the impression that all the other specks (galaxies) were moving away from him. This impression of outward expansion for all observers, in fact, has been termed the *cosmological principle.*

Back in 1948, however, there was not sufficient information available to test the big-bang theory. Fred Hoyle and the British astrophysicists argued for another theory, the steady-state theory, according to which the universe not only is uniform in space (cosmological principle) but also unchanging in time (perfect cosmological principle). Thus, the cosmological principle was extended so that it was "perfect" or "complete" and not conditioned by specific historic events. The steady-state theory is in direct conflict with the big-bang theory. In the latter concept, space becomes progressively emptier as the galaxies recede from one another. In the steady-state theory, one must postulate that new matter is continuously created in the space between the galaxies, in order that new galaxies may then form to take the place of those which have receded. The new material is believed to be hydrogen, which is the source from which stars and galaxies spring.

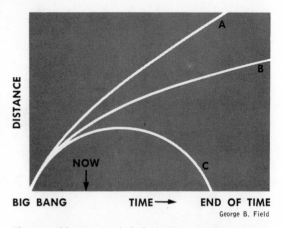

Three possible ways in which the big-bang universe is evolving, as described on page 333 of the text. Curve A represents a rapidly and continuously expanding universe. Curve B shows one expanding slowly; in C, expansion stops and contraction occurs as matter returns to its original state.

Continuous creation of matter from apparently empty space has met with considerable skepticism from authorities, because it seems to violate one of the basic laws of physics — the conservation of matter. Matter cannot be created or destroyed, but just converted into other kinds of matter or into energy. On the other hand, it would be difficult to disprove continuous creation directly, because the amount of matter, according to steady-state theory, is arising very slowly — about one atom per billion years in a volume of space equal to that contained in an average television set!

The steady-state theory in its original form has not fared well in the light of recent astronomical studies. Its chief failing appears to be its insistence on the uniformity of stars and galaxies. It would not predict that the average properties of nearby and distant galaxies would be different; and yet differences have been observed, especially by radio astronomers (see Index under Radio astronomy). There are far more faint radio sources than have been predicted by the steady-state theorists. Such effects, however, can be explained on the basis of big-bang theory, since it predicts that galaxies evolve with the passage of time. Because of the finite speed of light, we see various galaxies as they appeared at different stages in the past, as we have already pointed out. For very distant galaxies, billions of light years off, we see them as they were billions of years ago, when their characteristics were quite different. Because of these new facts, Hoyle and others have renounced the early form of the steady-state theory. Others are attempting to modify it, however.

The big-bang model has also run into difficulties. For one, the concept of all matter being compressed into one dense mass has been very difficult for present-day physics to describe or comprehend.* The explosion and consequent motion of this material may be compared to the possible flights of a projectile fired off the earth's surface. It may travel so fast that it easily escapes the earth's gravity and moves very quickly far out into space, and keeps doing so. Or it may just barely escape the earth and keep moving very slowly on outward. Or it may never have had sufficient velocity to rise free of earth's gravity; the projectile will eventually slow down, stop and then start falling back to earth, at increasing speed. The expanding universe may be acting similarly — expanding rapidly, or comparatively very slowly or finally so slowly that expansion may halt, being overcome by the gravitational attraction of matter for matter. Then contraction sets in, as all matter begins to "fall" back, faster and faster, toward its point of origin.** At the present time, observations have not been good enough to suggest which one of the three expansion processes, described above, may be operating in the universe. Yet, there is hope that in a few years the answer may come. Large telescopes are needed for the job, and there are simply not enough of them available.

Another stumbling-block to the big-bang theory is the age of the universe obtained mathematically from it. It seems just too small (less than 10 billion years) for a number of very old stars, whose ages have been determined independently from the amount of nuclear fuel they are supposed to have consumed. However, proponents of the big-bang theory feel that this method of stellar dating is not yet very accurate, and so they consider that it is not really a serious threat to their idea.

The present known proportion of helium in the sun and in many other stars averages about 30 per cent by weight. This agrees well with the amount predicted by the big-bang theory. Big-bang exponents say that the temperature of the cosmic blast first reached several billion degrees, but began to drop off after the event. At some stage many atomic nuclei began to form, including those of helium. The exact amount of early helium depends on several factors, particularly the temperatures prevailing then and now. Some trouble has been experienced in the theory in this regard. Critics also point out that the apparent agreement on present helium abundance between fact and theory may be only coincidence, and that later cosmic events influenced the helium concentration. Much more information on the distribution of chemical elements must be obtained.

The explosive fireball must have given off terrific amounts of high-energy radiation. Gamow and others said that remnants of this radiation might still be detectable, but at much lower frequencies now, because of the great loss of heat and energy since the big bang. In 1965 and later, such possible radiation was detected, in the microwave (see Index) region of the spectrum, at various wavelengths. It seems to come evenly from all regions in space, as would be expected from a universal fireball, and corresponds to a present temperature of from 2.5 to 3° above absolute zero (absolute zero = −273.16° C.). All these observations are in very close agreement with the predictions that have been made by theory.

If all these findings about fireball radiation and helium abundances finally prove to be correct, it would mean that at one stage the universe was 1,000 times smaller than it is today and, at a still earlier period, 300 million times smaller! Matter in this compact state could not exist as normal atoms, nor could it eventually come to form stars and galaxies, unless it exploded.

Editor's note: Extremely dense matter is thought to exist in some very small (dwarf) stars. A pint of this material at the earth's surface would supposedly weigh over twenty tons!

** *Editor's note*: Ultimately, the whole process may begin again, after matter has become sufficiently compacted to explode once more. How many times has this happened (if at all)?

THE WORK OF A STATE HEALTH DEPARTMENT

Safeguarding the Health

of the Community

BY WILLIAM LEVIN

WHEN you take a drink of water from a faucet, do you ever stop to think of the source of the water? Do you ever wonder what becomes of garbage after it has been collected? The chances are that you never give such matters a thought. Yet your health depends to a large extent on the purity of your water supply and the proper disposal of wastes.

The water that you drink, the food that you eat, the wastes of which you dispose, the air that you breathe, the diseases that threaten you — all these matters and others pertaining to health are of concern to public health departments. Charged with the protection of the community at large, they are to be found, in one form or another, in practically all civilized countries. At the international level, the World Health Organization (WHO) of the United Nations conducts research, provides information and carries out vigorous campaigns against various diseases.

In the United States, public health agencies may be operated by cities or other local units, counties or states. The Federal government also concerns itself with public health problems. Thus the United States Public Health Service, an agency of the Department of Health, Education and Welfare, works with the states in various health programs. It also operates nine research laboratories, known as the National Institutes of Health.

"Public health is purchasable," said a noted New York public health administra-

tor. In the United States, citizens buy it with the money they pay for taxes, for these are the main source and often the only source of support for public health agencies. It is important for all of us, therefore, to know what public health measures do for the health and welfare of the community. The present article aims to provide this information. It would be impossible to discuss in so short an article the health departments at all levels — city, county, state and Federal. I shall concern myself principally, therefore, with the work of state health departments, which play a major role in the health field. Our discussion will also serve to throw light on the work of other types of health agencies in this country and in other lands, for they face many of the problems that we shall consider.

The rise of the public health movement in general is discussed elsewhere in this set.* The first state health department, it is generally agreed, was established by the Commonwealth of Massachusetts in 1869. By 1900, most states had set up state health departments; they are now to be found in all the states. These departments, up to World War II (1939–45), were concerned mainly with the recognition, control and prevention of contagious diseases and with the sanitation of the environment. Several of the more populous and wealthier states had undertaken other programs. These included the production of vaccines and of biological and chemical agents for the prevention and treatment of disease. Since the war, there has been a wide expansion of activities.

Organization and activities of a state health department

At the outset, let me point out that a state health department is not the same thing as a state board of health. The state health department is the functioning, or working, agency of the state board of health, which is the policy-making body. The members of the latter body are appointed by the governor. In the past, only physicians were named. The present tendency is to include,

* Editor's note: See The Development of the Public-Health Movement, Volume 9, pages 36–42.

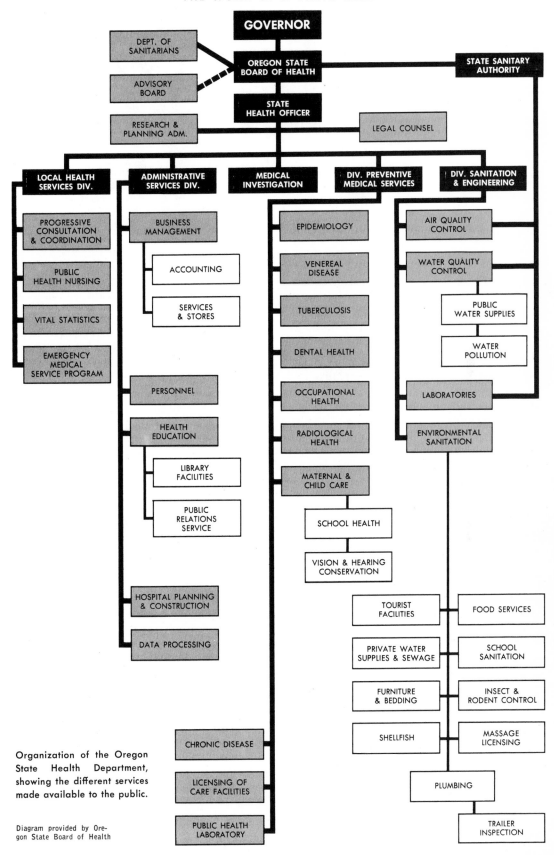

Organization of the Oregon State Health Department, showing the different services made available to the public.

Diagram provided by Oregon State Board of Health

besides physicians, representatives of other professions concerned with health (such as public-health engineers and pharmacists) and at least one person representing the general public. As a rule, a state board of health appoints its executive secretary, who is also known as the state health officer. He is the chief of the state health department and as such is responsible for its activities.

The organization of a given state health department depends on various factors, such as the size of the state; the density of its population; and whether the state is highly industrialized or mainly agricultural. The diagrammatic scheme of the Oregon State Health Department on the preceding page indicates the make-up of a typical department at the state level. The activities in which state health departments engage vary in scope from state to state; yet all have certain well-defined programs in common. These are carried out, with very few exceptions, in much the same manner throughout the country.

Following are some of the more important areas of activity of the typical state health department:

1. Controlling contagious diseases.
2. Controlling the sanitation of the environment.
3. Vital statistics.
4. Research.
5. Public health education.
6. Mental health.
7. Co-operation with the Federal government in medical-care programs.

The control of
contagious diseases

The control of contagious diseases goes back to ancient times when sufferers were isolated from the community or, in certain countries, even stoned to death. In the fourteenth century, the procedure called quarantine was adopted as a protection against the plague. Persons suffering from this disease or coming from plague-infested areas were isolated for a specified period, which was ultimately set at forty days.*

* This forty-day period, called *quarantina* in Italian, gave rise to the word "quarantine."

Oregon State Health Dept.

The author, Dr. William Levin, and an assistant in the Oregon State Health Department's Public Health Laboratory. Dr. Levin formerly directed this laboratory.

Since the agents that caused disease were unknown, it was thought that even if an individual harbored the disease, its effects would not last beyond the specified period.

In the nineteenth century, Pasteur, Koch and other famous scientists discovered that many contagious diseases were caused by minute forms of life — the so-called bacteria.*

Diseases such as cholera, typhoid fever, typhus fever and tuberculosis, which formerly claimed thousands or hundreds of thousands of victims yearly, could now be controlled. This was because the organism that caused a particular disease could be identified and because it had been learned how the organism entered and left the human body. The result was an entirely new approach to the problem of controlling communicable diseases.

Quarantine and isolation procedures are still used but under greatly modified conditions. The incubation period of most diseases (that is, the interval between exposure and appearance of the first symptoms) is well known, varying from a matter of hours to several weeks. Isolation of the patient, therefore, varies for each disease.

* Editor's note: For an account of this development, see the section on The Germ Theory of Disease in Volume 7, pages 378–85.

In a disease like diphtheria, for example, quarantine is usually lifted when two consecutive cultures from nose and throat, taken after the end of the illness, have proved negative. In typhoid fever, however, a carrier condition may last for months or even years following the illness. In such cases, the individual may be restricted in movement and prohibited from engaging in the handling or processing of food. He may even submit (voluntarily) to an operation to remove the carrier condition.

In carrying on the never-ending war against disease-causing germs, the state department has a laboratory staffed by bacteriologists and other highly trained specialists. Their duties include isolating the germ that causes an outbreak of disease; testing its virulence; and giving other pertinent information to the epidemiologist, or epidemic specialist. Such information may help not only to pinpoint the source of the infection but also to prevent its spread. The public health laboratory in which such information is collected is frequently housed in its own building, and in a number of states is responsible directly to the state health officer. Where the density of population or distance from the central laboratory requires it, branch laboratories are established.

The state epidemiologist, who may have several assistants, is a disease detective, trained to ferret out sources of infection. With the aid of the public health laboratory, he looks for carriers of disease germs or for persons suspected of being infected. He investigates all possible leads that may throw light on the cause or source of an epidemic. He studies reports to determine whether there is an increase in the rate of illness in any community in the state and attempts to determine the cause.

When the source of an epidemic has been pinpointed, clinics are held to immunize persons known to have been exposed to the disease. Special clinics may be set up for children. The state health department plays a dominant role in such clinics. It supplies its technical personnel and also

Thousands of specimens are tested in the laboratories of the New Jersey State Department of Health, in Trenton. Mixups in such materials would cause endless confusion. Hence an accurate identification of specimens, as illustrated here, is a necessity.

New Jersey State Department of Health

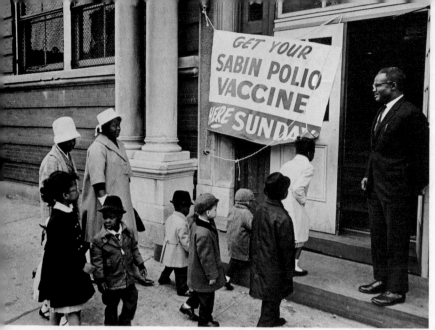

A health educator with the New Jersey State Department of Health watches parents and children enter a New Jersey school to receive immunization against poliomyelitis (infantile paralysis). Giant strides have now been made in the fight against this disease.

New Jersey State Department of Health

furnishes such materials as vaccines, toxoids (see Index) and other proven agents of immunization.

The private physician is supposed to co-operate fully with the local and state health departments by reporting promptly the existence or even suspected existence of a contagious disease. Unfortunately many epidemics get a good start because the health department is not informed or because the information comes too late.

Sometimes an epidemic may threaten a community as the result of an emergency situation caused, say, by a flood or an earthquake. If the local health department is unable to cope fully with such a threat, the state health department at once steps in. Mobile truck units for water purification and others for laboratory diagnosis are quickly made available. The state health department also distributes vaccines, which are used in local clinics. Private physicians may obtain the vaccines; they charge the patient only for their services, not for the vaccines.

Tuberculosis and the venereal diseases, all highly contagious, have been among the prime targets of health departments for many years. Great strides have been made in the recognition and treatment of these diseases, but control measures are still far from satisfactory. Social customs, prejudices, inhibitions and a devil-may-care attitude on the part of many persons hinder the application of measures known to be effective in the control of these diseases.

To combat tuberculosis, mobile X-ray laboratories are used by many state health departments, at times in collaboration with state tuberculosis and health associations. Free chest examinations are offered to all citizens. Tuberculosis suspects are notified of their condition and are advised to see their physicians or to go to health-department clinics. Follow-up measures are taken in all proven cases of tuberculosis.

Venereal-disease clinics are run at night as well as during the day to permit their use by working people. Free treatment is provided where necessary. To detect the existence of venereal disease, health-department laboratories in most states examine, free of charge, blood specimens from persons who may be infected.

An important member of the epidemiologist's staff is a public health veterinary doctor. The control or eradication of animal vectors (carriers) of diseases that can be transmitted to humans is extremely important in the control of contagious diseases. Tuberculosis, plague, psittacosis, rabies, ornithosis and tularemia are some of the diseases transmitted by infected mammals or birds. An increasing number of virus infections * arise from such sources.

Controlling the sanitation of the environment

"A wholesome living environment," according to the American Public Health As-

* *Editor's note:* See the article on The Viruses, in Volume 6.

sociation, "devolves largely upon the state health department." Pioneer health departments in the United States paid particular attention to such environmental factors as water supply and waste disposal. Later, there was increasing concern with milk and food and, in recent years, with air pollution, housing and radiation.

Water supply and sewage disposal. Diseases such as cholera and typhoid fever, which were caused by the drinking of polluted water, were responsible for many deaths in the United States until steps were taken to purify the water supply. The development of adequate methods of purification represents a triumph of the sanitary engineer. There have been no cases of cholera in the United States since 1873; typhoid fever is a vanishing disease in this country.*

A kindred problem is the adequate treatment of sewage that flows into streams or lakes. What we call sewage consists of liquid wastes plus a certain amount of solid matter carried off in these wastes. In practically all cases, the sewage must be treated before it is allowed to flow into any body of water.**

State health departments play an important part in the purification of water and in sewage disposal. Plans for the construction of water-supply and sewage-disposal plants must be submitted to these departments for approval. The public health engineering staff looks over the plans carefully. It then recommends alterations, additions or deletions, if any features of the plans are not in accordance with sound public health engineering practices. Regular and frequent laboratory tests are required to insure the purity of water supplies. Unless a qualified local laboratory can make such tests, samples have to be submitted to the state health laboratory. Monthly reports on both water and sewage plants are sent to the state health department.

The disposal of solid wastes. This is also a concern of the state health department. Such wastes are very often disposed of by incineration (burning). Some municipalities located on seacoasts dump solid wastes into the ocean after towing them to a considerable distance from the shore. In many cases, the sanitary-fill method is used. In this, garbage and other kinds of solid refuse are first compressed to a dense mass and are then covered by several feet of dirt. The most unsanitary method of waste disposal is the open dump, which is a haven for disease-carrying flies and rats.* The state health department keeps a close check on such dumps and instructs dumping agencies in the proper use and care of sanitary fills.

* *Editor's note*: Water-purification methods are discussed in the article on The Water Supply, in Volume 2.
** *Editor's note*: The methods of treatment are described in the article on The Disposal of Wastes, in Volume 5.

* *Editor's note*: For a fuller account of the disposal of solid wastes see the article on The Disposal of Wastes, in Volume 5.

This mobile laboratory, operating in Chicago, Illinois, gives free skin tests and chest X rays in order to detect possible sufferers from tuberculosis. This disease has been brought more or less under control, though vigilance is still required to combat it.

State health departments and other health bodies wage a never-ending war against water pollution. The aerial photo below gives a view of the pollution in Ashtabula Harbor, Ohio. Before proceeding against pollution, scientists must analyze the water. The right-hand photo shows different samples of water at the Oregon Public Health Laboratory. The samples will be examined fully for bacteriologic content.

E. G. Hoffman   Oregon State Board of Health

Inspection of milk and other foods. In some states, the inspection of milk supplies and the processing of foods are the responsibility of the state agricultural department. In others, the state health department has the responsibility. When, however, an outbreak of food infection or poisoning occurs or when a milk supply is suspected of having caused an outbreak of typhoid fever or septic sore throat, the state health department takes full charge. It has the responsibility of determining the source of the infection and of removing the supply of food or milk from the market, if necessary. Milk in particular is a medium in which germs can thrive. Besides typhoid fever and sore throat, infected milk can spread tuberculosis, brucellosis and diphtheria. A fairly common food disease is salmonellosis, which is caused by bacteria belonging to the genus *Salmonella*. Far more deadly is the food disease called botulism (see Index); fortunately, it is comparatively rare.

Air pollution. Air pollution, particularly in large cities and industrialized areas, is becoming a serious problem in various areas of the country and in many metropolitan areas throughout the world.* Many

* *Editor's note*: See the article on Air Pollution, in Volume 3.

factors contribute to air pollution : industrial plants belching out smoke, often containing mineral particles; exhaust from automobiles, trucks and buses; improperly burned fuel in private residences; the burning of leaves and trash. The consequences of air pollution can be most tragic. Consider what happened to Donora, Pennsylvania, in 1948. On October 27 of that year, a thick fog settled down on this town of 14,000 and remained suspended over the area for four and a half days. It was made up in considerable part of wastes discharged into the air from factories. It resulted in twenty deaths and 6,000 cases of illness.

State health departments, through their sanitary engineering personnel, now measure the amount of pollution in the air as well as the kinds of pollutants (polluting substances). This is done by stationary equipment and also by mobile units. When pollution becomes a real menace to health, warning is given to the public through the newspapers, radio and other mediums of communication. If conditions warrant, all traffic may be halted; the burning of trash may be forbidden; in extreme cases, factories may be shut down.

Housing. In certain states, health departments are charged with investigating housing conditions. Such investigation is usually confined to various matters of faulty sanitation. These include improper or insufficient toilet or bath facilities; unsafe plumbing connections; improper ventilation; and rodent infestation. Where local ordinances cover such delinquencies, action is taken by the city.

The housing problem really calls for co-operative action. It should be tackled not only by the health department but also by the state fire marshal's office and the other state departments concerned with safety and welfare. Federal assistance in housing projects is necessary to eliminate slums.

Vector control is another important function of state public health departments. A vector is an organism that transmits germs or other agents of disease. The rat, for example, helps spread plague, trichinosis and other diseases. Mosquitoes are responsible for the transmission of yellow fever and malaria; ticks are vectors of such diseases as spotted fever and Q fever.*

The presence of an entomologist (insect specialist) on a state health-department staff is of great help in determining the type and source of insect-borne infections.

Radiation control. A number of state health departments are now concerned with the control of radiation. Thirty states have established programs for inspections or surveys of radium installations. Five states require licensing of such installations and thirty-three others require registration of radium supplies. The increasing radioactive fallout from nuclear blasts, resulting in a certain amount of contamination of milk and other food products, caused grave concern in the United States for a time.** With the suspension of aboveground nuclear-weapon testing by the United States and Russia, the problem is not now critical in the United States. State health departments, however, are still on the alert.***

* *Editor's note:* It should be borne in mind that mosquitoes and ticks, like all other vectors, are not disease-producing agents; they simply carry such agents. Thus malaria is caused directly by the protozoan *Plasmodium malariae,* which is transmitted by mosquitoes belonging to the genus *Anopheles.*

** Radioactive strontium (Sr^{90}) is perhaps the deadliest product of radioactive fallout. For the effects of Sr^{90} on man see the Index, under Strontium—Radioactive.

*** Two other nuclear powers, France and China, are still setting off aboveground nuclear blasts.

Vital statistics

Public health bookkeeping, better known as vital statistics,* is concerned with keeping records of such happenings as births, deaths, marriages and divorces. In all states, with the exception of Alaska and Massachusetts, the state health officer is the registrar of vital statistics for his state, although he may delegate that authority to a member of his staff. As we shall see, the actual gathering of the data is in the hands of registrars on a lower level. On the national level, the Bureau of Vital Statistics is a part of the United States Public Health Service. Vital-statistics records form a basis for medical studies and research of various kinds.

Uniform reporting forms have been developed by the Federal government and adopted by the states so that significant comparisons may be made. Registration districts are not necessarily the same for all states. Local registrars are usually members of county health departments; in large cities, however, they may belong to the city health department. All reports are eventually sent to the state health department, which then becomes the official custodian of the records. Because of the great value of these records both to the state and to individual citizens, they are kept in fireproof vaults. Birth certificates are particularly useful. They provide proof of citizenship; they also serve to establish one's identity in the case of inheritance and for other legal requirements. Certified copies are obtained, generally for a small fee, by writing to the state registrar.

Vital statistics include the data relating to the incidence (occurrence) of disease within a state. Morbidity reports (reports of disease **) are usually made weekly by local health departments and are sent to the state health department, which collects and interprets the data. Figures on the incidence of certain diseases are wired weekly by the state health department to the Communicable Disease Center of the United

* Vital statistics means, literally, "statistics having to do with life." *Vita* is the Latin word for life.
** *Morbus* is the Latin word for disease.

States Public Health Service in Atlanta, Georgia. In return, reports obtained by the Public Health Service on the incidence of disease are sent out to each state health department.

Research activities

A noted public health professor, Dr. Wilson G. Smilie, has observed that "some portion of the time and attention of the personnel in each of the major divisions of the health department should be devoted to research and inquiry." States like New York, Massachusetts and California, to name a few, have contributed particularly important researches in public-health methods. Thus a series of notable studies by the Massachusetts Board of Health served as a basis for water-purification and sewage-treatment procedures for many years throughout the world. Certain public health researches have also served the cause of pure science.

An important reason for carrying on research activities within a public health department is the uplift in morale that it gives to the professional staff. The performance of routine work such as is required of the staff on a day-in-and-day-out basis becomes a tedious chore. It deadens the initiative and resourcefulness of persons who are qualified to think and act on their own. If they are given a chance to inquire, to search and to compare procedures, they will go about their work with greater enthusiasm, and the results may well be of lasting benefit to the public.

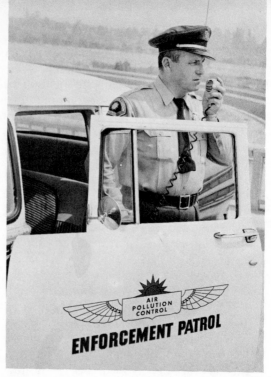

Los Angeles County, Air Pollution Control

This uniformed air-pollution-control inspector makes a daily patrol of a section of the Los Angeles Basin to detect sources of air pollution and perform other duties.

Education in public health

It has been said that if research in public health methods were to stop right now, it would take more than ten years before all the results of this research could be put to practical use. The state health department makes the results achieved by research available to its employees at all levels. For one thing, it conducts in-service training for its personnel. Also, its own professional staff as well as those of county health departments are encouraged to take

Portland Cement Co.

Aerial view of the three-million-gallon sewage treatment plant at Panama City, Florida. Drying beds are in the foreground. In the background are several tanks used in treating sewage.

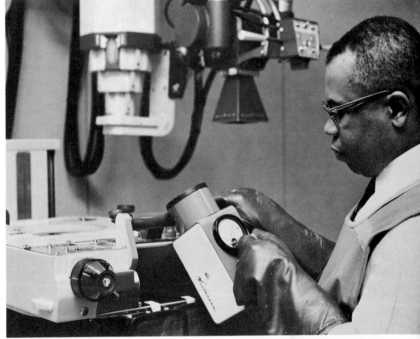

Modern state health departments must concern themselves with the control of radiation. Here a representative of the Radiological Health Program of the New Jersey State Department of Health checks a fluoroscope in a hospital. He wishes to make sure that it operates in accordance with requirements.

New Jersey State Department of Health

postgraduate training in their specialties. Both Federal grants and university fellowships have been made available for this purpose. A number of state health departments give orientation courses to new county health department personnel, paying for the expenses involved.

The educational program of state health departments is by no means restricted to health-department members. Either alone or in co-operation with the state medical school, the state medical association or volunteer agencies, state health departments offer refresher courses to private physicians. They also hold seminars or workshops for these physicians and help conduct clinics.

Some of the most important educational activities of the state health department concern the public at large. Education of the public has to be a never-ending process in the field of health. Superstition, bias, doubt and even wilful ignorance still hamper the work of public health agencies. The state health department has the obligation of informing the public on all matters pertaining to health. It explains why immunization is important in the case of the diseases for which vaccines are available, and it describes immunization methods. It provides infor-

mation through every existing channel of communication on how to guard against disease, accident and the various dietary deficiencies.

Printed material relating to such matters as infant care, nutrition and venereal disease is distributed by the state health department to persons requesting it either directly or through county health departments. Health literature and exhibits are also placed at county and state fairs. A film library is maintained covering all forms of health information and activities. Films are sent to schools, health departments and other responsible organizations interested in health matters. A number of health departments have developed their own films on health subjects for presentation on television. They sometimes have regular time on television or radio stations for programs of this type.

Bulletins dealing with health activities, vital statistics and other types of information are sent to physicians, health officers and other persons requesting them. These bulletins are issued monthly or at more frequent intervals. The state health department also issues an annual or biennial report, covering all its activities. This report has

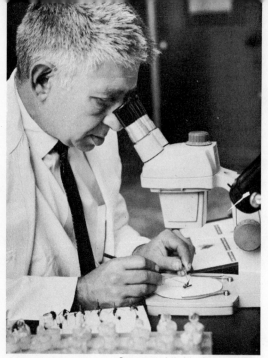

Department of Health—City of New York

Dr. George Bernstein, an entomologist of the New York City Health Department, examines an insect under the microscope. He plays a vital role in department activities.

proven to be of great value to the state legislature as well as to other interested citizens.

Mental health

It has been estimated that each year in the United States over a million persons are treated in mental hospitals. There is no question about the great need for recognition and care of mentally disturbed persons and also for their rehabilitation. Whether all this work should be carried on by a health department or some other department of the state is a debatable matter. There has been a tendency in the past few years to remove mental health activities from the state department of health and to assign them to some other agency. Not all state and county health officers are in favor of such a trend, particularly if their own health services have successfully coped with the problem. As a matter of fact, the American Public Health Association in 1965 is-

sued a policy statement to the effect that "the state health department has an obligation to maintain a view of the whole health of the whole people and should act to co-ordinate mental health and mental retardation services with all its programs."

Co-operation with the Federal government in medical-care programs

Federal aid to the states to bolster and enlarge public health activities has been provided since 1918 with the passage of various bills by Congress. Among the most important of these measures was the Hill-Burton Act of 1946. It provided for the construction or expansion of hospital facilities throughout the United States, with the state giving one dollar for each two dollars of Federal funds. All Federal moneys provided for hospitals under the Hill-Burton Act are paid to the state treasury and distributed by the state health department on vouchers, under conditions laid down by the government. Hospital construction plans have to be approved by the state health department and finally by the Public Health Service, the Federal agency mentioned above.

With the passage in 1965 of the Federal health insurance program known as Medicare, state health departments became involved in a field that had previously been given little consideration — geriatrics, or the care of the aged. The new legislation covered people of 65 years or older. Among other things, it provided payment for hospital bills, skilled nursing care after hospitalization and home health services. The

Oregon State Board of Health

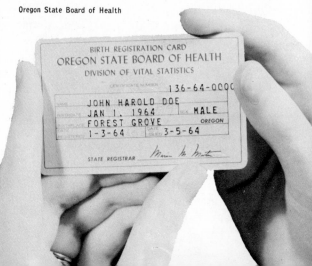

A pocket-size birth certificate issued by the Division of Vital Statistics of the Oregon State Health Department. Such certificates are extremely valuable. They provide proof of one's citizenship; they also establish the identity of a person in case of inheritance or other matters.

Oregon State Board of Health

Technician checking an educational film for damage. The typical state health department has a film library, with films covering various forms of health activities and health information. Films are sent to schools and to various other health departments.

hospitals, nursing homes and medical laboratories providing services for Medicare patients were required to meet Federal standards, which in many cases were more stringent than those set up by the state. State health departments were assigned the task of raising standards within a brief period so as to meet Federal requirements. This task has not yet been fully accomplished, but a great deal has been done. Certainly there has been none of the chaos that, according to many, would follow the introduction of Medicare.

Medicare is only one phase of the increasing attention now being given to the problems of the aged. Because of advances in medicine and public-health procedures, the average life span has been increased within fifty years or so from thirty-five years to about seventy. There are more senior citizens now than ever before, and their number will almost certainly increase in the years to come. It is well known that they require more medical attention and hospitalization than any other age group.

To help meet the problems associated with the increasing span of life, it is confidently expected that every state health department will have a section or bureau dealing exclusively with geriatrics.

The preceding pages have dealt with some of the many ways in which the state health department helps safeguard the health of the public at large. Its task is becoming increasingly difficult. More and more people, coming from every quarter, are crowding together in our metropolitan areas, which are swallowing up more and more of the surrounding territory. If an epidemic of smallpox, say, or typhoid fever were to sweep through such a community, it would have the most serious results. What is more, because of the ease and rapidity of transport by automobile, bus, train and airplane, it would probably soon spread throughout the state and then perhaps throughout the nation. Health agencies are a bulwark against any such calamity. *See also Vol. 10, p. 278: "Public Health Movement."*

THE DEFENSES
OF THE BODY

Structures and Processes
That Guard Us

BY W. W. BAUER

THE human body, moving over a long span of life, through a world filled with hazards, possesses a remarkable system of defenses against attacks from without — against accidents (or other violence) and disease. It has an outer parapet, many internal defenses and a highly ingenious regulatory system. A distinguished American physiologist, Dr. Walter B. Cannon, has described this elaborate series of defenses as "the wisdom of the body."

The senses and nervous
system provide warning

The organs of perception provide warning of violence, due either to accident or to intentional attack by man or animals. The eye can perceive, or the ear detect, the approach of danger. Man's sense of smell is less acute than that of many animals, but it is keen enough to help ward off danger of accident from fire or fumes or even to warn against attack. Skin sensation is useful in detecting contacts with crawling insects and other animals that may have a dangerous bite and in warning of excessive heat or cold. It also helps us to determine the texture of solid objects or the character of fluids with which we make contact.

Closely allied to the senses of perception is the action of the nervous system. A warning signal received through the eye,

the ear, the nose or the skin, is transmitted to the brain, which then directs appropriate action. If there is plenty of time, this may be a conscious action. You may be driving a car, and see a traffic jam in the next block. You slow up and look the situation over as you approach, then decide what to do next. But if the driver ahead of you suddenly puts on the brakes, you do the same before you have time to size up the situation. This is called reflex action. A reflex action takes place when you duck without thinking as a snowball is thrown at your head; in fact, the chances are that you will duck even if you know there is a heavy sheet of unbreakable glass between you and the oncoming object. Reflex action is at work, too, when you jerk your hand away, quicker than a wink, upon touching a hot stove.

This is how reflexes work. In the skin there are tiny organs called receptors, or receivers; there is a different one for each sensation: pain, heat, cold, pressure, texture and so on. From these, the nerve fibers go through various nerve trunks to a nerve center or ganglion, one of a chain which is just outside the backbone in the abdomen, chest and neck, and in various places in the head. Here the impulse is delivered to other nerve fibers, in much the same manner as a telephone relay carries the voice from station to station, and the message is conveyed to the brain. Action impulses then originate in the brain. They are transmitted to a nerve center in the spinal cord and from there, by other nerve fibers, to muscles that bring appropriate sense receptors, such as the eyes, nose or fingers, into play. Thus we look at, or smell or feel the object that had stimulated our skin receptors and learn what it is like.

But if there is an emergency, the whole action is short-circuited. We touch a hot stove, and the pain sensation flashes to the spinal-cord relay station. Here it is intercepted and transmitted to the appropriate nerve fibers bringing about action; these at once impel the appropriate muscles to get the hot contact broken without delay. The interception saves the longer time it would take for the danger signal to reach the brain, and there to be transferred through a num-

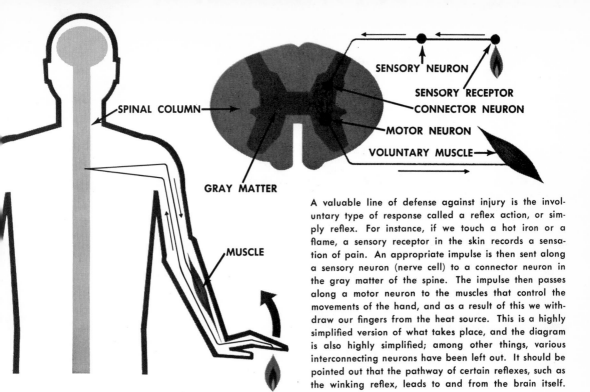

SPINAL COLUMN

GRAY MATTER

MUSCLE

SENSORY NEURON
SENSORY RECEPTOR
CONNECTOR NEURON
MOTOR NEURON
VOLUNTARY MUSCLE

A valuable line of defense against injury is the involuntary type of response called a reflex action, or simply reflex. For instance, if we touch a hot iron or a flame, a sensory receptor in the skin records a sensation of pain. An appropriate impulse is then sent along a sensory neuron (nerve cell) to a connector neuron in the gray matter of the spine. The impulse then passes along a motor neuron to the muscles that control the movements of the hand, and as a result of this we withdraw our fingers from the heat source. This is a highly simplified version of what takes place, and the diagram is also highly simplified; among other things, various interconnecting neurons have been left out. It should be pointed out that the pathway of certain reflexes, such as the winking reflex, leads to and from the brain itself.

ber of nerve paths and connections to the cells on the upper surface of the brain that ordinarily control voluntary actions.

Pain sensations occur in many parts of the body other than the skin and are manifested in different ways. The brain substance feels no pain, but the covering membranes do. The intestines are insensitive to cutting, but react painfully to twisting, pulling or distention with gas. Pains may be steady or intermittent, sharp or dull, shooting or burning. Pain is usually regarded as something to be avoided; actually it is a safeguard. It is a signal that something is wrong; properly interpreted and acted upon, it is a safety device, a protective function.

Closely related to pain are other uncomfortable sensations such as itching, nausea, dizziness and faintness, which indicate that some function is disturbed and needs attention. These sensations should be heeded, particularly if they are severe, if they tend to return at frequent intervals or if they are present for more than a few hours.

It is illogical to suppress these safety signals through the use of drugs. Merely dulling the pain does not remove its causes; it may even permit an illness which was mild in the beginning to become serious and perhaps even incurable.

The first line of defense —
the skin and mucous membranes

Diseases that attack the body from without are met with what military men would call defense in depth: that is, when one defense is breached, another stands ready to take over. The first line consists of the skin and the mucous membranes of the body. Attacking germs do not really get inside the body until they have penetrated either the skin that covers it or the mucous membrane that lines it. The digestive and breathing systems, commonly considered to be "inside" us, are really outside the body proper; they are covered with mucous membrane, which resists penetration.

The defenses supplied by the skin are of several different kinds. A natural barrier is provided by the outer layers of dead, flattened cells; they may be scuffed off without damage to the body and without pain. The oiliness of the skin, derived from the sebaceous glands, makes it waterproof and helps to prevent germ invasion. The blood vessels in the skin rush blood to the menaced area and thus bring to bear forces that fight germ progress.

Mucous membranes afford protection through the chemical composition of their secretions. The slightly acid saliva in the

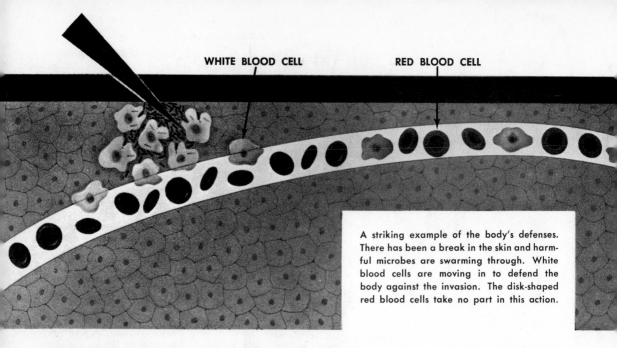

A striking example of the body's defenses. There has been a break in the skin and harmful microbes are swarming through. White blood cells are moving in to defend the body against the invasion. The disk-shaped red blood cells take no part in this action.

mouth and the more strongly acid stomach secretions both help to keep bacteria at a minimum. In the nose, the membranes have tiny cilia, or hairlike structures, which have a rhythmic waving motion toward the nostrils, thus moving secretion, dust and germs outward.

Invasion of the body by infectious agents

If the skin is broken, the way is prepared for the entry of infection. Small breaks heal quickly, first being sealed against invasion by the clotted blood, which not only prevents hemorrhage but also constitutes a defense against infection. If, however, infection has been introduced at the time of the injury, there may be a small center of inflammation around the affected area. It will become reddened; there will be pain or throbbing and heat; perhaps abscesses will form. A typical abscess on the surface of the body is a boil.

This is what happens when the infection sets in. More blood is rushed to the point of entry, accounting for the increase in local temperature, and the blood brings with it more white cells. These do not remain inside the blood vessels, but ooze through the thin and easily permeated capillary walls into the tissues, where they meet the invading organisms and attempt to engulf and destroy them. A cross section through an abscess in the early stages shows tissues swollen with blood and making a protective wall around the site of entry of the infection. If the infection is held at bay, the center of the abscess liquefies; in ordinary language we say it "comes to a head," or "points." It is then ready to open. The pus that is discharged contains fluid serum, white blood cells and bacteria, both dead and alive. If we open an abscess too soon, we may cut through the wall of protective inflammation and cause the infection to spread into deeper tissues or into the blood. Squeezing a pimple may produce the same unfortunate effects.

The invasion of the body by infectious agents—bacteria, viruses, molds—has been likened to war. There are local skirmishes at the points of attack, followed later by generalized battles. In this "war," the cells and the chemical constituents of the blood, tissue cells and body fluids represent the defending forces, or "armies," against the invaders. The white cells may be compared to the infantry, which does the hand-to-hand fighting and which mops up after the action. The outcome recalls the classic description of the successful campaigner — the one who "gets there fustest with the mostest." Either the enemy is repelled or the defenders are overwhelmed.

The invading bacteria direct a chemical attack against the body tissues; they produce chemical substances, called toxins, or poisons, which may be damaging or even fatal. These substances may be picked up from the site of the local invasion and may be carried through the whole body; they may do harm to vital organs, particularly the heart, the nervous system and the kidneys. A local infection, such as diphtheria or septic sore throat, may affect the entire body, producing fever and a feeling of illness.

Antibodies
to the rescue

Against the "poison attack," there is chemical defense. The invaded tissues soon begin producing substances called antibodies, which counteract the effects of the invading germs. There are several kinds of antibodies. The antitoxins directly neutralize the toxins; the agglutinins cause the invading bacteria to clump together and become inactive; the opsonins "soften up" the bacteria for the attacks of the white cells; the bacteriolysins dissolve the germs.

Lymph nodes as
a defense line

Suppose, however, that the body loses the local skirmish. The defending forces may be overwhelmed; or a person may squeeze a pimple or try amateur surgery on a boil or carbuncle. The local defenses are bypassed; the invading forces make a "breakthrough." Fortunately, the body has a second line of defense. Part of the tissue fluids drain through a series of vessels that parallel the veins and eventually convey these fluids (lymph) into two large veins. These lymph vessels lead through collections of spongy tissue known as lymph nodes, which constitute traps for infection. Lymph nodes are strategically placed at circulation "bottlenecks," which correspond to the easily defended posts, such as mountain passes, where a military commander would station his reserves. The tissue fluids from the hand, for example, pass through lymph nodes near the elbow, and again in the armpit; those from the foot, through nodes near the knee and in the groin. These nodes are filled with a special type of white blood cells, the lymphocytes. They may break down in the process of handling heavy infections and form abscesses; but they protect the main body structure and the vital organs. An infection which has overcome

local defenses may often be traced by angry red lines running from the point of injury up the arm or leg; these are the inflamed lymph vessels. There are systems of lymph nodes and drainage vessels that serve the internal organs in the same manner as the superficial nodes serve the extremities.

In certain instances of tuberculosis, the attack upon the lymph nodes is less violent but more persistent. If all goes well, nodules, called tubercles, will develop. These nodules will trap and hold the invading bacilli, sometimes permanently; ultimately they will become encrusted with calcium deposits. If, later, the body is weakened by fatigue, malnutrition or further infection, the walls of the nodules may break down, releasing the imprisoned bacilli. This may take place many years after the first attack.

Defensive substances that
keep circulating in the body

When the body forces have been mobilized for defense and have won the action, the local site of the skirmish clears up; the healing process takes place, and a scar often remains. Once they have gone into action,

Lymph nodes aid the body in its fight against infection by trapping microbes and removing them from the blood stream. Within the lymph nodes, the microbes are attacked by lymphocytes—cells that engulf invading germs.

LYMPH VESSEL WITH VALVE

←LYMPH NODE

the body defenses remain ready for further trouble. The tissues that have reacted against an invasion by a communicable disease do not cease reacting when the emergency has passed; they go on manufacturing the defensive substances, which circulate in the blood. For example, after a case of diphtheria, the body continues to manufacture antitoxin, which circulates in the blood for many years. The blood of a person who has recovered from typhoid fever contains agglutinins, which cause living typhoid bacteria to clump together. The presence of such antibodies gives a person protection which wears out only after a period of years, varying with the disease and the individual. That is why second cases of communicable disease are unusual; persons who do suffer such diseases a second time have defective powers of defense and may become more seriously ill than the normal person, or may even succumb.

Immunization
against disease

Man has taken advantage of the slowly unfolding knowledge of natural immunity provided after recovery from disease. An English country doctor, Edward Jenner, led the way in 1798 with his famous INQUIRY INTO THE CAUSE AND EFFECTS OF THE VARIOLAE VACCINAE (cowpox). In this monograph he showed how he could prevent smallpox by vaccination — that is, by inoculation with cowpox. Nowadays the practice of vaccination is universal among enlightened people, and smallpox exists only where vaccination is neglected. The same basic principle, with variations in detail, is used in immunizing children against diphtheria, whooping cough, tetanus (lockjaw) and poliomyelitis (polio). In areas where water supplies may be contaminated or the milk supply is of dubious quality, typhoid vaccination may be advised. (Nowadays the word "vaccination" refers to any type of preventive inoculation.) Persons traveling into certain infected areas, particularly in the tropics, the Orient and the Near East, may be advised or required to be vaccinated against cholera, typhus fever, yellow fever or other prevalent diseases for which there

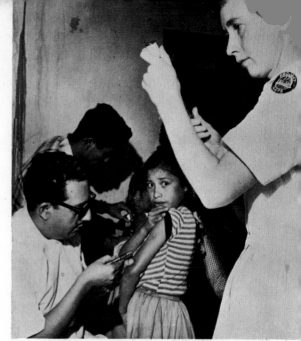

Project Hope

is available protection. The search for a polio vaccine has been one of the fascinating dramas of modern medicine: it is described in some detail in another chapter (see Index, under Poliomyelitis).

Certain diseases can be warded off by individual immunization, but not on a mass basis. For example, until recently measles was preventable only by immunizing with gamma globulin, or GG, a protein contained in the blood. Measles was so prevalent, however, and the supply of GG so limited that mass advance immunization was impracticable, even if the GG measles immunity were lasting, instead of being limited to a few weeks. Now, a practical measles vaccine for mass immunization is available.

There is no advance immunization against rabies. When a person has been bitten or licked by a dog which is known to be, or possibly might be, rabid, the Pasteur vaccination procedure begins. Usually it is in time to save the individual from the disease, which is invariably fatal.

Efforts to prepare advance immunization against the common cold have met with scant success. There is a cold vaccine, and its use is sometimes recommended, but both doctors and patients are divided in their opinions as to whether it is useful. It is harmless and may be tried if desired; but one should not expect too much from it.

There are various kinds of immunity. If it occurs as a result of having a disease

The ravages of poliomyelitis (more familiary known as polio) have been largely stemmed by immunizing children and adults with antipolio vaccine. At the left, we see children in the Peruvian town of Trujillo receiving shots of Salk antipolio vaccine, containing killed viruses. This type of vaccine must be administered by injection. The Sabin antipolio vaccine contains live viruses; it is not injected but is given by mouth. The above photograph shows students at East High School, Rochester, New York, taking doses of the Sabin vaccine.

and overcoming it, it is called natural; if it is acquired by a man-made procedure, it is called artificial. Both types of immunity depend upon stimulation of the body's own defenses; they are both described as active and they may last for many years.

Suppose that a child exposed to serious disease has not had previous immunization. Then, as in diphtheria, we may give the child a preventive injection of antitoxin. This does not stimulate the body mechanism, so this kind of immunity is called passive; its effect is only temporary.

The substances used to provide immunization are called antigens. Some, used in protecting against smallpox and rabies, are virus vaccines, containing living but greatly weakened viruses. Some are bacterial vaccines — killed bacteria in suspension. Some, called toxoids, are greatly weakened toxins. All have the property of stimulating the tissues to form antibodies, but they do not produce the disease; all provide active, artificial immunity. The substances known as antitoxins produce temporary protective immunity; they are not antigens.

Some persons find it hard to distinguish between vaccines, toxoids, serums and antitoxins. A vaccine is prepared from a virus or a culture of bacteria. A toxoid is prepared from the liquid culture medium in which bacteria or viruses have grown and produced their toxins. A serum is the liquid portion of human or animal blood that contains immunizing substances. An antitoxin is the purified immunizing agent derived from a serum. Use of serums is decreasing because of the danger that they may trigger allergic attacks. (See Index, under Allergies.)

General infections are particularly dangerous

Some infections are so massive or so violent that they immediately overwhelm all local and secondary resistance and enter the blood stream; in some cases infection is introduced directly into the blood. Unless there has been previous immunization, such general infections, as they are called, are often serious and sometimes fatal. They include rheumatic fever, typhoid fever and chronic infection of the heart valves by a streptococcus. They may be overcome by the body's own immunity mechanism, through the gradual development of antibodies. The course of the disease indicates the struggle between infection and resistance; the result is victory (recovery), defeat (death) or stalemate (chronic disease).

Recovery from disease, or injury or surgery

Even when the patient has recovered, certain organs or tissues may have been more or less seriously damaged. In such cases, the body may continue to function quite well, as long as there are no unusual

351

General Electric

EYE

OPTIC NERVE

BRAIN

In some cases, there is complete recovery from disease or injury. Thus bone heals well and full function is generally restored. Above, we see three stages in the healing of a fracture of the tibia and fibula (bones of the leg), with the photo at the extreme right showing the completely healed bones. There are cases, however, in which specialized tissue, once destroyed, is not replaceable by healing. Thus vision is permanently lost when the optic nerve, which leads to the eye (see diagram, left), is destroyed.

stresses. Scarlet fever, for example, before the days of modern drug treatment, frequently did serious injury to the kidneys, destroying some cells and damaging others. Under proper treatment, recovery would take place in some instances. If the injury to cells had not been too great, they would recover and resume their function. The cells which had been killed would be partially replaced by other cells of similar character or by fibrous scar tissue.

If the end result of the healing process, following disease or injury or surgical removal, leaves too much scar tissue and too little cell replacement, there is limitation of function. There is a final line of defense, even against such limitation. There is so much tissue reserve that in many cases there will be enough functioning tissue to meet the ordinary needs of the body. As a result, many persons with damaged organs or tissues may live long and well by exercising

due care and remaining under competent medical supervision.

Many tissues are replaceable after injury. Muscles, skin and even bone heal well, and full function is restored except in very severe injuries. Vital organs such as the heart have a high rate of recovery after serious injury as from diphtheria toxin, rheumatic fever or even a heart attack. There is much more kidney and liver substance than is required for ordinary living. The mucous membranes of the lungs, stomach, intestines and other internal organs are still able to carry on after they have been extensively damaged.

To some extent, certain organs may even take over the activity of others that have been impaired. The stomach can be almost completely removed, and digestion still goes on in the intestines with hardly diminished efficiency, if a few eating habits are modified. Removal or failure of glands can now be remedied by supplying the hormones they would normally secrete; thyroid feeding by mouth and insulin replacement by injection are prominent examples.

The more specialized tissues are not replaceable by healing, once they have been destroyed. When the nerve of hearing is gone, that function is lost forever; vision is lost when the optic nerve is destroyed. When cells of special sense nerves and of the brain and spinal cord are killed, they are not replaced by other nerve cells but by scar tissue. Thus when a brain area concerned with a certain function, such as muscle control in the hand or the foot, is destroyed, the hand or foot will be paralyzed, unless other muscles can take the place of the lost muscle. It is true that sometimes recovery or at least partial recovery may occur after a brain injury; but this is because the nerve cells have not been destroyed, but only injured. As they recover, function returns.

Many nerve cells have long filaments carrying impulses to a distant point or bringing them from that point. If such a filament is cut but the cell remains intact, function will return when a new filament has grown along the path of the injured one.

In the healing process involving the less specialized tissues, new cells are formed only to the extent that the tissue is made whole again and resumes its function. In the normal individual, regrowth and scarring after an injury or surgery seldom get out of control. In a few instances a scar may overgrow and form a structure called a keloid, which can usually be corrected by minor surgery.

Other defenses of the human body

In addition to all the defenses that we have considered hitherto, there are psychological and mental defenses, arising out of instinctive fears and acquired experience. The baby is born with fear of falling and of loud noises; as we grow older, we develop various patterns of cautious procedure that help to keep us out of trouble and reasonably intact most of the time.

See also Vol. 10, p. 276: "General Works."

Federal Nigeria Information Office

The scar that is left after injury to the skin consists of specialized fibrous tissue and does not represent replacement of the original cells. This scar tissue lacks elasticity, and the epidermis is not firmly joined to it. In some cases, scars represent deliberate patterns which are brought about by means of incisions in the skin in accordance with tribal rites. The incisions may be superficial, resulting in comparatively slight scars, like those on the face of the boy, above, belonging to the Yoruba tribe in Nigeria. If the incisions are deep, the corresponding scars are prominent, as in the case of the Western Australian aborigine shown in the lower photo.

Australian News and Information Bureau

Lofman-Standard Oil Co. (N.J.)

Tony Linck—Cities Service Co.

Above: a seismic exploration party, prospecting for oil, sets off a dynamite charge near Lewiston, Montana. Shock waves from the blast are reflected from underground rock layers and are recorded by a seismographic recording truck. A good idea of the contour of the rock layers is obtained and the search for oil can be narrowed down. In the right-hand photograph, we see a reflection seismographic record being inspected by an operator after a shot.

MODERN METHODS
OF PROSPECTING

How Hidden Ore and Oil
Deposits Are Located

FOR the past few generations, industry has been draining our mineral resources at an ever increasing rate. It is a matter of great importance, therefore, to find new sources of coal, iron, petroleum and the other minerals that are used in such vast quantities in peace and war.

Until comparatively recently, prospecting for new deposits was usually limited to a study of rock outcrops, shallow test pits and drill holes. Rock outcrops furnish the best key to what lies beneath the surface; unfortunately, in most mining and oil districts they cover less than 2 per cent of the total surface. Furthermore, in the temperate zone large areas are more or less masked by a thin veneer of soil; in the tropics the rock has been rotted so deeply and the vegetation is so dense that a geological report is sometimes impossible. In the northern United States and in Canada the continental glacier left behind an immense amount of debris, which in many cases directly conceals the rock crust. This crust is hidden, in other cases, under thousands of lakes and swamps occupying hollows in the glacial material.

In those regions where dependable rock outcrops are plentiful, a geologist can rather accurately foretell the underground structure; in most cases, however, such territories have already been most carefully studied. The really important areas for present and future prospecting are the hidden and as yet unidentified portions of the earth's crust. Prospectors seeking mineral treasure welcome any economical method that will pierce the covering mantle and reveal the presence or absence of ore deposits, as well as provide information about the structure of the underlying rock.

Perhaps the first method used to locate hidden deposits was a forked stick, like the hazel twig that is supposed to locate subsurface water. When a gold nugget was tied to the forked stick and the prospector walked over the territory that was to be examined, the stick was supposed to dip suddenly if it neared a lode of gold. Petroleum deposits were sought by means of a vial of petroleum attached to a forked stick. To the scientifically minded person, of course, all this seems absurd.

Yet in the present century some of the shrewdest oil operators in the United States actually took seriously a modern counterpart of the forked stick. This device, which was called a wigglestick, consisted of two coiled aluminum springs joined together so as to form a fork. A platinum vial was inserted in the fork; it contained a secret chemical that was supposed to have an affinity for oil. Needless to say, this curious device was a fraud.*

Today, oil prospectors seldom rely on direct methods for detecting petroleum; they seek structures that may hold oil. On the other hand, solid ore deposits are located directly by truly scientific devices. In general, the scientific detection of hidden ore bodies is based on the differences between the properties of the ore mass and of the enclosing medium. Where such differences do not exist, prospecting instruments can furnish no clue.

Where, however, the ore body differs from the surrounding rock in density, in electrical conduction, in magnetism or in the way it transmits earthquake shocks,

* However, chemical methods are employed in geological prospecting; for example, samples of mineral are tested, or assayed, for their content. Oil deposits may be detected by analysis of surrounding rock and soil for any hydrocarbons that have seeped into them from the oil.

modern scientific methods enable the geologist to locate hidden ore deposits. By way of illustration, we might compare the locating of ore deposits underground with the hunting of submarines underwater. During World War I, the detection of a motionless, submerged submarine was a difficult matter, since the propeller was not turning and therefore making no noise. However, experiments soon revealed that a submerged steel vessel has electrical and magnetic properties different from those of sea water and that it reflects sound waves. Ingenious instruments, based on all these discoveries, were then devised. It became a fairly easy matter, by the close of the war, to detect the presence of submerged underwater craft.

Modern methods of locating valuable hidden deposits work on much the same principles. They have nothing at all in common with the "wigglestick" and "forked stick" for which no scientific basis has yet been discovered. They make use of differences in certain physical factors — differences that are caused by the presence of ore deposits. Important factors in geophysical prospecting include magnetism, density, elasticity, electric conductivity, thermal (heat) conductivity and radioactivity. Since nature provides an infinite number of combinations of these factors in each situation, it would be unfair to expect all the methods to work equally well. Consequently, it is customary to make a preliminary geological survey to determine which method is best suited to the existing local conditions.

Magnetic methods

A compass needle free to swing around a vertical axis will point toward the earth's north magnetic pole in the Northern Hemisphere and toward the south magnetic pole in the Southern Hemisphere. These poles do not coincide with the geographic ones. Our globe is like a giant magnet, with many local variations in the intensity of its magnetism, due to differences in the composition of the earth's crust. The compass needle is used to indicate the horizontal variations in the earth's magnetism.

Vertical variations, known as "dip," are indicated by means of a needle mounted on a horizontal axis. Determinations of such variations have been made for many years at various stations. Specially prepared maps show points of equal magnetic intensity over all of the earth's crust.

Magnetic-intensity changes are detected more accurately by the deflection of a magnetometer, a device suspended on a knife edge. There are magnetometers for measuring the horizontal or the vertical component of the earth's field.

As we have said, the earth behaves like a giant magnet producing lines of magnetic force that radiate from the poles. These lines of force are affected by the composition of the earth's crust; they can penetrate some rocks better than others. Rocks that are very easily magnetized tend to warp or distort the magnetic lines of force, or magnetic gradient, as they are sometimes called. Each type of rock produces its own distortion pattern. The magnetometer measures the magnetic gradient in a given region; the distortions of the gradient make it possible to detect valuable deposits.

Although most of the earth's minerals are not very magnetic, a few are. One example is the mineral known by the ancients as "loadstone" and now called magnetite (Fe_3O_4), one of the oxygen compounds of iron. Magnetic substances distort the magnetic gradient by pulling the lines toward them. In Figure 1, we can see how a deposit of iron is acting like a small magnet. It has formed two distinct magnetic poles around which the lines of force have formed. A map such as this would probably indicate a workable ore.

Sometimes a valuable ore is commonly associated with a less valuable magnetic mineral. Certain ores are located by this means. In this case, the desired ore causes no magnetic distortion, but the surrounding material distorts the lines of force around the deposit. Magnetic maps show this deviation from the normal magnetic gradient. The valuable deposit is silhouetted by the magnetic distortion of the surrounding material. In this way, other types of deposits are found.

Fig. 1. This highly simplified plan shows several lines of equal magnetic attraction.

The magnetic exploration method is sometimes used in prospecting for oil deposits. These deposits are often found in places where there are salt domes within the crust of the earth. The domes, consisting of rock salt, have been forced up through various rock strata from salt beds lying deep in the earth. If certain strata have not been penetrated by the salt but have been pushed up as shown in Figure 2 (B and C), they provide fine reservoirs for petroleum. The magnetic method is used to detect salt domes because they are diamagnetic (not easily penetrated by magnetic lines of force) and therefore bring about a definite weakening of the magnetic field of the earth at its surface.

Magnetic prospecting instruments installed in planes and helicopters have been used in recent years to carry out exploratory surveys in various parts of the world. The instruments used record variations in magnetic intensity on a moving strip of paper as the plane or helicopter flies back and forth over the area that is being surveyed. This makes it possible to complete a survey in much less time than would otherwise be required.

Seismic methods

When an earthquake occurs or when a charge of dynamite is exploded, the sound travels through the air and the shock moves through the ground. Both travel in the form of vibration impulses, or waves. Shock waves traveling through the various

strata of the earth form the basis of the seismic, or earthquake, method of exploration. This method depends upon the measurements of the time intervals that elapse between the firing of charges of dynamite and the arrivals of vibration impulses at a number of sound detectors set up on the surface of the ground.

The speed with which a rock formation transmits the vibrations will depend upon the elasticity and density of the rock. The vibrations travel more rapidly through hard and solidly compacted rocks than they do through formations that are loose or entirely uncemented. They may go through loose sediment at the rate of only 1,000 feet a second, while they may attain a velocity of 17,000 feet per second when they make their way through salt domes.

It may take the shock waves less time to go from one point on the earth's surface to another by way of an underlying rock formation than by way of the earth's surface. In Figure 2, A represents the place where a charge of dynamite has been set off; D the place where the wave arrives. If D is far enough away from A, the wave going along the path ABCD will arrive at D before the wave that travels along the short cut AD. The reason is that the first wave will pass through much denser formations, including a salt dome.

Fig. 2. How the different strata are arranged in an area containing a salt dome.

In seismic exploration the dynamite charge, varying in weight from a few pounds to about a ton, is put in a hole drilled in the ground; this hole must be deep enough so that it will be below the soil or below the area containing fragments of weathered rock. The time when the charge is set off is recorded when the explosion

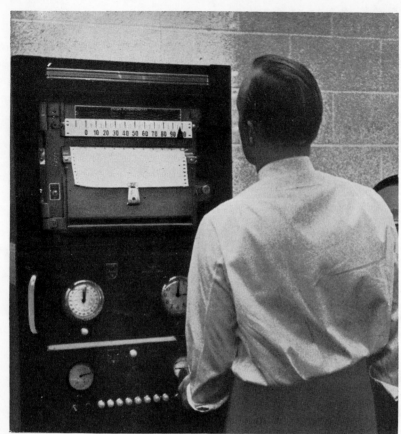

Fig. 3. The X-ray diffractometer identifies rock samples and it also aids in mapping various structures deep within the earth.

breaks an electric circuit carried through a wire imbedded in the dynamite charge.

The detectors, called geophones, are in small metal cylinders; they are set upon the ground at intervals. As the vibrations hit a geophone, they are converted into electrical impulses; these are transmitted through wires connected with a recording station installed on a truck. In the recording station the impulses are amplified and transmitted to a mirror galvanometer. This records the vibrations on moving photographic paper by reflecting a spot of light upon the paper. Impulses from a number of geophones can be recorded in a single station at the same time.

In the refraction method of seismic exploration, the shock waves are refracted, or bent, as they reach formations of greater or lesser density. Experts analyze the differences in speed of waves traveling through the different formations. In the reflecting method, waves are reflected back to the surface from underlying rock formations; the detectors are set comparatively near the place where the charge is fired.

Gravitational methods

According to the law of gravitation, the attraction between two bodies is proportional to the product of their masses and inversely proportional to the square of the distance between them. By measuring the force of gravitational attraction at a given area, the geological prospector can derive a good deal of information about the nature of the underlying rock formations, since these formations differ in density. We know, for example, that sedimentary rocks, such as mudstone, sandstone and shale, are not so dense as igneous rocks, such as granite and basalt. Obviously the gravitational attraction will be greater where the underlying rock formations are igneous than where they are sedimentary.

Any instrument that measures very small changes in gravity is extremely valuable in locating hidden deposits and in deciphering the underground structure of the earth's crust. Such an instrument is the torsion balance; with it, changes in gravity of one part in a million may be detected.

The torsion balance usually consists of a more or less horizontal bar that is suspended by its center from a vertical wire; at each end of the bar is a weight. Both weights are of equal mass and, as a rule, are set so that each one is at a different height above the (horizontal) surface of the ground. (In one form of balance, the bar itself hangs slanted at an angle to the horizontal; the directly attached weights are thus at different altitudes.) The torsion balance is free to move horizontally around the vertical wire axis that passes through its center.

When the balance is brought above an area of ground where the underlying rocks show differences in density, it rotates. This happens because the density variations have warped the gravitational field above the surface of the ground. In effect, the torsion instrument has become unbalanced with respect to the gravity prevailing in that region. Since the balance can move only horizontally to compensate, it rotates and twists the wire to which it is attached. The amount of torsion developed in this wire is recorded photographically and indicates the quantity of gravitational change in the area. Although a highly sensitive instrument, the torsion balance requires much time to operate and has been replaced in the United States by the gravity meter, or gravimeter.

Unlike the torsion balance, the gravimeter measures the vertical force of gravity directly. There a number of types, but most instruments employ a suspended metal spring with an attached weight or arm; the spring responds to rock-density and gravity changes by lengthening or shortening or sometimes by rotating (Figure 4). Since this motion is extremely small, it is magnified by means of electrical, optical or mechanical devices, which also record the changes involved.

At first, the gravimeter was not so efficient as the torsion balance, but it has since been perfected. It is now extremely sensitive as well as easy to use. The gravimeter is placed on the ground or is held above it on supports; it is also used on airplanes and ships. Light portable models have been developed to allow numerous readings over a wide range of country in a single day. Gravity meters are used extensively in prospecting and research, because of their sensitivity to density variations in rock — a widespread phenomenon.

At one time the pendulum was commonly used in the United States in gravitational prospecting. The period of motion of a freely swinging pendulum is affected by changes in the gravitational force to which the device is subjected. These time changes are recorded and measured. Today, surveys based on the use of the pendulum are restricted mainly to purely scientific work.

Electrical methods

There are several methods of prospecting by means of natural and induced electrical currents and waves. They have been successful to a limited extent, particularly where metallic ore bodies are sought. Electrical procedures have also been applied to petroleum exploration, as we shall note later on in this article.

The so-called self-potential technique relies on natural electrical currents generated by ore bodies. Electrochemical activity often results when a metal-sulfide mineral in the ground comes in contact

Fig. 4. These simplified diagrams show two types of gravimeters. The force of gravity is measured in the first of these devices (A) as a spring is lengthened or shortened; in the second one (B) as the spring rotates.

with mineral-water solutions. The associated differences in electrical potential (voltage) produced in different parts of such a mineral mass can be detected by sensitive instruments.

Wherever the rocks are not electrically active, current must be artificially generated in them, in the applied-potential methods. The simplest way is to place a pair of electrodes in the ground and pass current between them. More elaborate methods employ copper conductors up to thousands of feet long placed parallel to each other

Fig. 5. Diagram showing how the applied-potential method of electrical prospecting is employed. A portable alternating-current generator sends currents flowing through two bare copper conductors about 3,000 feet long and about 1,000 feet apart. In an area of equal conductivity, current flows through the ground between the wires in straight lines (dotted) at right angles to the wires. Lines of equal potential (solid) are also straight but parallel to the conductors. The area between the two conductors is searched with two movable electrode pegs, connected to an amplifier and earphones. If no sound is heard in the earphones, both pegs are on one equipotential line of force. The equipotential lines in the area can be mapped out in this way. An ore body, with different conductivity from that of the rest of the area, will affect the lines as shown.

along the surface of the ground and electrified by means of an alternating-current generator of low voltage, as shown in Figure 5. Ground currents then flow between the conductors at right angles to them. Naturally, along each electrical current there is a progressive change in electrical potential, measured in volts. Imaginary lines connecting regions of the same potential are known as equipotentials, generally running at right angles to the directions of the earth currents and parallel to the copper conductors (Figure 5).

The lines of equipotential are plotted by means of movable electrodes with earphones stuck here and there into the ground. As long as the electrodes are on the same equipotential line, no current flows through them, and the earphones are silent. But as soon as the electrodes are placed on different equipotentials, current flows into the phones, and the prospector hears a noise. In this way, the potential and current patterns are plotted; wherever distortions in these lines occur, a mass with marked electrical properties is probably responsible. It may be a body of ore, as shown in Figure 5.

The self-potential and applied-potential methods discussed above permit only a relatively shallow penetration of the earth. Other electrical operations probe deeper into the ground and provide a somewhat clearer picture of conditions there. Deep penetration of the earth can be obtained by the investigation of what are known as natural earth, or telluric, currents — broad sheets of electricity that sweep along the crust of the globe daily. Special instruments determine the patterns of earth currents; they have been used in detecting deep rock structures that may contain petroleum. Various layers in the crust react differently to the passage of the current; from this, it is possible to build up a picture of the situation at relatively great depths, up to several thousand feet.

Other deep-penetration methods use applied electrical currents. One of them measures the resistivity of various rock layers to the passage of electricity. Current is sent through the ground by means of two widely separated electrodes stuck into it. A second pair of electrodes is moved around between the current electrodes and traces the distribution of electric currents and potentials. Each rock layer affects, or "refracts," the paths of the applied currents differently. From all these measurements, the investigator calculates the resistivities of beds thousands of feet down to the transmission of the currents. The farther apart the current electrodes are located (sometimes over a hundred miles), the deeper the electricity penetrates the earth; however, there is a practical limit to the separation of the electrodes, for the currents would them become too weak. The entire procedure bears some resemblance to seismic refraction surveys, in that the paths of artificially induced disturbances (here, electricity instead of dynamite-explosion waves) are characteristically distorted by particular kinds of rock.

One electrical prospecting method uses electrical pulses sent underground; these pulses are then reflected back up from different rock layers somewhat as earthquake waves are in seismic reflection surveying. Another technique involves sending radio waves into the ground; in response, the latter may emit secondary radio waves if it contains metallic ores. In still another method, a magnetic field is induced in the ground by means of an electrified surface cable; the nature of the rocks affects this field, which is measured by means of detecting coils at the surface.

Electrical measurements in rocks are also made in wells being driven for petroleum — a process called electric well logging. The resistivities of various rock beds that have been drilled are taken by means of one or more electrodes lowered into the borehole. Current is passed between the electrodes and a source of electricity on the ground surface near the well; the rock surrounding the well (plus any metal casing in the hole) conducts the current. The electrical characteristics of the beds at different levels are taken in successive readings; they indicate the nature of the rocks. In some cases, current is not applied; the self-potential of the rocks is sufficient for measurement and study.

Radioactivity methods

Prospecting for radioactive minerals, containing uranium, thorium and radium, involves certain special techniques. Since radioactive materials give off radiation, they are most readily found by devices that detect this emission. Among them is the Geiger counter. This instrument consists essentially of a gas-filled tube containing a pair of electrodes. Normally the gas inside does not conduct electricity; but when radioactivity from an outside source passes through the tube, it electrically charges the gas. The latter then allows current to discharge between the electrodes, producing a loud click when it is amplified. The rate of clicking indicates the concentration of the radioactive mineral that is emitting the radiation.

A far more sensitive (and costly) radiation detector is the scintillation counter, or scintillometer. In this instrument, a crystal responds to atomic emission striking it by producing minute light flashes, or scintillations. These flashes are magnified and recorded by electronic tubes and meters. There are various types of Geiger counters and scintillometers on the market, suitable for the different conditions that are encountered in prospecting.

Radioactivity measurements are also taken in wells that are being bored for oil. A detector is lowered down the hole; as it passes through various formations of rock, it records the intensity of radioactivity found in each. This gives a clue to the nature of the earth below the surface.

Summary

We have sketched some of the more important scientific techniques involved in prospecting for mineral wealth. There are numerous variations of these methods, which are constantly being improved, and new procedures are being developed.

The selection of appropriate operations in a given area often poses a problem. Much depends on the extent to which the region has been previously explored (if at all) by conventional surface-geology methods, as well as on the expense involved and on just what is being sought. Seismic surveying is costly; magnetic and gravimetric methods, less so. Seismic, gravimetric and electrical techniques are often employed in petroleum work. The various methods may corroborate each other; sometimes they conflict or do not agree with the conventional geological picture. At least, they may indicate something unusual or unsuspected below the surface of the earth. Much depends on the correct geological interpretation of raw instrumental data.

THE DEFENSES OF PLANTS

How Plants Ward off Their Animal Enemies

IN THE constant struggle for life, plants develop a great variety of defenses to insure the survival of their species. Certain plants find safety in numbers. For example, the grasses, which are otherwise quite defenseless, grow so quickly and flourish so abundantly that there is little danger of their being completely annihilated by browsing animals, such as cattle and sheep. Other plants manage to survive because they have efficient defensive weapons. The mountain laurel and rhododendron, for instance, have a strong poison in their leaves; other plants are effectively protected by barbs or spines or disagreeable odors. Certain plants have developed ways of attracting insect friends that either aid in pollination or destroy other insects injurious to these plants. For example, flowers of many plants contain nectar, which attracts bees and moths; these insects distribute pollen in their trips from flower to flower.

Unfortunately for most plants that are in danger of being eaten, it is the green shoots and the leaves that are consumed by herbivorous, or vegetation-eating, animals. The green parts of plants contain chlorophyll, and photosynthesis (see Index) takes place in these areas. If they are destroyed, the plant loses its food-making machinery. Therefore any adaptations that protect these vital centers make it more likely that the plant will survive.

An adaptation is a characteristic feature that allows a plant to successfully live under certain environmental conditions. The environment includes not only the conditions of the soil, the amount of moisture, the temperature and so on, but it also involves the other plants and animals that live in the same general area. An adaptation is the result of a long series of evolutionary changes. These changes are due to variations in the plant's heredity. If the variations are favorable and if they are passed on to the offspring, the species as a whole will have a particularly good chance to survive. Plants developing favorable traits of this kind are said to be naturally selected.

The statement (often heard) that a single plant or a whole plant species adapts itself to a certain environment is not quite accurate. It implies that plants are able to know beforehand the problems that arise from a change in the environment. Furthermore, it suggests that plants can change their structures or manner of functioning in order to meet such problems. This has not been scientifically demonstrated. With our present knowledge of plants and their responses to the environment, it is better to say that they become adapted by the natural selection of hereditary variations.

A herbivorous animal, desiring food, does not reason that by eating the green parts of a plant it will destroy the plant's capacity to produce more food. Men act somewhat differently because they usually save enough of an individual plant or a sufficient number of plants to replenish what they have taken for themselves. But this protection given to plants through man's foresight is only extended to a very few species — namely, those that he requires for his food, clothing or other products of his civilization. If plants were dependent for survival upon man's foresight, they would be hard pressed indeed, for the plants that he seeks to protect because they are useful to him are few in number. Plants must, therefore, depend upon their own defenses for survival.

PLANTS DEFENDED
BY THEIR POISON

The leaves, flowers or fruits of the plants shown on this page are avoided by animals because they are poisonous.

Barberry (*Berberis thunbergii*).

Hellebore (*Helleborus niger*).

Nightshade (genus *Solanum*).

All photos except bottom right,
J. Horace McFarland

U. S. Forest Service

Some rhododendron blossoms.

Left: monkshood (*Aconitum napellus*).

There are a great many different kinds of plant defenses. Certain types protect the plant from all kinds of dangers, while others are effective only against certain enemies. There are defensive devices that serve only to repel enemies; others may do considerable harm to any animals that may attempt to attack the plant.

Plant poisons are efficient defenses

Among the most efficient plant defenses are the plant poisons, which take effect when the plant is touched or eaten. It is interesting to note that not all parts of the plant are equally toxic, or poisonous. Most of the poisons are concentrated in the plant parts that are most susceptible to attack: the leaves, in which food is manufactured, and the fruits and flowers, which serve for reproduction.

Different poisons produce varying effects on different animals. Poison ivy (*Rhus toxicodendron*), for example, brings about a very unpleasant skin rash in human beings, but it serves as the main source of food for certain insects which devour the leaves of the plant.

The many kinds of plant poisons

The plant poisons are made up of complex organic compounds — alkaloids, glucosides, resinoids and organic acids. They produce a variety of symptoms in the victims. Plants that are poisonous by contact, such as poison ivy, secrete a number of poisons belonging to the alkaloid group. The main effect, as we pointed out, is a rash — the condition known as contact dermatitis.

Plants such as sorghum, arrowgrass and certain species of wild cherries secrete a glucoside-type poison called prussic acid.* This poison kills within minutes after animals feed on a plant containing it. Another active ingredient in many plant poisons is the compound known as tremetol,

---

* Prussic acid (HCN) is more properly known as hydrocyanic acid; in its dilute form, it is called Scheele's acid. Its gaseous form, hydrogen cyanide, is one of the most deadly and fastest-acting poisons known." Hydrogen cyanide gas is used in gas chambers for the execution of criminals.

which is found in the white snakeroot and the rayless goldenrod. Tremetol causes the disease called "trembles" in grazing animals; it is characterized by muscular weakness and shaking. This form of animal poisoning is of particular concern to mankind, because the poison is very soluble in cow's milk and can be transmitted to man through that medium. In the human form, the disease is commonly known as "milk sickness."

Plants that secrete photosensitizing poisons

Some plants secrete what are known as photosensitizing poisons. These substances make an animal highly sensitive to light. If the animal remains in the shade, it will be unaffected, but if it steps into strong sunlight, it will develop a wide variety of symptoms; death may result. Photosensitizing poisons are secreted by such plants as the buckwheat and St.-John's-wort.

Some poisonous plants do not manufacture their poisons at all, but take them up directly from the soil. These plants are often referred to as seleniferous because their poison is so commonly the element selenium. They can absorb this element through their roots from certain types of shale. The locoweed, wild aster and prince's-plume are plants of this type. They cause the conditions known as alkali disease and "blind staggers."

Substances that make plants undesirable as food

Other plants take up from the soil certain substances which, though they are not toxic, render the plants undesirable to animals looking for food. One of the most common substances of this type is silica, the oxide of silicon. In the stems of horsetails, the leaves of rhododendrons and the needles of certain evergreens, one finds large deposits of silica. As a result, the plants become unappetizing and quite indigestible for animals. The same is true of certain kinds of vegetation found in the Australian bush.

Plants have found other ways of making themselves undesirable as food for animals.

The sharp spines of the cactus.

The thistle is a prickly plant.

PLANTS THAT WARD OFF THEIR FOES

The leaves of the eryngo plant, above, have several sharp spines along the edges.

The leaves of the aloe plant (left) have a very sharp apex and their margin is spiny.

In order for an animal to like a food, it must have a pleasant taste. Certain plants are either very bitter or very sour. Most animals sampling vegetation of this kind will leave it severely alone thereafter. The sense of taste is very closely allied to that of smell. Plant defenses may be in the nature of more or less offensive smells, which cause animals to pass by what might otherwise be considered as a palatable food. The dog fennel and the hound's-tongue are among the plants whose odor is evidently very disagreeable to the ordinary grazing animals. In the case of poisonous plants with unpleasant odors, such as the water hemlock and the tobacco plant, an odor of this kind will protect not only the plant itself, but also the grazing animal, which will seek its food elsewhere. In fact, many of the poisonous plants that give off foul odors are also disagreeable to the taste — an effective double protection for the plants and for the animals that otherwise might be tempted to feast upon them.

Evil-tasting substances
in fruits, flowers and seeds

In some plants, such as the peppers, mustard and horse radish, the leaves are not the worst-tasting parts. It is the reproductive structures — the fruits, flowers and seeds — that contain particularly unpleasant, though not poisonous, substances. These substances are chemically related to the poisons found in some plants. For example, the taste of mustard comes from a glucoside that is transformed by myrosin, an enzyme, into an oil (C_3H_5NCS). (You will recall that many of the plant poisons are glucoside- and alkaloid-type compounds.) Pepper gets its flavor from an alkaloid called piperine. Horse radish contains a volatile oil, butyl sulphocyanide, which is related to one of the deadliest poisons known to man.

Drops of water
may protect plants

Most grazing animals do not care for plants on whose leaves drops of water or dew are present. Some plants have developed a special capacity for retaining drops of water, derived from dew, much longer than other plants do. Among the varieties using this defensive device are the teasel and the compass plant.

How animals are able
to avoid poisonous plants

Although the species of poisonous plants are comparatively few in number, the number of individuals is large. With so many poisonous plants occurring over a wide range, one might wonder how animal life has survived so well. The answer is that animals seem to be able, in some way that we do not understand, to avoid these dangerous forms of vegetation.

It is an old belief that in the jungle, if a man eats only what he sees monkeys eat, he will run no risk from poisonous vegetation. Certainly, animals do seem to know instinctively which plants are safe for them to eat. As we have seen, they shun some plants because they give off an unpleasant odor. Even if poisonous plants do not give off any odor — or at least an odor that is perceptible to human beings — animals seem able to avoid them. Certain grazing animals also keep away from various mosses and ferns which, as far as we know, are not poisonous. We can only guess that such plants are harmful to the animals in some way.

Sharp weapons
that defend plants

Some plants protect themselves by warding off their enemies with sharp, pointed weapons such as spines, prickles and thorns. Spines are modified leaves. The spines of the cactus plant, for example, are formed when most of the leaf dries up and falls off, leaving only its central structure. The spine-type leaf helps the plant conserve water by presenting much less surface for evaporation. Thorns are modified twigs; they serve exclusively for protection. Prickles are derived from epithelial, or surface, tissue. They also serve only for protection.

As in the case of plant poisons, the spines, thorns and prickles are distributed strategically on the plant so as to protect its important parts — the leaves, fruits and flowers. They are arranged in such a way as to come in contact with any animal attempting to feed on the plant. The distribution and size of the protective structures depend upon the kind of animal most likely to attack the plant and the probable point of attack.

The huge floating leaves of *Victoria regia* are protected only on the under surface and at the margins, because only at these points is it vulnerable to attack. Other plants are armored only at the lower portions of their stems. Above a certain height, they are quite safe from the attacks of grazing animals.

Defensive structures that protect young plants

In some cases, a plant has defensive structures only during a part of its life. A young plant that is weak and tender may be armed with thorns until it grows into a more sturdy individual that is much less likely to be attacked. Plants that are armored only on their lower parts are of this particular type.

Earlier in this article, we mentioned that the leaves of certain plants are undesirable as animal food because they contain silica deposits. Other leaves are not suitable for grazing animals because they are formed in such a way as to cut the mouths and internal organs of animals that try to eat them. The pine needle is a case in point. It is interesting to note that not only are such leaves very similar to needles in appearance, but that in certain parts of the world they are actually used by the natives as sewing needles.

Defensive weapons determined by geography

Plants with needlelike leaves are very common in dry, arid regions; the leaves protect the plants and help conserve water. Protection against animals is especially important in these areas because of the scarcity of other types of plants on which the animals can feed.

Similar in shape to the needlelike leaves are the long, narrow sturdy ones of the South African aloe plant. This type of leaf is not only long but also pointed; an animal would have to be something of a sword swallower to eat it. The margins of the leaf are protected by small spines.

Spines that are like the teeth of a saw

A number of other plants have spines along the margins of their leaves for defensive purposes. The spines are like the teeth of a saw; they cut the lips and mouths of any grazing animals foolish enough to try to eat them. To reinforce these cutting edges, the leaves are often impregnated with silica deposits. Some plants, such as cut-grass, contain so much silica that the leaves do not even require spiny margins. They cut like knives and are capable of inflicting serious wounds.

The hypodermic needle of the stinging nettle

Certain plants have combined the needle defense with poison to produce even more effective protection. The stinging nettle is of this type. Its barbs act in much the same way as hypodermic needles, piercing an attacking animal and injecting poison at the same time.

When one brings one's hand in contact with certain leaves, such as those of the stinging nettle, there will be unfortunate effects. Stinging hairs, each composed of one large cell, will break off from the leaves and will fasten securely upon the hand. They will inject an irritating substance into the skin — a substance related to formic acid ($HCOOH$), which is the "venom" of certain red ants and some other insects. If a number of hairs, concentrated in a small area, have penetrated the skin, the injected substance may bring about considerable inflammation.

The defenses of the stinging nettle are effective only against attack from above. The hairs, which are quite elastic, are pointed upward; they are also restricted to the leaves, the lower parts of the plant being bare. If one passes one's hand upward so as to press down upon the hairs on the leaf, the hand will glide over them without mishap; the hairs will simply be pressed against the leaves. But if one reverses the direction of motion, the slightest touch will break off a number of hairs, releasing their poison.

Plants, therefore, have a great variety of natural defenses. Essential plant parts, such as leaves, fruits and flowers, may be disagreeable in odor and in taste or even poisonous to animals that might want to feed upon them. Some plants are provided with spines, prickles or thorns that discourage browsing animals. Others are protected by pointed, barbed and stinging hairs.

Plants that protect themselves by mimicry

Plant defense, however, is not entirely a matter of nature's having provided actual defensive weapons. The plant has still other resources. It may turn to subterfuge, for example, to protect itself. Thus we have very curious instances of mimicry, where a striking resemblance to another plant or object is unmistakable. Perhaps the best-known example of this kind of mimicry is the common dead nettle. It takes its name from the fact that in general appearance it looks extremely like the common stinging nettle. Actually, however, it has none of that plant's unpleasant properties. Some plants in South Africa look very much like pebbles, while others greatly resemble in coloration the ground in which they grow.

Nature's ingenuity is seldom shown more clearly than in the relationships that come under the general heading of symbiosis (from the Greek word that means "a living together"). This term describes a relationship formed for the mutual benefit of two dissimilar organisms. These may be two different kinds of plants or animals, or a plant and an animal. In many cases, the two organisms involved can live independently, although their association brings benefit to them both.

The lichen provides an example of symbiosis

The lichen is perhaps the classical example of the working of symbiosis, for it is a plant that has developed entirely from the interaction of two other plants upon each other. These two plants are an alga and a fungus, each of which contributes, by its own characteristics, to the formation of the lichen. The alga is a colony of green cells embedded in the fungus. In the alga the process of photosynthesis goes on, while the fungus threads absorb necessary moisture and extract needed minerals from the air and water.

Certain plants, or trees, known as ant plants, form an almost symbiotic type of relationship with ants; they provide the ants with food or protection, or both. In return, the ants protect the plant from the invasion of other insects. The actual protection here may be carried out by the

The leaves of the aquatic Victoria lily are often five feet across, with a rim several inches high.

William Lavarre, from Gendreau

ants' hurling their excretion of formic acid against the unwelcome visitors. Sometimes ants have a kind of symbiotic relationship with plant lice. Their attempts to maintain too large a population of lice on a given plant may destroy that plant. The corn-root louse, for example, is cared for by an ant that lays bare the roots of the corn plant and then places the lice on the exposed root surfaces and thus greatly damages them.

Surrounding water may protect plants

A gardener may surround a plant with water, to protect it from some of its small enemies that can neither fly nor swim. He may stand the potted plant in another pot containing water. Many water plants, such as the water lilies, are protected by nature in a similar way. Bees and other flying insects that visit the plant in search of nectar and pollen are not kept from the plant, while the injurious snails and insects, such as ants, are effectively warded off. In some cases, a slight reservoir of water habitually accumulates at the base of the plant leaves, as in the compass plant and the teasel, and this water pocket serves much the same purpose, though on a considerably smaller scale.

Sticky secretions may provide protection

Even more common is another kind of effective defense. Extremely sticky secretions from the plant tissues lie upon the surfaces of some plants, to trap insects that crawl over them. This excretion may come from the epidermis (the external skin or coating) or from special glands or hairs. It is most commonly found on the flower stalk or on the principal stem. The protection derived from such sticky secretions sometimes extends not merely to the flower but to the whole foliage, as in some of the primulas and saxifrages. On the leaves of these plants the dead bodies of insects are often found, caught in the sticky protective substance.

A waxlike covering, present in so many flowering parts, is still another means of protecting the flower. It is no defense against snails, which can pass over it with no difficulty, but it does protect the plant against the many varieties of hard-bodied little insects that so often launch such extremely damaging attacks on both leaf and flower.

Plant defenses against winged insects, usually in the form of hairlike structures inside the flower, are constructed in various ways. In addition, the actual arrangement of the flower structure itself, especially as regards the hiding and protection of the nectar, is often of the greatest ingenuity.

How undesirable insects are kept away from nectar

In many plants, nature has provided mechanical arrangements to protect the flower nectar against insects that could creep up the stems from the ground. One of the most interesting of these is found in some of the balsams. Special glands developed from the stipules at the leaf bases secrete a sweet discharge that attracts insects climbing up the stems. They come in contact with a drop of this sweet substance at the base of each leaf and find it as satisfying as they would the flower nectar. It also has the advantage of being closer at hand. Ants in search of nectar go so far, therefore, and no farther, and the nectar is safe. In the absence of such sweet stuff at the leaf bases they would, of course, go on to search out the nectar within the flower itself and thus interfere with the visits of the winged-insect pollen-carriers, which are so essential for the successful development of the plant.

Plant defenses may attract as well as repel

Plant defense involves not only the repelling of enemies but the attracting of friends. Under this heading we include nature's many devices to attract insects to different parts of the plants where they will find food; the arrangements of petals to aid in cross-pollination; the provisions for the dispersion of seeds and fruits and their protection.

The French physician Laënnec, inventor of the stethoscope, using the instrument in auscultation. This drawing has been adapted from a painting by Chartran.

SCIENCE AND PROGRESS
(1815-95) VII

BY JUSTUS SCHIFFERES

NEW DIRECTIONS IN MEDICAL RESEARCH

AT the beginning of the nineteenth century, medicine had come a long way from the unscientific mumbo jumbo that had disgusted the sixteenth-century anatomist Vesalius (see Index). Yet much remained to be done. The basic causes of disease were still unknown. Medical men were ignorant of just what happened in vital processes like respiration and digestion; they knew little about the true functioning of the liver; the pancreas was a fascinating mystery to them. When in doubt, they had recourse to bleeding (the drawing of blood by surgical instruments) and leeching (the application of the blood-sucking worms known as leeches). Safe anesthesia and antiseptics were unknown. Surgery was still a pretty crude affair. Surgeons were often considered to be no more proficient than the barber-surgeons of former times; their workshops — the hospitals — were feared as death houses.

In the nineteenth century remarkable progress was made in almost every field of medicine. Improved methods of diagnosis were developed. New light was thrown on the functioning of the body organs. The germ theory of disease revolutionized the treatment of many human ailments and gave promise of controlling epidemics of communicable diseases. The introduction of anesthesia and the use of antiseptics made surgery safer, and as a result its scope was greatly widened.

The groundwork for these spectacular advances was laid in the first five or six decades of the century. For one thing, this period saw the development of an instrument — the stethoscope — that has since become indispensable in diagnosis.

Its inventor, René-Théophile-Hyacinthe Laënnec (1781–1826), was a native of the French province of Brittany, a regimental surgeon in the French Revolution, a physician in two famous hospitals in Paris and a professor of medicine at the College of France.

Laënnec has told us the story of his invention of the stethoscope. "In 1816," he wrote, "I was consulted by a young woman presenting general symptoms of disease of the heart. Owing to her stoutness, little information could be gathered by application of the hand and percussion [tapping the chest with flexed fingers]. The patient's age and sex did not permit me to resort to direct application of the ear to the chest.

"I recalled a well-known acoustic phenomenon; namely, if you place your ear against one end of a wooden beam, the scratch of a pin at the other end can be distinctly heard. It occurred to me that this physical property might serve a useful purpose in the case with which I was then dealing.

"Taking a sheet of paper, I rolled it into a very tight roll, one end of which I placed over the chest in front of the heart. To the other end I put my ear. I was both surprised and gratified at being able to hear the beating of the heart with much greater clearness and distinctness than I had ever done before by direct application of my ear."

On the basis of this principle, Laënnec proceeded to build his stethoscope (from two Greek words meaning "chest-observer"). In its original form, it was a short wooden tube, up to twelve inches in length, and widening somewhat toward each end. (The modern version has two ear tubes with flexible attachments.) In 1819 Laënnec published a treatise in which he described the use of the stethoscope.

Through the use of Laënnec's invention, physicians could now make more accurate diagnoses of diseases of the heart and lungs; they could follow fairly well the spread of these diseases. They could also detect the presence of the fetus in a pregnant woman, since the heart of the fetus beats almost twice as rapidly as that of an adult woman.

There were a number of outstanding developments in physiology in this period. Our scene now shifts to an American frontier army post, where a United States Army surgeon, William Beaumont (1785–1853), has just taken charge of a serious gun-shot case. To quote the good doctor: "Alexis St. Martin [the victim] was a Canadian of French descent, about eighteen years of age, of good constitution, robust and healthy. He had been engaged in the service of the American Fur Company . . . and was accidentally wounded by the discharge of a musket on the sixth of June 1822 . . .

"I saw him in twenty-five or thirty minutes after the accident occurred; and on examination found . . . a protrusion . . . which proved to be a portion of the stomach, lacerated through all its coats and pouring out the food he had taken for his breakfast through an opening large enough to admit the forefinger."

By skillful surgery and constant attention, Beaumont effected a cure. When the wound healed, the stomach remained exposed to the outer air through an aperture about two and a half inches in circumference. It dawned upon Beaumont that he now had a unique opportunity to study the functioning of the stomach, since food could be readily introduced into St. Martin's stomach through the aperture and could be just as readily withdrawn. He therefore proposed to the young French Canadian that he should serve as a living laboratory; in return he agreed to provide the young man with food (and drink) and

lodging. St. Martin agreed, and in 1825 Beaumont began the experiments that were to win him lasting fame in the annals of physiology.

He has thus described one of these experiments: "August 1, 1825. At twelve noon I introduced through the opening into the stomach articles of diet, suspended by a silk string and fastened at proper distances, so as to pass in without pain. [These "articles of diet" included highly seasoned beef à la mode, fat pork, lean beef, salted beef, a piece of stale bread and a bunch of raw, sliced cabbage.] . . . At 1:00 P.M. withdrew and examined them. Found the cabbage and bread about half digested; the pieces of meat unchanged. Returned them into the stomach. At 2:00 P.M. withdrew them again. Found the cabbage, bread, pork and boiled beef all clearly digested and gone from the string; the other pieces of meat but very little affected. Returned them into the stomach again . . . At 3:00 P.M. examined again. Found the à la mode beef partly digested; the raw beef was slightly macerated on the surface. Returned them again." There was little change the next time Beaumont withdrew the string. But St. Martin decided that his patron had done enough experimenting for that day; and so the doctor set to work analyzing his notes.

A classic of medical literature

St. Martin proved to be an exasperating sort of laboratory. He was constantly running away and had to be brought back at great trouble and expense. Furthermore, Beaumont found it hard to carry on his experiments, since War Department orders kept him moving frequently from one post to another. However, he persevered and at last, in 1833, presented his findings in a little book — OBSERVATIONS ON THE GASTRIC JUICE AND THE PHYSIOLOGY OF DIGESTION — published at his own expense. It was perhaps the most important single work ever written on the digestive process. It established once and for all the essential chemical nature of this process; it provided basic information

John Wyeth & Brother, Inc.

William Beaumont withdrawing gastric juice from the stomach of Alexis St. Martin. From a painting by Cornwell.

about the secretions of the stomach and its functioning. All modern studies of nutrition, all modern diet tables are based upon this remarkable little book. The author's experiments, performed under backwoods conditions, represented something more than a landmark in the history of physiology. They proved that the progress of science does not necessarily depend on the amassing of great funds for research and on the construction of big laboratory buildings.

Another great name in the history of physiology is that of Claude Bernard. This distinguished French doctor was born at Saint-Julien in 1813. He studied medicine at Paris, becoming a pupil of the eminent physiologist François Magendie. Bernard completed his medical schooling in 1843; ten years later he became a doctor of science. In the year 1855 he succeeded Magendie as professor of physiology at the College of France. Bernard was an accomplished teacher and lecturer, but his achievements in physiological research were even more outstanding.

He was the first to show how the pancreas functions; in the course of time this discovery pointed the way to the control of diabetes, a disease in which the pancreas fails to function properly. Bernard also made some remarkable discoveries concerning the functioning of the liver. He demonstrated that the liver modifies the glucose (a form of sugar) that reaches it, turning it into a substance called glycogen, which simply means "sugar-maker." This substance is then stored in the liver. When and if the concentration of glucose in the blood falls below a certain level, the liver transforms part of its store of glycogen into glucose and releases it in the blood stream.

Bernard called the conversion of glycogen into sugar an "internal secretion." Today physiologists would no longer so label it, since sugar is not a specific product of the liver. But Bernard's researches pointed the way to the discovery of bona fide internal secretions — those of the pituitary gland, the thyroid gland, the parathyroid glands, the pancreatic islets of Langerhans and the adrenal glands.

Bernard also did important research on the vasomotor nerves, which control the size of the blood vessels. He demonstrated that vasodilator nerves cause the arteries to dilate, and that vasoconstrictor nerves cause these blood vessels to contract.

This great physiologist won many honors in his lifetime. He became an officer and later a commander of the Legion of Honor; he was appointed to the renowned French Academy and he became the founder and first president of the French Biological Society. Upon his death in Paris, in the year 1878, he was given a truly magnificent public funeral.

The first half of the nineteenth century saw a frontal assault on the disease known as puerperal, or childbed, fever, which attacks women in childbirth. This ailment had long taken a fearful toll. The death rate among women admitted to lying-in hospitals was particularly high. One of the first physicians to call attention to the contagious character of this disease and to the manner in which it was carried from one victim to another was the Yankee medical man, poet and essayist Oliver Wendell Holmes (1809–94).

At a meeting of the Boston Society for Medical Improvement, in 1843, Holmes read a paper, The Contagiousness of Puerperal Fever. He pointed out that the disease "is so far contagious as to be frequently carried from patient to patient by physicians and nurses." And why? Because these doctors and nurses did not clean themselves properly before attending their patients. To Holmes this seemed a particularly blameworthy offense. "The woman about to become a mother, or with her newborn infant upon her bosom, should be the object of trembling care and sympathy . . . God forbid that any member of the profession to which she trusts her life . . . should hazard it negligently, unadvisedly or selfishly!"

Holmes' paper aroused the indignation of Dr. Charles Meigs, professor of obstetrics at the University of Pennsylvania. Meigs took Holmes' remarks as a direct slur upon the members of the medical profession as a whole. Holmes answered Meigs with another paper called Puerperal Fever as a Private Pestilence; in this, he pointed out that a certain obstetrician called Senderein had scrubbed his hands with chloride of lime before attending his patients, and that as a result the mortality rate among them had dropped amazingly. Not long afterward Holmes became professor of anatomy at the Harvard Medical School. He seems to have become so absorbed in his new duties that he lost interest in the controversy over puerperal fever.

The war against this disease was to be carried on by the man whom Holmes had called Senderein and whose name was really Semmelweis. Ignaz Philipp Semmelweis (1818–65) was a native of Budapest, Hungary, who received his medical training in Vienna. After completing his schooling, he became an assistant in the lying-in hospital in Vienna. It consisted of two different departments, or divisions.

OLIVER WENDELL HOLMES

PUERPERAL FEVER

IGNAZ PHILIPP SEMMELWEIS

Medical students were taught in the first division; in the second, the women who were to become midwives received their training. In the first division, over a period of six years, there had been 99 deaths per 1,000 births; in the second division only 33. Semmelweis came to the conclusion that puerperal fever was a wound infection transmitted by the hands of the physicians and medical students who examined women during and after childbirth. Sometimes they would turn from one patient to another without troubling to wash their hands. If they did take the trouble, they used only soap and water, and they never quite succeeded in removing all the germ-bearing particles that adhered to their hands.

Semmelweis, who was in charge of the first division, now insisted that all the students should wash their hands in a solution of chloride of lime before examining a patient. The results were truly startling. At the time when Semmelweis issued his order, the death rate from puerperal fever was 120 per 1,000 births; after seven months, the death rate had dropped to 12 per 1,000 births.

Semmelweis' hasty temper had aroused the dislike of his superiors, and he was continually harassed by petty persecution.

At last he could endure no more, and he returned to Budapest. In time he became the director of the lying-in hospital in his native city. Here, too, he was the object of much criticism; as a result, his mind was affected. In 1865 he left for Vienna to consult a specialist in mental diseases. In the course of a routine examination it was discovered that Semmelweis had contracted the same type of infection that he had spent his life in combating. Soon afterward he died of the infection.

The validity of the position taken by Holmes and Semmelweis was not fully appreciated until the germ theory of disease was later demonstrated. Today puerperal fever is no longer a menace in maternity wards. No longer is infection carried, as Holmes had put it, "from bed to bed as rat-killers carry their poison from one household to another."

As a young man Holmes had studied in Paris under Pierre-Charles-Alexandre Louis (1787–1872), the founder of medical statistics. This is an exceedingly important branch of medicine. It is difficult to prove that one method of treatment or control of disease is better than another; often, only accurate statistics can provide this information. Louis showed the possibilities of the statistical method.

A MEMORABLE VICTORY OVER PAIN

On the 16th of October, 1846 — celebrated in Massachusetts as Ether Day — a great victory was won over one of man's most terrible scourges — pain. That day saw a public demonstration of the first safe anesthetic, ether — or sulfuric ether, to give it its full name — in the Massachusetts General Hospital, in Boston. The discovery of the anesthetic effects of ether was due to three Americans — Morton, Jackson and Long — and it represents one of America's most notable contributions to the progress of science and the welfare of mankind.

Before Ether Day, it is true, anesthetics of sorts had been administered to patients about to undergo an operation. The soporific (sleep-producing) and anesthetic

(pain-killing) effects of intoxicating liquids and of the poppy seed — source of morphine, cocaine and laudanum — were well known. The luckless victim of accident, war or disease was sometimes drugged with alcohol or morphine before he took his place on the dirty operating table. But this did not happen as often as one might imagine, for surgeons had discovered that patients drugged with alcohol or morphine were particularly likely to die during or after operations. Often, therefore, the surgeon refused to administer any opiate, and the patient had to bear his pain as best he could. Necessarily cruel, surgery had to be mercifully swift. Naturally, operations lasting hours at a time — like some that take place quite frequently today —

were impossible under such circumstances.

The discovery of a safe anesthetic changed all this almost overnight. Not only did ether make it possible to abolish pain during a surgical operation, but the surgeon no longer had to hurry in order to reduce to the minimum the sufferings of his patient. Many operations now became feasible that would have been quite unthinkable before this time.

Ether was known to chemists years before it was put to practical use to deaden pain. In the 1840's students at the Harvard Medical School occasionally indulged in "ether frolics" — that is, they would inhale the vapor of ether for the mild form of intoxication that it produced. One of the teachers at the Medical School, Dr. Charles Thomas Jackson (1805–80), observed that while under the influence of ether the students seemed to be oblivious to pain. Jackson now began to experiment with sulfuric ether as an anesthetizing agent. One of his students, Dr. William T. G. Morton (1819–68), a dentist who was studying medicine at the Harvard Medical School, became greatly interested in these experiments.

Morton had long sought an effective painkiller that he could use in his dental work. His friend and former partner, Horace Wells, had used nitrous oxide ("laughing gas") to deaden pain in dental treatments, and Morton had been greatly impressed. But unfortunately one of Wells' patients had died from the effects of this anesthetic; shocked, Wells withdrew from practice. Morton realized that he would have to seek a safer anesthetic than nitrous oxide. It now occurred to him that ether might prove to be ideal for this purpose. He experimented with the substance in his own home, first putting his dog to sleep and then testing the effects of the anesthetic on himself. Finally he employed ether on a patient; he removed a tooth without causing any pain.

Morton thought now of the possibility of using ether as an anesthetic in surgical operations. He persuaded Dr. John Collins Warren (1778–1856), senior surgeon of the Massachusetts General Hospital, to let him give ether to a patient who was about to undergo an operation. The date of this demonstration was set for October 16, 1846. A young medical student, Washington Ayer, has left the following eyewitness account of what happened:

"The day arrived; the time appointed was noted on the dial when the patient was led into the operating room. Dr. Warren and a board of the most eminent surgeons in the state were gathered around the sufferer ... It had been announced that 'a test of some preparation was to be made for which the astonishing claim had been made that it would render the person operated upon free from pain.'

"Those present were incredulous, and, as Dr. Morton had not arrived at the time appointed and fifteen minutes had passed, Dr. Warren said with significant meaning: 'I presume he is otherwise engaged.' This was followed by a derisive laugh and Dr. Warren grasped his knife and was about to proceed with the operation.

"At that moment Dr. Morton entered a side door. Dr. Warren turned to him and in a strong voice said: 'Well, sir, your patient is ready.' In a few minutes he was ready for the surgeon's knife, when Dr. Morton said: '*Your* patient is ready, sir.'

"Here the most sublime scene ever witnessed in the operating room was presented, when the patient placed himself voluntarily upon the table, which was to become the altar of future fame ... That was the supreme moment for a most wonderful discovery. Had the patient died under operation, science would have waited long to discover the hypnotic effects of some other remedy [than ether] of equal potency and safety. It may be properly questioned whether chloroform would have come into use as it has at the present time.

"The operation was for a congenital tumor [a growth existing at birth] on the left side of the neck ... The operation was successful; and when the patient recovered, he declared he had suffered no pain. Dr. Warren turned to those present and said: 'Gentlemen, this is no humbug.' "

Morton and Jackson, joining forces, tried to patent ether under the name of

Letheon. They proposed to issue permits for a considerable fee to physicians who wished to use the new anesthetic. This scheme was doomed to failure as soon as doctors recognized that Letheon was simply sulfuric ether. Morton and Jackson soon parted company. Each of the former partners insisted that he was the sole discoverer of anesthesia. That honor was also claimed by Horace Wells, who, as we saw, had used nitrous oxide as an anesthetic.

In 1849, Morton petitioned Congress to give him a substantial reward for his work in developing a safe anesthetic. Jackson also pressed his claims before Congress; the friends of Wells, who had died, likewise entered the lists. For several years the controversy raged. At last a measure appropriating $100,000 for Morton was being actively pushed in the Senate, when one of the senators rose to protest. He pointed out that Dr. Crawford W. Long (1815–78), of Georgia, had used ether in a surgical operation in 1842 — four years before the historic demonstration at the Massachusetts General Hospital. Long's patient, James Venable, had declared under oath in 1849:

Dr. William T. Morton administering ether to a patient before an operation.

"In the early part of the year [1842] the young men of Jefferson and the country adjoining were in the habit of inhaling ether for its exhilarating powers. I inhaled it frequently for that purpose and was very fond of its use.

"While attending the academy, I was frequently in the office of Dr. C. W. Long, and having two tumors on the back of my neck, I several times spoke to him about the propriety of cutting them out, but postponed the operation from time to time. On one occasion . . . I agreed to have one tumor cut out and had the operation performed that evening after school was dismissed. This was in the early part of the spring of 1842.

"I commenced inhaling the ether before the operation was commenced and continued it until the operation was over. I did not feel the slightest pain from the operation and could not believe the tumor was removed until it was shown to me."

Congress took no further action on the $100,000 appropriation after Venable's affidavit had been revealed. To this day the question of priority in the matter of the discovery of anesthesia is shrouded in doubt. It is important to observe that Venable's affidavit was not given until 1849, three years after Morton's public demonstration. The only compensation that Morton ever received for his work on anesthesia was an honorary degree from an American university and a gold medal from the French Academy of Sciences. He died poor and embittered in 1868.

The news of the successful use of ether as an anesthetic flashed quickly around the world. British surgeons, notably James Syme, the tutor of Lister, and James Y. Simpson (1811–70), professor of obstetrics at the University of Glasgow, hastened to adopt this new medical procedure; so did eminent surgeons in other lands.

On November 4, 1847, Simpson announced that chloroform, which had been discovered by the French chemist Jean-Baptiste-André Dumas, could also be employed as a safe anesthetic; he had used chloroform to ease the pains of a woman in childbirth. Simpson was greeted by a perfect hail of criticism. He was denounced by clergymen and others who claimed that painless childbirth was a violation of God's will. They quoted Scripture (Genesis, III:16): "Unto the woman [God] said, I will greatly multiply thy pain and thy travail; in pain thou shalt bring forth children." Simpson answered these objectors in 1847 in a famous paper called Answers to the Religious Objection against the Employment of Anesthetic Agents in Midwifery and Surgery. He failed to silence his critics. But then, in April 1853, Queen Victoria consented to take chloroform during the birth of her seventh child, Prince Leopold. The opposition to pain-killing in childbirth collapsed as if by magic. Chloroform was often administered to women in childbirth thereafter. Nowadays, however, most obstetricians favor so-called "natural childbirth."

THE GERM THEORY OF DISEASE

For many centuries mankind had lived in constant fear of epidemics — a fear that was aggravated by a sense of utter helplessness. The germ theory of disease did much to free man from this terrible nightmare of dread. The theory was one of the great scientific triumphs of the nineteenth century — indeed, of all time.

It had a strange and humble origin — the study of fermentation. Men had been making and drinking alcoholic beverages since time immemorial. Yet not until after the middle of the nineteenth century did anyone know the why and wherefore of fermentation, which turns grapes into wine, and hops, malt, rice, barley and other cereal grains into beer, ale and mead. The chemists of the early nineteenth century, led by Liebig, had said that fermentation was a chemical reaction.

The French chemist Louis Pasteur showed that it was due to the activity of certain living organisms, called bacteria. Continuing his study of bacteria, he launched his truly epoch-making theory that some of these tiny creatures — also called microbes, or germs — could overwhelmingly invade the human or animal body and thus cause disease.

Today this theory is almost universally accepted. But until Louis Pasteur entered the scene, certain learned professors were still maintaining that earthquakes brought on the plague; and others attributed fevers to such factors as marshes, night air and bad odors. A few men, indeed, had at least some idea of the true facts in the case. The sixteenth-century Italian physician Fracostoro (see the Index) had expressed his belief in "seeds of contagion." John Snow (1813–58), a Yorkshire-born London physician, almost hit upon the truth when he traced a cholera epidemic in London in 1854 to the polluted water of a certain street pump — the infamous Broad Street pump. He showed that cholera epidemics would not arise if the water used for drinking and preparing food was not contaminated with the contents of cesspools, house drains, sewers and other sources of pollution. But Snow had no idea that cholera was caused by a specific germ existing in the polluted water. It was Louis Pasteur who not only first proposed the germ theory of disease but who established it in the minds of men by rigorous scientific demonstration.

This gentle scientist was one of the greatest benefactors of mankind. A humble and pious man, he was not only the founder of the germ theory but also the father of bacteriology, the discoverer of immunity from disease and the victor over the mad-dog disease — rabies, or hydrophobia.

Pasteur was born in Dôle, France, in 1822. His father, a veteran of Napoleon's army and a tanner by trade, taught the lad the history of France, and Louis was ever afterward a passionate patriot. He went to a little country school and then to the Normal School in Paris. His education was often interrupted because of lack of funds, but his absorbing interest in his studies overcame all difficulties. From the first he was deeply interested in the natural sciences, and he was determined to devote his life to science, as both researcher and teacher. "Armed with science," he once wrote to his parents, "one can rise above one's fellows."

After graduating from the Normal School, Pasteur began to teach in a high

The French chemist Louis Pasteur (left) was the first to propose the germ theory of disease.

school in Paris; in due course he married the principal's daughter. His researches on the structure of crystals attracted wide attention and won him a professorship of chemistry at the new University of Lille. As a university professor, Pasteur was a civil servant. The Government did not hesitate to call upon him to help businessmen and others who had problems that could be solved more or less readily by chemical methods.

Soon Pasteur was requested to find out why the wine in Orléans was turning sour. After careful research, he discovered that fermentation was brought about through the activities of certain minute organisms. He showed the vintners how to keep their wine from spoiling by gently heating it to a temperature of 55 degrees centigrade — the process that we now call pasteurization. The heating destroys the tiny organisms that sour wine, beer and milk. "I found," wrote Pasteur, "that all real fermentations depended on the presence and multiplications of organic beings [that is, bacteria]."

The chemists of the old school were unconvinced; they maintained that fermentation was a chemical phenomenon and that living things like microbes had nothing to do with it. "Where did these microbes come from?" they asked. "They are found in the air," was Pasteur's response. He now devised an experiment that silenced his opponents. First he caused air to be sucked through a tube filled with cotton wool. The dust particles that collected in the tube were transferred to a sterile sugar solution in a gooseneck flask. The neck was then sealed. In a few days great colonies of bacteria were found inside the sealed flask. Obviously these colonies had descended from the original bacteria drawn from the air. Pasteur showed also that if the dust and sugar solution in the flask was boiled, no bacteria grew. He won a prize — and many adherents to his new germ theories — as a result of the crucial experiments.

Another practical problem was now thrown into his lap. The silkworms in Alais (Alès) were dying of a mysterious

disease and the silk industry of southern France was in danger of extinction. His old teacher, the chemist Jean-Baptiste-André Dumas, begged him to investigate the problem. "I have never had anything to do with silkworms," protested Pasteur; but in the year 1865, he packed his trusty weapon, the microscope, and went south to attack this new problem.

By the year 1868, Pasteur had discovered that the silkworms of southern France were dying not from one disease but from two. What was even more important, he had demonstrated conclusively that each of these diseases was caused by a specific microorganism. Pasteur devised a method for preventing contagion as well as for detecting diseased silkworms — and the silkworm industry was saved.

Pasteur now turned his attention to the study of the germs causing chicken cholera and anthrax. He cultivated the germs of chicken cholera in a kind of chicken soup — a culture medium in which the microbes could find suitable food. One day he injected an old, stale culture into a few hens. The fowl became slightly sick but soon recovered. Then it occurred to him to inject fresh, germ-full cultures into the hens. Nothing happened. In some unique way, the old, thinned out cultures had strengthened the hens' defenses against infection with fresh germs. This is an example of the phenomenon of immunity, or the mobilization of the body's defenses against bacterial invaders.

In May 1881, Pasteur and his associates proved that immunity to anthrax could also be acquired. In a demonstration at a farm near Melun, twenty-five sheep and six cows were injected with vaccines made from old cultures of the anthrax bacillus (germ). An equal number of cows and sheep were not vaccinated. Then all the animals were infected with living anthrax germs. To the astonishment of the veterinarians and farmers who were following the experiment, the vaccinated sheep and cows remained in excellent health, while all the unvaccinated animals quickly sickened and died.

Pasteur's researches in the dread disease called hydrophobia, or rabies, made a particularly dramatic story. Hydrophobia attacks many animals, including dogs, cats, wolves, foxes and jackals; it is transmitted to man by the bite of infected animals. The most striking feature, perhaps, of the disease is shown at an advanced stage. The patient is tormented by thirst and yet is seized with a violent choking fit when he attempts to swallow water. In fact, the very thought of water may bring on such an attack; hence the name "hydrophobia" ("fear of water," in Greek). Until Pasteur, hydrophobia victims always died after suffering the most frightful agonies.

After extended experiments with saliva from infected animals, Pasteur came to the conclusion that the germ — or as it later turned out, the virus — of the disease was concentrated in the nerve centers of the victims. He found, for example, that when he introduced matter from the spinal cord of an infected dog into a healthy animal, he could produce the symptoms of hydrophobia. He also discovered that he could prevent dogs from dying of the disease by a series of injections of the dried spinal cords of infected rabbits.

On the morning of July 6, 1885, a nine-year-old Alsatian lad, Joseph Meister, who had been cruelly bitten by a mad dog, was brought to Pasteur's laboratory in Paris for treatment. Pasteur had never tried his vaccine on a human being, and he hesitated to do so now. "The death of this child," he wrote afterwards, "appearing to be inevitable, I decided, not without lively apprehension, as may well be believed, to try upon Joseph Meister the method that I had found constantly successful with dogs." The treatment proved to be entirely successful; the boy speedily recovered.

Soon Pasteur was besieged by patients from all over the world, seeking treatment for the bites of mad dogs and wolves. A grateful world honored the great scientist's name by contributing funds to build a series of Pasteur Institutes, where vaccine could be manufactured, treatments given and research on immunization undertaken.

Pasteur died quietly, full of years and honors, in 1895. His career emphasizes an important point: that efforts to solve immediate and practical problems of industry may lead to the discovery of immensely valuable theories in pure science. Thus Pasteur's work on the problems of vintners and silkworm-growers in France led to the establishment of the germ theory of disease, the science of bacteriology and the doctrine of immunization.

The world of science and the general public eagerly accepted Pasteur's demonstration of the thesis that tiny organic beings cause disease — that is, the germ theory of disease. In the first flush of enthusiasm, it was thought that all diseases were probably germ diseases; but twentieth-century physicians have come to recognize that this is not the whole story. There are many important classifications of disease for which no "germ" can be found; for example, heart disease, cancer, and a host of psychosomatic (mind-body) ailments, in which the effect of emotions on bodily states is the predominating factor. We know now that the causes of disease are multiple. To understand and control them, we must study the host of the disease (that is, the sick person), the agent of disease (which may be, but is not always, a germ) and the environment of both.

After Pasteur, the science of bacteriology, dealing with the study of bacteria, moved ahead at an exciting pace and for perhaps half a century dominated all thinking about the nature of disease and the means of preventing it. There were two trails leading to the conquest of communicable diseases — one the bacteriological trail, uncovering the specific agents of specific diseases; the other, the epidemiological trail, noting and finding means of preventing the transmission of disease. Often these trails overlapped as the microbe

ROBERT KOCH

hunters discovered both new agents of disease and unexpected methods of transmission.

Perhaps the greatest microbe hunter after Pasteur was Robert Koch (1843–1910), a German doctor. He was an exceedingly painstaking man of science, who established a series of postulates, or rules, for determining the identity and the specific character of disease germs. He discovered how to stain bacteria with dyes so that they could be seen and studied under the microscope. He isolated and described the anthrax germ in 1876; in 1882 he discovered the tubercle bacillus, the germ that causes tuberculosis; in the following year he identified the comma bacillus, the germ of Asiatic cholera.

Koch electrified the whole world in 1890 by announcing that he had discovered a substance — tuberculin — that could cure tuberculosis. Koch had prepared this substance by sterilizing the medium in which tubercle bacilli were grown in the laboratory, filtering it and concentrating it by evaporation. It soon became evident that tuberculin could not live up to the extravagant claims that Koch had made for it as a cure for tuberculosis. Eventually, however, it proved to be useful in diagnosing the disease, and it is employed for this purpose at the present time. Despite the failure of his tuberculosis "cure," Koch continued to enjoy the esteem of the scientific world. He investigated many other diseases — notably African sleeping sickness. In 1905 he was awarded the Nobel Prize in medicine.

Other microbe hunters made notable finds in the exciting final quarter of the nineteenth century. Armauer Gerhard Henrik Hansen discovered the bacillus causing leprosy in 1874; this germ is often referred to now as Hansen's bacillus. In 1879, Albert Ludwig Siegmund Neisser isolated the gonococcus, the germ that causes gonorrhea. In the following year the bacillus of typhoid fever was identified by Karl Joseph Eberth. In 1881, George Miller Sternberg in the United States and Karl Fraenkel in Germany discovered the bacterium that causes lobar pneumonia; the great Pasteur isolated this germ at about the same time. The bacillus causing diphtheria was first described by Edwin Klebs in 1883 and isolated by Friedrich August Johannes Loeffler in 1884. Arthur Nicolaier discovered the bacillus of tetanus (lockjaw) in 1894.

Once the agents that caused communicable diseases were discovered, it became imperative to find out how they were transmitted. It was found that certain hosts will harbor the bacilli of specific diseases. It was also demonstrated that certain kinds of food and drink could carry and transmit disease germs. Thus, the burly British doctor David Bruce (1855–1931) found out in 1887 that the microbes of Malta fever, or undulant fever, can be carried in goat's milk. The disease is transmitted to humans when such infected milk is drunk. Undulant fever can be transmitted from cow's milk; milk derived from tubercular cows can also infect human beings with tuberculosis. That is one reason why we insist on pasteurized and certified cow's milk today.

It was discovered by nineteenth-century microbe hunters that insects also transmit disease germs. Men had long suspected that the fly was a vector (carrier) of disease; but the guilt of the insect was first definitely established in 1869, when it was demonstrated that the fly carries the germs of anthrax. Four years later an English nurse, who was in the Near East during a cholera epidemic, noted that the epidemic abated when flies vanished. In Washington, D. C., it was shown that these insects carried the germs of typhoid fever from insanitary privies to kitchens and parlors. A United States Army Medical Commission report revealed that flies carrying typhoid fever had killed more soldiers than bullets had killed during the Spanish-American War.

Fleas turned out to be another vector of disease. In 1894 the Japanese Shibasaburo Kitazato and the Swiss Alexandre-Emile-John Yersin discovered the bacillus of bubonic plague in the fleas that infest rats. International health activities have done much to protect the world from this ancient scourge; but it has not yet been exterminated. Plague bacilli have also been found in the fleas that infest the rats' fellow rodents, particularly the ground squirrel.

The story of how the tick was proved to be the vector of Texas fever is particularly engrossing. It carries us to the Old Chisholm Trail, over which Texas cattle were driven north for fattening and marketing. The hero of this tale was a city-born doctor, Theobald Smith (1859–1934), an employee of the United States Bureau of Animal Industry in Washington, D. C.

The bureau had been called upon to solve a serious problem confronting the cattlemen of the West. When southerners brought their cattle northward and set them to graze together with northern cattle, the southern cattle remained fat and healthy. But the northern cattle, after a month or so, took sick with the disease called Texas fever. They stopped eating, lost weight and died. Why? Smith went out west to solve the mystery. Cowpunchers, he found, claimed that the disease was due to ticks. Smith sought to find out whether or not this was the case.

It was a strange laboratory in which he worked; it consisted of six dusty fenced-off fields, in which there were northern cows, southern cows and ticks. Some ticks were so small that they could be detected only with a magnifying glass; others — big female ones gorged with cow's blood — were half an inch long. Through microscopes Smith and his co-workers spotted little pear-shaped microbes in the blood cells of sick cows and in the bodies of the ticks. But ticks have no wings; they do not jump from cow to cow; they live their whole lives on a single host. How then can ticks carry Texas fever from a Texas cow to a Montana cow? Smith pondered the question.

One hot summer day in 1890 he found the answer. After infesting southern cattle, adult female ticks dropped to the ground where they laid microbe-infected eggs. In about three weeks, the eggs became baby ticks whose bodies and stingers harbored the microbes of Texas fever. When a baby tick crawled up a northern cow's leg and bored its way in, it carried the fever germs with it. The southern

U.S.P.H.S.

Disc-shaped rat guards are placed on the mooring lines of ships coming from plague-infested ports. The rats on board may harbor the fleas transmitting bubonic plague.

cows, source of the infection, did not become sick because they had developed an immunity to the disease.

In 1893 Smith issued a report on his findings, called INVESTIGATIONS INTO THE NATURE, CAUSATION AND PREVENTION OF TEXAS OR CATTLE FEVER. His solution of the Texas fever problem was a simple one. "Dip your cattle clean; kill the ticks," he said, "and the disease will disappear." Later investigations have shown that ticks also carry germs of diseases — like Rocky Mountain spotted fever — that attack man.

Smith had opened the way to a whole new field of inquiry in the matter of disease control — the sciences of epidemiology and preventive medicine. He put David Bruce on the trail of the tsetse fly, which turned out to be the vector of African sleeping sickness in horses, wild animals and men. Most important, he influenced the men whose work put the mosquito at the top of the list of insect vectors of disease.

The mosquito is the vector of the most prevalent disease on the face of the globe — malaria. This fact was brilliantly demonstrated, just before 1900, by the British poet-physician Sir Ronald Ross (1857–1932), serving in the Indian Medical Service, and the Italian physician Giovanni Battista Grassi (1854–1925). Mosquito control is the essence of malaria control. Only a few species of mosquitoes, of course, carry disease.

A dramatic demonstration of the role of the mosquito in carrying disease occurred in the case of yellow fever, sometimes called yellow jack. Havana, Cuba, was infested with the disease. A Cuban physician, Carlos Juan Finlay (1833–1915), suspected that the mosquito might be the carrier of the disease, but he could never definitely prove that his theory was correct. Following the Spanish-American War of 1898, the United States took over Cuba, formerly a Spanish possession, and faced the problem of combating yellow fever.

The United States Army sent a distinguished commission to Cuba to investigate the disease. It was headed by Major Walter Reed (1851–1902) and included Dr. Jesse William Lazear, who died a martyr to the investigation. At a crucial point in the proceedings, it became necessary to find human volunteers who would risk contracting yellow fever. Two soldiers and one civilian employee of the Army offered themselves without pay for this experiment, acting, as they said, "solely in the interests of science and for humanity." With the help of these volunteers and other devoted men, Reed and his associates were able to prove conclusively that the mosquito called *Aëdes aegypti* is the carrier of the virus that causes yellow fever.

A unique engineering triumph — the building of the Panama Canal — was due in large part to this discovery. The French had tried to build the canal in the 1880's under the guidance of Ferdinand-Marie de Lesseps, the promoter of the Suez Canal. The appalling death rate among workers because of yellow fever was one of the factors that brought operations to a standstill. When the American Government decided to go ahead with the canal in the

America's Reed Commission investigated yellow fever in Cuba.

John Wyeth & Brother, Inc.

early 1900's, it was recognized that the first job to be tackled was that of cleaning up the Canal Zone. The task was entrusted to Colonel William C. Gorgas (1854–1920). He knew how yellow jack was carried; he kept down the mosquito population and the canal was pushed through.

We can look upon the Panama Canal as a monument to the devoted men who demonstrated that *Aëdes aegypti* carries yellow fever; to Theobald Smith, who showed how insect vectors could be tracked down; to Louis Pasteur, who gave the world the germ theory of disease.

SURGICAL OPERATIONS BECOME SAFER

Modern surgery is based upon anesthesia and asepsis. The word asepsis means complete exclusion of disease-producing bacteria in order to prevent infection. This idea, based on the germ theory of disease, was new to the nineteenth century. Before asepsis came antisepsis — the process of actually killing microbes by application of chemicals.

The man who brought antiseptic methods into surgery was a gentle, clear-eyed and high-minded Quaker wound-dresser, Joseph Lister. He was born at Upton, in the English county of Essex, in 1827, the son of a wine merchant who devoted his leisure hours to making microscopes. Lister attended the Quaker schools at Hitchin and Tottenham; he then studied medicine at University College, in London. After completing his medical course, he went to Edinburgh armed with an introduction to the eminent Scottish surgeon James Syme (1799–1870), professor of clinical surgery at the University of Edin-

burgh. Lister became a house surgeon under Syme; three years later he married Syme's daughter.

Lister was appointed professor of surgery in Glasgow in 1860. He was particularly interested at that time in the infections that originated in wounds and that caused the formation of pus — "laudable pus," the surgeons of that time called it, because it was supposed to be a sign of healing. What was the source of the putrefaction — that is, the infection — that caused the formation of pus?

In 1865 a colleague of Lister called his attention to Pasteur's demonstration that putrefaction is caused by microbes present in the air. It occurred to Lister that, if such were the case, one might be able to prevent surgical infection and the consequent formation of pus by killing the microbes. For this purpose, Lister decided to use carbolic acid, which had served previously to disinfect sewage. He painted the wound of a patient suffering from a compound fracture with undiluted carbolic acid and then dressed it with cloths that had been dipped in diluted acid. The wound healed beautifully. In the course of the following two years Lister used this method on many patients with excellent results.

On August 9, 1867, he reported on the method at a meeting of the British Medical Association in Dublin. "I left behind me at Glasgow," he said, "a boy, thirteen years of age, who, between three and four weeks previously, met with a most severe injury to the left arm, which he got entangled in a machine at a fair . . . Without the assistance of the antiseptic treatment, I should certainly have thought of nothing else but amputation at the shoulder joint . . . Now I did not hesitate to try to save the limb by wrapping the arm from the shoulder to below the elbow in the antiseptic application . . . Before I left, the discharge was already somewhat less, while the bone was becoming firm . . . I feel sure that if I had resorted to ordinary dressing when the pus first appeared, the progress of this case would have been exceedingly different." In other words, the injured boy would have lost his arm.

Lister ended his address by pointing to the revolution that the introduction of antisepsis had brought in hospital methods of treatment. "Previously to [the introduction of antisepsis]," he said, "the two large wards in which most of the cases of accident and operation are treated, were among the unhealthiest in the whole surgical division of the Glasgow Royal Infirmary . . . I have felt ashamed when recording the results of my practice to have so often to allude to hospital gangrene and pyemia [pus in the blood stream] . . .

"But since the antiseptic treatment has been brought into full operation, and wounds and abscesses no longer poison the atmosphere with putrid exhalations, my wards, though in other respects under precisely the same conditions as before, have completely changed their character. During the last nine months not a single instance of pyemia, hospital gangrene or erysipelas [inflammation of the skin] has occurred in them."

Since undiluted carbolic acid irritates the tissues of the body, Lister mitigated its effects by blending it with shellac. In

Joseph Lister supervising the use of dilute carbolic acid in the form of a spray, in one of the earliest "antiseptic" surgical operations.

order to get rid of the germs that might be floating around in the operating room, he used a spray apparatus to disinfect the air with a dilute solution of carbolic acid. Lister and other surgeons soon saw that it was not essential to kill germs in the air — a possible but unlikely source of wound infection in the operating room. It was only necessary to take sensible precautions to keep germs away from the operative wounds and the surgical field. This could be done by sterilizing all the instruments used in operations, by using sterile clothing and by keeping the hands aseptically clean. Surgery moved from antisepsis to asepsis.

Lister won the respect and esteem of the men of his generation. He was President of the Royal Society from 1895 to 1900; in 1897 he was raised to the peerage as Baron Lister of Lyme Regis. When he died, in 1912, he was buried in Westminster Abbey, reserved for Britain's greatest men. His chief monument, perhaps, is the Lister Institute of Preventive Medicine in London, modeled after the Pasteur Institute of Paris.

With the advent of anesthesia, antiseptics and scrupulous cleanliness in the operating room, surgeons all over the world began cutting into the human body more deeply than ever before. They penetrated the abdomen; many surgeons devised elaborate operations which they named after themselves. Soon all the organs in the abdomen — the stomach, the gall bladder, the pancreas, the intestines and the appendix — could be operated on successfully. Countless human lives were saved as a result. For example, before Lister's time, appendicitis (inflammation of the vermiform appendix) had probably been about as common as it is today. But surgeons had never operated on the appendix, and the patient had always died. With the perfection of abdominal surgery, an appendectomy (removal of the appendix) became a relatively simple operation.

Later developments made it possible for the surgeon to invade the chest cavity, where the lungs and heart are located. In the twentieth century, surgeons found safe ways of getting deep into the skull cavity.

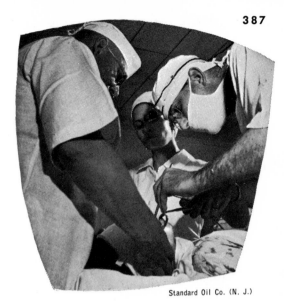

A surgeon removing a patient's tonsils in a modern hospital.

The great American surgeon Harvey Cushing (1869–1939) finally reached the pituitary body, a small gland that lies at the very base of the brain. The ancients had considered this gland or a nearby one — the pineal — as the "seat of the soul." Actually, the pituitary gland exerts a great effect upon the chemistry of the human body — and particularly on the reproductive system.

The advancing science of surgery gave new impetus to pathology — the study of diseased tissues. Toward the end of the eighteenth century, the problem of tissue changes in disease had been attacked by Marie-François-Xavier Bichat (1771–1802), who had served as a surgeon to the armies of the French Revolution. An appointment as physician to a famous hospital, the Hôtel-Dieu in Paris, gave him the opportunity to perform numerous autopsies. In a period of six months he opened some six hundred bodies in order to study the changes brought about in human tissues by disease.

The man who put pathology on a modern footing was a vigorous little German anatomy professor, Rudolf Virchow (1821–1902). He was perhaps the greatest medical figure in Berlin in the last half of the nineteenth century. He made many important contributions to histology (the science of tissues) and to the study of various diseases. In his book CELLULAR PATHOLOGY, published in 1858, Virchow gave a striking account of what happens in disease states.

Virchow was probably the first to point out that white blood cells — leucocytes — mobilize to defend the injured part of a body. The Russian-born bacteriologist and zoologist Elie Metchnikoff (1845–1916) later explained that the white cells gobble up germ invaders. He found a fine mouth-filling word for this process:

"phagocytosis" ("cell-eating process," in Greek). Metchnikoff's work on immunity won him a Nobel Prize in medicine (with Paul Ehrlich) in 1908. This many-sided scientist made a study of syphilis and prescribed calomel ointment as a protection against it. He was also interested in gerontology — the science that studies the process of growing old. It has taken on added importance in our own day. A world made safer by surgery and sanitation contains far more old people than ever before.

"THE QUALITY OF MERCY IS NOT STRAIN'D"

"The quality of mercy is not strain'd,
It droppeth as the gentle rain from heaven
Upon the place beneath."

These magnificent lines from Shakespeare's MERCHANT OF VENICE apply admirably to the noble profession of nursing. It is hard to realize that until about the middle of the nineteenth century, nurses (except for women in religious orders) were held in almost universal scorn. As the London TIMES put it, in 1857: "Lectured by committees, preached at by chaplains, scowled on by treasurers and stewards, scolded by matrons, bullied by dressers, grumbled at and abused by patients, insulted if old and ill-favored, talked flippantly to if middle-aged and good-humored, seduced if young — they are what any woman would be under the same circumstances." They were, generally, disreputable, dowdy and, all too often, drunken.

This sad state of affairs was changed chiefly through the efforts of a high- (and strong-) minded Victorian lady, Florence Nightingale (1820–1910). Through her ideas and ideals, her widely heralded errands of mercy and her skill as an administrator she made nursing a highly honored profession.

A gentlewoman by birth, Florence Nightingale received an excellent classical and mathematical education at home with her father as teacher. Instead of settling down thereafter to the conventional life of an aristocratic young lady, she shocked her friends by showing a deep interest in nurs-

FLORENCE NIGHTINGALE

ing. She underwent a regular course of training as a nurse at the Institute of Protestant Deaconesses, located at Kaiserswerth, Germany, and operated by Pastor Theodor Fliedner. After she had completed the course, she underwent further training in hospitals in London and Edinburgh and studied nursing problems in London.

Miss Nightingale's opportunity to show the world the need of scientific methods in nursing came in 1854 during the Crimean War. The scene of the fighting was the Crimea, a peninsula on the Black Sea; the British and French were pitted against the Russians. After the manner of poets, Tennyson later glamorized a relatively minor episode of the war — the charge of the Light Cavalry Brigade at Balaklava. But as a matter of fact, there was precious little glamour in the Crimean War. The fighting was bitter; losses were heavy; the sufferings of the wounded and sick on both sides aroused the horror of the world. "The soldier knew some one had blundered," wrote Tennyson of the order that sent the gallant Light Brigade "onward into the valley of death." But the chief English blunderers were those who had failed to provide suitable medical care for the British Army.

Conditions at the British base hospital at Scutari (Üsküdar, Turkey) were abominable. The alleged hospital was a dirty, stinking yellow barn, infested with rats and vermin and without any comforts or conveniences. When British war correspondents revealed these conditions, there was a great public protest, and a royal commission of inquiry was set up. Florence Nightingale wrote to her friend Sidney Herbert, the War Secretary, offering her services and he gladly accepted them. Accompanied by thirty-eight trained "sisters of mercy," she set sail on October 21, 1854, and two weeks later arrived at Scutari. Miss Nightingale and her associates went to work immediately; they scrubbed, they washed, they re-arranged, they cooked for the sick and wounded. The sight of Florence Nightingale walking through the wards late at night with a lamp in her hand, inspecting and comforting, became an inspiration to the patients and to the nurses who worked with her.

The "Lady with the Lamp" had much to contend with. The military authorities resented what they considered her interference. They did what they could to thwart her, but she had the backing of the War Secretary and she overcame all obstacles. The results were truly astounding. In February 1855 the death rate in the hospital was 42 per cent; by June it had dropped to 2 per cent.

Upon her return to England in 1856, Florence Nightingale founded the Nightingale Home for Training Nurses at St. Thomas' Hospital, with a fund of £50,000 ($250,000), which had been raised by subscription in recognition of her services. Soon the nurses who had been trained at St. Thomas' were in great demand, and other nurses' training centers were set up in the United Kingdom. In time the ignorant and dirty slatterns who had served in the hospitals were replaced by well-trained and self-respecting women who inspired in the patient the will to live.

War, serving as a whip to mercy, had provided the impetus for Miss Nightingale's reform of the nursing profession. It also led to the formation of the Red Cross societies — those wonderful national organizations that seek to alleviate and prevent human suffering. The founding of the International Red Cross goes back to the year 1859, when the French and Sardinians fought a bloody battle at Solferino, Italy, against the Austrians. A young Swiss banker, Jean-Henri Dunant (1828–1910), was an eyewitness of the battle; after the fighting was over, he organized a corps of volunteers to search out and nurse the wounded left unattended on the field of battle. The experience touched him so deeply that in 1862 he struck off a pamphlet, called MEMOIR OF SOLFERINO, in which he proposed the formation of an international society to provide aid to the wounded and sick in wartime.

In 1864, a conference for this purpose was held at Geneva, with twenty-six delegates from sixteen governments attending. This conference, known as the Geneva Convention, witnessed the official birth of the Red Cross organization. Its identifying symbol was to be a square red cross on a white field — the flag of Switzerland reversed. This emblem was to be a sign of impartial help to both sides in a war; it was never to be fired upon. Since that time, the Red Cross societies have widened their scope by peacetime activities. They have provided relief in disasters; they have worked for public education in health matters, for public-health nursing and for improved health conditions generally.

Many other voluntary health agencies have also entered the lists to battle against disease and needless suffering. They bear eloquent testimony to the medical progress of the nineteenth century — progress that has brought new hope for happier, healthier living to mankind.

Continued on page 251, Volume 8.

TRANSMITTING CYLINDER

IMPULSES

PHOTO CELL

LENS

LIGHT SOURCE

COMMUNICATION

FACSIMILE TRANSMISSION*

How Pictures and Printed Matter Are Sent by Wire and Radio

A PLANE crashes in a residential district in the outskirts of Chicago and causes terrible havoc. A half hour or so later, a photograph of the flaming wreckage is wrapped around a horizontal cylinder in a Chicago office. An attendant pushes a button. A facsimile of the picture is then sent at lightning speed through the wires of telephone circuits or by radio to hundreds of stations on a press-association network. In a matter of minutes, newspaper offices in New York, Boston, Pittsburgh, New Orleans, San Francisco and many other places will have an almost perfect reproduction of the original picture. In an hour or so, hundreds of thousands of readers will be looking at the photograph in their favorite newspapers. Facsimile transmission like this would have seemed like black magic a hundred years ago. Today we take it just as much for granted as we do television, jet planes, spacecraft, laser beams and other modern miracles.

Suppose we wish to transmit a facsimile of a photographic print over a telephone circuit. First the picture is wrapped, picture side up, around the horizontal cylinder of the sending machine. The descriptive material accompanying the picture is typed at the sending station on a strip of gummed paper and pasted to one end of the photograph. This typed matter is transmitted together with the photograph itself.

When an attendant presses a button on the transmitting machine, the cylinder begins to rotate. A beam of light is thrown through a tiny aperture about one-hundredth of an inch square and traces a continuous spiral over the picture as the cylinder turns. This process is called scanning. It is somewhat like the scanning system used in television but is much slower. It takes a tele-

Photos on these two pages, Associated Press

How facsimiles are transmitted by the Association Press (AP). The picture is wrapped around a cylinder, or drum. As this cylinder rotates, a beam from a light source is directed through a lens, which focuses an intense spot of light on the picture. Reflections from the picture strike a photocell, and they are converted into electric impulses. Amplified, these impulses are sent along the AP Wirephoto network to receiving units. The photo shows an AP Portable Wirephoto transmitter. The picture to be sent out is being mounted on the drum.

vision camera only one-thirtieth of a second to scan a complete picture; it takes a facsimile machine several minutes.

The beam of light is reflected from the photographic print to a photoelectric cell mounted on a carriage that moves alongside the cylinder. (In certain facsimile machines, it is the cylinder that moves.) The photoelectric cell transforms the reflected light rays into electrical impulses. The lighter a given area of the picture is, the stronger the impulse will be. The impulses are greatly amplified before they are sent out over a telephone circuit.

The receiving machine converts the electrical signals into the blacks and whites

* Article prepared with the assistance of the Associated Press and the Western Union Telegraph Company.

RECEIVING CYLINDER

LENS

GLOW LAMP

In one reception method, electrical impulses from the Wirephoto network are received through a glow lamp, which converts them back into light impulses. These are focused by a lens onto undeveloped photographic film, which may be developed and printed normally. If photographic paper is used instead of film, a positive print may be obtained directly. In photo A, print paper is being mounted on the receiving cylinder of an AP Wirephoto Recorder. Photo B shows an AP Photofax Recorder, after the reception of a picture and weather map by the electrolytic process we describe on this page.

and grays of the original picture. The earliest method was a photographic process, and it is still in use for certain purposes. In this process, unexposed photographic film is wrapped around the receiving cylinder, which starts to turn at the same time as the sending cylinder.

The electrical impulses from the sending machine pass to a glow lamp, which brightens or darkens in proportion to the strength of the current. The light from this lamp is focused through a lens upon the film on the rotating receiving cylinder. The film is exposed as it is struck by the light, which is now bright, now relatively faint. When the transmission is completed, the film is taken to a darkroom a few steps away from the machine. Here the negative is developed and a print is made. In some receivers, photographic paper is used on the receiving cylinder instead of film. This makes it possible to obtain a positive print directly.

In recent years, the so-called electrolytic process has come to the fore and is rapidly replacing the photographic method in the transmission of pictures by news agencies. In the electrolytic process, the glow lamp of the recording device is replaced by a stainless-steel blade. This presses upon a paper as the latter passes over a rotating horizontal cylinder, on which a wire has been spirally wound. The paper has previously been treated with an electrolyte—a substance that conducts electricity in solution.

As current passes through the paper moving over the rotating cylinder, marks are made in the paper through an electrolytic reaction. (See Index, under Electrolysis.) These marks are in different shades of gray, depending upon the strength of the current. The paper is automatically dried as it passes from the cylinder. In fact, the entire process is automatic; the copy is available almost immediately after transmission has taken place. Facsimile reproductions by the electrolytic process are not quite so faithful as those produced by the photographic method. They are cheaper, however, and they are entirely satisfactory for newspaper reproduction and for various other purposes.

Picture transmission over a network of telephone lines was begun in the United States on an experimental basis in 1925. In 1935, the Associated Press put into operation its Wirephoto picture-transmission

A high-speed facsimile transmission system serves the weather network of the U.S. Air Force Strategic Air Command. In this scene at the Air Force Weather Relay Station at Suitland, Maryland, the technician in the foreground observes a weather map being received from one of the network stations. The technician in the background is inserting a completed map on a transmission drum, prior to sending the latest forecast to other stations.

system over a network covering twenty-four newspaper offices. This network has since been greatly expanded. Other press associations send facsimiles over their very own networks.

The apparatus used to transmit pictures and other matter over radio links is much like that which we have just described. This kind of picture transmission is called radiophoto.

The facsimile-transmission system is used nowadays to speed the delivery and pickup of telegrams. Western Union, a pioneer in developing modern facsimile, processes over 50,000,000 telegrams a year by

A milestone in the history of facsimile transmission was achieved when an entire facsimile edition of the *New York Times* was transmitted daily from New York to San Francisco over a television cable for a five-day period during the Republican convention in San Francisco in September 1956. Photo A shows the transmitting station in New York. The man at the right is taping two full-sized page proofs to the sending drum. Photo B was taken at the receiving end. The man at the left is warming a receiving drum while maintaining telephone contact with the New York transmitting station. The other man is wrapping a page-sized photographic film on another receiving drum. The proof pages from New York were recorded on the film and photoengravings were made from the latter. Matrices were prepared from the photoengravings. Finally stereo plates for rotary presses were cast in the usual way. Press runs for the *Times* facsimile edition ranged from 16,000 to 19,000 a day.

New York Times

the use of more than 40,000 compact Desk-Fax facsimile machines in business offices. The sender places his message on the cylinder of the Desk-Fax and presses a button. A tiny electric eye then scans the telegram and flashes an exact picture of it to a Western Union office. In a similar manner, the businessman receives telegrams from the Western Union office. The Desk-Fax is used for messages sent over short distances.

Western Union has developed other types of facsimile equipment for long-distance transmission of public messages, business documents, weather maps and other materials.* The device called Letter-Fax is used for public facsimile service, linking five major cities coast-to-coast, as well as for private-wire service for government agencies and industrial firms. Letter-Fax equipment can send or receive any type of document, diagram or line drawing up to $8\frac{1}{2}$ inches by 11 inches in size. Larger transmitting and receiving equipment, capable of handling maps up to 18 inches by 36 inches, has also been developed. It serves the two major weather networks in the United States: the United States Weather Bureau network and the Air Force Strategic Air Command network.

* Generally speaking, short-range transmission is carried over wire; long-range transmission, by radio.

Metropolitan Museum of Art,
Fletcher fund, 1925

Honeywell

CERAMICS*

A Survey of One of the World's Oldest Industries

Ancient and modern applications of ceramics. Left: an Etruscan vase, which goes back to the seventh century B.C. Right: close-up of the ceramic spin motor of a space-guidance gyroscope.

THE shards of cooking pots from prehistoric campsites; decorative urns; spark plugs; the tail pipes of rockets — all these objects have more in common than one might think. They were made of earthy materials, shaped by man and turned into useful or ornamental objects through the application of high heat. The art of processing objects in this way is called ceramics, or ceramic, from the Greek word *keramos,* meaning "burnt substance." ** The word "ceramics" also refers to the articles made by the process.

The art of making ceramic products goes back beyond the era of recorded history. Yet, as late as the early years of the present century, ceramics were produced more or less by trial and error. In recent years, chemistry and physics have unlocked many of the secrets of ceramic materials. This has resulted in better ware and has pointed the way to a multitude of products formerly unheard of. The scope of the industry has been broadened greatly. As a matter of fact, there is at present not simply one ceramic industry but a long list of industries that have in common the ceramic

process. The glass industry is included among them; we do not discuss it in the present article since it is dealt with elsewhere in these volumes.*

Ceramic scientists and engineers have been called on to produce materials that can withstand the stress and heat imposed by the supersonic speeds of aircraft ** and by nuclear reactors. Ceramics has also come to play a vital role in space exploration. Critical parts of rockets and spacecraft — including nose cones, rocket exhaust nozzles, guide vanes and heat-resistant windows — must be of ceramic construction to meet the high temperatures encountered upon reentry into the earth's atmosphere. Ceramic materials are also used for electronic parts in the communication and control assemblies of spacecraft.

Raw materials for ceramics and their preparation

The element oxygen is the most abundant one in the earth's crust, and the second most abundant element is silicon. The oxide *** called silica, made up of oxygen and silicon, is particularly common in the crust and is to be found in most of the

---

* Article written with the assistance of the American Ceramic Society, Inc.
** This is the generally accepted definition of ceramics. If it seems rather sketchy, it should be pointed out that ceramic products are so varied in materials, methods of forming and uses that no inclusive definition exists.

* See the article The Story of Glass, in Volume 3.
** See the article Supersonic Flight, in Volume 10.
*** An oxide is a compound in which oxygen is combined with another chemical element.

STACK

CHARGE OF
POTTERY

FUEL

W. S. Dickey Clay Mfg. Co.

The above photograph shows a group of periodic kilns, in which large-diameter clay pipe is being processed. Because of their shape, these kilns are often referred to as "beehive kilns." They are often gas-fired so that the temperature may be closely controlled. The diagram at the left shows a charge of pottery being fired in a periodic kiln. The hot gases first pass upward, then downward through the pottery charge and up a stack.

earthy materials used in ceramic production. Other oxides serving as ceramic raw materials include those of magnesium, aluminum, zirconium, thorium, titanium and boron. However, not all ceramic materials are oxides; man-made carbides (compounds of carbon) and nitrides (compounds of nitrogen) are coming into quite wide use.

Ceramic raw materials must be ground to a uniform consistency before they can be given further processing, and mineral impurities must be removed. The cleaned materials then go into the ceramic mix — the mixture of materials from which the finished product will be made. Besides the clay or other basic plastic material, the mixture commonly includes potter's flint and feldspar. Potter's flint consists of finely ground silica; it reduces the shrinkage that comes about in the firing and drying processes. Feldspar has a comparatively low melting point. It is added so that the batch may be fired at a somewhat lower temperature than would otherwise be necessary.

The methods of
forming ceramic

There are a great many forming (shaping) methods; we can mention only a few of the more important ones here. The hand shaping of materials serves mostly today in the production of artware. The jigger, a modern adaptation of the potter's wheel (described below) is used in the mass production of dinnerware. Certain ceramic pieces, such as sanitary ware, are cast. Other products, including electrical insulators, are formed by hydraulic presses. In some cases, as in the manufacture of brick, the plastic mass is extruded — that is, it is forced through a die containing the desired cross section of the finished product. The extruded material is then cut to the desired size. We shall have more to say about these forming methods and others later in this article.

After the ceramic material has been formed, it is dried in a dryer or oven. It is then ready for the firing operation.

The firing of
ceramic materials

Firing, or subjecting to intense heat, is a basic part of the ceramic process. The required heat may range from as low as 900° F. to more than 4,000° F. The object of firing is to bring about physical and chemical changes that will make each ceramic part strong and durable. A vital change is the transformation of silica. Before this compound is subjected to the firing process, it has a crystalline structure: that is, it is made up of crystals whose atoms form a regular pattern. Silica is liquefied

Right: clay pipe ready for firing in a tunnel kiln. Mounted on a car, it will soon enter the kiln. The pipe has been transferred to the entrance of the kiln on the tracks running at right angles to the latter. Other tracks, which are not shown here, run through the kiln, and it is along these tracks that the car containing the pipe will pass. In the diagram, we show one type of tunnel kiln.

W. S. Dickey Clay Mfg. Co.

STACK
EXHAUST FAN
PREHEATING SECTION
BURNERS
COOLING SECTION
BLOWER
MOVEMENT OF CARS

in the firing operation. Most of the silica does not recrystallize after cooling. It becomes a glassy material that bonds together the crystals in the finished ware. The process of heating to the glassy state is called vitrification, from the Latin word *vitrium*, meaning "glass." Bonding is an essential end result of all firing operations, regardless of the contents of the ceramic mix.

Because clays and other ceramic raw materials vary so much in their composition, even a chemical analysis cannot always indicate how these materials will react in the firing operation. Hence the engineer's analysis must be supplemented by firing test pieces and by "pilot runs."

Firing takes place in a furnace known as a kiln * and built of refractory (heat-resistant) brick. There are hundreds of different kinds of kilns, most of which are variations of two principal types: periodic and tunnel.

The periodic kiln, also known as the "beehive," is circular in shape; it has a domed roof that is from 20 to 30 feet in diameter. The ware is carefully stacked in this kiln, in order to permit the even circulation of heat, and the door is closed with refractory brick and mortar. Heat is then produced by the burning of coal, oil or gas. The temperature is gradually raised to a

* Ceramists pronounce this word as "kill."

point that will bring about vitrification or other desired changes in the ware. Then the temperature is slowly lowered. Finally, the kiln is opened and the ware inside it is removed. As can be seen, this is not a continuous but a periodic operation; hence the name "periodic kiln."

In recent years, tunnel kilns have come into general use because they make more economical use of fuel. The ware that is to be fired in such a kiln is loaded on cars, and these are moved slowly through three zones of heat in the long tunnel kiln. In the first zone, the temperature of the ware

Pyrometric cones, used to check the temperature in firing kilns. Cones 2, 3, 4 and 5 have different softening points. Cone 2 will bend over first after firing begins; then, in turn, cones 3, 4 and 5. Cone 5 should remain upright throughout; otherwise, it is an indication that overfiring has taken place. Upper photo: the cones before firing; lower photo: the cones after firing.

Furnished by the Edward Orton Jr. Ceramic Foundation

is gradually increased. The firing process is completed in the second zone; the third zone is for slow cooling.

It is most important to control the temperature in the kiln. Underfired ware will be soft and lacking in strength. If the ware is fired at too high a temperature, it will slump and will become misshapen. If it is cooled too quickly, it will crack.

Ordinary thermometers, of course, cannot be used in the kiln, because mercury found in such devices boils well below the temperatures required for ceramic processes. In the ceramic kiln, temperatures are measured by optical pyrometers, or thermocouples * or pyrometric cones.

Pyrometric cones are extensively used in the industry and are particularly interesting because they themselves are ceramic products. They are small three-sided spires, about three inches high; they are made of carefully compounded materials with known softening points. Three or more pyrometric cones are placed in the kiln with the ware and are observed from outside of the kiln.

* For optical pyrometers and thermocouples, see the Index.

The left-hand photo shows clay sewer pipes before the firing process. Note that each of the pipes has an enlarged section, known as a bell, at one end. In the right-hand photo, the pipes have been fired and glazed.
Swindell-Dressler Corp.   W. S. Dickey Clay Mfg. Co.

Cones of different softening points are selected. When the first one bends over, it indicates that the desired temperature is near. When the next-to-the-last one goes down, the right temperature has been reached. The last cone should remain upright; if it too goes down, it is an indication that overfiring has taken place. Cones are available in about 60 grades with softening points ranging from 1,085° F. to 3,659° F.

Glazing of ceramic ware

A great many ceramic products, including dishes, bathroom fixtures and wall tile, are glazed. The glazing material, called a frit, is a mixture of finely ground glass, clay (a small amount) and water. The frit is applied to the ware by dipping, spraying or brushing and is dried; then firing takes place in the kiln. After the firing process, the coating becomes a smooth, nonabsorbent surface that is easily cleaned and that protects the ware. More details of the glazing operation are given later in this article.

Ceramic colors

The brilliant and durable colors displayed by wall tile, ceramic artware, porcelain enamels, glass and glazed brick are not easily obtained. Because the pigments are fused at high temperatures, they must have good heat stability and must not react with molten glazes. The search for materials to make ceramic colors has led to the testing of a wide variety of chemical elements and compounds. Uranium was used in quantities to produce red and yellow ceramic colors long before the atomic bomb based on radioactive uranium was conceived. Cobalt yields blues and violets; manganese gives pinks and browns. Copper and chrome are used for the many shades of green. Nickel, vanadium and antimony have made their contributions to the ceramic rainbow with colors that will endure for a great many generations.

Ceramic colors may be classified according to the methods of application.

Body stains are produced by pigments mixed with the raw clay. This assures a

This designer is shaping a fine vase. Starting with a lump of clay, he models it from the bottom up as the wheel turns, as in the earliest days of pottery-making. Later, a mold will be prepared from the finished model.

Both photos, Lenox, Incorporated

The worker at the left is shaping a cup with a jigger. Details of the device are shown in the above diagram. A plaster mold is set on a turntable, which is rotated by a shaft. The clay is pressed on the mold; then the jigger tool is brought down on the revolving mass, working it to the desired shape.

color that goes through the entire piece of ware. Body stains are applied to some types of tableware and unglazed floor tile.

Glaze stains are added to the frit, or glazing material, as it is being ground. As the glaze is melted in the kiln, the color is bound to the surface to which the glaze has been applied.

Underglaze colors are applied mostly to dinnerware and pottery. A clear glaze is applied over the colored design, after which the ware is fired.

Overglaze colors, as the name implies, are applied on top of the glaze, which has already been fired. Another firing then takes place. These colors, applied to cheaper ware, are not so durable as underglaze.

Glass enamels are used on tumblers, bottles, lamp bulbs and other glass articles for permanent labeling, brand names and decoration. They are made of ceramic colors and are applied by stamping, silkscreen processing or spraying.

Whitewares are
important ceramics

Dishes, bathroom fixtures, electrical insulators and wall tiles are four extremely important ceramic products, known by ceramists as whitewares. They are so called because they are made from materials that burn to a white body. Usually they are glazed. Whiteware bodies are classified as vitreous or semivitreous. Vitreous bodies are fired to a higher heat than the semivitreous variety and, as a result, are entirely impervious to moisture. The lower temperatures at which semivitreous ware is fired produces a body that has the required strength but that will absorb moisture. Semivitreous ware is less expensive to produce because less fuel is required in the firing process.

The most commonly used types of clays used for whitewares are kaolin, ball clays and stoneware clays. Kaolin is the whitest of the clays, with low iron content. Ball clays are fine-grained and easily formed; they have a high dry strength. Stoneware clays have good working properties and are favorite materials for pottery.

The clay-forming method called jiggering is widely used in the production of dinnerware. The jigger is a modification of the ancient potter's wheel—a horizontal disk rotating on a vertical spindle and bearing the clay to be shaped by the potter's hand. As in the case of the potter's wheel,

397

A jewellike effect is created on a fine china cup by means of hand-applied raised enamel dots. A high degree of skill is required for an operation such as this.

Above: pressing the foot of a cup into place while both foot and cup are soft. The handle is attached in the same way. Below: slip casting. A souplike mixture called slip is poured into the mold cavity. The dry mold absorbs some of the slip. The rest is poured off and then the thin coating on the mold is left to dry.

the basic part of the jigger is a rotating horizontal disk. A plaster mold is centered on the disk top. The mold has the shape of one side of the piece to be formed, such as the upper side of a dinner plate. The clay is pressed firmly on the mold which is set to rotating. Then the jigger arm, a heavy blade having the profile of the plate bottom, is brought down on the revolving mass of clay and works it to the desired shape and thickness. If the piece is to be hollow, as in the case of a cup or bowl, the plaster mold has the shape of the outside of the ware; the jigger blade forms the inside. Cup handles are cast in a mold, a dozen or so at a time. They are pressed onto the cups while both the cup and handle are still soft.

The method called slip casting is used in the manufacture of whitewares with intricate shapes. The form for the outside of the piece that is to be produced is a plaster mold made of several interlocking sections. A souplike mixture called slip is prepared; it consists of water and finely ground clay, mixed with feldspar, talc or nepheline syenite. The slip is poured into the mold cavity and is allowed to remain in it for a short time. The dry plaster mold sucks water out of the slip, causing the clay that is nearest to the mold to solidify. Then the slip in the center, which has remained liquid, is poured off, leaving a hollow center. When the mold parts are removed, the piece of ware is revealed. The mold must be dried before it can be used again.

Most whitewares are glazed. Generally, they are fired once before the glaze is applied; then the glaze is added. Another firing takes place at a lower temperature. In the case of the translucent ceramic ware called porcelain, it is the first firing (the so-called bisque firing) that is at the lower temperature. Glaze and decoration are applied after the bisque firing. Then the ware is fired again to a higher temperature in order to bring about the required degree of vitrification.

Ceramic wall tile is generally made from talc, ball clay and flint, with minor additions of other raw materials as required to get good working qualities. In some plants, wollastonite or pyrophyllite are being used to replace some of the talc. After mixing, grinding and the addition of moisture, the batch is fed into automatic presses that stamp out the individual tiles. In some plants, the tiles are dried and fired to semi-vitreous bodies before glazing and a second firing. Elsewhere, the glaze is sprayed on after the body has been formed; body and glaze are then subjected to a single firing. By either method, the glaze is melted, causing it to fuse with the surface of the tile. Inorganic coloring matter, mixed with the glaze, provides a wide variety of colors and patterns for the finished product.

Refractories—
masters of fire

The ceramic materials called refractories can withstand unusually high heat as well as abrasion and the corrosive effects of acids and alkalis. They are found in furnaces, stills for the cracking of petroleum, ceramic kilns, boilers, incinerators, electrolytic cells for aluminum production and the interior of the family fireplace. They are an important constituent of nuclear reactors. Jet engines would not last very long without refractory parts.

Fireclay, formed into firebrick and hundreds of specialized shapes, is an important raw material for refractories. In recent years, nonclay refractories have been developed to meet increasingly severe demands. They are being made of alumina, zirconia, silicon carbide, chromia, magnesite, graphite and other less common materials. The cost of these refractories is much higher than

that of fireclay. However, their use in critical parts of a furnace will keep it in operating condition for longer periods, with less time taken out for repairs.

Methods for the production of refractories follow in general the common ceramic processes. Materials are crushed, screened and ground; then they are put through magnetic separators to remove ferrous (iron-containing) impurities. Mixed with small amounts of moisture, they are shaped by dry pressing, extrusion, hand molding or casting. Drying and kiln firing complete the process.

Porcelain enamel—
fusing ceramic to metal

Porcelain enamel is produced by fusing a film of glass to a metal, usually iron or steel. This useful ceramic material is specified where metal must be protected against heat, corrosion or abrasion. It is to be found in sinks, bathtubs, ranges, farm silos, hot-water tank interiors, linings for furnaces, chemical apparatus and parts for jet engines and gas turbines.

Ceramic engineers specializing in porcelain enameling find that their skills are being called on more and more to devise ceramic-to-metal seals. Such seals must be provided for the places where wire, tubes or other metal parts enter a laboratory vessel, manufacturing device or spacecraft that must be kept airtight and gastight.

In the processing of porcelain enamel, the metal is first formed into the desired shape and thoroughly cleaned. Then the enamel material — a frit, made of finely ground glass — is applied. Two enameling processes are in general use. Dry-process enameling consists of heating the metal piece and then sifting powdered frit onto the hot surface. Here the frit melts to form a hard, impervious layer. For wet-process enameling, the frit is mixed with water and clay, forming a paintlike liquid that can be applied by brush, dipping or spraying. After this has dried, it is fired so as to fuse to the metal. Most enamels are fired at temperatures of from 1,350° F. to 1,600° F. Lower-melting frits have been developed to make possible the application of enamel to alumi-

CLAY MIX

AUGER MACHINE   DIE

CLAY COMPRESSED AND MOVED
TOWARD DIE BY SCREW ACTION

J. C. Steele and Sons, Inc.

Most brick is formed by extrusion, the process illustrated in the diagram at the left. Clay is prepared in the form of a stiff mud. In an auger machine, it is moved by screw action to a die; it comes out of the die as a continuous column of approximately the length and width of a brick. It is then cut by a machine, such as the one shown in the above photograph, to brick thickness.

num, copper and other metals with low melting points. These frits can be fired at from 950° F. to 1,000° F.

Commercial enameling is generally a two-coat process. The frit used for the first coat contains cobalt or nickel and fuses well with the metal; the result is a dark blue or brown enamel. For surfaces that are usually not visible, such as the interior of a kitchen oven, this "ground coat" may suffice. A second coat is usually applied where appearance is important, as in a range top or a bathtub. In this cover coat, selected materials, such as titania, zirconia, antimony oxide or tin oxide, are added to cover the first coat and to add color. Methods for producing white enamels in a single-coat process have also been developed. They require unusual types of steel and added preparation before the enamel is applied.

In the past, porcelain enameling was apt to chip under heavy blows or bending. This has become less of a problem with the development of better materials and methods of application. The general rule is that the thinner the enamel coat, the better the adherence.

Structural
clay products

Brick, sewer pipe and tile, all made of clay, have been among man's building materials from a very early period of his civilization. Generally speaking, today's construction materials of clay are much the same as they were thousands of years ago. The chief differences are that they are now made by machines, instead of being hand-formed, and that they are burned to a greater degree of hardness. A new development is the introduction of light-weight brick and tiles. They are made of carefully selected clays and shales that explode when subjected to high heat. The products formed from these exploded materials are about a third lighter than ordinary brick or tile.

Common brick, which has no special surface finish, can be made from a wide variety of clays. Carefully selected clays must be used for face brick. This type has one or more specially finished surfaces and is used for the "face," or outer surface, of a structure.

Most brick are now made by extrusion. The clay is prepared in the form of a stiff mud. This is forced through a die, and it comes out as a continuous column that is approximately the length and width of a brick. Wires strung on another machine quickly cut the column to brick thickness. After being dried, the brick are fired in a kiln.

Many colors, sizes and textures are available in face brick. Clays from different pits will burn to a variety of colors. Other colors can be achieved by different firing techniques and by the amount of air admitted to the kiln. Even greater variety is obtained by adding sand, coloring powders or stains to the face of the brick before it is dried. Wire cutting, special molding techniques and other methods are used in great variety to produce unusual effects.

Chimney flue liners, drain tile and conduits for underground electrical wiring and telephone circuits are also formed by extrusion. So are sewer pipes. In this case, however, the pipes must be formed individually. This is because at one end of each pipe there is a "bell" — an enlarged section that fits over the end of the next pipe in line, to make a joint. Most sewer pipe is also glazed. In this process, salt is thrown on the fire in the kiln. The salt vaporizes and goes through the kiln, reacting with the clay to form an impervious glaze on all surfaces of the pipe.

Quarry tile — unglazed tile used for floors — are closely related to these structural clay products. The tile, which are usually a half-inch thick, are particularly useful in plants where a high degree of cleanliness must be maintained, or in places where acids are likely to be spilled.

Roofing granules for the shingles that cover so many homes are a ceramic product. They are made from crushed rock, screened to uniform size and then coated with a ceramic mixture that adds color and protection. The asphalt-shingle industry uses the granules in huge quantities.

Miniaturized electronic circuits

The ceramic wafers used as a base for electronic circuits are so small that a complete circuit, containing a number of wafers, can fit into a cube measuring about a third of an inch to a side. Such miniaturized circuits are used, among other things, for hearing aids, proximity fuses and tiny radios that could fit into the cap of a fountain pen. The light weight and tiny volume of the miniaturized circuits make them especially useful for different types of artificial satellites and space vehicles.

Most of the tiny wafers are made from alumina (aluminum oxide); they are pressed out by automatic machines and then fired. Materials with desired electronic properties are applied to the surface of each wafer as a powder, ribbon paste or other convenient form; then the applied substance is fired, fusing it to the wafer. After the

Radio Corp. of America

Three stages in the production of a ceramic circuit, set next to a paper clip to show how small this circuit is. A shows the circuit in the unfired state. B is a circuit after firing; a transistor and a diode have now been mounted in place. In C, the active elements have all been sealed in and the whole assembly is ready for use.

Below are some memory cores, greatly enlarged, for an electronic computer. The arrow leading from the circle shows the place it would occupy in a circuit plane, made up of hundreds of memory cores. We also see a stack consisting of numerous planes.

UNIVAC Division of Sperry Rand Corp.

3/100 INCH

Indiana General Corp.

various electronic parts, in this wafer form, are assembled in a stack in the proper order, wires along the sides are attached to terminals on each wafer, completing the circuit. All are then sealed into a cube, making a neat package ready to slip into the major circuit.

Ceramic doughnuts
as memory cores

The small doughnut-shaped ceramic rings that provide the "memories" for many electronic computers and control systems are known as ferrite memory cores. These rings, with outside diameters as small as 0.03 inch, are pressed from a composition that is principally iron oxide. They are formed with high-speed automatic presses and sent through small tunnel kilns in refractory trays known as boats.

The cores are mounted on wire grids (circuit planes), with hundreds of cores to a grid. There are a great many grids in an electronic computer. Each memory core stores one bit of information, retaining it or releasing it at the operator's command.

Ceramics applied to
the making of gems

A ceramic process is used to create gems that rival in beauty the stones found in nature and used as jewelry. These man-made gems have many industrial applications. The electronics industry relies heavily on them because they are "grown" under controlled conditions and with known materials to provide specified electrical and optical properties. They are used, among other things, in transistors, lasers and solar cells.

Artificial diamonds have been produced under high pressures, applied together with high heat. This process is described elsewhere in THE BOOK OF POPULAR SCIENCE.* At present, only diamonds for industrial grinding are in production.

Portland cement is made
by a ceramic process

Portland cement, widely used for making concrete and in mortar for masonry work, is prepared by a ceramic process. It is made up of about 60 per cent lime, 25 per cent silica, 10 per cent alumina and traces of other materials. The manufacturing process begins with the conversion of great slabs of limestone to the form of a powder. The powdered limestone is then mixed with finely ground clay and gypsum, is put into a rotary kiln and is fired under a temperature of about 2,700° F. The mixture comes out in a form known as "clinker," which is then ground to a fine powder. This is the

* See the article Man-made Diamonds, in Volume 4.

This rotary kiln, used in making portland cement in a Pennsylvania cement plant, is 341 feet long. As it slowly rotates, every part of the raw materials it contains is thoroughly heated. At the same time, since the kiln is mounted at a slight inclined angle, the materials being processed move slowly to the lower end of the kiln, whence they are discharged.

F. L. Smidth and Co.

Left: two big ceramic-clad nose cones, or re-entry vehicles, of intercontinental ballistic missiles (ICBM's). Each of the cones represents the third stage of an ICBM—the part that reenters the earth's atmosphere on its way to the target. Right: a nose cone after its passage through the atmosphere. Note the effect of the heat of re-entry on the cone.

Photos, Avco Corp.

familiar portland cement. After it is mixed with water it returns to the hardness and strength of rock.

The rotary kilns used for making portland cement are among the largest pieces of moving machinery used in a manufacturing operation. They are huge steel tubes, lined with fire brick and mounted at an inclined angle. Some are as much as 12 feet in diameter and 500 feet in length. They revolve about once a minute, causing the raw materials within them to be thoroughly exposed to the great heat of the kiln. At the same time, these materials move slowly from the upper end of the kiln down to the lower end, from which they are finally discharged. The process takes about four hours.

Spark-plug manufacture

Ceramic insulators are required for the many millions of spark plugs used in motor vehicles. These insulators are made from alumina (aluminum oxide), ground to a powder and mixed with water. The mold is a flexible, rubberlike material, shaped like a spark-plug insulator. After the mold has been filled with alumina, it is subjected to high pressure by air or liquid. This pressure, applied evenly from all sides, compacts the alumina into a dense, hard body. After the body has been fired, it is stamped with the brand name and then sprayed with a glaze. A second firing fuses the glaze to the alumina, making it impervious to dirt and moisture.

Another ceramic operation is required when the metal parts are attached to the insulator body of the spark plug. A glass composition that melts at a lower temperature than the metal parts involved is used to connect metal to ceramic, creating an airtight seal.

The ceramic process applied to abrasives

Grinding wheels, whetstones and abrasive powders are now mostly made by the ceramic process. Alumina (aluminum oxide) and silicon carbide, a man-made compound, are the sources for hard, sharp particles that are capable of cutting any materials known to man. Even diamonds can be worn down by these abrasives.

Granules of aluminum oxide or silicon carbide are converted by a ceramic process into grinding wheels. The granules are first screened to uniform size and then mixed with one of a variety of compositions, usually made up of a glass frit, quartz and clay. This mixture, to which some water is added, is formed under pressure into the shape of the desired wheel. After drying, the wheel is fired in a kiln until the binding composition is vitrified into a glass, holding the abrasive in a durable bond. Grinding wheels made in this way are more uniform than those processed from natural stone.

This, in brief, is the story of ceramics. Older than civilization, ceramic products are in greater demand than ever before to meet the expanding needs of modern technology. It is fortunate, indeed, that there never will be a shortage of the necessary raw materials, since so much of the earth's crust can be treated by ceramic methods.

See also Vol. 10, p. 282: "Ceramics."

MASERS AND LASERS*

Revolutionary Radiation Devices

CRYSTALS that amplify the faintest of radio signals from trillions of miles out in space; devices that measure time more accurately than any mechanical clock; light beams that burn holes through steel or that carry radio or television programs — these are some of the applications of the revolutionary devices called masers and lasers.

The maser (from *M*icrowave *A*mplification by *S*timulated *E*mission of *R*adiation) absorbs electrical or electromagnetic energy. Then when it is acted on by the very short electromagnetic waves called microwaves,** it emits energy and greatly amplifies the microwaves. The laser (from *L*ight *A*mplification by *S*timulated *E*mission of *R*adiation) is based on the same general principle as the maser. However, it amplifies and, more importantly, generates light waves (and also infrared and ultraviolet waves) instead of microwaves. Many substances have been made to "mase" and "lase" — that is, to behave like masers or lasers.

The absorption and emission of radiation

To understand how masers and lasers absorb or emit radiation, it is necessary to bear in mind that atoms and molecules are not inert building blocks but veritable bundles of energy. Thus the electrons — particles of negative electricity — spin and wobble as they revolve in various orbits around the nucleus of the atom. The atoms and molecules of solids vibrate in their fixed posts in the crystal lattice (see Index); the atoms and molecules of liquids and gases move about. They are all subjected to various forms of energy — heat, light, magnetism, electricity and so on.

Atoms and molecules can exist in different energy levels, separated from one another by definite steps. Suppose that radiation from without acts upon a substance. If a given atom of the substance is at a low energy level, it will absorb energy; the incoming radiation, therefore, will be decreased by that amount. If the atom is at a high energy level when it is stimulated by radiation of the appropriate frequency, it will drop to a lower energy state. It may even do so without any specific stimulation by a wave — that is, spontaneously. Ultimately, it will emit radiation corresponding to the stimulating wave or, in the absence of the latter, waves corresponding in frequency to the difference between the higher and lower energy level. Where there is stimulating radiation, this will be reinforced by the additional radiation. Under ordinary conditions, most materials will absorb much of the energy falling upon them since most of their atoms are in the lower energy levels.

The absorption and emission of radiation is normally a disorderly random process. For one thing, the incoming radiation is usually a mixture of frequencies. Moreover, as atoms and molecules vibrate, they interact with one another, making the energy transformations even more complex. But what if we could make the atoms behave in a more disciplined way? What if we could make them jump up and down the energy steps all together at the physicist's bidding, like a troop of circus animals? That is precisely what has been accomplished with the maser and laser.

The basis of masing and lasing action

The medium employed in a maser is either a gas or a solid, which has been selected because its atomic or molecular structure has favorably arranged energy levels. It is led into or is enclosed in a cavity resonator. This is simply a metal box from whose walls incoming radiation can be appropriately reflected.

---

* Article prepared with the assistance of Bell Telephone Laboratories, Inc.
** For an account of electromagnetic waves, see the article Electromagnetic Radiation, in Volume 7.

beam in the form of red light. The
beam is reflected back and forth
between a pair of mirrors, one at
either end of the rod. As it is
reflected, the beam stimulates other
high-energy atoms to drop to lower
levels and to emit red light in their
turn. When the original beam has
become energetic enough, it passes
out of one of the mirrors, which
is more transparent than the other.

MIRROR

RUBY ROD

LASER BEAM

MIRROR

First, it is necessary to increase greatly
the number of atoms in the high-energy
state as compared with those in the low-
energy level. This can be done in several
ways. In one method, the low-energy atoms
are filtered out through the use of an appropriate electrical field. This was the method
employed in the first operational maser —
the ammonia maser devised by J. P. Gordon,
H. J. Zeiger and C. H. Townes. In another
method, the temperature is greatly lowered
by means of liquid helium or nitrogen, thus
bringing the great bulk of the atoms to the
low-energy state. Then these atoms are
raised, all together, to the high-energy state
by "pumping": that is, by introducing into
the system electromagnetic energy that is at
a different wave length from the stimulating
wave length that will be used later.

The next step is to introduce a stimulating wave — a microwave of the appropriate frequency — at one wall of the cavity
resonator. It will excite a number of the
high-energy atoms in its path. Each of them
will then emit electromagnetic energy of the
same wave length as the stimulating wave.
Thus to the energy of the original microwave will be added that emitted by the stimulated atoms. The wave will now bounce
off one of the cavity-resonator walls and
will excite more atoms on the rebound. As
it bounces back and forth between the walls
of the cavity resonator, the wave will continually grow in strength. By the time it is
emitted from the maser, it will have been
greatly amplified. This amplified microwave will reproduce weak signals with great
fidelity and very little noise. In the am-

monia maser, only two energy states are
involved. Most masers (and lasers, too)
are based on three or more energy levels.

There are basic similarities, as well
as differences, in the operation of masers
and lasers. In the laser, atoms are raised
to a high-energy state before they begin to
emit. Unlike the maser, however, the laser
puts forth a beam of intense light or ultraviolet or infrared radiation, instead of microwaves. Furthermore, the laser does not
usually function as an amplifier of a weak
signal coming to it from the outside.*

Light or electrical energy is used to
raise the energy level of the atoms in the
laser material. The now activated, high-
energy atoms began to drop back to low-
energy levels. As they do so, they begin
to give off the characteristic laser radiation, or beam. Since this beam is rather
weak at first, it must be reflected back and
forth through the laser between a pair of
semitransparent mirrors, one at each end
of the laser apparatus. As this happens, the
beam stimulates other high-energy atoms
to drop to lower energy states and so emit
radiation of the same kind. This reinforces,
or amplifies internally, the original laser
beam. When it becomes sufficiently energetic (in the merest fraction of a second),
it passes out of the laser through one of the
mirrors, which is more transparent than
the other or has a special "window."

The beam of light emitted by a laser is
almost pure in color — that is, it has a very

* The laser can be adapted as an amplifier of light
signals of the right frequency coming from the outside, by
pumping it to a point just before it would begin to "lase"
by itself.

Left: a Bell Telephone Laboratories engineer inserts a traveling-wave ruby maser assembly into a vacuum vessel containing liquid helium, which is at an extremely low temperature. The maser operates most effectively under such conditions. This particular maser was later installed in the cab of the horn antenna at the satellite station at Andover, Maine. The maser served to amplify the exceedingly weak signals coming from the Telstar communication satellite.

Right: applying the laser to television. Microwave signals have been generated, corresponding to the picture that is being transmitted. The pattern of the microwave signals is impressed on a laser beam (at the left of the photo). The beam is picked up by the phototube of the receiving apparatus and is converted into microwave signals. When these are transformed into the video image, Soviet premier Nikita Khrushchev appears on the screen of the television set.

Bell Telephone Laboratories

General Telephone and Electronics Corp.

narrow range of frequencies instead of being spread over a broader range, as in the case of ordinary monochromatic ("one-colored") light. The laser beam does not spread out widely in space, because its waves are coherent — that is, close together in frequency and timing. Within its frequency range, a laser beam may be very powerful.

The first laser — the ruby laser invented by T. H. Maiman in 1960 — worked only in short, discontinuous pulses. Continuous operation has since been achieved, not only with the ruby laser but with other kinds (gaseous and crystalline) as well. The first continuously operating laser was a gas device containing a mixture of helium and neon, developed by Bell Telephone Laboratories. Argon and oxygen have also been used; other gas mixtures are being tested.

By subjecting lasing materials to various types of energy — electrical, magnetic, even sonic — scientists have been able to change the laser output in various ways for the purposes of signaling, communication and general experimentation. Various patterns can be imposed upon a beam. Its color can be changed by passing it through another substance, such as a crystal.

Applications of
masers and lasers

Masers are excellent amplifiers because of their low noise level. They serve in long-distance radar and microwave communication. They are also used in combination with radio telescopes to amplify weak radio signals originating in outer space.* The ammonia maser is not used as an amplifier of sound. It has great possibilities, however, as an "atomic clock" of high accuracy. As the ammonia atoms in this device are excited, they set up steady oscillations. These serve as signals with which to control another oscillating device outside of the maser.

The laser has already shown itself to be a remarkably versatile device. For one thing, it has great possibilities as a research tool. The slender, powerful laser beam can be used in starting and controlling chemical reactions on a molecular scale. It can serve to investigate fine details of a molecular structure and even atomic structure. The purity of the frequencies generated by the laser may revolutionize the study of light. The sensitivity of the laser to physical changes and distortions enables it to detect the presence of active forces, such as earthquake waves. It could be made to function as an effective seismograph.

A ruby laser produced by the Raytheon Company created a sensation when its beam punched a hole in a safety razor blade in a burst of energy lasting a fraction of a second. Another ruby laser has cut through steel an eighth of an inch thick. Some researchers are trying to develop a laser beam that would serve as a military weapon — as a "death ray." It is believed that the power

* See the article Radio Astronomy, in Volume 9.

The revolutionary laser radar, which can give target details hundreds of times sharper than those provided by the conventional radar set. The device has shown its effectiveness in many experiments. In operation, the light beam from the laser radar flashes from the transmitting telescope (right), strikes the target and then bounces back into the receiving telescope (left). The two smaller scopes shown here have been used in the experiments to photograph targets and align the system.

Performing a painless eye operation with a laser at New York's Columbia Presbyterian Hospital. The operation consisted of removing a tumor from the retina of an eye of the patient. The tumor was destroyed by a laser beam, which was focused by a mirror, as shown.

Above: two components of a miniature assembly have been welded together by the beam of a ruby laser. The size of the welded area is indicated by comparison with the eye of the needle shown at the right of the photo.

of the laser beam could also be harnessed for more peaceful uses. It serves in cutting metals in the manufacture of various miniature components of instruments and machines. It has also been used by surgeons as a "scalpel" in delicate operations.

Laser beams show great promise in the field of communication. Because of their narrow range of high frequency, they could provide hundreds of thousands of wave channels for the exchange of messages, in contrast to the hundreds, or, at most, thousands of channels obtainable by radio waves and microwaves.

The laser has already been applied to television. In the laser television apparatus developed by the General Telephone and Electronics Corporation, modulated microwave signals are generated, corresponding to the picture that is being transmitted. Next, the pattern of the microwave signals is impressed on a gas-laser beam. The now modulated beam is picked up by the phototube of a receiving apparatus. The beam is then converted into microwave signals and these are transformed into the video image.

Lasers will probably play an important part in the exploration of space. The ring laser, developed by the Sperry Rand Corporation, can be used to measure and correct the motions of space vehicles. Another Sperry Rand device, the laser radar, can measure the speed of distant moving objects to an accuracy of .00004 miles an hour or less. It should prove invaluable in command guidance systems for vehicles in outer space. (See the article Guidance in Space, in Volume 8.)

It is expected, too, that the laser will find application in the electronic computer. As we point out in the article The Electronic Computer, in Volume 9, this device is based on the binary number system, in which there are only two symbols—1 and 0. The laser, with its lower and higher energy states, would be ideally suited for computer use. The "one" and "zero" of the computer would correspond to a high-energy level and a low-energy level, respectively, of the laser. Laser computers would be much faster than the fastest computers in existence today. Since glass fibers of minute diameter can be made to lase and carry light beams effectively, they would make possible laser computers of great complexity but of extremely small size.

THE ASTONISHING GIANTS

Elephant, Hippopotamus, Rhinoceros, Giraffe

THERE was a time when giant mammals roamed over the forests and plains of the world. There were early members of the elephant family — the mastodon, the mammoth and the *Dinotherium*. There was the truly colossal *Baluchitherium,* an early hornless rhinoceros that stood eighteen feet at the shoulder. These creatures have vanished from the face of the earth, and we know of them only from their fossil remains, found in the rocks. We might well distrust the evidence of our own eyes as we examine these fossils were it not for the existence, in this twentieth century, of certain survivors of the age of monsters — particularly the elephant, the rhinoceros, the hippopotamus and the giraffe.

These animals are not closely related, but they form part of the large group of hoofed mammals, or ungulates — a group that includes the horses, cattle, tapirs, pigs, camels and so on. They show certain similarities in the form of the teeth and in the structure of the limbs; they feed almost entirely on vegetation. Elephants, rhinoceroses and hippopotamuses have the same type of skeleton. The backbone, to which are attached many ribs, serves as a girder balanced on the strong forelegs. The large, heavy head counterbalances the weight of the body. The hind legs provide the chief thrust in walking or running.

The elephant is among the most interesting of beasts. Besides its huge size and its well-developed brain, it has a most unusual elongated snout — the trunk — which is remarkably well adapted for collecting the quantities of food that the animal needs.

In the course of its evolution, the elephant grew larger and larger. It consumed more food and gradually grew larger teeth for grinding it. The study of the teeth, in fossil form, of extinct elephant species has furnished important evidence in reconstructing the animal's past.

The modern African and Indian elephants are two of a long line of animals that goes back some forty to fifty million years and that includes the mastodons, the mammoths and numerous more primitive elephantlike types. The earliest known member of this line was *Moeritherium* of Africa. A comparatively puny creature, it stood only two feet high. It possessed small tusks on both upper and lower jaws, and it probably had a short snout, like that of a tapir. From this type at least two branches of elephant development arose.

One branch led to the *Dinotherium* of Eurasia and Africa. It was a distinct type of elephant having no tusks on the upper jaw but possessing down-turned tusks on the lower jaw. It became extinct perhaps less than a million years ago.

The other branch led to the *Gomphotherium* of Africa, Eurasia and North America. This animal, which had elongated, tusk-bearing upper and lower jaws, flourished some 25,000,000 years ago. From this long-faced elephant came mastodons (of which some had a lower as well as an upper pair of tusks), mammoths and present-day elephants. The mammoths differed from the mastodons in having a much higher and shorter head and a short, tuskless lower jaw. Our modern elephants resemble the mammoths more closely than the mastodons.

Woolly mammoths were depicted quite frequently in Stone Age drawings. Well-preserved carcasses of these huge animals have been found embedded in the soil of Siberia. Apparently they had bogged down in deep mud, which later had become frozen.

In the early part of the last century, a mammoth was discovered in a marvelous state of preservation near the mouth of the Lena River, in Siberia. Its flesh and hair and internal organs were intact; in fact, its last meal of shoots and cones of pine and fir was still undigested in its stomach. Its brain was quite uninjured. The big animal had undergone astonishingly little change since it had met its doom.

Scientists have been at a loss to explain just how these huge beasts came to be so well preserved by freezing. According to one theory, freezing must have occurred very quickly, before the mammoths knew what was happening. It has been suggested that some unusual weather or astronomical phenomenon caused a terrific sudden fall in temperature in the particular localities where the mammoths were later found. Siberia has been called a mortuary of mammoths. At one time the Russians exported considerable quantities of ivory derived from these huge animals.

Mammoths measuring thirteen feet in height have been found; but the average seems to have been about ten feet. These animals were comparable in height, therefore, to the elephants of the present day. Mammoth tusks were very long; in extreme cases, they may have extended over ten feet from the sockets in which they were imbedded. They were more slender, however, than those of modern elephants. The mammoth was covered with very long hair that almost reached the ground. The tail was short; a tuft at the end was provided with stiff bristles. The ears were small and they were covered with fur.

Apparently the mammoth was the only member of the elephant family that became adapted to conditions of extreme cold. In France, it maintained itself until toward the very end of the glacial period. It may have survived even longer in the tundras of northern Siberia.

The trunk of the elephant was a key factor in the animal's evolution. This powerful, muscular organ, which is actually an elongated snout and upper lip, serves as the chief tool of the ungainly creature in the struggle for survival.

The trunk developed through one of those experiments of nature whereby, as an animal changed in size or habits, it changed its means of getting food. Since the early elephants were browsing animals, it seems that as they grew in stature, they either had to increase the length of their necks or find another way to reach the ground with their mouths. The head was so heavy that it was impossible to grow a longer neck and the accompanying muscles to support it. Instead, the early elephants, such as *Gomphotherium,* for example, developed elongated lower jaws.

As the lower jaw lengthened, the nose and upper lip gradually grew beyond the upper jaw. But as the snout, or trunk, increased in length, the necessity for the long lower jaw disappeared. As a result, this jaw began to shorten and the trunk became the means for getting food. The two remaining incisor teeth of the elephant's upper jaw developed into continually growing tusks. The tusks were weapons and also served perhaps to dig up roots.

The trunk has become a versatile organ

From an exaggerated, piglike snout, like that probably found in *Moeritherium,* the elephant fashioned a trunk that was capable of grasping objects. The powerful muscles needed to manipulate it arose chiefly from those parts of the facial muscles that in other mammals move the sides of the nose. As a consequence, the trunk of modern elephants is far more satisfactory than a long neck, for not only can it reach the ground but it can be moved upward, backward and sideways as well.

The elephant can do a great many things with its trunk. It uses the organ, for one thing, to draw in water. However, contrary to popular belief, it does not actually drink water through the trunk. Water is sucked into the organ and is then sprayed into the mouth. The trunk is also used to convey food to the mouth. By means of this useful organ, the elephant can feed on the vegetation on the ground and in the trees above its head. Among the big animal's favorite foods are the tender twigs and branches from the upper limbs of trees. Without the elephant's trunk, most of these delectable tidbits would be quite beyond its reach. Occasionally the desired twigs are too high for even the trunk to reach. In this case, the animal solves its feeding problem in a remarkably simple and practical way; it pushes the tree over, using its head as a battering ram.

The trunk of the elephant serves as a sort of fifth limb, and a very powerful one, too. With it, the animal has been known to lift as much as a thousand pounds. It does not carry heavy loads on its trunk, however. A ponderous log, say, would be lifted by the trunk to a position across the tusks and then held in place by the trunk. With this organ, the elephant would test the weight of the log before lifting it to the tusks, where it would be carried, perhaps for a considerable distance.

Strong as the elephant's trunk is, it is capable of quite delicate work. On the end of the Indian elephant's trunk, there is a fingerlike lobe, which the animal can manipulate with quite amazing dexterity. (The African elephant has two such lobes.) Consider for a moment how the animal grasps the comparatively tiny peanuts that are fed to it by child visitors to the zoo. The lobe of the trunk is also a very sensitive organ of touch.

The trunk serves as the elephant's organ of smell. The animal's eyesight is poor and its hearing is not much better; hence it depends to a considerable extent on its sense of smell — one of the most acute in the animal kingdom — to keep it in touch with what is going on. If one were to observe an elephant in the wilds for any length of time, he would see that the trunk is constantly in motion sniffing the air and inspecting the objects in the immediate vicinity of the animal.

Elephants belong to the order Proboscidea and are the largest land animals in the world. At the present time they are represented by only two species — the African and the Indian. The African elephant is slightly larger than the Indian. African bulls normally reach a height of eleven feet, and a weight of six tons; occasionally,

individuals thirteen feet tall have been found. Females are about a foot and a half shorter, on the average, than the bulls. Indian bulls usually attain a height of nine or ten feet. One consequence of the African elephant's greater size is that it rarely lies down after reaching maturity. As the animal grows older and larger, it becomes more and more difficult for it to lift its great bulk to a standing position once it has reclined. It may spend the last thirty or forty years of its life on its feet — even while sleeping. Indian elephants, on the contrary, lie down quite regularly. Only old members of this species sleep on their feet.

There is a good deal of controversy in naturalist circles today concerning the intelligence of the elephant. There is no doubt that the animal is one of the most intelligent of the mammals (not including man, of course), but there is much disagreement as to how it compares with the dog, the horse and the great apes. In one respect, indeed — in its ability to learn from man — the elephant has few peers among the lower animals. Because of this ability, it has served humans in various ways for a good many centuries.

The big animal figures quite prominently in ancient warfare. When Alexander the Great invaded India in 326 B.C., the Indians sought to stop his advance by using elephants in their attacks. Apparently Alexander's troops were not intimidated. In the battle of Heraclea (280 B.C.), King Pyrrhus of Epirus hurled massed charges of elephants against the Roman legions and routed them. The famous Carthaginian general Hannibal employed elephants successfully in warfare. They played an important part in his famous victory over the Romans at Cannae in 218 B.C.

The elephant is one of the most reliable of show animals and among the mainstays of any circus. The first captive elephant to be brought to North America was a female, shipped from Calcutta, India, to New York in 1796. It became the feature attraction of the first American circus. Undoubtedly the most famous of circus elephants was Jumbo, which was originally exhibited in the Royal Zoological Gardens in London. It won renown because of its huge size; it stood ten feet nine inches at the shoulder and weighed six tons. The American showman Phineas T. Barnum bought the animal in 1882 for $10,000 and exhibited it in the Barnum and Bailey Circus for three years. Jumbo was killed by a railroad train in Canada in 1885. Its skeleton has been preserved for posterity at the American Museum of Natural History and its mounted skin at Tufts College, in Medford, Massachusetts.

Circus elephants can be trained to do many things. They can carry riders on their backs, play ball, stand on their hind legs or on their heads and bring a huge forepaw to within inches of the head of a trainer lying prostrate on the ground. They are gentle with children and graciously accept the peanuts that youngsters offer them. Only female elephants are used as performers; the bulls are apt to become unreliable at certain times.

Elephants are noted as work animals, performing remarkable services for man. Among other things, they have been used for centuries in logging operations in India and Burma. They played an important part in the construction of some of the outstanding architectural masterpieces of India. The big animals were used to carry and stack timber and to place masses of masonry in position.

The intelligence of elephants is attested in many ways. They have been taught to understand as many as twenty-five different commands. The big animals have been known to make tools for their own use. They remove branches, strip them of all but the topmost leaves and use them as fans to brush away flies. Sometimes they pull up stakes and use them as

Amer. Mus. of Nat. Hist.

African elephants with young at a training-station camp located in the Republic of the Congo.

back-scrapers. In passing spears to their riders, the animals have been trained to present them handle first. When traveling through a wooded area, an elephant will protect its rider from low-hanging twigs and branches.

The elephant leads a very interesting life in its natural habitat. It travels in herds of two hundred or more under the guidance of a big bull. The diet is strictly vegetarian; the herd moves from one place to another in search of fodder. The big animals lumber along, in single file, at about six miles an hour; no animal can travel farther in a single day.

Elephants may mate at any time during the year. At certain periods, the males go into a state of sexual excitation, called "musth." During such periods, a strong-smelling liquid runs from glands near the eyes, and the bulls are moody and ill-tempered. The period of gestation is about twenty-one months; the female bears a single calf at each birth. She may have six to eight young during her lifetime. Calves are covered with hair at birth; they stand about three feet high and weigh approximately two hundred pounds. They are suckled on a single pair of mammaries between the mother's forelegs and are not weaned until about the beginning of the third year.

The ungainly hippopotamus

The word "hippopotamus" comes from two Greek words meaning "river horse." The animal is a river-dweller, indeed; but the "horse" part of the name is not particularly appropriate, because the hippopotamus is more closely allied to the hog family. There are two living species: the common hippopotamus and the pigmy, or Liberian, variety. These animals belong to the family of the Hippopotamidae.

The common hippopotamus (also called the hippo) once ranged over much of Europe, the British Isles and Africa, but it is now restricted to a portion of the African continent, north of Zululand. As civilization advances and more and more areas are settled, the hippo becomes a prob-lem because of the damage it does to crops. As a result, it is mercilessly hunted and its numbers have been greatly reduced.

The hippopotamus is the second largest land-living animal, by weight, in the world. The average specimen weighs about four tons; some individuals, as much as five. The massive head alone may weigh a ton. The animal is from twelve to fourteen feet in length and stands about four and a half feet at the shoulder. The huge, barrel-shaped body is supported by short, pillar-like legs. The hippo can open its huge mouth wider than any other animal, except the whales. The skin is very thick over most parts of the body, reaching a maximum thickness of two inches over some of the upper areas.

The internal organs of the hippo are of equally amazing dimensions. The stomach may reach a length of over ten feet. To fill this vast cavern, the animal may consume five or six bushels of vegetation in the course of a single day. The hippo's great appetite has proved useful to mankind, because it impels the animal to feed voraciously on river growths that would otherwise choke the streams.

Hippos live in herds of twenty to thirty individuals. Each herd keeps to the river most of the day, moving up and down the stream for considerable distances in search of food. Hippos can remain under water for as long as thirty minutes, if necessary; the normal interval, however, is from five to ten minutes. The animals can float on the surface or sink to the bottom at will. Nostrils and ears can be hermetically sealed, voluntarily, as the animals sink to the bottom of the river. Hippos are excellent swimmers; they can also walk along the river bottom at quite surprising speed — eight miles an hour, according to certain authorities.

At night, the members of the herd occasionally leave the river for short periods of time to feed on vegetation along river banks. A hippo will never go too far, and it will return before morning along the same path, following its own scent back to the river. Should a heavy rain wash away the scent, the animal will

Elephant plowing a field in the Naini Tal Terai forest area of India. Indian elephants, such as these, are somewhat smaller than the African species.

A sturdy pachyderm worker moving huge teakwood logs near Rangoon, in Burma. There, elephants play an all-important part in logging operations.

be lost. On land, the animal can walk about as fast as a man and it can even gallop after a fashion. While it is on land, special skin glands pour forth an oily, reddish liquid that prevents the skin from drying out. The fact that this liquid resembles blood in appearance has given rise to the perfectly absurd belief that the hippopotamus sweats blood.

Hippos mate once a year. The bulls fight savagely at mating time, and their battles sometimes have a fatal outcome. The gestation period is about nine months; the female gives birth to a single calf. Even a baby hippo weighs a hundred pounds or so at birth and its weight increases rapidly. Usually it is suckled in the water. It travels from one place to another by riding on its mother's back.

The pigmy hippopotamus is found in Liberia and Sierra Leone, in West Africa. It stands only about three feet high at the shoulder, is about six feet long and weighs a mere four hundred pounds. Though far less bulky than the common hippopotamus, the pigmy resembles the larger animal in both appearance and habits.

A surly heavyweight
— the rhinoceros

The rhinoceros is found today in the warm regions of Asia and Africa and also in Indonesia. This big, clumsy animal has a thick hide that makes it invulnerable to attack by even the largest flesh-eaters. The head, which is concave in front, is armed with one or two horns. These structures are outgrowths of the skin; they consist of compacted masses of hair. The horns continue to grow during the lifetime of the animal. The rhinoceros, or rhino as it is often called, is a plant-eater; it feeds on grasses and foliage of various kinds. It belongs to the family Rhinocerotidae, a name derived from the Greek and meaning "nose-horned animals."

The rhinoceros has a most unusual partnership with a bird called the tick bird, which spends its time removing ticks and insects from the rhino's hide. Thus it provides food for itself and contributes to the comfort of its big companion. At the approach of an enemy such as man, the bird sounds a warning with loud screeching and much flapping of its wings. It is a most effective sentinel.

Most rhinoceroses have uncertain dispositions. They are not very intelligent and have poor eyesight and appear to be at a loss when confronted by a prospective enemy, such as man. They are likely to seek refuge in flight; but they are quite as apt to make a sudden charge. Since a rhinoceros cannot turn quickly, it is usually possible to side step its charge unless one yields to panic.

The commonest rhino of Africa is the black rhinoceros, which stands some five feet at the shoulder and weighs up to three thousand pounds. It has two horns, the front one being the larger of the two. Generally it is a solitary creature, except at mating time. Mating can take place at various times during the year. A single calf is born after a gestation period of some eighteen months. The mother suckles its young for two years or so.

The largest rhino is the white, or square-lipped variety, found in Central Africa. The animal is not really white, but a rather sooty gray in color. It weighs up to four tons and stands six and a half feet at the shoulder; like the black variety, it has two horns. Sometimes it lives in a small group.

The great Indian rhinoceros, which ranges over the plains of northern India, Nepal and Assam, has only one horn. Its hide is in the form of plates, hinged at the joints; hence it is sometimes called the "iron-plated rhino." The skin is dark gray in color. Other rhinos include the Javan, which has one horn, and the Sumatran, which has two.

The giraffe is the
tallest land animal

We now come to a different type of giant, the giraffe, which is the tallest of all living land animals. The males average over fifteen feet in height and the females thirteen to fourteen; nineteen-foot specimens have been reported. The giraffe belongs to the family Giraffidae. It was

Right: the Indian rhinoceros (*Rhinoceros unicornis*). Note the deep folds of the rhino's skin.

THREE THICK-SKINNED GIANTS

Left: the black rhinoceros (*Diceros bicornis*). It is found in Africa, to the south of Ethiopia.

Photos, N. Y. Zool. Soc.

Right: the hippopotamus (*Hippopotamus amphibius*), one of the heaviest of the world's mammals.

called the cameleopard by the Romans, because it was supposed to be the offspring of a camel and a leopard. The giraffe travels in herds. Generally, each herd is made up of a full-grown male and several females with calves.

The forelegs are longer than the hind legs; hence the neck is thrust upward instead of forward. The neck itself, though it has the normal number of seven vertebrae characteristic of most mammals, is enormously elongated. The head can be placed on a line with the neck, so as to extend the reach still farther. The tongue, too, can be thrust out to an amazing extent.

The giraffe is one of the most specialized of animals. If the tree foliage on

which it feeds were ever to become scarce, the animal would be hard put to it to find food. Ground-feeding is a difficult maneuver for the giraffe. It must straddle wide with its front legs in order to bring its mouth in contact with the earth. On the other hand, with its great reach and its flexible, prehensile lips and tongue, the animal can readily pluck the leaves of trees, avoiding thorns.

It has often been said that the giraffe is mute because it has no vocal cords. As a matter of fact, giraffes have been known to utter sounds. They groan when they are injured; the females call to their young when the latter stray. It is true that the vocal cords are quite undeveloped; yet

This striking photograph will give an excellent idea of the enormous mouth capacity of the hippopotamus.

Black Star

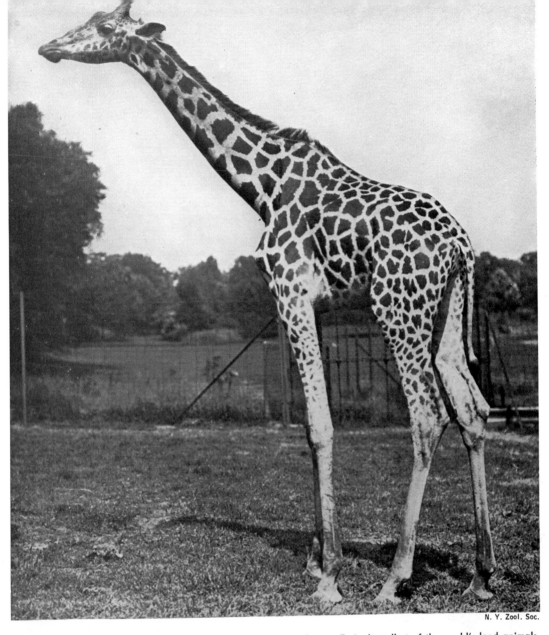

A fine specimen of Nubian giraffe in captivity. The giraffe is the tallest of the world's land animals.

somehow the giraffe can produce audible sounds without them.

Zoologists have long been puzzled by the giraffes' fantastic ability to withstand thirst. Restricted to Africa, south of the Sahara Desert, these animals are found, among other places, in the Kalahari Desert. In this arid region, as far as we know, they cannot find water for seven or eight months of the year. One must take into account, of course, the possibility that desert animals may know of water sources of which men are ignorant. Perhaps the Kalahari giraffe's supposed abstention from water may be somewhat exaggerated.

The giraffe is a most inoffensive animal and is even quite friendly in tourist areas. The horns are useless as weapons of attack, since they are covered with soft fur; however, the animal can deliver a powerful blow with its feet or its head.

A comparatively short-necked relative of the giraffe is the okapi, found in the upper Congo region in Africa. Its existence was not confirmed by zoologists until the turn of the present century. The male stands a little over five feet at the shoulder; its body is considerably more compact than that of the giraffe.

See also Vol. 10, p. 275: "Mammals."

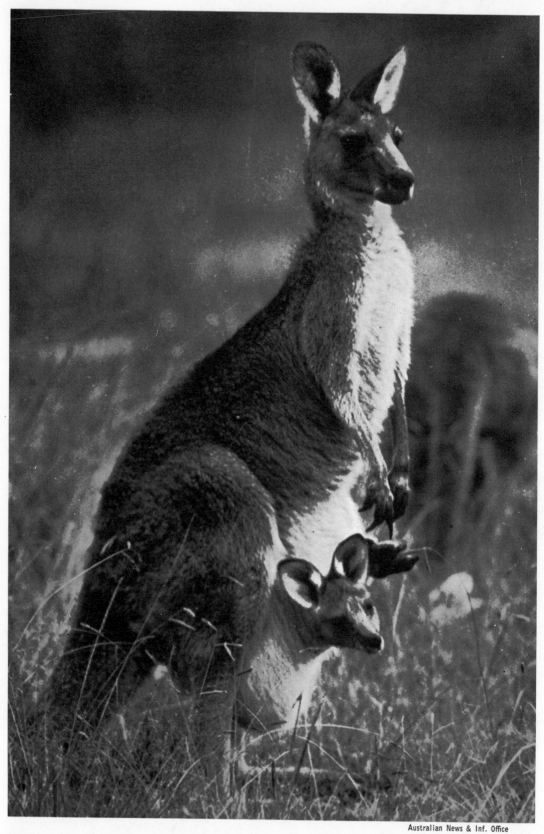

Female Australian kangaroo, with her young in her pouch. Baby kangaroos, about an inch in length at birth, are suckled in the pouch. There they stay some time after they are born.

THE POUCHED MAMMALS

Kangaroos, Opossums and Other Marsupials

THE curious creatures known as the pouched mammals form a unique order of animal life. Their mode of reproduction, in particular, differs radically from that of the general run of mammals, such as moles, bats, mice, cats, apes and elephants. Most mammals, greatly as they may differ from one another in size and habits, reproduce in much the same way. The female produces a tiny egg cell that has very little yolk in it. This cell is fertilized within the body of the female, and after a time it comes to rest in her womb, or uterus. As the egg develops, membranes are formed around it. One of these membranes fuses with the wall of the uterus so that a firm connection is made between the developing young, or embryo, and its mother. This connection, which is called a placenta, is richly supplied with blood vessels. It serves as a passageway, by which nourishment and oxygen are passed from the mother to the embryo. After a certain length of time, varying with different species, the now well-developed young is forced from the womb and is born — that is, leaves the mother's body. The mammals that reproduce in this way are sometimes called placental mammals, or placentals.

The female pouched mammal brings forth its young in a different fashion. It produces an egg with a much larger supply of yolk than that of a typical placental egg. This egg is fertilized within the body of the female but no placenta is developed. (The rabbitlike bandicoot of Australia is an exceptional case; a primitive and only partly developed placenta is formed within its body.)

The embryo in the womb of the female pouched mammal is nourished on the yolk of the original egg cell; a nutritive solution, called uterine milk, in which the embryo is bathed, also furnishes a certain amount of food material. The embryo does not remain long in the mother's womb; it is forced out of the body at a very immature stage of development. The young of the opossum leaves the mother's body eight days after the fertilization of the egg; the young of the kangaroo remains in the womb for only thirty-nine days.

When the baby pouched mammal emerges from its mother's body, it is an almost shapeless bit of flesh. Hardly an inch in length, it is blind and naked. No external ears show; the hind legs and tail are mere buds. Surprisingly enough, however, the front legs are equipped with large clawed hands, whose nerve centers are well developed. By means of these hands the baby crawls up the mother's belly and finds its way to the pouch, or marsupium, which is located there. This pouch has given rise to the name marsupials, often applied to the group of pouched mammals.

The baby animal finds shelter and warmth in the marsupium. Within it are the mother's teats, through which the tiny little creature draws milk. The baby fastens on one of the teats, or nipples, with its mouth, so that the nipple is thrust far down into its throat. The upper and lower lips of the little animal grow together at the corners around the nipple, and the nipple itself swells. As a result the baby is securely fastened to its source of nourishment. Thus enclosed within its mother's pouch, the young marsupial feeds and grows. It leaves its snug shelter only when it is fairly well developed and capable of eating and digesting other kinds of food besides its mother's milk. But it does not leave its pouch sanctuary permanently, even at this stage of its development. As we shall see, it hops back into the pouch quite frequently, particularly if danger threatens.

In order to understand the relationship between the marsupials and the placental animals, we must go back to the early history of the mammal group. The earliest mammals, which were descended from mammallike reptiles, were in all likelihood small creatures that lived in trees. They had to remain inconspicuous in order to survive at a time when giant reptile carnivores were ruling the earth. The little mammals had sharp teeth, but because of their small size their prey was limited to worms and insects. They also fed upon eggs and, perhaps, fruits and buds.

From these early animals various mammal types evolved. Some of these flourished for a time and then became extinct. One type, which reproduced its kind by laying eggs, succeeded in maintaining itself; today it is represented by the platypus and the spiny anteater of Australia. Two other groups of mammals managed to survive, and became the ancestors of our modern placentals and marsupials. At the early stages of their development, both these types of mammals were small; they ate insects and various other kinds of food.

The early marsupials were opossumlike. They had small brains, but they were far more intelligent than any of the reptiles that were then living. Gradually marsupials spread throughout the tropical and temperate regions of the world. In the course of time they came into competition with the placentals and almost invariably succumbed to their rivals. Gradually the marsupials were driven out of Eurasia, Africa and North America. They continued to thrive in South America and Australia.

Various marsupials and herbivorous placentals had migrated to South America by way of the Isthmus of Panama. This intercontinental bridge had been broken off in the course of time and South America had become an island continent. The marsupials flourished there and evolved into quite dissimilar types. Some of them were rather short-legged, large-skulled carnivores, as large as bears; they preyed on other marsupials and on herbivorous placentals. One marsupial flesh eater had long piercing tusks, like those of the saber-toothed tiger. Other marsupials remained more or less opossumlike.

About a million years ago, the land bridge to North America was re-established. Great numbers of highly developed placental mammals pushed their way into the South American continent. The marsupials could not withstand this onslaught, and most of them perished. Today a few scattered species, including the opossums, are the only surviving representatives in the two Americas of what

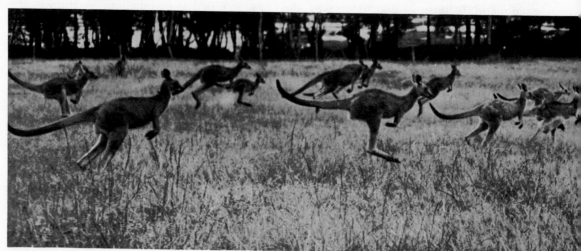

Australian News & Inf. Service

A lively group of kangaroos on a New South Wales plain. These animals are often pests.

was once a flourishing population of marsupials of many different kinds.

The marsupials of Australia fared much better than their American cousins. A number of opossumlike animals had invaded Australia when it was still connected to the Asiatic mainland. About 70,000,000 years ago, Australia became isolated from the rest of the world. Fortunately for the marsupials, no placental mammals, except for bats and several species of rats, had entered the now isolated continent. The marsupials, therefore, dominated this vast land, in which they increased their numbers and evolved into many different types.

The development of different types of marsupials

One group became carnivorous. There were catlike marsupials (today called native cats), wolflike creatures (represented by the modern Tasmanian wolf) and a wolverinelike animal, from which the modern Tasmanian devil descended. Another group was insectivorous; it included marsupial anteaters with long snouts, marsupial moles with reduced eyes and well-developed fore limbs, and pouched mice, resembling the shrews of other parts of the world. A third group, including phalangers, kangaroos, wallabies, wombats and koalas, became herbivorous.

The phalangers were tree dwellers; they had prehensile tails, by which they could cling to branches. Some even developed extensions of skin along the sides of their bodies, so that they could soar from one treetop to the next. Kangaroos and wallabies became ground-dwelling plant eaters; they hopped about on their hind legs. The wombats became tailless, stout-bodied animals with rodentlike grinding teeth. The koalas became strikingly bearlike.

Giant marsupials of the Australian continent

As is quite frequently the case with an actively evolving group, some of the Australian marsupials became giants, though they were not comparable in size with the dinosaurs that lived in previous eras. There was a lionlike marsupial species

The tree kangaroo, found in New Guinea and in northern Queensland, Australia.

that had a skull a foot in length. A giant kangaroo stood almost ten feet high. *Diprotodon,* an extinct relative of the wombat, was about the size of a rhinoceros, reaching a length of twelve feet.

The disappearance of marsupial giants like these is a puzzling problem. Changes in climate, decreasing food supply, the spread of poisonous plants, the outbreak of disease — all these factors may have been involved. The British biologist A. Dendy proposed the following theory to account for the disappearance of giant marsupials. He observed that many groups of animals, in the course of their evolution, have shown a marked tendency to increase enormously in size and that this tendency has been accompanied by the development of grotesque and utterly useless bodily structures. He believed that such untoward developments might lead in the course of time to the utter destruction of the species.

It is well known that the growth of the bodies of animals is controlled by internal secretions, the products of various glands. Dendy held that in the absence of certain growth-inhibiting secretions, various organs of an animal would continue to grow far beyond the normal limits. When a useful organ begins to develop and assumes some new function for which an increase of size would be advantageous, natural selection would favor those individuals in which the organ grew most rapidly and attained the largest size in the individual's lifetime. If growth were normally inhibited by some specific secretion, natural selection would favor those individuals in which the glands producing the secretion were least developed or least efficient. This tendency toward greater size would be handed on, from generation to generation; in time, excessive size would no longer be an advantage to the animals in question.

Marsupials adapted to a variety of environments

The extinct giant marsupials are just one example of many animals that began their evolution as well-adapted organisms but became nonadapted in altered circumstances and so died out. Other marsupials of Australasia, however, were more successful than their giant relatives and have survived to modern times. They exploited the opportunities at hand and so spread out into a variety of habitats. The force in evolution whereby evolving animals enter new environments and become quite different from one another is called adaptive radiation. Some marsupials became predators and developed teeth for their flesh-eating habits; others took to the trees and developed organs for climbing; still others became burrowing animals. The marsupials of a particular way of life came to resemble the placentals of other lands who had the same kind of habits. This phenomenon in evolution, in which basically different animals with similar habits take on similar characteristics, is termed convergence.

In modern times the marsupials of Australasia have seriously decreased in numbers; some species have become extinct. The primary causes seem to be man and his introduced animals. The marsupials have been hunted by man for food and fur and wantonly killed for "sport." Man's agricultural and stock-raising activities have drastically taken away good grazing land from the herbivorous kangaroos and wallabies. The introduced animals, especially the dingo, the fox and the domestic cat, have destroyed thousands of marsupials. Since they reproduce slowly, usually having but one or two young a year, they cannot quickly replace their lost numbers. During a period of drought, many herbivorous marsupials and the introduced rabbits will starve. When favorable conditions return, the prolific rabbits soon re-establish themselves and consume much vegetation, whereas the marsupial population seldom recovers itself completely and must constantly compete against the voracious rabbit population for food.

The kangaroo family is a varied group of marsupials

Our survey of the Australasian marsupials begins with the kangaroo family (family Macropodidae), a varied group ranging in size from the kangaroos, which stand six feet, to the musk kangaroo, which is only rat-size. The kangaroos, wallaroos, wallabies and rat kangaroos all belong to this family. The front legs are relatively short and undeveloped; the hind legs are enlarged and muscular. The hind feet are elongated. The fourth toe is the longest; the short second and third toes are fused together; there is no first toe. These marsupials are all hopping animals.

There are no specific differences between kangaroos, wallaroos and wallabies except size and body build. All have front teeth specialized for clipping grasses, shoots and leaves; the molar teeth have ridges on their crowns for grinding this vegetable food. Canine teeth are lacking or merely rudimentary.

The kangaroos (genus *Macropus*) are large, powerfully built animals capable of bounding at speeds up to thirty miles an hour for short distances. When moving at a slow pace they spring a distance of four to six feet at a single bound; as they in-

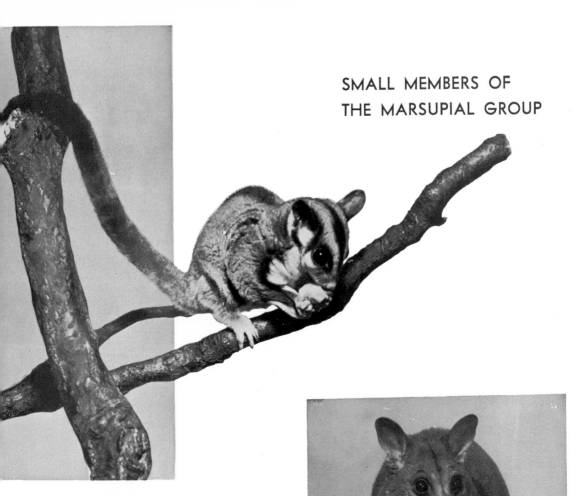

Above: New Guinea phalanger.

Right: gray phalanger.

Below: vulpine phalanger.

Above: murine opossum.

Photos: N. Y. Zool. Soc.

crease their speed they may make leaps of twenty-six feet. While they are moving rapidly, the heavy, thick tail is held out almost horizontally to counterbalance the forward thrust of the body. The tail is also used as a rudder to swing the body when the animal wants to make a turn at full speed. When the kangaroo grazes, its arched body rests on all fours. To move, the animal pushes its tail against the ground, at the same time lifting its hind legs together and swinging them forward.

The red kangaroos are plains dwellers, whereas the great grey kangaroos inhabit brushy country and open forests. Both are gracefully-built animals with exceedingly long hind legs and thick but tapering tails. Wallaroos are stockily built kangaroos that live in rocky regions of the mountains. They have roughened soles on their hind feet which prevent slipping as they leap from rock to rock. Kangaroos and wallaroos have a special stomach sac in which the cellulose and other carbohydrates of their vegetable food is broken down by means of bacteria.

The mother kangaroo gives little aid to her newborn young

Kangaroos mate but once a year and have one or, rarely, two young. The only help the mother seems to give her tiny offspring in finding the pouch is to lick a path in her fur from the opening of the birth canal to the entrance of the pouch. If the infant embryo loses its way in her fur or drops to the ground, she does not aid it. The time taken for the young to make the journey to the pouch is judged to be about fifteen minutes with the great grey kangaroo and from five to thirty minutes with the red kangaroo. Once the weaned young leaves the maternal pouch, it does not stray far from its mother, jumping back into its retreat at the first sign of danger from fox, dingo or eagle. If a female, carrying a young one, is chased by dogs or a hunter on horseback, she will dump her offspring from the pouch. Whether she does this to lighten her load or allow the young to escape is not known. It is said that if she survives the chase, she returns to the spot where the young was dropped. Kangaroos can fight savagely when cornered, propping themselves on the tail while kicking with their hind legs. Their hands grip strongly.

Wallabies are of medium and small size

Wallabies are kangaroolike in habits and appearance but are of medium and small size. The smaller ones dig ground burrows that have an open exit some distance from the entrance. When frightened, they dash for the burrow from some lookout point close by the entrance. Larger wallabies seek refuge in ground hollows scooped out under bushes. The brush wallabies (*Protemnodon*) are large, gracefully built and often distinctly marked and handsomely colored. Scrub wallabies, or padamelons (*Thylogale*), are smaller and are thick-tailed. They live in dense scrub areas and have tunnellike runways through the heavy undergrowth. Rock wallabies (*Petrogale*) are skilled in climbing and bounding over the rocks in mountainous areas. Their foot pads, like those of the wallaroos, are roughened; this gives traction on slippery surfaces. Nail-tailed wallabies (*Onychogalea*) get their name from the horny projection at the tip of the tail; they have silky fur. The hare wallabies (*Lagorchestes*) are solitary animals, much like hares in habits and appearance.

The forest-dwelling tree kangaroos (*Dendrolagus*) differ somewhat from the rest of the family because of their tree-dwelling habits. The hind foot is comparatively shorter and broader; though not a grasping organ, it has curved, sharp claws and roughened soles. The fore limbs are more equal in length to the hind, and the broad hands serve admirably in climbing. The tail is long and slender but not prehensile. Tree kangaroos ascend trees to sleep, feed on leaves and fruit and escape from predators. Though compact of body, they climb agilely, using the tail as a prop and balancer. Usually they descend a tree tail first, but if hard pressed they leap downward twenty or thirty feet to another tree or to the ground where they easily alight on all fours.

Australian koala, or native bear.

The rat kangaroos (subfamily Potoro-inae), diminutive members of the kangaroo family, are agile, ground-dwelling marsupials with prehensile tails. They feed on grasses, fungi, tubers and refuse. Rat kangaroos dig burrows or shallow depressions sheltered by bushes or a fallen tree. They make nests of stringy bark or grass; these materials are carried in small bundles to the nest site in a loop of the prehensile tail. Some rat kangaroos dwell together in colonies, but others live in pairs or are solitary. The female produces young several times a year, one or two at a birth. With one species, the infants remain in the maternal pouch four months.

The musk kangaroo (*Hypsiprymnodon*) seems to be a link between the kangaroos and the phalangers, or "possums." The hind legs are not so disproportionately large; the tail is opossumlike, hairless and scaly. Unlike the kangaroos, the musk kangaroo possesses a big toe; this is not opposable to the other toes.

The phalangers (family Phalangeridae) are cat-size or smaller marsupials, specialized for tree living. They have sturdy limbs and curved claws. Unlike the kangaroos, they possess a first hind toe; this is opposable to the other toes and is used for gripping. The tail is either prehensile or, as with the gliding phalangers, is extravagantly furred, almost featherlike, and serves as a rudder. The phalanger's head is somewhat squirrellike; the well-formed maternal pouch opens toward the front. The second and third toes are joined together but have separate claws; this arrangement serves as a comb to preen the fur. Phalangers are night-roaming and feed on insects and vegetation.

The honey mouse, or honey possum (*Tarsipes*), is a tiny phalanger with an elongated, trunklike muzzle, which can be thrust deeply into flowers for nectar and pollen. The pygmy possums (*Cercaërtus*) are small phalangers that hibernate in cold weather. Other noteworthy phalangers include the striped possums (*Dactylopsila*), which are handsomely marked with black and white and distinguished by their long, probelike fourth fingers; the ring-tailed phalangers (*Pseudocheirus*), which get their name from the habit of curling the end of the tail in a ring; the common possums (*Trichosurus*), which are somewhat foxlike with a thickly bushed tail, large ears and a pointed muzzle; and the cuscuses (*Phalanger*), which have small ears and a prehensile tail with a naked and scaly tip. The gliding phalangers belong to three separate groups, but all possess gliding membranes along the sides of the body. The graceful glides of the greater flying phalanger (*Schoinobates*) sometimes cover 120 yards.

The quaint koala, or native bear (*Phascolarctos*), appears to be related to the phalangers, but it differs from them by having only a rudimentary tail and well-developed cheek pouches; the maternal pouch faces to the rear instead of forward. The koala is completely arboreal, climbing by means of its strong limbs and powerful claws. This robust marsupial, which has a woolly coat, feeds exclusively on the leaves of only a few species of eucalyptus. Koalas usually breed only once every two years. One young (sometimes two) is born. When the young abandons the pouch it climbs to the mother's back where she carries it until the cub is almost full grown. A curious habit of the female koala is to manufacture a pap, or soft food, of eucalyptus leaves in her body at the time when the young one is being weaned. The cub eats this pap, which contains no excrement, from the mother's anal opening; apparently this food greatly speeds up the young's growth.

Unlike the phalangers and koalas, the wombats are ground-dwelling marsupials, being heavy-bodied with short, stout legs. They are excellent burrowers and will sometimes excavate an underground tunnel extending a hundred feet in length. Their front feet carry powerful digging claws; their rodentlike front teeth gnaw through any roots that obstruct their tunneling activities. The tail is a mere nubbin, and the head large. These nocturnal animals live alone, pairing only at mating time. Grasses, fungi and the inner bark of some trees and shrubs make up their diet. The common wombat (*Phascolomis*) is distinguished by having short, rounded ears, coarse hair and a naked area on the muzzle. It is fairly large, measuring three and a half feet. The hairy-nosed wombat (*Lasiorhinus*) is smaller; it has soft, silky fur and longer, tapering ears.

The bandicoots (family Peramelidae) are ratlike or rabbitlike marsupials having

Tasmanian devil, a marsupial carnivore.

pointed muzzles and large ears. Their hind limbs are fairly long, with the second and third toes fused; the front limbs are small. These curious little animals are both herbivorous and carnivorous. They eat various kinds of vegetable matter; they also feast on insects, mice and lizards. Australia's bandicoots include the short-nosed, long-nosed, pig-footed and rabbit bandicoots.

The marsupial mole (*Notoryctes*) is outwardly completely molelike. Its body is small and compact, its muzzle cone-shaped; the tiny ears lie buried in the short fur of the head, the legs are short and stocky, the fingers have enlarged digging nails and the tail is a rudiment. The non-molelike feature, of course, is the pouch, which

The common wombat of Australia is a rodent-like marsupial that is specialized for digging burrows in the ground.

Photos, N. Y. Zool. Soc.

opens to the rear. This little marsupial plows through the desert sand about three inches below the surface, coming above ground at intervals. It feeds on ants and probably other insects and worms.

Another insect eater, the banded anteater (*Myrmecobius*), feeds on ants, termites and their eggs and larvae. This marsupial is rat-size and has a long, bushy tail, prominent ears and a pointed muzzle. Its tongue, by which it captures insect prey, is long and thin. The female marsupial anteater lacks a pouch; the young are protected only by her fur as they cling firmly to her nipples.

lizards. This animal is short-legged, with a large head and strong jaws. Like the marsupial wolf, it is confined to Tasmania. The Tasmanian wolf (*Thylacinus*) lives only in the most inaccessible parts of its island home. The largest marsupial carnivore, it is strikingly doglike, running on its toes more than does any other marsupial. It has piercing canine teeth, flesh-shearing premolar teeth and bone-crushing molars. The animal is nocturnal, hunting alone or in pairs for wallabies and other marsupials, rats and birds.

Aside from the pouched mammals of Australasia, the only other marsupials in-

N. Y. Zool. Soc.

Female common opossum with young. Six to eight young make up a normal litter.

The pouched mice (subfamily Phascogalinae) are also insectivorous. They are similar to mice but have numerous needle-like teeth and more tapering muzzles; some species live in trees, while others are ground dwelling. The native cats (*Dasyurus*) supplement their insect diet with birds and birds' eggs. These white-spotted carnivorous marsupials are weasel- or marten-like and are mostly nocturnal and tree-living. The Tasmanian devil (*Sarcophilus*) is a fairly small though powerful flesh eater. It can climb but usually lives in rocky areas, where it hunts for the smaller wallabies, rat kangaroos, rats, birds and

habit the New World. These include the South American opossum rats (*Caenolestes*), which are ground-living and have no pouches, and the arboreal woolly, murine and common opossums (family Didelphidae) of South, Central and North America. Most possess naked, prehensile tails. The females bear many young at one time. Those that lack the pouch carry their young at first attached to the nipples. Later the infants climb to the mother's back, wrapping their tails around hers.

One species of opossum, the yapock, or water opossum, seems to be the only marsupial specialized for an aquatic life. It is found along the rivers and other bodies of water from Guatemala to southern Brazil. Above, it is ashy gray, with broad black cross bands; it is whitish below. This aquatic marsupial is about two and a half feet long. It has webbed feet, a marsupial pouch and a naked, prehensile tail. The yapock feeds upon aquatic animals; it is particularly fond of fish.

The most familiar of the opossums is the Virginian, or common, opossum (*Didelphis virginiana*). This is the animal to which the name "opossum" (from the language of the Virginia Indians) was first applied. It ranges from New York to Florida and from the Atlantic coast to the Great Lakes and south to Texas. It is about as large as a cat; its tail is some fifteen inches long. It has a long pointed snout, sharp teeth, prominent ears, a long, almost naked prehensile tail and a marsupial pouch. It has long, grizzled gray external hairs and short, whitish underfur. Its den is comfortably bedded with leaves and dry grass; there, five to fifteen young are born once or twice a year.

The fecundity of the opossum is one reason why it has survived since Mesozoic times, for it is the prey of many predatory animals, including horned owls, wildcats, foxes, wolves and bears. Man hunts the opossum, too, for its fur and its flesh.

N. Y. Zool. Soc.

The yapock (*Chironectes panamensis*).

The animal is particularly exposed to attack by its enemies when it seeks its food on the ground.

The varied diet of the opossum

Opossums are nearly omnivorous. They eat fruit, mushrooms and other vegetable matter; they hunt for the eggs and young of birds; they pounce on wild fowl and rabbits at night; they search smokehouses and even farm kitchens at night for rodents and insects; they raid chicken coops. According to one writer, "the opossum will catch a hen and drag the squawking victim off. It will not abandon its prey until the dogs that have been aroused by the clamor have overtaken the robber and have fastened upon it with their teeth."

The origin of the phrase "playing possum"

Often when this animal (or any of its tropical relatives) finds itself cornered, it will fall suddenly limp and apparently dead; whence the well-known phrase "playing possum." When this takes place, the opossum draws back its gums from its glittering teeth, acquiring a truly cadaverous appearance. It will not stir, even if it is picked up by the tail or rolled around with one's foot. If one turns one's back, however, the animal is likely to start up suddenly and run away.

Generally this "playing possum" is considered to be an instinctive feigning of death. It is true that some people have attributed it to "paralysis by fear," but this is not very likely. As a matter of fact, the opossum will not always resort to this stratagem; if it has a fair chance it will fight, particularly if it is a mother defending the young. It shows a courage and a ferocity in the use of its teeth that may be quite disconcerting.

The ruse of "playing possum" is not always a safeguard, since many animals will seize an opossum that is feigning death as readily as one that is active. The artifice seems to be a vestige of some very ancient habit of defense.

See also Vol. 10, p. 275: "Mammals."